CAN WE SOLVE THE FARM PROBLEM?

An Analysis of Federal Aid to Agriculture

COMMITTEE ON AGRICULTURAL POLICY

THE SPECIAL COMMITTEE listed below, appointed by the Fund in connection with this project, was asked to study the research findings and to formulate a program of action to deal with the problems disclosed by the research. The committee's report, for which the committee is solely responsible, is given in Chapter 12 of this volume. Chapters 1 through 11 contain the findings of fact and their analysis, for which the committee has assumed no responsibility.

JESSE W. TAPP, *Chairman*

Chairman of the Board of Directors,
Bank of America, National Trust and Savings Association

JOHN D. BLACK

Professor of Economics,
Harvard University

HARRY B. CALDWELL

Master of the North Carolina
State Grange

CALVIN B. HOOVER

Chairman, Department of
Economics,
Duke University

DONALD R. MURPHY

Editor,
*Wallaces' Farmer & Iowa
Homestead*

EDWIN G. NOURSE

Past Chairman,
Council of Economic Advisers

MARGARET G. REID

Professor of Economics and
Home Economics,
University of Chicago

QUENTIN REYNOLDS

Formerly General Manager,
Eastern States Farmers'
Exchange, Inc.

THEODORE W. SCHULTZ

Chairman, Department of
Economics,
University of Chicago

ANDREW STEWART

President,
University of Alberta

LOUISE LEONARD WRIGHT

Midwest Director,
Institute of International
Education

OBED A. WYUM

Chairman, Policy and Program Committee,
North Dakota Farmers Union

CAN WE SOLVE
THE FARM PROBLEM?

AN ANALYSIS OF
FEDERAL AID TO AGRICULTURE

Murray R. Benedict

With the Report and Recommendations
of the Committee on Agricultural Policy

NEW YORK • THE TWENTIETH CENTURY FUND • 1955

FOREWORD

FOR THE PAST thirty years "the farm problem" has been a major political issue in the United States. Pressure for far-reaching government aid to farmers began during the 1920s and was intensified with the disastrous break in farm prices after the end of that decade. In an effort to meet these demands, the federal government launched a wide array of programs designed to rehabilitate agriculture and improve farm conditions. These programs, most of which have been continued and expanded since their initiation, have involved a heavy charge on the taxpayer and have brought about marked changes in the relation of government to agriculture. They have therefore given rise to much public interest and concern.

Despite this widespread interest, the public has not been well informed about the nature and significance of the current farm problem and of the programs relating to it, or even about the older, more orthodox body of farm legislation that had grown up in the years prior to 1930. In an effort to provide a better basis for intelligent public action relating to this important part of the national economy, the trustees of the Twentieth Century Fund in 1951 launched a comprehensive study of the government's farm programs. Its aim was to provide a compact, readable description and analysis of this complex array of activities in order to contribute to public understanding of farm problems and to wiser and more realistic decisions by farmers, farm organizations and the general public.

The study has been carried out under the direction of Murray R. Benedict, Professor of Agricultural Economics at the Giannini Foundation of the University of California, Research Director for the project, and Oscar C. Stine, formerly Assistant Chief of the Bureau of Agricultural Economics, the Associate Research Director. They have been assisted by a small research staff and have received aid and counsel from many qualified people both within and outside the government.

The study here presented is the first of a contemplated two-volume report on the results of this research. It deals with the agricultural programs as a whole; the reasons for them, the institutional arrangements under which they operate, the over-all costs and the general nature of the results. This volume has been written by Dr. Benedict with the counsel of Dr. Stine and assistance of other members of the staff. The second volume, scheduled for early release, will analyze in considerable detail the various specific commodity programs. It is being prepared jointly by Dr. Benedict and Dr. Stine.

The Fund also established a consultative committee of well-known and widely experienced agricultural economists, farm leaders and representatives of the public to review the findings and formulate recommendations for public action. While that committee has reviewed the text of the research report here presented and has contributed valuable suggestions and criticisms, responsibility for the report rests entirely with the author. The committee's own report, which appears at the end of the volume, is solely the responsibility of the committee and constitutes its major contribution to the project as a whole.

In presenting this volume to the public, the Fund wishes to express its appreciation to the members of the committee for the genuine public service they have rendered and to Dr. Benedict for his diligence and scholarly competence in the difficult task of analysis to which he addressed himself.

J. FREDERIC DEWHURST
Executive Director
The Twentieth Century Fund

330 WEST 42D STREET
NEW YORK 36, N. Y.
SEPTEMBER 1955

ACKNOWLEDGMENTS

SPACE PERMITS mention of only a few of the many people who assisted in one way or another in the preparation of this book. To many of them who, for practical reasons, must remain anonymous, I can only express my deep appreciation of their generosity and courtesy in supplying needed data, criticizing drafts and making helpful suggestions.

Special recognition and my personal gratitude are due to Dr. Orville F. Poland, who served as principal research assistant on this phase of the study. He took a leading part in assembling data, maintaining contacts in the various federal agencies and exploring the archives for pertinent legislation and reports. His keen interest, high standards and frank criticism have been invaluable. I, of course, take full responsibility for the views expressed and the general tone of the book, since the task of writing it was my own. However, most of the statistical summaries should be credited to Dr. Poland, and he has given generously of time and effort in checking sources, interviewing specially qualified people and going over the numerous drafts of the various chapters.

Dr. O. C. Stine, Associate Director of the project, has given generously of counsel in the shaping of this volume, though his principal responsibility has been in preparing materials and analyses for the companion volume which deals with the commodity programs. Again, though his counsel has been most valuable and many of his suggestions have been taken into account in preparing this study, I do not wish to imply agreement on his part with all of the views and findings here presented.

Dr. David MacFarlane sat in on the discussions of some of the early drafts of a number of the chapters and contributed many helpful suggestions. Miss Patricia Gustafson also participated in staff sessions during the summer of 1952. The index is the work of Dr. Elizabeth Kelley Bauer, to whom I am deeply indebted for the comprehensive and workmanlike job that has been done on it.

Many people in the Department of Agriculture have been most generous in supplying needed information, criticizing preliminary drafts and checking data. I am especially indebted to C. Kyle Randall, Wayne Rasmussen and Gladys Baker of the Agricultural Marketing Service; to Almon T. Mace of the Farmers Home Administration; to R. C. Engberg and Ralph Battles of the Farm Credit Administration; and to Frank D. Brenchley and Thomas Thornburg of the Commodity Stabilization Service. Harry McKittrick of the Bureau of the Budget and Irving Sensel of the Bureau of Land Management also were very helpful. Needless to say, none of these people should be held in any way responsible for the specific form the report has taken or the conclusions implied.

I am deeply appreciative of the unfailing and cordial cooperation of both Evans Clark, the former Executive Director of the Twentieth Century Fund, and J. Frederic Dewhurst, the present Director, and that of the Fund's home office staff. Though the study has required more time than was anticipated, the understanding and encouragement of the Directors and staff of the Fund have helped greatly in bringing it to a stage where this first and more general section is ready for publication.

In addition to the counsel and criticism mentioned above, all members of the special committee have reviewed and discussed the manuscript and offered helpful suggestions and criticism.

MURRAY R. BENEDICT

CONTENTS

TABLES

APPENDIX TABLES

AUTHOR'S NOTE

No STUDY designed for the general reader can present in detail the many features of an industry so vast and complex as American agriculture. It is not, in fact, an industry but rather a great aggregation of industries, the leaders and representatives of which tend to join forces in seeking certain types of legislative action when their interests coincide.

Neither is it possible to define sharply a specific "farm problem." The "farm problem," as the term is commonly used, relates to the whole array of grievances and aspirations that cause farmers to seek government aid in achieving ends they consider appropriate and desirable. Chapter 1 outlines in broad terms the more important forces that have given rise to a farm problem in times past, and the report of the special committee, in Chapter 12, discusses more specifically the problems that are currently most important. The intervening chapters deal mainly with the programs and institutions set up to aid agriculture in the depression decade and the way in which they have affected the situation in the more recent war and postwar period.

The various programs must necessarily be dealt with in broad terms since the mass of detail would otherwise obscure the essential elements of the problems discussed. The activities described pertain to scores of commodities and have been carried on by tens of thousands of public employees over a period of more than twenty years. They have related to or impinged upon more than five million farms, each of which is a separate operating unit with its own special set of problems and conditions.

Fortunately, it is neither necessary nor desirable to describe these programs and their results in great detail. The things of importance, to both farmers and the general public, are the principles involved, the general effects of the programs, and the public and private costs resulting from them. Illustrations rather than masses of data can best bring these out. There has also been little attempt to identify or describe minor legislative and administrative changes. These often are very important to administrators, and to particular groups of farmers, but they do not affect over-all conclusions significantly.

Separations and Categories

Question may properly be raised as to the warrant for discussing each phase of the program, such as credit, price supports, conservation or food subsidies, as though it stood by itself instead of being interrelated with the other programs. Though this is a legitimate criticism, the decision to use a topical rather than a chronological plan of organization was made deliberately. Certainly the interrelations among the various programs are many and complex. Eligibility for price supports and loans may depend on what is done about conservation or cutbacks in acreage; surplus removal and susidies may be interrelated with price-support programs; and some of the agencies, such as the Commodity Credit Corporation, are not independent entities. Instead, they are integral parts of an over-all program that has many different facets. Even research and the operations of the credit agencies have numerous interconnections with the other activities described.

Yet, the alternative to a seemingly too sharp separation of the chapters dealing with the various agricultural agencies and programs is to undertake to describe them all in context with each other and period by period. This, in addition to creating almost insuperable difficulties from the standpoint of presentation, seemed likely to provide the reader with a less clear understanding of the various programs than if each is discussed independently of the others. It is exceedingly important, however, that the reader keep in mind that these programs were not carried out *in vacuo* but were going on simultaneously and were, to some extent, affecting each other. A given farmer might be, and often was, working with the Farm Credit Administration, the Agricultural Adjustment Administration, the Soil Conservation Service and other agencies all at the same time.

We have chosen in this volume to follow the movements of each of the armies in this more or less coordinated attack on the farm problem rather than to jump from front to front as the battle progressed. In the companion volume, where each chapter deals with a specific commodity or a group of related commodities, the procedure, from the standpoint of writing, has been to attempt to describe and measure progress in each separate field of operation where two or more of the agencies might be working in cooperation or, in some cases, even at cross purposes.

Costs More Measurable Than Returns

There are important conceptual difficulties even in the measurement of dollar costs for programs that vary so widely as those carried on in behalf of agriculture during the past twenty years. But the problem of measuring the results of such expenditures is incomparably more difficult. On the cost side, we have such problems as these: Should the data be on a realized cost basis or on an accrual basis? What is the real value of the vast commodity holdings of the Commodity Credit Corporation? How much of the cost of a surplus removal program is a cost in behalf of agriculture and how much of it a contribution to the recipients of the commodities moved? Countless other conceptual and practical difficulties have had to be considered and dealt with.

Costs have been handled in two ways, depending on the nature of the operation. For loan and corporate funds, the estimated cost of the money to the government was determined; program expenditures were added; and returns to the government were deducted in order to arrive at a net figure. Thus accrued but not yet realized returns and losses are not included.

For other programs, expenditures have been used if feasible and cash returns to the government have been deducted. However, in many cases it was necessary to use amounts obligated instead of expenditures (that is, the amounts committed by the agency though actual payments may not yet have been made). For the most part, obligations and expenditures differ, if at all, only as to the year in which they appear. However, it should be recognized that the cost data presented represent, in many cases, general magnitudes of expenditure rather than precise dollar figures. In most cases, the larger figures have been rounded to the nearest tenth whether it be millions or billions. Exceptions will be found in items for which very precise official data are available. No attempt has been made to evaluate permanent assets such as buildings, equipment and so on, though these, in some cases, are assets of some consequence.

There are some minor discrepancies in published data purporting to show the same thing. Revisions and corrections are continually being made by the Department of Agriculture as new information becomes available. Most changes of that kind do not affect the larger aggregated figures significantly. In general, the data for the most recent years are the ones that are least settled and most likely to be modified as a result of later computations and more complete information. The cost of the Commodity Credit Corporation program is almost certainly understated. It is virtually inconceivable that the stocks now held can be moved without further heavy losses, but there is no way of estimating, with dependability, what those losses will be.

On the credit side, the problem is still more difficult. What valuation can be placed on an outlay that enabled a farmer to retain his farm when he would otherwise have lost it, or on an expenditure that raised the efficiency and living standard of a "low-income" farmer? How, for example, can the results achieved in a soil conservation program be measured and, if they can be measured, what value should be put on them?

The policy followed in respect to returns fom the expenditures has been, so far as possible, to describe the nature and general extent of the results achieved, leaving it to the judgment of the reader as to whether the expenditure was or was not a wise one. Even this is, of course, not always feasible or meaningful. At best, the appraisal of returns is a highly subjective affair. The individual valuations placed on any given result will vary widely.

The Approach and Point of View

The study presented is not strictly an economic analysis of farm policies and programs. Such an approach, though well suited to the analysis of individual crop programs, would be unrealistic and superficial if applied to a comprehensive program such as the one here discussed. National farm policy includes many elements that do not lend themselves to formal economic analyses of the conventional type. Political factors play a very large role. Parts of the program have resulted from the particular circumstances of past periods and cannot be discussed realistically without taking account of the situations that brought them into being.

The program as a whole is an intricate web of activities that has a time dimension as well as the timelessness assumed in many types of formal economic analysis. Hence, if the development of the program and its significance are to be understood in realistic and human terms, it must be approached from a variety of angles: economic, historical, political and possibly even sociological. This, in fact, is the way it is looked at by the farmer, the man on the street and the general reader. They do not think in terms of formal academic disciplines. It is for these groups that the book is written. The aim is to contribute to broad understanding of the issues involved rather than to provide the refinements that would perhaps be of greater interest to economists and others already familiar with the main outlines of the program.

Approached in this way, the treatment inevitably includes a good many value judgments, either stated or implied. The aim has been to keep these at a minimum and to present to the fullest extent possible a readable, factual and objective description and analysis of the various programs. However, it is only fair to the reader to state, though surely in a sketchy and inadequate way, the basic premises and attitudes underlying the study. He can then take them into account in arriving at his own interpretations and conclusions.

In broad terms, the philosophical framework implied is that of an economy in which main reliance is on the decisions of the five million or more operating farmers in their efforts to make the best use of their resources, but with full recognition that government can and should help to make that system work better. The role of the government, as seen here, is that of attempting to keep the economy as a whole stable and prosperous and of giving help in overcoming gross inequities as among the various groups that make up the economy. It is assumed, too, that government should give positive aid in correcting maladjustments that have come about through actions of the government itself or objectives established by it in furthering the national interest, as, for example, the distortions resulting from wartime production programs. Government also can and should take positive action to overcome or alleviate hardships that result from widespread depression whether in agriculture or in other parts of the economy.

There are in addition certain continuing maladjustments and pathological conditions which, in a free-enterprise economy, either are not corrected automatically or are corrected too slowly. Among these are such things as the progressive deterioration of soils, the static or retrogressing situation of some groups of farmers and farm workers, and the regional and interregional maladjustments that grow out of profound changes in international trade, major technological revolutions or shifts in population.

The point of view here described looks to a larger responsibility and opportunity on the part of government than would have been considered appropriate thirty or forty years ago, but to avoiding reliance on government in matters that can be equally well or better handled through individual action. For those whose philosophies and values look to a larger degree of government management and control than this implies, and also for those who favor a minimum of government participation in economic affairs, the interpretations and conclusions here presented will require modification. It is hoped, however, that the factual foundation has been provided in sufficiently objective form to make possible more informed judgments by people who have widely varying points of view.

Many of those professionally concerned with one or another phase of this very broad and complex group of activities will not find as much detail about their particular parts of the program as they would like. No single study could provide that. Some will feel that their particular kinds of activity have been understressed or dealt with too harshly. However, a conscientious effort has been made to obtain criticisms from officials of the Department of Agriculture, and many of these have resulted in constructive improvements in the text or in the data used. Virtually all of the chapters have been reviewed by people active in the programs described and by many qualified people not in the federal service. It is hoped that mistakes or inadequacies of presentation, if found, will not be numerous or of major proportions.

CAN WE SOLVE THE FARM PROBLEM?

An Analysis of Federal Aid to Agriculture

Chapter 1

Causes and Nature of the Farm Problem

AGRICULTURE, like other industries, has always had its own special problems. During most of its long history these have not seemed to call for direct intervention by government. Farmers were plagued by the uncertainties of weather, by pests and diseases and by the vagaries of the market, as well as by periods of general depression, but there seemed to be little the government could do about it.

Until the 1900s, these difficulties were taken in stride. They, or problems like them, were common to all kinds of business. Farmers did not feel they needed to be singled out for special treatment either adverse or favorable, though some of the things they advocated were primarily for the benefit of agriculture, notably cheap money and lower freight rates. They sought government action to enable them to develop and settle the public domain. They fought for better and cheaper transportation and demanded a more adequate money and credit system. They took part in the struggles over tariff policy and were active in the efforts to control monopolies. But, in the main, these were not merely farm problems. Most of them affected business and labor groups as well.

By the latter part of the nineteenth century both the farm groups and the national Congress became interested in research and education that would make agriculture more efficient. After 1900 there were vigorous demands from farmers for help in correcting abuses in the marketing system, and they sought government aid in creating for themselves a specialized credit system so they could be financed on terms more nearly in keeping with those available to other industries. In general, they like most other groups sought to create and maintain conditions favorable to unrestricted competition.

Over the past thirty years this attitude has changed. The government itself, at the behest of the representatives and spokesmen of agriculture, has initiated a body of activities that run counter to these views which were so widely accepted only a few decades ago. Through their operation, agriculture has to some extent been removed from the diminishing area of the economy in which the free-market price system is permitted to determine how much of various products will be produced, and what the rewards of the producers will be. To understand how an industry which historically has been the bulwark of individualism has become one in which there are very complex direct governmental controls, and to understand the incidence of the costs and benefits of these programs, it

3

is necessary first to review the nature and characteristics of the farm industry itself and of the setting in which it operates.

From about 1880 on, the government's official policy was against monopolies and critical of "big business." But the trend of the times was away from the small-unit type of competitive economy which had so long been accepted as normal by farmers, by the general public and by most businessmen. Industrial and marketing organizations were becoming larger and were able to exercise monopolistic powers of various kinds. Labor was becoming more highly organized and was adopting policies that modified significantly the old ideas of a completely free market.

Agriculture, however, remained competitive. Its five to six million entrepreneurs could not control production, establish prices or bargain collectively. It thus found itself, along with small retailers and unorganized workers, the last remaining stronghold of the kinds of competition that were assumed to be normal in the nineteenth century environment.

During the first decade of the present century prices were rising and the national economy was expanding rapidly. Workers could move freely from one industry to another or start new small businesses in or out of agriculture. Under these conditions, the real earnings in agriculture could not get far out of line with those in other kinds of business. The sudden drop in demand for farm products which came in the early 1920s and the still more severe disruption of price relationships which occurred in the 1930s caused the farm groups to turn more and more to this pre-World War I period as a suitable criterion of equitable price relationships.[1] Since the middle 1920s they have contended that farm and nonfarm earnings and prices were approximately "fair" during those years. While this has been, to some extent, a rationalization designed to support demands for higher farm prices, it has also had a logical foundation that has attracted widespread and continuing political support.

In the period just preceding World War I, farm prices had moved up substantially from the very low levels of the late 1800s. As compared to those of the 1890s and the early 1900s they were relatively satisfactory to farmers though farm people still contended that agriculture was not keeping pace with the progress in other parts of the economy. Nevertheless, it is apparent that this was a comparatively stable period so far as

1. In the years just following 1920, the 1910–14 period was adopted as a base for most index series mainly because it was the most recent one in which prices were not distorted by war and postwar changes in demand and costs. By the middle 1920s the prewar base period began to be regarded as an equitable standard in determining relationships between farm and nonfarm prices. This view has become more and more firmly established in the thinking of farmers and farm-state congressmen and has become a central feature in the farm legislation enacted by the Congress. Farm prices that bear the same relationship to nonfarm prices as those which existed in the period 1910–14 are now referred to as "parity" prices. There have been some changes in the concept but it still is the underlying principle on which the laws relating to "parity" prices for farm products are based.

farm and nonfarm prices were concerned and one in which farmers were relatively better off than they had been at any time since the Civil War.

THE CHANGE IN CONDITIONS AFTER 1920

The conditions described above were radically changed by the disturbances that accompanied and followed World War I. Prior to 1914, farm people had various safety valves that tended to ameliorate, to some extent, the pressures resulting from the excess population produced in the rural areas. There was relatively easy entry into rapidly expanding urban occupations and businesses and, until 1900 or after, young farmers could and did find outlets in the homesteading of unoccupied lands. Possibly more important was the fact that there was an almost unlimited market abroad for farm products not needed in the United States. Prices might be low but there seldom was much difficulty in selling in the world markets almost any amount that might be produced.

This large and receptive world market (chiefly in western Europe) resulted from the very rapid industrialization and population growth then occurring in that area and from the fact that, on balance, the people of the United States still owed large amounts of money to foreign investors. United States exports could be larger in dollar volume than imports, the difference being made up through payment of interest and dividends on foreign capital invested in this country, freight charges paid to foreign ship-owners, insurance premiums, immigrant remittances and expenditures by American travelers abroad.

Thus exports could exceed imports continuously without creating exchange difficulties and there was a good deal of flexibility in the arrangement. An unexpectedly large surplus could be disposed of in the very elastic world market either by building up exchange balances abroad or by retiring U.S. indebtedness at a faster than normal rate. If U.S. crops were poor, European supplies could be drawn more largely from other surplus producing countries. World production of the major export crops, except cotton, was normally rather stable.[2]

World War I and the years following it caused a drastic change in the trade balance of the western world. The United States, instead of continuing as a debtor nation, suddenly became the world's largest creditor. England, France and Italy owed us huge amounts of money they were unable to pay. They still needed food and fiber from abroad but no longer were able to pay for them out of earnings on their foreign investments. Even their industries, which normally produced goods to exchange for imported raw materials, had been seriously disrupted by conversion to war use, by enemy action and by depreciation. Furthermore, U.S. industrial production was growing rapidly and we were less

2. Since the world supply of cotton was largely produced in the United States, a short U.S. crop could, of course, disturb the international market more than for most other staple crops.

and less dependent on imported manufactured goods for supplying our own needs. Germany, which had previously been a heavy buyer of U.S. farm products, was even more severely shorn of foreign assets and was forced to rely almost wholly on her own agricultural resources.

United States credits to the allied nations were terminated in 1920 and little aid was given to Germany until private credits began to be extended later in the decade. As a result, most of western Europe had to re-establish and expand its agricultural production as quickly as possible. Thus the large and elastic world market which had been a foundation stone in American agricultural prosperity was severely restricted at the very time when the wartime efforts to expand U.S. agricultural production were coming into effect.

These conditions alone would have made the postwar adjustment in American agriculture extremely difficult. In addition, an enormous inflation of agricultural prices, land values and short-term debt had occurred. Farmers entered the postwar period far more heavily indebted than they had been when the war started and their assets were bound to shrink rapidly in value. The stage was set for a major depression in American agriculture and the crash came in the summer and fall of 1920. Prices fell drastically. Funds were not available for paying obligations as they fell due or even, in many cases, for meeting current expenses.

Orderly Readjustment Needed

The problem of agriculture in this period was that of making an orderly adjustment to the radically changed foreign market situation and of working out from under the heavy load of debts and taxes that had come about through wartime inflation. It was not a situation in which entirely free competition, unaided by government action, was likely to work well. Production could not be adjusted downward quickly and the domestic market for most staple agricultural commodities was very inelastic.

In the absence of any provision for absorption of excess supplies and with almost no emergency loan facilities, agriculture was hard hit. Farm prices fell from 228 (1909–14 = 100) in 1919 to 128 in 1921. Hundreds of thousands of farmers, rural banks and businessmen in the wheat and corn areas faced disaster. For almost the first time in the history of American agriculture there was a vigorous demand for direct government aid. Farm organizations grew rapidly and began to exert a strong influence in Congress especially through the "Farm Bloc," which was organized in the spring of 1921.

Though the need for some action to alleviate the desperate situation in the farm areas was widely recognized, the leaders of most of the farm organizations were torn between a desire for quick remedial action and

3. U.S. Department of Agriculture, *Agricultural Statistics, 1937,* p. 400.

a reluctance to demand large-scale government intervention in agricultural affairs. The Farm Bloc pushed through a number of agricultural acts but these were mostly in keeping with traditional farm policy and were not important as emergency measures.

The major effort of the farmer groups in the early 1920s was of a different kind. It looked to the creation of large-scale commodity cooperatives organized and managed by farmers themselves and without government aid or supervision. They were designed to raise prices through more aggressive merchandising of farm products and the exercise of some degree of monopoly control. This was a significant change in farmer attitudes, one which was to become far more important in succeeding decades. Farmers had long been in the forefront of the drive against monopoly practices. Many of them now swung over to the view that agriculture must adopt policies and practices similar to those used by "big business" and thus put itself in a position to deal on more even terms with other groups in the economy.

The movement thus started proved abortive and was becoming less important by the middle of the decade. Farmers were too numerous, too difficult to organize and too hard to keep in line to make such an ambitious scheme work on a voluntary basis. It was a recognition of this fact that led eventually to a more general acceptance of the idea that government should be urged to help farmers carry out this program which they had found themselves unable to carry through without government aid.

This shift in attitude and strategy was by no means sudden or complete. There was much resistance to the idea of government intervention and many farmers still were unconvinced that a monopoly-type approach was either feasible or desirable. Nevertheless, such techniques were to become prominent and widely favored, in the McNary-Haugen plan so vigorously pushed in the last half of the 1920s, in the mildly monopolistic approach sponsored by the Federal Farm Board in the early 1930s and in the more drastic program of acreage controls, marketing agreements and quota systems that came in 1933 and after.

Disparity in Farm and Nonfarm Price Levels

A major factor in the changing attitude of farmers was the difference in behavior of farm and nonfarm prices in the 1920s. Whereas farm prices as a whole fell to little more than half their wartime levels, some of them to less than half, nonfarm prices fell only about 25 per cent and then leveled off. This meant that farmers had to trade a far larger quantity of their products for a given quantity of nonfarm goods than they had had to do in the prewar period. They attributed the inequality to more effective controls over production and prices in the nonfarm economy.

Such controls were undoubtedly responsible in part for the differences in price behavior. Business and labor organizations were growing in size and power and were more able to control production, prices and wage rates than in earlier periods. This was not, of course, a full explanation of the differences observed. In part they stemmed from the sharply curtailed and very inelastic market for farm products, and from the nature of agricultural production which makes downward adjustment very difficult even in the face of extremely low prices.

In earlier periods, under a more generally competitive, small-unit economy, farm and nonfarm prices tended to rise and fall more or less in unison, as a general reaction to over-all levels of prosperity or depression. Here, almost for the first time, the two did not move together and the disparity became very evident to the farm groups affected.

The fact that the depression was most severe in the areas producing the major export crops (especially wheat, corn and hogs) and the emphasis on price relationships, led to a major campaign to induce the government to intervene with a view to keeping domestic prices above those prevailing in the world markets. This effort took shape in the intensive and sustained drive for passage of the McNary-Haugen two-price plan.

Under that plan, sales of major export crops for domestic use would have been limited to amounts that would sell for the world price plus the tariff while the export surplus would have been sold abroad at the world price.[4] Though this plan was vigorously debated through five sessions of the Congress and eventually gained congressional approval, it was twice vetoed by President Coolidge and thus failed to become law. Nevertheless, it was an important forerunner of the programs that were later undertaken both by the Federal Farm Board and by the Agricultural Adjustment Administration.[5]

Fundamental Problem Not Recognized or Faced in the 1920s

Despite the vigorous campaigns that were carried on in the 1920s, there was little in the way of clear recognition of the real nature of the problems facing American agriculture in this period. The McNary-Haugen plan, even had it been adopted, would not have solved the problem. It could perhaps have eased the situation somewhat for the wheat growers and possibly for the cotton and tobacco growers. Its usefulness to the corn-hog, livestock, dairy and other groups is highly questionable.

Basically, the problem was one of adjustment to a new world market situation and of working out as painlessly as possible from the inflation and speculative excesses that had marked the war and postwar years.

4. In the early versions of the plan the domestic price was to be held at a "fair-exchange" relationship with nonfarm prices; that is, at what would now be called "parity." In its later forms the plan called for a domestic price that would equal the world price plus the tariff.
5. For a more detailed discussion of these developments see M. R. Benedict, *Farm Policies of the United States, 1790–1950,* Twentieth Century Fund, New York, 1953, Chapters 10, 11 and 12.

Some downward adjustments in production were also needed in view of the slacking off of the abnormally high war needs for which the agricultural economy had been geared.

Wheat acreage, for example, had been expanded from 52 million in 1913 to more than 73 million in 1919. The January 1 hog population had grown from 54 million to nearly 64 million. Tobacco acreage was up 50 per cent and cattle numbers had increased by more than 25 per cent. Yet the foreign market for most of these products was less healthy than in the prewar years.

The United States adopted, in 1921 and 1922, a strongly protectionist program which weakened still further the buying power of the principal customer nations, whose exchange relationships were already badly demoralized by war and by the shift of the credit balance to the United States. The interests of the producers of export crops in the United States lay in fostering imports that might create buying power for their products. However, the legislation they supported implicitly accepted the protectionist policy and would, in fact, have strengthened it by applying it to surplus commodities as well as those of which we did not produce enough to supply our domestic needs.

Certainly no action we could have taken at that time would have strengthened the foreign markets enough to absorb at good prices the farm surpluses we wanted to sell. Nevertheless, some steps looking toward adjustment to our new position in world trade could well have been taken. Actually the legislation passed and proposed looked in the other direction.

The second type of action needed was one that would restore quickly and with less hardship a more suitable balance between amounts produced and the effective market for them. With devices since developed, some assistance could have been given by the government in making this difficult adjustment. As of that time such procedures had neither been proposed nor discussed, except for the limited efforts made in the annual agricultural outlook statements designed to guide farmers in their production plans.

Farmers could also have been aided by more adequate emergency credit. For those who had become heavily involved in debt on assets that were shrinking in value, there was no easy way out. But many more of them could have saved themselves if given time and a chance to convert their short-term mortgages into long-term amortized obligations.

Such aid was given, and on the whole very successfully, in the more severe depression of the 1930s. But in the early 1920s, only limited funds were available through the recently established federal land banks. Even the small amount of mortgage credit they were able to provide was on such a conservative basis that few of the heavily mortgaged farmers could make use of it. Second mortgage loans, such as were later provided through the Federal Farm Mortgage Corporation, were not available and no plan for providing them was seriously proposed.[6]

The adjustment problem of the 1920s illustrates one of the major difficulties in stabilizing agricultural prices and incomes. The demand changes associated with war are largely external. The requirements of the domestic market during the war years could easily have been met. The pressure was for increased output so that more could be shipped abroad. This was a national objective rather than an agricultural one. After the war, the need was for readjustment downward but no mechanism had been developed to help correct a situation which the government itself had been instrumental in creating.

The national interest requires that agriculture be in a position to expand output substantially and quickly to meet increased offshore needs in time of war. But the nature of the agricultural industry is such that it cannot quickly reverse the process when the abnormal needs have receded. Here as in many other industries the mechanics of quicker and less painful adjustment need further study. The unstabilizing influence lies outside the United States but the adjustments must be made internally.

THE FARM PROBLEM OF THE 1930s WAS DIFFERENT

In the 1930s the farm problem was of a different kind. Basically the trouble stemmed from an enormous shrinkage in the buying power of domestic consumers and a further decline in foreign demand. Agriculture continued to produce at about a normal rate. From the standpoint of the national interest no major downward adjustment of agricultural production was needed, except possibly in cotton, wheat and tobacco, which depend heavily on export markets.

The principal difficulty stemmed from the sharp reduction in nonfarm output, with its accompanying heavy waste of human and capital resources, and from the sharp decrease in the volume of purchasing power. Industrial production declined from 110 (1935–39 = 100) in 1929 to 58 in 1932. Bank loans and discounts shrank from $41.4 billion in 1929

6. In the depression of the 1920s conditions were much less favorable for a successful and constructive refinancing operation than in the 1930s. Between 1910 and 1920 the valuation of farm lands and buildings increased from $35 billion to $66 billion. Much of this increase was due to inflation and speculation. Prospective long-term earnings did not justify the high land prices prevailing in 1920. Hence loans at high percentages of these inflated values could not have been made with reasonable safety to the lender and probably would not have been a real advantage to the borrowers, since they still would not have been able to liquidate them. By 1930, the valuation of farm land and buildings had receded to $48 billion and by 1935 it was down to $33 billion. Thus with the speculative and inflation-created valuations squeezed out, loans could well be made up to a relatively high percentage of value with comparatively little risk to the government and with a good prospect that the farmer could save his farm and eventually pay off his debt.

to $20.4 billion in 1935. Employment in manufacturing fell off 37.5 per cent and payrolls were down 58 per cent.[7] Agriculture was thus in the position of offering about a normal amount of its products in a market where the supply of nonfarm commodities was greatly reduced and where the buying power of consumers had shrunk by half.

The effect of this unbalance was clearly apparent in the relative prices of things sold by farmers and those bought by them. To be sure, the prices of goods bought by farmers declined, but only from an index of 150 in 1929 to 102 in 1932 (1910–14 = 100). Prices received by farmers fell from 148 in 1929 to 65 in 1932.[8] Thus farmers were able to buy with a given quantity of farm products only about 60 per cent of the amount of nonfarm commodities they had been able to buy in the period prior to World War I.

This does not mean that they were only half as well off as nonfarm people. With their full-scale production, their total buying power had shrunk in a roughly similar proportion to that of people not engaged in agriculture.[9] Nonfarm wage workers who continued to have employment were better off than before. They were getting farm products and many other things at bargain prices. However, the unemployed urban workers, variously estimated at from 10 million to 15 million or more, were less well off.

The crux of the problem lay in the fact that agriculture, continuing its full-scale production, felt the impact of the depression mainly in the form of disastrously low prices while industry could and did reduce production, thereby contributing to a vast reduction in national real income and to large-scale unemployment.

Farmers who were able to retain their farms continued for the most part to have employment, a place to live and a considerable part of their foodstuffs in the form of home-produced commodities. Urban workers who were unemployed lacked these elements of security, except as they might be provided on a minimum scale through public or private relief.[10]

7. U.S. Bureau of the Census, *Statistical Abstract of the United States, 1942*, pp. 887, 291 and 389.

8. *Agricultural Statistics, 1952*, p. 618.

9. Net income to persons on farms, from farming, declined from $6.7 billion in 1929 to $2.3 billion in 1932. Income to persons not on farms declined from $79.2 billion to $41.3 billion. Income to persons not on farms continued to decline, reaching a low of $39 billion in 1933. Farm income recovered slightly, to $3 billion, in 1933. *Agricultural Statistics, 1945*, p. 441.

10. The brief and broad generalization made above is, of course, a less than adequate explanation of the complex relationships involved. Many charges such as those for transportation and various other services remained relatively unchanged thus tending to maintain prices paid by farmers and to cause the prices received by farmers to decline by a greater percentage than the prices paid for farm products by urban consumers. Prices at the factory also declined more than did the prices paid at retail by farmers and other consumers. This was due largely to the relative rigidity of the costs of distribution, particularly costs of transportation.

Price Objectives Emphasized

Agricultural entrepreneurs, like businessmen and urban wage workers, tend to be more aware of price changes than of such fundamentals as over-all national production, volume of buying power and amount of unemployment. The basic need of the economy was a restoration of buying power through re-employment and a larger volume of industrial output. Had it been possible to bring these about, there would have been little occasion for any marked reduction in farm output except in a few major export crops.

The emphasis on prices and wage rates tended to obscure these more basic problems, and the initial effort in the National Recovery Administration was in the direction of raising prices and wage rates rather than of restoring volume of production and employment at a lower level of prices.

The agricultural leaders and administrators took a similar view. The major purpose of the farm programs of the 1930s was to raise the prices of farm products relative to those of nonfarm commodities and to protect the equities of farmers who were in debt. In part, this involved efforts to reduce farm output, thus applying in agriculture, with government aid, much the same type of solution as that adopted privately in most nonfarm industries.

It would be unwarranted to imply that the need for an over-all revival of production, buying power and employment went unrecognized. The Administration initiated various measures looking to that end. It was also contended, and there is some evidence to support the view, that a reversal of the downward trend of prices would in itself stimulate production and activity. The farm groups, in particular, contended that a restoration of buying power in the farm areas would be a strong stimulus to the revival of industrial activity.

This view undoubtedly was somewhat overemphasized as a means of gaining acceptance of strongly interventionist government action to aid agriculture. The contention that the prosperity of the economy as a whole rested heavily on the maintenance of a strong and prosperous agriculture had, however, been vigorously asserted almost all through the preceding decade and was widely accepted in agricultural and congressional circles.

That a restoration of the full $4.4 billion required to put agricultural incomes at their 1929 levels could somehow multiply in such a way as to expand national income by the $45 billion or more required to bring it up to the 1929 level requires more evidence than has been presented either theoretically or empirically. Nevertheless, the farm segment of the economy did present one facet of the problem in which some steps looking to the start of recovery seemed feasible. Also some adjustments in output appeared to be in order, to offset the shrinkage in foreign outlets if for no other reason.

Such adjustments did come about shortly, largely as a result of droughts rather than of government programs. The general tone of the markets for the major export crops was markedly improved by the opportunity afforded for liquidating the burdensome stocks that had kept them depressed.

Whatever the merits or demerits of the arguments and rationalizations used, the underlying purposes of the major farm programs of the 1930s were to refinance farm indebtedness, so as to prevent further loss of ownership, and to raise agricultural prices and incomes. Coupled with these were a number of longer-term programs designed for other purposes, notably the conservation of soils, the improvement of credit facilities and aid to low-income farmers.

PROBLEMS OF THE 1940S AND EARLY 1950S

The 1940s brought a new set of conditions, problems and goals that was different from that of either the 1920s or the 1930s. Beginning in 1941 the objective of the government's farm program was abruptly changed. Instead of seeking to cut back agricultural output it suddenly sought to increase most types of production as fast and as much as possible. Restraints were soon abandoned and various incentives for increased production were provided. Demand increased to such an extent that the problems lay almost wholly in the fields of production and price control.

Here for the first time in a decade the objectives of the government and those of the farm groups came into conflict. The government wanted to hold prices stable. It was willing, however, to make some concessions in respect to farm products in view of the long period of subnormal prices that had prevailed. Prices were to be allowed to rise to "parity," that is, to a relationship with the prices of other commodities which would be similar to that prevailing in 1910–14. At that point they were to be checked, except where special inducements for increased production were needed. Since demand was by then strong enough to push some farm prices well above parity, a major problem was that of preventing an inflationary spiral such as that which had occurred in World War I.

Many farm and congressional leaders objected strongly to any restraint on the upward movement of farm prices, contending that agricultural prices had so long been depressed that they should now be allowed to rise above parity as an offset for the hardships of the earlier years. The government's position was, however, that, regardless of the merits of this contention, failure to place limits on the rise in the prices of essential foods would make it impossible to stabilize wages and prices generally. Without such stabilization the cost of the war would be enormously increased and the war effort would be hampered.

The government maintained its position in general, though with many concessions to both agriculture and labor. Agricultural prices and incomes were above parity with nonfarm prices and incomes from 1942 on. A main feature of the compromise under which the farm representatives accepted in principle the establishment of price ceilings at parity was a guarantee that most farm prices would be supported at 90 per cent of parity for two years after the close of the war.[11]

This provision was intended partly as a means of assuring all-out production during the war years without fear of a sudden and disastrous postwar break in prices such as that which had caused such havoc in 1920 and 1921. In part, however, it was the beginning of the campaign for continuous support of farm prices at or near parity.

The attitude which developed then and which has been prominent since reflected a distrust of free-market prices as an equitable distributor of returns throughout the economy. If continued after the period of postwar adjustment it implied a considerable amount of government control over production or heavy federal subsidies or both. The Congress and many of the farm leaders appeared to be willing, at least for the time being, to accept the controls and costs so implied.

The expected postwar slump did not materialize. Farm prices moved up rapidly after the removal of price controls and were well above parity in the years 1946, 1947 and 1948. By 1949, the expected readjustment seemed to be getting under way. The parity ratio (for farm products as a whole) dropped back to 100 and continued at that level in 1950. It had been up to 115 in 1947 and stood at 110 in 1948. Price supports at 90 per cent of parity for many of the farm products were continued in the legislation of 1948 and 1949 and later acts. This resulted in heavy accumulations of some commodities in the 1949–50 season.

The outbreak of war in Korea in June 1950 created new demands and caused a temporary upsurge in farm prices which eased the situation significantly. The parity ratio was up to 107 in 1951 but dropped back to 100 in 1952.[12]

The Nature of the Problem in the 1950s

The 1950s have brought problems of a different kind. American agriculture has now been prosperous for more than a decade. The financial position of farmers is stronger than it has ever been in the past. Land prices are not notably inflated. The problem is how to make certain

11. It should be noted that a price support at 90 per cent of parity does not mean the same thing as a loan at 90 per cent of the market price. In most lines a loan of 90 per cent of the market price is considered a high-risk loan. Parity price may, however, be equal to or even well above the free-market price. "Parity" is normally a goal or an objective rather than an actual price in the market.

12. By April 1953, it was down to 92. It remained at approximately that level during 1953 and the early part of 1954. The April 1954 ratio was 91. U.S. Department of Agriculture, *Statistical Summary*, May 13, 1954, p. 2.

1950

needed adjustments associated with the tapering off of the abnormal war and postwar demand and how to maintain stability and prosperity in the years ahead.

A new and more extensive war would, of course, defer the adjustment and bring back the insistent demand of the war years. A serious recession in the nonfarm economy would complicate the problem and make difficult if not impossible the maintenance of a satisfactory situation in agriculture. The possibility of a series of bad crop years which could cause concern over the adequacy of food supplies also cannot be overlooked.

Weather conditions, on the whole, have been extremely favorable since 1936 and production has been at record levels. No period of equal length between years of serious and widespread drought is observable in the record of crop yields and production, which dates back to the 1860s. Improvements in techniques and the development of more resistant strains of crops have lessened to some extent the dangers of crop failure even in dry years, but it is still not evident that these could offset significantly the effects of a drought as severe as that which afflicted the country in the years 1934 through 1936.

If we disregard these unpredictable disturbances, the principal problems before us are those of making adjustments in such war-expanded crops as wheat, developing a soundly conceived program for reserves and maintaining a reasonable adjustment of output to the needs of the market. As of this writing, heavy stocks of some of the farm commodities are again being accumulated, and a more severe test of the workability of the existing types of price support than any that have occurred in the past seems to be in the making.

Acreage allotments and marketing quotas have been imposed for wheat and cotton and acreage allotments are in effect for corn. These will no doubt ease the situation to some extent. The longer-term reaction of farmers to rigorous controls of this kind is difficult to assess fully and the question of what to do with the stocks now held is still a perplexing one. The problem might recede into the background, temporarily at least, if widespread and severe droughts should occur within the next year or two or if new large-scale war demands should arise. It seems clear, however, that sooner or later the practical workability of the present type of storage and price-support program will require re-examination.

Consideration obviously will have to be given also to the level of prices and incomes the nation chooses to maintain in agriculture. If this is to be above that resulting from the free play of market forces, subsidies or market controls, possibly both, will be required. A possible alternative is the establishment of a policy that will prevent extreme recessions in farm prices and incomes while leaving production and prices largely to the free play of economic forces in periods of relatively stable and prosperous conditions. Some means will no doubt be sought for achieving greater stability in the returns for perishable products since these do not lend themselves to stabilization through storage operations.[13]

Revival of World Trade Would Help

Much of the difficulty could be lessened if world markets could again become as effective as they once were in contributing to stability of supply. Until 1914, exports and imports were the natural shock absorbers to take care of excess production in this country or to make up deficits if they occurred. The prospects do not appear bright that the international markets can soon reassume this role. Nevertheless, to the extent that they can be made to do so the difficulties of maintaining a sound and stable domestic agriculture will be eased.

The agricultural depression of the 1920s was in large measure a result of efforts to expand production to meet the needs of our allies and of the subsequent disruption of normal exchange relationships which grew out of World War I. That of the 1930s was associated with almost worldwide depression and seriously demoralized international markets. Again in the 1940s we expanded production far beyond the requirements of our own population, particularly in wheat, pork and eggs, in order to supply other peoples during the war and postwar years.

Such maladjustments as are now apparent stem partly from abnormal export demands, partly from changes in consumption habits and partly from other factors. The problems of the future will center to some extent around the effort to re-establish more normal and healthy international markets. In the main, however, they will be those involved in making an orderly transition from the present situation to one better adjusted to prospective domestic and foreign demand for our products.

Though the principal emphasis in this study is on the farm programs that have come into prominence since 1930, the nature of the farm programs and the reasoning back of them cannot be well understood without taking account of the peculiarities of agriculture as an industry and the special problems it presents. The industry and its special characteristics are therefore described in Chapter 2.

An analysis of the relation of government to agriculture would also be incomplete if it did not take account of the very extensive programs of government aid which date back to the nineteenth century. These activities have taken many forms and have had profound effects on the

---

13. Over-all national policy has moved strongly in the direction of providing safeguards against extreme hardship in all parts of the economy. Unemployment insurance, old-age insurance, relief and old-age assistance have been provided for most of the nation's urban workers. Government fiscal policies are modified consciously with a view to keeping business active. Most of these provisions contemplate placing a floor under earnings and incomes rather than maintaining them at high levels. In this the farm price-support program now in effect differs from the others in that it seeks to maintain farm prices at prosperity levels rather than to provide a floor that will prevent undue hardship.

industry. They still constitute a very large part of the farm program, though one which is less controversial and more generally accepted than the price-support programs which have been so widely discussed in recent years.

Not only has there been a far-reaching development of research, education and service work relating to agriculture. There has also been a $2 billion refinancing program, carried out in the 1930s, and a vast electric power development for rural areas which has involved an investment of more than $2 billion. In addition there has been an extensive program designed to aid low-income farmers and farm wage workers, carried out mainly through the Farm Security Administration and the Farmers Home Administration. Crop insurance has been provided on an experimental basis, and surplus removal programs, including food stamp aid to low-income consumers and school lunches, have been undertaken. These very diversified types of activity are described in Chapters 3, 5, 6 and 8.

Chapter 2

Characteristics and Importance of Agriculture

FARM PEOPLE constitute less than one sixth of the nation's population. As recently as 1930 they were nearly a fourth and only forty years ago more than a third. At the time of the first census, in 1790, more than 90 per cent of the population was classed as rural and even the majority of those engaged in urban pursuits had farm backgrounds and close social and economic ties with agriculture.[1]

Since the early part of this century the number of workers in agriculture as well as the proportion of farm to nonfarm people has been declining. The number of workers on farms reached its highest level in 1910, at approximately 12 million. It has been declining slowly but consistently since that time.[2]

Though the number of workers has declined, the output of agriculture has increased enormously in the past 40 years. This is a reflection of the rapid gain in technological efficiency. It is also a result of the change from horse and mule power, which has freed some 60 to 70 million acres of land formerly used in producing feed for horses and mules. Using 1935–39 as 100, the index of farm output rose from 79 in 1910 to 144 in 1952.[3] Most of this gain has occurred in the past fifteen years.

This rapid stepping up of productivity has contributed greatly to national well-being and to international objectives in the decade just past. However, it has also created problems that must now be faced as the abnormal demands of the war and postwar years slack off. These can best be understood by taking account of the peculiarities of the industry

1. The distinction between "farm" and "rural" population as used by the census should be noted. Rural population, broadly speaking, includes all persons living outside of cities or incorporated places of 2,500 or more (with some exceptions to take account of urbanized areas that are not parts of cities or incorporated places). Rural population thus includes many who cannot properly be classed as farm people. It is only in recent censuses that the farm population has been segregated from the rural nonfarm.

2. The proportion of the nation's labor force engaged in agriculture stood at a little over 70 in 1830, and had declined to less than 20 per cent by 1940. U.S. Bureau of the Census, *Trends in the Proportion of the Nation's Labor Force Engaged in Agriculture 1820 to 1940,* Series P 9, No. 11, March 28, 1942.

3. "Farm output" as used by the U.S. Department of Agriculture means the amount produced for human use. It should be distinguished from "gross farm production," which includes products grown to feed horses and mules. Because of the extensive shift to tractor power the index of farm output has risen much more sharply than that for gross farm production. In addition to the shift to tractor power, the transfer to the towns and cities of many functions formerly performed on farms has made possible a considerable reduction in the manpower requirements of agriculture.

which make quick adjustment to changes in demand difficult and uncertain, especially those involving reductions in output.

Agriculture a Very Diverse Industry

Agriculture is by far the most widely dispersed and probably the most diverse of the major industries. The wide differences in type of product and form of organization make generalizations difficult. They likewise complicate the problem of devising and applying procedures designed to improve conditions in agriculture, since the impact of any given plan of action is very uneven. Some farms produce mainly for the market; others mostly for home use. Some produce perishable products, others mostly things that can be stored. Some are heavily dependent on markets abroad while others find all or most of their outlet in the home market.

Though these important differences exist, there are elements of unity in the industry which tend to make farmers stand together on many issues affecting agriculture. Among these is the fact that agriculture is an industry of small units. No single farm is large enough to affect importantly the over-all output of the product. Consequently, adjustments in supply are difficult and usually slow, unless government takes a hand in the process. Large-scale storage and price-stabilizing operations are also unmanageable except through government action. Hence, though the various farm groups do not all have the same problems and do not all want the same kinds of help from the government, many of them want government assistance of one kind or another and they frequently join forces to get omnibus legislation that will authorize government actions of several different kinds.

For the great majority of farms, the management function and most or all of the labor are combined in the same person. As a result, the tendency for agriculture to maintain production in times of falling demand and prices is very strong. Most farmers cannot release the labor customarily used since it is that of themselves and their families. Hence it is usually more practical for them to continue approximately full-scale production than to cut down output and have their labor resources less than fully used. This is in contrast to the situation in nearly all of the larger urban industries where management and labor are not combined in the same person. Here management can reduce its labor force, thus cutting down expenses and reducing the output of the firm, thereby helping to prevent disastrous declines in price.

While this difference in the organization of agriculture as compared to urban industry is of great significance in explaining differences in behavior, it should not be pushed too far. There are of course important incentives for the maintenance of full production in urban industries as well as in agriculture. Notable among them is the high level of fixed costs and the consequent increase in total per unit cost with declining output.

Nevertheless, the very important element of entrepreneurial cost represented by labor can be more readily adjusted in nonfarm industries than in agriculture.

Spatial Differences Create Problems

The enormous differences in the space requirements of agriculture and those of the nonfarm industries are not easy to grasp. The land area of the United States (omitting outlying areas) is roughly three million square miles. Of these, nearly 1.8 million, or 60 per cent, are in farms. In contrast the area occupied by all cities, parks, highways and railroads amounts to only about 111,000 square miles, or 3.7 per cent of the total land area.[4] Thus the producing plant of American agriculture occupies an area that is some sixteen times that of all other industries combined, including urban residential areas, roads, parks, and railroad rights of way. The agricultural plant is spread over distances as great as the 3,500 miles from Maine to California and the 4,000 miles from the State of Washington to Florida.

These differences in area affect importantly the problems and interests of the two groups of industries. Personal contact, exchange of ideas, and unity of action are far more difficult in agriculture than in most urban industries. Agricultural labor is also much more difficult to organize than urban labor, and not so effective in bargaining collectively.

This great dispersion of agricultural work and life likewise accounts for important differences in emphasis in the publicly supported activities sought by the two groups. Farmers long have shown a keen interest in highway improvement, in the wider availability of electric power, and in access to schools. Most urban employers and large parts of urban labor take these things for granted; or, if roads, electric power and schools are not directly available, can bring them in without prohibitive expense.

Great Differences in Types and Sizes of Farms

The diversity of types among the 5.4 million farms enumerated in the agricultural census can be illustrated in a variety of ways. They differ in size, in income, in kinds of products grown, and in many other ways. Among the more important differences are those of size and value of product. More than 1.3 million farms, or nearly a quarter of the total number, are under 30 acres; while at the other extreme more than 300,000, or over a twentieth, have an area of 500 acres or more. The great variations in size are shown in Table 1.

More informative from an economic standpoint is a classification based on value of products. Some large farms are very extensively

4. There are, of course, many industries and business establishments that are located outside urban areas. However, the figures given do indicate in a general way the great differences in compactness of most urban industries as compared to farming.

TABLE 1

NUMBER OF FARMS BY SIZE IN ACRES, 1950

Size of Farm	Number of Farms	Percentage of Total Number of Farms	Cumulative Percentages
Total	5,382,162	100.0	
Under 30 acres	1,338,522	24.9	24.9
30 to 69 acres	1,051,129	19.5	44.4
70 to 179 acres	1,723,476	32.0	76.4
180 to 499 acres	965,409	18.0	94.4
500 acres and over	303,626	5.6	100.0

Source: U.S. Census of Agriculture, 1950, Vol. II, General Report, pp. 774–75.

operated, and have small incomes, while some small farms are very intensively operated and have large incomes. The most significant measure of size is therefore the value of products. About a quarter of the farms have a value of products sold that amounts to less than $400 per farm, while a little less than one tenth of the farms have sales amounting to $10,000 or more. Aside from the very small farms, the largest groups are in the $1,000 to $2,500 range and in the $2,500 to $6,000 bracket. About a fifth of all farms listed fall in each of these two groups.[5] Values of products sold, in 1949, are shown by size groups in Table 2.

TABLE 2

NUMBER OF FARMS BY VALUE OF PRODUCTS SOLD, 1949

Value of Products Sold	Number of Farms	Percentage of Total Number of Farms	Cumulative Percentages
Total	5,382,162	100.0	
$0- $399	1,345,341	25.0	25.0
400- 999	836,282	15.6	40.6
1,000-2,499	1,098,360	20.4	61.0
2,500-5,999	1,106,480	20.6	81.6
6,000-9,999	502,445	9.3	90.9
10,000 and over	493,254	9.1	100.0

Source: U.S. Census of Agriculture, 1950, Vol. II, General Report, pp. 764–66.

It is apparent that agriculture is an industry made up predominantly of small units. More than 1.3 million places classed as farms in the 1950 Census of Agriculture had cash sales amounting to less than $400. Nearly a million others with sales ranging from $400 to $1,000 were of small importance economically. Unless supplemented from other sources

5. It should be noted that these data are for value of products sold, not total production. They also do not include income from nonfarm sources.

these small incomes could not provide an adequate standard of living or contribute importantly to the buying power of the economy.

It would be incorrect to assume that such farms, as a whole, do not have other sources of income. Many are part-time farms, the operators of which draw income from work on other farms or from a different occupation. Some are essentially rural residences of elderly people, or of those whose primary interests and incomes are not agricultural. Some are farms that experienced crop failure in the year of enumeration; some may be new farms that have not yet come into full production.

Off-Farm Work Important as a Source of Income

Some 2 million farm operators (about 35 per cent of the total) reported some off-farm work in 1949. About a million and a quarter of them engaged in off-farm work for more than 100 days and thus had undoubtedly a substantial outside income. About 835,000 worked less than 100 days off the home farm. These, though receiving some supplemental income from off-farm work, probably depended mainly on their incomes from farming. Some, of course, received other income, from pensions, returns on investments and so on.

It will be noted that the number receiving income from off-farm work corresponds roughly to the number having cash sales of farm products amounting to less than $1,000. They are probably, in the main, the same group, though there still are considerable numbers of farmers who receive very small total incomes even when off-farm income is included. Many of these are in the older age group and live on farms as a way of spending their years of semi-retirement. Others live on very poor or small farms, often in areas that are chronically backward.

Despite these qualifications it is evident that some two million of the 5.4 million farms included in the census have minimal significance in the over-all national farm economy, either as sellers of farm commodities or as buyers of goods purchased with the proceeds from farming operations. Putting it another way, about 95 per cent of the cash income from farming is received by about 55 per cent of the farmers (those having cash sales that amount to more than $1,200 per year).[6]

Thus in one sense the farm problem breaks roughly into two parts: that of the 50 to 60 per cent of all farmers who produce the bulk of the nation's farm commodities that are sold, and who are likewise important buyers of nonfarm commodities, and a group nearly as large which is characterized by small production per farm, low income from farming and relatively low buying power. For this latter group, though prices are important, a mere increase in price or reduction of costs, within ranges that are conceivably practical, will not alter income levels importantly.

6. *U.S. Census of Agriculture, 1950,* Vol. II, General Report, pp. 1128–29 and pp. 1132–33.

Other Differences

Still other differences in farm type and problems should be noted. The Bureau of the Census classifies the farms of the United States roughly into ten major groups as follows: cotton; cash grain; other field crops; vegetable; fruit and nut; dairy; poultry; livestock farms other than dairy and poultry; general; and miscellaneous.

These classifications are made on the basis of the relationship of the sales of the particular types of products listed to the total sales of all farm products produced. If more than 50 per cent of total sales consist of a given type of product such as cotton, vegetables or fruits and nuts, the farm is classed as a cotton, vegetable or fruit-and-nut farm.[7]

Because of variations in climate, soils, rainfall, topography, and proximity to markets, there are pronounced regional variations in the concentrations of these various types of farms. These contribute to sectional differences in policy objectives. Livestock production centers heavily in the Corn Belt and intermountain areas, general farming and dairying in the Northeast and the Middle West, wheat, cotton and tobacco in the Middle West, the Plains area and the South, and fruits, nuts and vegetables mainly in the coastal areas, though with some important exceptions. Seldom do all of these regions have a similar outlook on the nature of the farm problem and what should be done about it.

AGRICULTURE IS HIGHLY COMPETITIVE

Because of its structure and the nature of its labor force agriculture is one of the most competitive industries in the national economy. Since no unit is large enough to dominate the market or to affect significantly the national output of a given type of product, the individual grower does not find it to his advantage to restrict his production as a means of raising the price of the product. Neither is it feasible for him to establish class prices, divert to inferior uses or specify prices to be charged for the product.

His situation differs markedly from that of many large industrial enterprises and of the members of the larger and stronger labor unions. Usually his product must move into a market where prices will be determined by the free play of competitive forces based on supply and demand. Most of the markets are characterized by many suppliers and many buyers. Under these conditions prices tend to be very sensitive to changes in supply or demand.

In contrast, the prices of most of the things farmers buy are likely to be very slow in responding to changes in demand, and the amounts put on the market tend to be regulated by managerial decision in such a way as to keep prices from breaking sharply. Organized labor likewise tends

7. *Ibid.*, pp. xxx-xxxi.

to resist very strongly any reduction in wage rates, preferring to take the impact of a reduced demand in the form of increased unemployment rather than in lower rates of pay. Thus the farmer feels, with some justification, that he is often at a disadvantage in trading his products for those of other economic groups.

Inelasticity of Demand Complicates the Problem

The exchange relationships described above are made doubly difficult from the farmer's standpoint by the fact that for a number of the major products demand and the amounts produced are relatively inelastic. When employment is high and incomes good, people eat about so much regardless of price, within moderate ranges. If more is produced, perhaps as a result of favorable weather, prices may go very low without causing the amounts purchased to be increased significantly. This, of course, is less true for specific products, particularly the minor ones, but even here increased consumption of one product may cause a decrease in the consumption of some other one.[8] For many industrial goods and services the unfilled wants are much larger and price reductions or intensified sales campaigns may expand purchases markedly.

This inelasticity of demand operates also to increase farm prices sharply if supplies are short. Generally, however, agricultural production has been sufficiently plentiful to prevent large price rises except under the abnormal conditions resulting from war. The principal need from the farmer's standpoint has been for some means of providing more stability in prices through support of the market in times of pronounced weakness resulting either from sudden changes in demand or from abnormally large production.

The sudden changes in demand arise most commonly and importantly from changes in the amounts exported. Domestic demand for farm products as a whole is relatively stable, except in times of acute depression. Sharp changes in export requirements pose problems of quick adjustment which agriculture is poorly equipped to meet.

Supply Response Also Inelastic

If unaided, agriculture's supply response is slow and fumbling. Once resources have been committed to a given use they cannot readily be shifted to something else. The tendency is to continue to produce even

8. Such generalizations must, of course, be accepted with some reservation. There is a tendency to overstate the inelasticity both of the demand for foodstuffs and the amount produced. Note, for example, the very marked increase in per capita consumption of foods that occurred between 1939 and 1945 and the very significant adjustments that have been made at various times in wheat acreage, hog and poultry production and cotton output. However, such adjustments do tend to be slower and less coordinated for farm products than for many other commodities. In the short run both the demand for and the supply of the major farm products are very inelastic.

when prices fall to levels that provide little return for the labor and capital used. Since the farmer cannot discharge himself or the members of his family, he tends, for some time at least, to continue to produce at about the same pace regardless of the price he gets for his product. Short-time production changes result mainly from larger or smaller yields caused by variations in weather conditions. Seldom do the more important variations in demand and supply correspond in such a way as to result in reasonably stable prices.

These characteristics of the industry and its markets point up the possibility that some types of government action may be constructively helpful to agriculture, and possibly also desirable from the standpoint of society generally. For storable farm commodities, the vagaries of weather can be offset to some extent by absorbing stocks in some years and releasing them later. Some of the difficulties resulting from changes in demand can also be ameliorated in this way, that is, by acquiring and holding burdensome supplies in such a way as to give time for adjustments in output and consumption.

Such actions, if directed toward stabilization of supplies and prices rather than to keeping prices continuously above the free-market level, may be socially desirable as well as an aid to farmers. If used as a means of keeping prices continuously above those that would result from the free play of supply and demand they are likely to lead to burdensome accumulations that may ultimately prove depressing rather than strengthening to prices. It is much more difficult to liquidate such stocks than to accumulate them.

For the major export crops, the traditional stabilizer in situations of this kind is a freely operating export market. To the extent that this can be restored to something approaching its previous ways of functioning it will simplify the task of maintaining stability in the domestic markets. This type of automatic stabilization has not been effective since 1914 and probably cannot be fully restored. However, an effort to move in that direction is warranted.

For the perishables quite different types of problems arise. These, too, are subject to gluts and scarcities. The variations in price may be even greater than for the storable commodities. Hence the perishables tend to be more speculative than the staple crops. However, though the demand for them is almost wholly domestic, it tends to be more elastic than for such crops as wheat, cotton and tobacco. For most perishables, except tree fruits, past history indicates that adjustments will be made more quickly than in the major staple crops. Depressions, if they occur, will not be so deep and lasting. The problem of aiding the producers of perishable crops is more difficult than for storables but some help can be given, through diversion of temporary oversupplies, promotional campaigns and channeling to underprivileged groups of consumers or publicly supported institutions. These products do not lend themselves to purchase, loan and storage programs of the types that have been used for the major storable commodities. They have therefore been omitted from the more specific types of price support provided for the so-called "basic" crops in the legislation of recent years.

Tendency to Maintain Output Benefits Consumers

While the inelasticity of output which characterizes agriculture presents problems for farmers, especially in times of depression, it is an asset nationally. The nation's food needs do not vary greatly, except through population growth and dietary change. Hence the tendency for farmers to keep on producing, and to absorb the fluctuations in demand through lower or higher prices, means that the nation does not go short of food and fiber when depressions occur. If other parts of the economy reacted in the same way, production would be maintained but prices would fluctuate more than they do now.

Obviously the most desirable national objective is to maintain demand and buying power in such a way that both output and prices can be kept reasonably stable. That objective has been accepted and officially adopted in the Employment Act of 1946. To the extent that it can be achieved, many of the problems that plagued agriculture and other industries during the 1930s will be avoided.

It is not apparent that society would benefit by reducing agricultural output enough in times of severe depression to maintain at full parity the prices of farm products. This would mean reducing the whole economy to a low level of output and consumption. Devices to maintain nonfarm production and thus to assure continuance of a high level of consumption throughout the economy would obviously be desirable. However, the structure of industry, commerce and credit is not such as to lend much encouragement in seeking such a solution.

Unless economic activity as a whole can be kept at high levels it seems inevitable that industrial production, employment and the buying power of urban consumers will be cut back sharply in times of depression. Since they constitute by far the largest part of the national population the impact on agriculture, one of the few industries that tends to continue full-scale production, is especially severe.

Farmers contend, however, that they should not be penalized for continuing to make their normal contribution to society and that their prices should be maintained in such a way that they will at least suffer no more income reduction than do the groups that do not continue to supply society with its normal complement of goods and services. However, in striving for the maintenance of pre-existing price relationships they are, of course, demanding something more than comparable incomes. Full-scale production, even at lower relative prices, would yield them incomes that might be as large as or even greater than those of the nonfarm groups.[9]

This illustrates one of the difficulties of using a price objective alone. It can be argued that higher relative incomes to agriculture in times of depression are warranted because it continues to produce a normal volume of goods. The two arguments more commonly used, however, are that agricultural incomes tend to be below parity with those of nonfarm workers even in times of prosperity, and that the maintenance or restoration of the flow of income into agriculture will help to increase nonfarm activity and restore prosperity. Further discussion of this aspect of the problem is deferred to Chapter 11 since it will be more understandable in light of the later descriptions and analyses of the recent and current agricultural programs.

Adjustment to Changes in Foreign Demand

Though the domestic demand, in terms of real need, is relatively constant, this is not true of the amounts required for shipment abroad. Foreign takings and requirements have fluctuated widely over the past 40 years. It is these changes that create the most serious problems in adjusting output of the major export products of agriculture. For example, World War I brought an insistent demand for more wheat and pork for shipment to the allied nations. During the 1920s the export demand for these products was notably weak. In the 1930s it became still weaker. In the 1940s, exports were again expanded in such a way as to call for amounts far in excess of the requirements of the domestic population.

It is in making quicker adjustments to these fluctuations in foreign demand and supply that farmers especially need help. They have repeatedly been faced with situations in which the impact of a radically changed world situation has impinged heavily on the relatively small number of farmers in the United States. It is here that the justification for direct government aid in making adjustments both up and down is most apparent. While agricultural production could, without too great difficulty, be kept in fairly good balance with domestic requirements, its inflexible supply makes its adjustment to these changes in external demand very slow and difficult.

Since the changes in foreign demand are in part at least a result of decisions by the government, they create certain responsibilities on the part of the government to aid in solving the problems created by them. More important is the fact that the national interest will usually be

9. The same may well be true for labor and industry but as yet no satisfactory procedure has been devised for inducing or forcing price and wage adjustments in industry, labor and distribution which will cause the prices paid by farmers to be anything near as flexible as are the prices of farm products under free-market conditions.

furthered by quicker adjustments than agriculture by itself is able to make.

The kinds of program needed differ, however, as between times when quick expansion is required and when contraction is in order. When the demand is suddenly increased, as in wartime, the resulting price rise usually provides the incentive. The most effective aids to quick adjustment will be the provision of ample credit, help in obtaining labor, fertilizer and machinery, and informational guidance as to how and what to produce.

The reverse situation is much harder to deal with both for the farmer and the government. Land once plowed up cannot easily be put back into more extensive, lower-grade uses. Equipment, buildings, labor force and the general organization of the farm, once they are brought into shape for larger production, are hard to demobilize. Usually a cutback cannot be made without loss. It is this fact which causes agriculture to keep on producing even when prices fall to extremely low levels.[10]

The problem here is to create incentives for the farmer to reduce acreages, usually of the export crops, and to provide financial help that will enable him to weather through until adjustments can be made or until demand revives. Since 1930, the government has accepted a responsibility to aid in making these changes. This has come about partly through the exercise of political power by the farm groups and partly as a result of a widely held belief that improving agricultural incomes will contribute importantly to general prosperity.

During World War II the government gave important assurances in regard to price supports in the postwar years, as a means of overcoming a fear that the war would result in overexpanded production and a sharp break in farm prices such as occurred in 1920. Somewhat similar assurances were given to industry and labor: for industry the privilege of rapid charge-offs of plant and equipment for income tax purposes; for labor, some assurances, under the Employment Act of 1946, that the government would not stand idly by and let unemployment become serious.

Agricultural Output in Relation to National Requirements

During the past forty years, the output of U.S. farm products has increased by about the same percentage as the U.S. population. This comparability is due mainly, however, to the great increase in farm production that occurred in the 1940s. From 1916 to 1940 the rate of population growth was greater than that of agricultural output. (See Table 3.)

10. The need of the farmer to meet fixed obligations such as taxes and interest forces him to keep on producing, sometimes even to increase his production, in periods of very low prices. These factors also affect production and price behavior in many nonfarm activities as well, especially in the smaller concerns.

TABLE 3

RELATIVE RATES OF GROWTH IN FARM OUTPUT AND U.S. POPULATION, 1910–1952

(*Indexes; 1910=100*)

Year	Farm Output	Population	Agricultural Exports a
1910	100	100	100
1911	100	102	124
1912	110	103	119
1913	99	105	115
1914	109	107	149
1915	111	109	133
1916	101	110	128
1917	109	112	109
1918	109	113	157
1919	108	114	146
1920	116	115	138
1921	103	117	148
1922	113	119	122
1923	114	121	113
1924	114	123	133
1925	118	125	115
1926	120	127	147
1927	120	129	122
1928	125	130	128
1929	123	132	108
1930	120	133	100
1931	132	134	109
1932	128	135	95
1933	118	136	94
1934	100	137	62
1935	122	138	72
1936	108	139	65
1937	137	139	89
1938	133	140	72
1939	134	142	80
1940	139	143	32
1941	144	144	62
1942	162	146	70
1943	158	148	85
1944	165	149	81
1945	163	151	122
1946	168	153	127
1947	162	156	114
1948	175	159	138
1949	173	161	123
1950	172	164	118
1951	176	167	141
1952	182	170	104

Sources: For farm output: U.S. Bureau of Agricultural Economics, *Agricultural Outlook Charts, 1954*, p. 32. For population: U.S. Bureau of the Census, *Historical Statistics of the United States, 1789–1945*, 1949, p. 26, and, for later figures, *Statistical Abstract of the United States, 1953*, p. 13. For agricultural exports: based on data from U.S. Department of Agriculture, *Agricultural Statistics, 1952*, p. 556.

a. Year beginning July.

The step-up during the 1940s in the rate of production increase as compared with the rate of growth in population was due partly to favorable weather and strong incentives for all-out production and partly to the larger portion of gross farm production that could be made available for human use, because of the shift from horse and mule power to tractor power. There were also important gains from increased use of fertilizers and from the adoption of better methods and varieties.

Gross farm production, which includes farm-produced feed for work animals, increased only 29 per cent between 1929 and the late 1940s whereas agricultural output, that is, production for human use, increased 44 per cent.[11] The gains from further substitution of mechanical for horse and mule power cannot be expected to be so large as in the past three decades, though the number of horses and mules is still declining. The production of feed for horses and mules was estimated to require 18 million acres of land in 1952 as compared with 25 million in 1949. However, if this entire acreage were to be released it would amount to less than a third of the acreage gained by this means over the past thirty years.

The incentives for maximum effort to produce may not continue as strong as in the decade of the 1940s. During that period farm prices were advancing more rapidly than costs, and profits were high. There was also much emphasis on war needs. More recently, farm costs have been increasing and farm prices declining. The profit margin has been narrowed significantly.

This is not to say that American agriculture cannot or will not continue to increase its output. The opposite is obviously true. But the rate of gain may very possibly be slower than that of the past ten years. Much land still is used inefficiently and more can be brought into production, but in most cases at higher costs per unit of output. Some of the farm labor force still is inefficiently employed, and technological improvements now known have by no means been universally adopted, but it is not likely that inefficiencies of these kinds can be overcome quickly.

Rate of Population Growth High

On the other hand, the rate of population growth continues high, and is much above that predicted by population experts as recently as 1940. Predictions in this realm are beset by many difficulties, but all indicators now available point to the need for a substantial upward adjustment of the population estimates that were commonly accepted a few years ago. Apparently there is prospect of a closer balance between agricultural production and domestic requirements than has prevailed in the past.

This balance, however, depends largely on the levels of employment and national income. These have provided an unusually strong demand

11. See U.S. Department of Agriculture, *Agricultural Statistics, 1952*, p. 661.

for farm products during recent years. Any significant recession from this high level of demand, especially if it occurs while population numbers are near their present levels, will undoubtedly increase the concern over farm surpluses. Even at present levels of employment and income, some kinds of farm products have become available in embarrassingly large quantities and the prices of most of the major groups of farm products have receded substantially from the high levels that prevailed in the postwar years.

The nation can, of course, retain a larger portion of the farm products now being exported if more is needed to supply our growing population. But, though foodstuffs available for export do constitute a reserve that could be retained if low production in this country should make that desirable, the most severe strains on food resources have come during and after wars, and have not been a result of our inability to feed our own population but rather of our desire to feed people in other countries when their supplies were inadequate.

A general appraisal of the trends and conditions discussed above seems to indicate a long-run situation in which farm surpluses will usually not be so large as to be unmanageable, and one in which there may be some concern over the adequacy of the supply of some of the farm commodities, particularly meats. If expansion is needed the problem will not be that of inability to produce more but rather that the additional production may be attainable only at higher cost per unit.

If in the future, needed increases have to be achieved in part through resort to poorer qualities of land and the use of more labor per unit of output, a situation will have developed in which agriculture will find it easier to adjust to the needs of the market. Expansion in the face of increasing cost is less likely to have severe repercussions on the price structure than if such expansion involves reduced costs per unit of output, as has been the case in the recent period of extremely rapid mechanization.

TECHNOLOGICAL CHANGES AND THEIR SIGNIFICANCE

Continuing technological advance has been a distinctive feature of American agriculture almost from the time of the Revolution. With the possible exception of Canada, Australia and New Zealand, no other nation has experienced such a rapid change in the character and efficiency of its agricultural operations. During the nineteenth century the change was mostly mechanical and at a pace that did not cause major disturbances in the industry. The adoption of horse-drawn implements occurred at a comparatively moderate pace, partly because none of the new inventions had such universal application as the tractor, and partly because the rate of invention was such that the change was a step-by-step process rather than an industrial revolution. Furthermore the introduction of horse-drawn implements did not constitute such a significant increase in the power resources of agriculture as that which came with the widespread adoption of tractors and automobiles.

America's rate of population growth during the nineteenth century was probably the fastest known to man, at least for any large area. Thus in spite of the fast pace of settlement, and the quick adoption of machine methods, the markets were not seriously overburdened except in the later decades of the century. The rapidly growing urban population was requiring an ever larger supply of food and fiber and the international setting was such as to provide a large and receptive market for huge quantities of farm products not needed by the domestic population.

Thus the mechanization of agriculture did not lead to large-scale technological unemployment, such as that which accompanied the industrial revolution in England or might be expected to result from the sudden introduction of machine methods in the agriculture of older nations where industrialization is not occurring rapidly. Furthermore a large segment of American agriculture, the cotton South, continued almost exclusively on a hand labor basis.

Largest Growth in Mechanization Occurred After 1940

The shift to horse-drawn equipment for major farm tasks had largely run its course by the turn of the century. Little further change in the power resource of agriculture was apparent until after 1920. Even then, the areas and crops for which tractor power was best adapted were those most seriously affected by the depression. Buying power was low and labor relatively abundant. These factors were even more in evidence during the deep depression of the 1930s.

Not until the 1940s did all elements in the situation combine to favor the kind of dramatic shift to new methods which characterized that decade. By then farm labor was in short supply and wages high, farmers had greatly increased buying power, and the outlet for farm products was almost unlimited. With the further incentive of a patriotic urge for all-out production no more favorable setting for the quick adoption of all known aids to production could be conceived.

Even in the 1920s and the 1930s the rate of increase in the use of tractors was striking. Whereas the official estimates indicate only about 1,000 tractors on American farms in 1910 the number had grown to 246,000 by 1920 (most of the increase occurring after 1915).[12] By 1930 the number had almost quadrupled (to 920,000). A further increase of more than 60 per cent brought the number up to 1.5 million by 1940. In the thirteen-year period following 1940 the number of tractors was

12. See U.S. Department of Agriculture, Miscellaneous Publication No. 630, *Progress of Farm Mechanization,* by M. R. Cooper, G. T. Barton and A. P. Brodell, 1947, pp. 30–36.

more than doubled again, reaching 4.4 million by January 1953.[13] The increase in availability of electric power, and the rapid introduction of electric equipment of many kinds, have also been important factors in reducing the amount of labor required on farms.

Other important labor-saving machines have likewise been added at a rapid rate. Farm motor trucks numbered less than 1,000 in 1910, but had reached 2.5 million by 1953. Nearly a million of these have been added since 1946. Between 1910 and 1952, the number of farm automobiles increased from around 50,000 to 4.4 million; grain combines from 1,000 to 887,000; corn pickers from none to 588,000; and farms with milking machines from 12,000 to 686,000.[14]

This growth in the use of power machines means, of course, that an important part of the farm economy has been transferred to the cities, mines, and oil fields. Tractors are built by city labor, iron and coal are mined by nonfarm workers, and oil is produced off the farms. Consequently the gain in agricultural output resulting from mechanization is not a net social gain. A significant saving has obviously been achieved but not so large a one as that implied by the crude figures for agriculture alone.

Impact of Mechanization Severe in the 1920s and 1930s

This rapid increase in mechanized farming was particularly severe in its impact on agriculture in the 1920s and 1930s. It was a labor-saving, production-increasing change occurring at precisely the time when agriculture had a redundant labor supply and a shrinking market. Thus the complex of technological improvements, of which the machine power revolution was a part, was causing production to be maintained even in the face of low prices and of positive efforts on the part of the government to cut it down.

The rate of technological advance between 1920 and 1950 was apparently such that this factor alone would have kept farm production high and prices low until the transition had run its course had it not been for the great increase in demand in the 1940s. In other words, there is every reason to think that if the war had not occurred American agriculture would have remained in a relatively depressed condition up to 1950 and beyond, probably in spite of governmental efforts to better its situation. It was thus the advent of war and its aftermath of world-wide need that prevented a more prolonged period of painful adjustment to a mechanical

13. U.S. Bureau of Agricultural Economics, *Agricultural Outlook Charts, 1954*, pp. 34–35.

14. *Agricultural Outlook Charts, 1953*, p. 32. By January 1953, grain combines numbered 940,000, corn pickers 635,000 and farms with milking machines 700,000. (*Ibid., 1954*, p. 34.) The machines mentioned are by no means all of those that are changing the labor requirements of agriculture. The pick-up hay-baler, the sugar-beet harvester, the cotton picker and many others have come to be very important in some types of farming.

and technological revolution that, for American agriculture, was somewhat comparable to the one which affected English industrial labor so profoundly in the period around 1800.

Other Improvements in Technology

While interest tends to center on the mechanical revolution discussed above, other important but less dramatic technological changes were being made. The introduction of machines and gasoline power was primarily a labor-saving device; that is, a means of cutting down the amount of labor used directly in agriculture. Paralleling this, there was a type of technological change which may be characterized as yield-increasing. This, in the main, was biological. It undoubtedly will continue to be important in the future. An example is to be seen in the quick adoption of hybrid seed corn in place of the types formerly used. This improvement, in the short space of a few years, came into almost universal use in the major corn areas and may have increased average yields by as much as 10 to 15 per cent or more.

Other changes, most of them less widely recognized, were being made at a very rapid rate during the 1930s and 1940s. Among them were improved methods of feeding, better control of animal diseases, much more use of fertilizer and better practices in the management of soils. In considerable measure these marked the fruition of agricultural research programs initiated many years earlier. The state agricultural experiment stations had been started in the 1880s and research in the United States Department of Agriculture got under way at about the same time. During the years that followed, the whole scientific equipment of society made great strides. In agriculture a groundwork was laid which was to make possible a far wider range of practical application than was apparent in the early years of research activity.

Wider Dissemination of New Knowledge

Not only had these new discoveries and new techniques become available but the mechanism for bringing them quickly into use had also been provided. From 1914 onward the federal and state governments developed a nationwide agricultural extension service for carrying directly into the farm communities the results of research on methods of production, disease control, soil management and improved varieties. By the 1930s these services had become well organized and ably staffed, and farmers had become receptive to the recommendations made by them. Thus there was brought about a much wider and faster adoption of improved methods than had occurred in any previous period.

It is perhaps futile to attempt to assign specific weightings to the various types of technological change in bringing about the unusual increases in farm output that marked the war years and those immediately following. Here, as in the industrial realm, the great body of knowledge that had been accruing during earlier years was brought to bear in raising output as far and as fast as possible. The amazing record of industry in turning out war goods is well known. That of agriculture is similar but with the important difference that it could not quickly build new plant and did not enlarge its work force.

Whatever the weighting assigned to the various types of technological progress, it is clear that agriculture now has as part of its working capital not only a tremendous investment in physical goods for efficient production but a vast accumulation of know-how that was not in existence a decade or two ago.

Agriculture as a Contributor to National Income

Over the past twenty years the income to farm operators for their labor and investment in farming has ranged from about 4 per cent of total national income to a high of 8.6 per cent. The low point both in total farm income and in percentage of national income occurred in the depression years 1932 and 1934. The highest percentages came in 1935 and 1946. The higher proportion received in 1935 was due both to a doubling of incomes to farm operators and the continuance of a very low national income. That of 1946 resulted from the heavy demand for foodstuffs to meet European needs and the abandonment of price controls. Farm prices and incomes moved up in advance of those in most other parts of the economy.

Except under abnormal conditions, such as those just mentioned, farm income tends to remain rather consistently within a range of 5.5 to 8 per cent of total national income.[15] The net incomes from farming, to persons living on farms and those not living on farms, as computed by the Bureau of Agricultural Economics are shown in Table 4.

In most years the portion of total net income from farming which goes to people not living on farms ranges between 12 and 16 per cent. In the severe depression years, 1930 through 1934, this portion was more than 20 per cent of the total, almost 25 per cent in 1932. However, the people living on farms receive income also from nonfarm sources.

Between the extremely depressed year 1934 and the prosperous year 1952, per capita net income from all sources to people living on farms increased from $150 to $905, about sixfold, while in the same period per capita net income to persons not on farms increased from $467 to $1,842, or a little less than fourfold. These figures are stated in current dollars and do not take account of the rise in consumer prices. For the period since 1933 the incomes to persons living on farms, both from

15. U.S. Bureau of the Census, *Statistical Abstract of the United States, 1952*, p. 255, and *Historical Statistics of the United States, 1789–1945*, 1949, p. 12. The figures given do not include adjustments in inventory for agriculture nor do they take account of losses and gains attributable to changes in the valuation of land and buildings.

TABLE 4

Net Income from Farming for Persons Living on Farms and Those Not Living on Farms, United States, 1930–1952

(Millions)

Year	Total Net Income from Farming	Total Net Income from Farming to Persons Living on Farms [a]	Net Income from Farming Paid to Persons Not Living on Farms			
			Total	Farm Wages [b] to Laborers	Farm Mortgage Interest [c]	Net Farm Rent [d]
1930	$6,214	$4,935	$1,279	$371	$570	$338
1931	4,746	3,779	967	277	553	137
1932	3,166	2,396	770	195	526	49
1933	3,677	2,866	811	176	472	163
1934	3,815	2,927	888	191	430	267
1935	6,575	5,587	988	219	396	373
1936	5,602	4,571	1,031	245	364	422
1937	7,362	6,324	1,038	282	341	415
1938	5,996	5,029	967	283	320	364
1939	6,032	5,017	1,015	288	305	422
1940	6,323	5,299	1,024	300	293	431
1941	8,719	7,390	1,329	368	284	677
1942	12,865	11,167	1,698	483	272	943
1943	14,697	12,800	1,897	603	246	1,048
1944	15,025	13,079	1,946	659	230	1,057

1945	$15,425	$13,441	$1,984	$691	$220	$1,073
1946	18,107	15,736	2,371	761	216	1,394
1947	18,964	16,467	2,497	837	222	1,438
1948	21,352	18,871	2,481	898	229	1,354
1949	16,909	14,719	2,190	854	242	1,094
1950	17,428	15,194	2,234	815	264	1,155
1951	20,554	18,100	2,454	869	291	1,294
1952 e	18,794	16,258	2,536	891	319	1,326

Sources: U.S. Department of Agriculture, *Agricultural Statistics, 1952,* pp. 698–99 and *ibid., 1953,* pp. 615–16.

a. Includes government payments.

b. Cash wages and value of perquisites.

c. Interest charges payable during the calendar year on outstanding farm-mortgage debt. This includes some payments made to other farmers.

d. Gross rent to nonfarm landlords minus their share of expenses. However, prior to 1940, farm mortgage interest paid by nonfarm landlords has not been deducted.

e. Preliminary.

farming and other sources, and the incomes to persons not on farms and for the nation as a whole are given in Table 5, together with the relative numbers of people in the two groups.

THE PEOPLE IN AGRICULTURE

Other stratifications in agriculture affect its well-being and behavior in important ways. Some farmers are owner-operators, others are tenants, and many are hired farm workers. Owner-operators benefit (or lose) from changes in the value of land as well as from ups and downs in current income.[16] Tenant farmers gain little and lose little through the rise and fall of land prices and hence concern themselves more with current incomes and costs.

As of 1950 about 3.1 million (57.4 per cent) of the nation's farms were operated by full owners; about .8 million (15.3 per cent) by part-owners; and 1.4 million (26.8 per cent) by tenants.[17] Nearly a fourth of the tenants were croppers, that is, operators who contribute little capital or management and are paid by receiving a share of the crop.[18]

The percentage of farms operated by tenants at the time of the 1950 census was lower than for any census since 1880, when information on tenure was included for the first time. This reflects the marked improvement in farm incomes that occurred during the 1940s which enabled many tenants to become farm owners. The improvements made during the 1930s in the credit arrangements available to farm purchasers also facilitated this transition. Until 1935, the percentage of tenancy had been increasing continuously from the time when data on it first began to be collected. In 1940, nearly 40 per cent of all farms were operated by tenants even though some of the farm programs devised during the 1930s were for the specific purpose of reducing the amount of tenancy.[19]

16. These gains are, to be sure, somewhat illusory so far as the operating farmer is concerned. Higher land values do not in themselves make farmers more prosperous, except as they sell their farms and get out of the business. For the farm-owner who continues in business, higher land values may result in higher taxes and possibly in a tendency to assume larger indebtedness. For the farmer seeking to purchase land they are, of course, a distinct disadvantage. Also the gains in assets during the 1940s from higher valuations on land were largely if not entirely offset by decreases in the value of the dollar. The fact remains, however, that most farm-owners do look upon higher land values as a gain to them.

17. The part-owner group is becoming more significant since the rental of additional land is one of the ways in which owner-operators adjust the sizes of their farms to the possibilities of gain from the use of modern large-scale machinery. Lands which may not be available for purchase, or for which outright purchase would involve too large an outlay of funds, may be combined with owned land through rental arrangements. The 1950 census showed a slightly larger amount of land operated by part-owners than by full owners (426 million acres as compared to 419 million). See U.S. Bureau of the Census and Bureau of Agricultural Economics, *Farm Tenure, A Graphic Summary, 1950,* 1952, p. 6.

18. *U.S. Census of Agriculture, 1950,* Vol. II, General Report, pp. 922-23.

19. For a fuller analysis of the trends and relationships here discussed, see *Farm Tenure, A Graphic Summary, 1950.*

TABLE 5

NET INCOME OF PERSONS LIVING ON FARMS AND THOSE NOT LIVING ON FARMS, UNITED STATES, 1934–1952

Year	Net Income (Millions) Persons on Farms: From Farming [a]	From Nonagricultural Sources	Total	Persons Not on Farms: Total	Total National Income	Population (Thousands) Farm	Nonfarm	Per Capita Net Income Persons on Farms	Persons Not on Farms
1934	$2,927	$1,900	$4,827	$43,897	$48,724	32,305	94,069	$150	$467
1935	5,587	2,000	7,587	49,237	56,824	32,161	95,089	236	518
1936	4,571	2,300	6,871	57,931	64,802	31,737	96,316	216	602
1937	6,324	2,500	8,824	62,852	71,676	31,266	97,559	282	644
1938	5,029	2,300	7,329	58,969	66,298	30,980	98,845	236	597
1939	5,017	2,500	7,517	63,675	71,192	30,840	100,040	244	636
1940	5,299	2,700	7,999	70,068	78,067	30,547	101,575	262	690
1941	7,390	3,100	10,490	84,471	94,961	30,273	103,129	346	819
1942	11,167	3,800	14,967	108,204	123,171	29,234	105,626	512	1,024
1943	12,800	4,200	17,000	134,237	151,237	26,681	110,078	637	1,220
1944	13,079	4,400	17,479	146,342	163,821	25,495	113,902	686	1,285
1945	13,441	4,200	17,641	145,895	163,536	25,295	114,633	697	1,273
1946	15,736	4,300	20,036	147,404	167,440	26,483	114,906	756	1,283
1947	16,467	4,900	21,367	162,172	183,539	27,124	117,002	788	1,336
1948	18,871	5,100	23,971	182,965	206,936	25,903	120,728	925	1,516
1949	14,719	5,200	19,919	182,889	202,808	25,954	123,284	767	1,484
1950	15,194	5,300	20,494	198,443	218,937	25,058	126,619	818	1,567
1951	18,100	5,600	23,700	226,972	250,672	24,037	130,323	986	1,742
1952 [b]	16,258	6,200	22,458	243,468	265,926	24,819	132,162	905	1,842

Source: U.S. Department of Agriculture, Agricultural Statistics, 1953, p. 615.   a. Includes government payments.   b. Preliminary data.

Characteristics of the Hired Farm Worker Group

The other major agricultural group consists of hired farm workers. It varies greatly both in composition and numbers from season to season and from area to area. Some are employed regularly throughout the year and occupy a status not greatly different from that of most workers in other industries. Other large groups work mainly during certain seasons of the year and include many who migrate from one seasonal task to another.

Not all seasonal workers in agriculture are migratory. Some are operators of small farms who supplement their incomes by working as employees on other farms. Others are nonfarm residents living in the communities in which the employing farms are located. Among these are many housewives and high school or college students who do not desire continuous work throughout the year. Still other large groups consist of foreign nationals who may be in this country either legally or illegally, but who do not, in the main, contemplate permanent residence in any given community or in fact in the United States.

Data concerning the numbers and characteristics of the hired farm labor population are somewhat sketchy but certain broad generalizations can be made. About half the farms reported some expenditure for labor in 1949, but only 13 per cent reported the employment of hired labor in the week preceding the enumeration in April 1950.[20] This indicates the great variation in numbers of wage workers employed in agriculture during the year and the very seasonal nature of the work available to such workers. More than 60 per cent of the expenditure for hired labor was on the 9 per cent of the farms which had a value of products sold of $10,000 or more. The principal suppliers of labor on the great majority of farms were the farmers themselves and members of their families.

During 1952, about 2 million persons worked on farms, for wages, to the extent of 25 days or more. However, almost 50 per cent of them worked less than 75 days as farm wage hands.[21] Most of these probably were employed in other occupations during part of the year. The number employed on farms varies from about .9 million in January to about 3.7 million in the fall months.[22] It is probable that more than 4 million different persons are employed as wage workers in agriculture at some time during the year. About half a million of these are migratory, not counting an unknown number of Mexican workers who enter illegally each year.

The regularly employed group consists mainly of white workers, including Mexicans, plus about one third as many who are Negroes. The migratory group, which becomes much more significant in the summer

20. *U.S. Census of Agriculture, 1950,* Vol. II, General Report, p. 1124.
21. U.S. Bureau of Agricultural Economics, *The Hired Farm Working Force of 1952,* 1953, p. 2.
22. U.S. Bureau of Agricultural Economics, *Farm Labor,* February 10, 1953, p. 11.

and fall months, includes large numbers of workers who are not U.S. nationals, the dominant foreign group being citizens of Mexico.

Interests of Hired Workers Differ from Those of Farmers

The interests of the hired labor group in agriculture, which constitutes roughly one fifth of its labor force, are, of course, markedly different from those of the farm operators. Most government farm programs do not touch this group significantly except in indirect ways.[23] Nevertheless, farm wage workers are better off in times when agriculture is prosperous than when it is in depression, and especially when the demand for labor is strong in nonfarm activities. Thus its interests are touched much more significantly by policies relating to levels of activity and prosperity in the economy as a whole than by those specifically designed to benefit agriculture.

Tendency for Farm Population to Remain Overexpanded

Though the number of people employed in agriculture has been declining since 1910, and has shrunk very markedly as a proportion of total population, the manpower remaining in agriculture has continued larger than the needs of the industry in most periods. Only when industry and commerce are very active, and in time of war, has the pull of the urban labor market been strong enough to absorb a good portion of the underemployed and unemployed labor in agriculture.

The distribution of agricultural underemployment is uneven. Certain regions with high rural birth rates and limited agricultural resources tend to be chronically oversupplied with farm workers. This is notably true of the southern Appalachian area and parts of the Old South. Here the wage rates in agriculture tend to be low, both in relation to agricultural wage rates in other areas and to those in urban industries. On the other hand, those rural areas in which living standards are high, and where mechanization has progressed rapidly, are tending more and more to have both birth rates and a wage pattern that approach more closely those of the urban areas.

Some other sections, particularly those heavily engaged in specialty crop production such as the Pacific Coast states, the Gulf states, and those of the Atlantic seaboard, are chronically short of farm labor resident in the areas. In these, heavy reliance is placed on migratory workers brought in from other areas and from outside the United States. Here the factors contributing to low farm-worker incomes are not so much an excessive number of workers as the shortness of the period of work,

23. An exception is the provision in regard to minimum wage rates and the use of child labor in the production of sugar beets and sugar cane. The sugar program is the only one that contains such a requirement.

the inferior social and economic status of the workers, and the unavailability of alternative outlets for the qualifications they have to offer.

By and large the characteristic situation in agriculture, except in times of abnormally high employment as in the 1940s, is that of an industry prone to produce and retain more workers than it can use efficiently. This in turn is a contributing factor to the relatively unfavorable bargaining position of farm people both as farmers and as farm employees.

The increasing mobility of farm people and the vastly enlarged area of contact between rural and urban people, some of which has been a result of the extensive migrations of men in the military services, may well result in a permanently better balance between urban and rural work opportunities. As yet, however, the rural areas produce and educate a larger than proportionate share of the nation's work force.

For the nation as a whole, children under 15 years of age constituted, in 1950, 33.3 per cent of the farm population but only 24.5 per cent of the urban.[24] Nearly 40 per cent of the urban population consisted of people in the most active working ages, 20 to 44 years, whereas only about 30 per cent of the farm population fell in this age group. These divergences are even more pronounced for some groups and some areas. For example, 41.9 per cent of the nonwhite farm population was under 15 years of age in 1950 as against 27.5 per cent for the comparable urban group.

Conditions of Life in Rural and Urban Areas

No brief comment can explain or illustrate the differences in living conditions in urban and rural areas. Both show extreme variations. However, certain broad relationships and trends are of some significance in understanding the nature of the farm policy problem.

Pioneer agriculture in the United States was characterized by physical isolation, a high degree of self-sufficiency and a considerable amount of independence from the ups and downs of the rest of the economy. For most types of agriculture, all of these distinguishing characteristics have been rapidly disappearing in recent decades.

Farmers who produce mainly for the market have come to be much affected by prosperity and depression in the nonfarm economy. They depend heavily on purchased production goods, foodstuffs, and other items bought through off-the-farm, commercial channels. Physical isolation has declined greatly as a result of good roads, the automobile, the telephone and rural free delivery. Even the school facilities and social activities are becoming more like those of the urban communities. Thus the differences both in opportunities and in cash costs of living are becoming less marked.

24. U.S. Bureau of the Census, *Census of Population: 1950,* Vol. II, Characteristics of the Population, Part 1, 1953, pp. 173–74.

There still remains, however, a sizable group of farm families that has retained much of the old, self-sufficient way of life, a group which, by present-day standards, lives in extreme poverty. Its way of life is not so much a retrogression from earlier and higher standards as a standing still while the more progressive elements in agriculture, and most urban groups, moved forward to a much higher standard of living in terms of material welfare.

This divergence presents serious difficulties both in devising appropriate over-all farm policies and in interpreting data concerning the relative well-being of farm and nonfarm groups. Generalized comparisons of the incomes of farm and nonfarm families, if these large groups of relatively unproductive farm families are averaged in, can be highly misleading. Furthermore, general programs designed to overcome an apparently large discrepancy between the incomes of farm and nonfarm people may even increase the great disparity between groups within agriculture, disparities that are greater than those between farmers and urban workers. Such unevenness of impact on the various segments of agriculture may likewise result in wholly abnormal and unwarranted benefits to some individuals, through government payments and otherwise, while giving almost no aid to those most in need.

It is apparent therefore that an enlightened farm policy must take account not only of the declining significance of the relative supposed advantages of urban life but also of the great differences that exist within agriculture itself. In the more advanced types of agriculture, the prevalence of good roads and the availability of the automobile, the tractor, and other power machines may well have made farming more attractive than many types of urban employment. At the same time it may have lessened markedly the advantages formerly derived by farm families from lower cash costs of living. But large numbers of farmers who still use more primitive methods continue to be relatively self-sufficient and less vulnerable to the fluctuations of the general economy. However, this greater stability is at the cost of a lower standard of living.

Per Capita Incomes Low in Agriculture

The incomes of farm people as compared to those of people not on farms have been markedly improved in recent years. It should be recognized, however, that the per capita cash income in agriculture has long been low in comparison to that of urban workers. Even with the great improvement which occurred in the 1940s, per capita cash income of persons living on farms was only $905 in 1952 as compared with $1,842 for persons not on farms.[25] The comparable figures for 1934, a depression year, were $150 and $467. By 1940 the per capita income of

25. *Agricultural Statistics, 1953,* p. 615.

farm people had advanced only to $262 while that of people not living on farms had reached $690.

These figures cannot be taken at face value as measuring the well-being of farmers and nonfarmers. It is clear that a comparison that will achieve universal acceptance cannot be made. Both ways of life involve many intangible values both plus and minus. Both contain some elements of nonmonetary return that do not appear in income data, and both conceal very wide variations from family to family within the group. Some analysis of the kinds of differences in income and the reasons for them will, however, make more understandable the nature of the relationship between the two which has occupied so prominent a place in the discussions of farm policy in recent decades.

In the first place the two groups are not of the same composition. Approximately 8 million persons, or about one third of the farm population, are children under 15 years of age and not normally in the work force except in an incidental way. If the urban population had a correspondingly high proportion of children the number in the age group 15 years and over would be smaller by some 8 million persons. That would mean undoubtedly at least 3 million fewer workers to contribute to the incomes of urban families. This fact in itself causes a significant distortion of the per capita cash income figures. Agriculture has a smaller proportion of income earners. At the same time, however, it produces and maintains during their nonproductive, early years an important portion of the workers who later are included in the urban labor force.

Cost of Living Differences

As a partial offset to its inferior cash income position, agriculture has available very important possibilities for economizing in the cash cost of living. Housing expense on the farm is usually only the cost of upkeep and taxes, whereas the urban dweller normally pays a substantial portion of his income in the form of rent. The farm home is likely to be poorer in amenities and quality but may be richer in spaciousness and some other intangibles. However, these values are by no means all in favor of the farm family. Its access to schools, health facilities and recreation may be distinctly below that of the urban dweller. Yet it still is true that one man's meat may be another man's poison. Many urban dwellers would require a substantial bonus to live on farms while many farmers, and some urban people, greatly prefer the complex of values that goes with life in the country.

However that may be, the farm family can ordinarily live in its accustomed way at a cash cost for housing that may be as much as $400 to $600 less than that of the city family of comparable status. This difference may offset as much as $150 to $200 of the difference in per capita incomes.

In like manner the farm family may, and usually does, produce an important part of its food supply instead of paying cash for it. The rising prices of foods, particularly of meats, and the rapid introduction of deep-freeze units on the farms, may well make a difference in cash outlays for food of $400 or more per year as between many farm families and their urban counterparts. These differences, because of the difficulty of measurement and the unevenness of incidence, are frequently omitted or understated in making comparisons of the incomes of the two groups.

THE INVESTMENT IN AGRICULTURE

As of January 1, 1953, the investment in American agriculture was about $136 billion, this being made up as follows (in billions): [26]

Real estate	$92
Livestock	15
Machinery and motor vehicles	17
Crops, stored on and off farms	9
Investment in cooperatives	3
Total	$136

In addition, farmers had about $10 billion in household furnishings and equipment, $14 billion in bank deposits and currency, and $5 billion in United States savings bonds.

Against these assets the industry had liabilities of about $15 billion constituted as follows: real estate debt, $7 billion; non-real estate debt, excluding Commodity Credit Corporation loans, $4 billion; loans held or guaranteed by the Commodity Credit Corporation, $1 billion; and obligations to other creditors, such as merchants, dealers and so on, $3 billion.

The total assets listed above represented an increase of about 207 per cent as compared to the values given in 1940, which stood at $54 billion. The level attained by 1953 was partly a recovery from the sharp decline that marked the 1920s and early 1930s, and partly a substantial increase in the investment in farm machinery, motor vehicles and liquid assets. The value of livestock and crops held has likewise increased greatly.

Valuations in Terms of 1940 Prices

If the valuations given above are adjusted to 1940 prices, the real changes in the assets of American agriculture become more apparent. Comparisons made on this basis are shown in Table 6. In 1940 dollars, physical assets increased 22 per cent between 1940 and 1953. This figure does not take account of changes in the value of real estate. The value of livestock has remained about constant in terms of 1940 dollars. The

26. U.S. Bureau of Agricultural Economics, *The Balance Sheet of Agriculture, 1953,* Agriculture Information Bulletin No. 115, p. 2.

TABLE 6

VALUE OF AGRICULTURAL ASSETS IN 1953 STATED IN TERMS OF
1940 DOLLARS

Assets	Value in 1940 (Billions of dollars)	Value in 1953 (Billions of 1940 dollars)	Net Change, Percentage
Physical assets			
Real estate [a]	$33.6	$33.6	0
Livestock	5.1	5.2	+1
Machinery and motor vehicles	3.1	7.5	+141
Crops stored on and off farms	2.6	3.1	+19
Household furnishings and equipment [b]	4.3	10.0 [c]	+134
Financial assets (valued in current dollars)			
Deposits and currency	3.9	14.2	+264
United States savings bonds	0.3	5.0	+1567
Investments in cooperatives	0.8	2.7 [c]	+237

Source: U.S. Bureau of Agricultural Economics, *The Balance Sheet of Agriculture, 1953,* Agriculture Information Bulletin No. 115, p. 4. Percentages are as given in the source cited and were computed from unrounded data.

a. Figures do not reflect net physical improvements or net depletion of productivity of agricultural lands.
b. Not deflated. Estimated value in 1940 plus purchases and minus depreciation.
c. Preliminary data.

principal changes are in the value of machinery and motor vehicles, stored crops and household equipment. Liquid assets have also increased greatly.

The most significant change is in the investment in farm machinery. Agriculture's assets in the form of real estate have remained substantially unchanged but the value of farm machinery and motor vehicles owned has more than doubled since 1940, reflecting the fastest rate of mechanization in the history of the industry. There has also been substantial betterment in the equipment of farm homes. The other major change is a vastly improved financial situation on the part of farmers. Even allowing for the decreased purchasing power of the dollar, farmers now have well over twice as much buying power in the form of liquid assets as they had in 1940.

Changes in the Financial Situation of Farmers, 1920–1953

While the data on farm incomes and gains in assets reflect the marked improvement in agricultural prosperity during the decade of the 1940s, this period followed one of some twenty years in which the industry was in almost continuous financial difficulties, at times in desperate straits.

The high farm incomes of 1916 to 1919 followed a decade and a half in which the relative position of agriculture had shown marked improvement as compared to that of the latter part of the nineteenth century. However, the inflated incomes of World War I proved to be only an illusory gain for agriculture. Though the industry received during those years some $18 billion more in income than it would have had if prices, costs and output had remained at 1914 levels, much of the gain was dissipated through speculation in land and purebred livestock, unwise purchase of stocks, and an era of generally free spending.

The sudden and unexpected decline in farm prices which occurred in 1920–1922 found farmers with a mortgage debt some 2.5 times that of the prewar years, and inflated costs that did not recede proportionately as prices went down. In contrast, the rest of the economy gained momentum, after a brief recession following 1920, and the prices of nearly all commodities and services the farmer had to buy remained high relative to prices of things he had to sell.

He was thus caught in a squeeze which was made doubly irksome by his growing desire for automobiles, better roads, improved schools and additional production equipment. Many of the major products of agriculture, particularly wheat, hogs, beef cattle and wool, fell to levels which would have threatened the solvency of the industry even without the heavy burden of debt carried over from the war and early postwar years. Great numbers of banks in the rural areas were forced to close their doors and credit became difficult to obtain.[27] The result was an upsurge of demand for special relief to agriculture that exceeded any such movement previously experienced in the United States.

Slow Recovery in the 1920s

During the 1920s agriculture made slow but significant recovery. The overexpanded acreage in war crops was cut down, war inventories were liquidated, costs were reduced and there was a larger than usual movement of farm people out of agriculture.[28] By 1929 many farmers had

27. Between 1921 and 1929 nearly 6,000 banks closed their doors. (*Statistical Abstract, 1950*, p. 404.) This was a substantially larger number than all that had been forced into liquidation in the long period between 1864 and 1920, during which time at least two other major depressions had occurred. The loss of banks and the accompanying credit stringency were notably severe in the rural areas, particularly in the Great Plains wheat belt.

28. The net outmovement from agriculture reached 1,137,000 in 1922, a record for such shifts up to that time. (See *Historical Statistics of the United States*, p. 31.) This transfer from agriculture to urban employment in that period was not, however, sufficiently large to step up markedly the per capita income in agriculture. A much larger shift occurred during the early 1940s. Net outmovement reached more than 1.3 million in 1941 and was at an all-time high of 2.8 million in 1943. The rate of transfer declined thereafter until 1945. It was then reversed, and about 1.3 million more people returned to the farms than left them. This latter movement out of and into agriculture was, of course, in large part, a movement into the armed forces and war industries and a return to agriculture after the war.

regained a tolerable level of well-being and a debt structure that was manageable. Prices still were low in terms of the relationship to nonfarm prices that had prevailed prior to World War I, but there appeared to be a prospect that the two would eventually come into better balance.[29]

Farm mortgage debt had been reduced only moderately but the marginal and submarginal borrowers had for the most part been liquidated. The long campaign for special farm legislation was still being pushed, but with less vigor than in the earlier years of the decade. It was in this somewhat less tense setting that the program of the Federal Farm Board was launched, a program which, in its original formulation, contemplated mainly a reorganization and improvement of the farm marketing system rather than a rescue operation for a desperately impoverished agriculture.

Effects of the Stock Market Collapse of 1929

The economic collapse which began with the stock market crash of 1929 caught farmers in the middle of a period of readjustment and recovery which had not yet run its course. The major impact of the depression, so far as agriculture was concerned, was on its price structure. The index of farm output stood at 97 in 1929 (1935–39 = 100). It dropped off to 95 in 1930, largely as a consequence of droughts, but rose to 104 in 1931 and stood at 101 in 1932. The sharp reduction that marked the years 1933–1936 was largely a result of catastrophic droughts rather than of intentional restrictions on production.[30]

The prices of farm products fell off by more than half between 1929 and 1932. Several of the major products of agriculture fell to levels lower than any experienced since the turn of the century. The financial situation of farmers was even more desperate than it had been in the 1890s, since their public and private commitments required much higher cash outlays than in the earlier period.[31]

Most industrial enterprises made sharp cutbacks in production. Iron and steel output dropped from an index of 133 in 1929 (1935–39 = 100) to 32 in 1932. Lumber production fell off from 152 to 49, machinery from 130 to 43, and chemicals from 89 to 68. Even the output of important consumption goods such as shoes declined from 89 in 1929 to 75 in 1930.[32]

29. The ratio of prices received by farmers to prices paid by them reached 92 in 1928 and 1929 (1910–14 = 100) and had been as high as 95 in 1925.

30. Except for such reductions as were brought about by the government's agricultural adjustment program, which is discussed later. The index of farm output fell off to 93 in 1933, and to 79 in 1934. It recovered to 96 in 1935 but dropped again, to 85, in 1936. Thereafter, with more favorable weather and price conditions, it remained consistently at a level well above that of 1929. *Agricultural Statistics, 1950,* p. 604.

31. The *wholesale* prices of farm products stood at 68 in 1932. Their lowest levels in the depression of the 1890s were 56 in 1896 and 60 in 1897. At that time, however, the all-commodities index stood at 68 as compared to 95 in 1932 (from the Warren and Pearson index as given in *Historical Statistics of the United States,* p. 231).

32. *Agricultural Statistics, 1950,* p. 601.

The price index for all commodities bought for use in production and family maintenance in agriculture declined from 150 to 102, or 32 per cent, but farm prices fell by more than 56 per cent. At the same time farm taxes, though lower than in the 1920s, were still more than twice what they had been before World War I, and interest obligations were some 85 per cent above those prevailing in 1910 to 1914.

More Than a Million Farmers Lost Their Farms

By 1932, hundreds of thousands of farmers were in desperate financial straits. The foreclosure rate, which had customarily run in the order of three to four per thousand farms before World War I, was now around 30 per thousand. In addition, great numbers of sales listed as voluntary were actually forced transfers from mortgagors to mortgagees, without going through the process of foreclosure. It is estimated that about 1.4 million operating farm owners, about one out of every 4, lost their farms during the tragic years between 1930 and 1937. Many who did not lose out completely saw their equities reduced to almost nothing.

The large-scale rescue operation carried out by the federally sponsored farm credit agencies from 1933 on brought stability to the financial situation in agriculture and reduced the foreclosure rate to about the pre-World War I level. Thereafter, increasing incomes, downward adjustments in expenses and the improved methods of payment that had been introduced in the 1930s resulted in a substantial reduction in the amount of farm mortgage debt. By 1940 it stood at $6.4 billion as compared to $9.7 billion in 1929.[33] Agriculture still was in a less than prosperous condition when the outbreak of war in Europe brought into being conditions that were to give it the most prosperous period in its history.

The decade of the 1940s was marked by continuously high farm production, very favorable prices, and a rapidly improving financial situation. Farm mortgage debt was reduced to less than $5 billion by 1945; many tenants had become owners; and the liquid assets of farmers had been built up to all-time highs.

The amount of mortgage debt owed on American farms, in 1945, was the lowest since 1914. Thereafter, it increased moderately. It stood at $5.6 billion in 1950 as compared to $4.9 billion in 1945. However, the average equity per mortgaged farm had increased from $6,672 to $11,125. The increase in mortgage debt between 1945 and 1950 was uneven as between different sections of the country. For the West it was 55 per cent; in the South, only 24 per cent, while in the North the amount declined by 1.5 per cent.[34]

33. A good part of this decrease was a result of the foreclosures described above. When a farm mortgage is foreclosed the farm often passes to the mortgagee on a debt-free basis.

34. Data from U.S. Bureau of the Census and Bureau of Agricultural Economics, *1950 Farm-Mortgage Debt*, 1952, pp. 7-8.

Chapter 3

Research, Service and Educational Programs

THE SLOGAN "equality for agriculture" was coined in the 1920s. This, however, was not the beginning of the effort to equalize urban and rural opportunities. The federal government began to take steps looking in that direction at least as early as 1862 when the land-grant colleges and the United States Department of Agriculture were established.

The land-grant colleges were launched as a means of providing technical and general education at college level for young people contemplating careers in agriculture and the mechanic arts. The stated purpose of the Department of Agriculture was "to acquire and to diffuse among the people of the United States useful information on subjects connected with agriculture in the most general and comprehensive sense of that word, and to procure, propagate and distribute among the people new and valuable seeds and plants." Though collection of statistics and the distribution of seeds and plants were stressed, the carrying on of "practical and scientific experiments" was also specified as one of the purposes of the new department.[1]

Some twenty-five years later, federal aid to agriculture was broadened by the provision of annual grants to the states for the creation and maintenance of agricultural experiment stations.[2] Such grants have been continued and greatly enlarged since that time.

The Department of Agriculture began to develop a research program shortly after it was created, though its activities in this realm did not become important until later. A Division of Chemistry was established in 1862 and divisions of Entomology and Fibre Investigations in 1863. The analysis of soils was put on a similar basis in 1865. Investigations relating to animal diseases were begun in 1878 and the Bureau of Animal Industry was created in 1884.[3]

1. Congressional committees on agriculture had been established earlier (in the House in 1820 and in the Senate in 1825). From then on publications relating to agriculture were authorized from time to time and the collection of agricultural statistics was begun officially in 1839.

2. Fifteen of the states had already set up agricultural experiment stations with funds appropriated by the state legislatures. The federal aid provided caused this movement to expand quickly to all of the states and eventually to Hawaii, Alaska and Puerto Rico. Federal participation not only gave stimulus to the movement but provided leadership and cohesiveness as well.

3. For a fuller account of departmental growth and problems in this period see Earle D. Ross, "The United States Department of Agriculture During the Commissionership," *Agricultural History*, July 1946, pp. 129–43.

The Department of Agriculture was raised to Cabinet status in 1889. From then on, it grew rapidly and various additional activities were assigned to it, some of them not closely related to agriculture. For example, the Weather Bureau was transferred from the War Department in 1891, the Office of Road Inquiry was created in 1893 and the Biological Survey, established in 1885, was raised to bureau status in 1905. In 1914, a further important step was taken through creation of the state-federal system of agricultural extension services designed to carry the results of agricultural research into the farm communities.

In the meantime, and in the years since, many other general services relating to agriculture have been provided by the federal government. Some, such as meat inspection, grain inspection and market reports, are for the benefit of society as a whole. Others, such as rural mail delivery, rural electrification and farm-to-market roads, increase farm efficiency and remove some of the handicaps of life in the country. They also facilitate sales by urban businessmen and contribute in many ways to the well-being of the community, both urban and rural.

It is the purpose of this chapter to indicate the nature of these programs, explain how and why they came about and to provide a general analysis of their significance, costs and implications.

Two Types of Aid to Agriculture

Most of the many federal programs relating to agriculture can be grouped into two broad categories, those designed to increase the efficiency of agricultural production and marketing and those set up to improve the *relative* prices, incomes and living conditions of farmers. Some activities do not fall easily into either classification but most of the important ones do.

From activities of the first kind, society as a whole gains along with agriculture. It may, in fact, be the principal beneficiary in the long run. In this class are most of the research and educational programs carried on by the federal and state governments and much of the regulatory and service work as well. Such things as improved farm-to-market roads, rural mail delivery and the provision of electric power also fall partly in this category. Programs of this kind usually result in lower costs. Since agriculture is a very competitive industry, lower costs tend to be reflected in lower prices to consumers.

For example, the introduction of hybrid seed corn has raised yields and lowered costs substantially. It is a direct result of long-continued research on genetics. Between 1931 and 1933 we used from 109 to 113 million acres of land to grow about 2.5 billion bushels of corn. In the late 1940s we were producing about 3.3 billion bushels on less than 90 million acres, except in 1947 when corn yields were cut heavily by drought.

Had yields continued at the levels of the early 1930s we would have needed around 40 million more acres to produce the amount of corn we used in the late 1940s. Not all of this gain was from the use of hybrid seed. Some of it resulted from heavier fertilization and better methods of farming, but these too were products of research and education. Without such gains in yield it is obvious that much more land and labor would be needed to produce the amount of corn we now use. The prices of hogs and cattle would have to be higher or we would have to do with fewer of them.

Other Gains Important

Few of the gains are so striking and identifiable as the introduction of hybrid seed corn, but great strides have been made in other fields as well. The losses from hog cholera in some years have run as high as 6 million head valued at as much as $65 million. This disease has largely been brought under control, though at some continuing expense for immunization. The control of tuberculosis in swine has reduced the number of condemned carcasses from around 65,000 annually to about 9,000. Cattle carcasses condemned have been reduced from about 46,000 per year to less than 1,000. The incidence of tuberculosis in cattle stood at 4 per cent in 1922 but had been reduced to 0.6 per cent by 1935.[4]

Growers of cotton in the lower Rio Grande valley estimate that controls applied to the pink bollworm increased their production for 1947–49 by an amount valued at $35 million. The steps taken to reduce stem rust in wheat, which cut production by some 200 million bushels in 1916 and forced resort to bread rationing, apparently brought these losses down to around 40 million bushels annually in the period 1918–1924. Wheat yields averaged above 17 bushels per acre from 1944 through 1948 as against approximately 14 bushels in the years 1930–1932, which were good wheat years. We have been producing in recent years on 20 to 25 million acres about the same amount of cotton as we were producing on more than 40 million acres in the period around 1930.

Examples of this kind could be listed at great length but these are sufficient to indicate the nature and magnitude of the gains from agricultural research and education. Equally important gains could be shown in milk production per cow, eggs laid per hen and improvements made in quality of product, reduction of losses in shipment and so on.[5] The significance of the over-all change in agricultural productivity is illus-

4. U.S. Department of Agriculture, *Yearbook of Agriculture, 1936*, pp. 90–91. This was the most extensive veterinary campaign conducted in any country at any time. It resulted in the detection and slaughter of some 3 million tuberculous cattle.

5. U.S. average milk production per cow increased from 3,646 pounds in 1906 to 5,326 pounds in 1951. Egg production per hen from less than 90 in 1909 to more than 140 in 1950. Byron T. Shaw, *The Role of Research in Meeting Future Agricultural Requirements,* paper presented at the 44th Annual Meeting of the American Society of Agronomy, Cincinnati, November 18, 1952, U.S. Department of Agriculture, pp. 7 and 20.

trated more strikingly in a recent paper by Dr. Harry R. Wellman, Vice President, Agricultural Sciences, University of California. He comments as follows:

In 1940 the labor force engaged in agriculture numbered 11,800,000 persons, including both farm operators and hired workers. With the same level of productivity per worker as existed in 1940, it would have required 14,500,000 farm workers to produce the enlarged output of 1950. Because of the increase in productivity per worker, the 1950 output was actually produced with 10,400,000 workers. Annual earnings per farm worker in 1950 averaged $1,432. At the same rate of earnings, the aggregate cost of an additional 4,100,000 workers would have been about six billion dollars.[6]

As to the factors which have led to this great increase in productivity, Dr. Sherman E. Johnson commented as follows: "the foundation for the wartime and early postwar increases in production was built up in the 20-year period between the two World Wars. It was built on the tremendous improvements that have been made in mechanization, in land use, in conservation, fertility, and cultural practices, in development of new crops and new varieties, and in increasing the efficiency of livestock production." [7]

Not all of this gain in output per man in agriculture resulted from technological changes on the part of agriculture alone. Some of it has come about through the increased use of things produced by nonfarm people; for example, tractors, motor trucks and other mechanical aids; and increased use of commercial fertilizers, gasoline, pesticides and so on. However, a very large part of the increase is undoubtedly due to technological advances within agriculture itself.

Significance and Incidence of Technological Gains

It is technological advances of these and other kinds that have made possible the great upsurge in food and fiber production in recent years and have enabled the United States to supply both its own people and other nations through the efforts of an agricultural labor force that numbers about a sixth of our total number of workers. If, like some primitive countries, we still had to use 50 to 80 per cent of our labor force to produce food and fiber we would have had to forego the tremendous gains in industrial productivity and standards of living which we have achieved in recent decades. The continuance of the upward trend in standards of living and the adequacy of future food supplies obviously depend on continuing progress in agricultural production that will keep agriculture in step with the technological progress being made in other parts of the economy.

6. Paper read before Central Coast Council of the California State Chamber of Commerce, October 2, 1953, University of California, Berkeley.
7. Sherman E. Johnson, *Changes in American Farming*, U.S. Bureau of Agricultural Economics, Miscellaneous Publication No. 707, December 1949, p. 12.

Much of the gain from improvements of the kinds described above accrues at first to the relatively small groups of progressive farmers who first put them into practice. Their production is increased and their costs reduced without changing significantly the over-all volume of production. As the improved methods come to be widely adopted they affect production, costs and prices throughout the industry, and most of the gains are passed on to society in the form of larger supplies or lower prices.

Similar social gains result from genuine economies in the marketing of farm products. The cost of market operations constitutes the spread between the prices received by farmers and the prices paid by consumers. To the extent that these processes can be made more efficient, the gains flow partly to farmers and partly to consumers. The actual incidence depends on complex supply and demand relationships and kinds of market organization that differ as between products and time periods. In this category are such things as the establishment of standard grades, the licensing of warehouses, the dissemination of market news and so on. This generalization of course does not tell us which activities are wisely conceived, how much should be spent on each of them or whether they are as efficient as they might be.

Programs Designed to Improve Farm Living Conditions

The activities designed to improve farm incomes and living conditions are mainly for the benefit of farmers, though they have broader significance as well. They can be divided roughly into two general types of programs, those designed to equalize rural and urban facilities and services and those having as their principal purpose the raising of farm prices and incomes relative to those received by other economic groups. The price and income programs are dealt with in succeeding chapters. Here we are concerned mainly with services supplied as a means of improving the conditions of life in rural areas by extending to them facilities that are commonly available to people who live in cities and towns.

Some of these activities antedate the price programs commonly associated with the idea of equality for agriculture but they have been considerably expanded in recent years. They include such things as rural mail delivery, parcel post, the improvement of farm-to-market roads, home economics extension work and, more recently, rural electrification and rural telephone development.

Here the purpose is to offset the disadvantages of farm life that grow out of the widely scattered nature of the industry. Comparable services are available to most urban residents, but at less cost per person because the distances to be covered are so much smaller. By providing services of this kind at public expense the government has moved in the direction of equality of real incomes as between farm and nonfarm people, though not in the form of prices and cash incomes. This type of aid has now been carried to a point where most farmers can have a good many of the conveniences of life that formerly were available only to people living in towns and cities.

The "Action Programs"

The so-called "action programs," to be described later, differ from those mentioned above in a number of ways.[8] Since most of them are designed to give farmers a larger share of the total national money income, they constitute by implication an effort on the part of the government to raise the prices paid by consumers. This makes them much more controversial. Furthermore, they require far larger inputs of federal funds than do the older types of program. Also, they involve much more extensive intervention by government in the processes of production, marketing and price-making than had ever been contemplated previously, except in the controls over rates charged by public utilities.

The benefits of such programs presumably accrue mainly to farmers rather than to the general public except for such indirect benefits as come from increased buying power and more stable conditions in the farm areas. They are not cost-reducing or efficiency-increasing so far as society as a whole is concerned. If the heavy expenditure of public funds and the far-reaching changes in government structure and functioning are to be justified it will have to be on different grounds than in most of the older types of government assistance to agriculture.

Such justification is claimed on the ground that other economic groups have gained at the expense of agriculture because of the changing structure of the economy and new concentrations of power. Partly, of course, the extensive entry of the government into these fields of activity came as a result of much stronger, more militant and more class-conscious organization of farmers. The political power of the farm groups grew enormously during the 1920s, as a result of the rapid development of organization and of techniques for exerting political pressure. The danger of disintegration in the economic structure of agriculture in the 1930s also played a part. The breakdown of credit, the increase in tenancy and the migration of displaced farm families were matters of general public concern.

But the older types of activity have not been replaced as a result of these new developments in attitudes and mechanisms which have come to be regarded as the "farm program" of the federal government. In fact they too have been expanded and strengthened in recent years. It may

8. The term "action programs" was coined in the 1930s to designate those types of programs in which the government intervenes directly in marketing and production for the purpose of controlling supply, raising prices or transferring income. The term is somewhat vague and undefinable in that many of the other programs look to the improvement of farm incomes and living conditions. However, it has some usefulness in distinguishing the very direct and positive types of income-increasing programs from the more general ones such as those providing for education, research, pest control and so on.

be that they will prove the most enduring and perhaps the most fundamental of the various kinds of aid to agriculture. Certainly they are the
least controversial. In order that their place in the over-all program
relating to agriculture may be recognized and understood they are briefly
described and analyzed before taking up the more controversial programs
that have been so much discussed in recent years.

THE RESEARCH AND EDUCATION PROGRAMS

The creation of the land-grant college system was the first step in the
development of the far-reaching network of specialized research and
educational agencies now serving agriculture at the state and local levels.
The procedure used was to assign to each state an amount of public-
domain land equal to 30,000 acres for each senator and representative
in Congress. This land was to be sold by the states, the proceeds to be
used in creating an endowment fund for the support of a college of
agriculture and mechanic arts. Hence the name "land-grant colleges and
universities" which is now applied to these institutions.

Through the sale of some 17 million acres of lands so assigned, endowment funds amounting to approximately $53 million were created.⁹ The
income from these funds has been supplemented by continuing annual
appropriations of federal funds under a series of later acts, the Second
Morrill Act (1890), the Nelson Amendment (1907) and the Bankhead-
Jones Act (1935), and by very large contributions from the state and
territorial governments. Under the acts mentioned above, the federal
government in 1953 was contributing to the support of the land-grant
colleges at the rate of $5,030,000 per annum, in addition to the income
derived from the land grants provided in the act of 1862.¹⁰

These colleges and universities have grown enormously in the ninety
years since they were established. Most of them have come to be the
principal publicly supported institutions of higher learning in their re-
spective states and territories. Most of their support now comes from
state and territorial appropriations and private sources.

9. U.S. Office of Education, *Statistics of Land-Grant Colleges and Universities,* year
ended June 30, 1952, Bulletin No. 1, 1953, pp. 50–51. As of June 30, 1952, the remaining
unsold lands amounted to 581,321 acres valued at $6,003,154. Income on the invested
funds and from rentals was $1,672,861 for the year ended June 30, 1952. The proceeds
from the sale of these lands were to be invested "in stocks of the United States or of
the states, or some other safe stocks yielding not less than five per centum upon the par
values of said stocks." The data given above are for the lands granted in 1862. As of
June 30, 1952, other federal grants to the land-grant colleges had resulted in an inventory of $8,837,558 in unsold lands and a fund of $27,776,001 which are in addition to the
endowment derived from the 1862 grants.

In somewhat similar manner, sizable grants of public lands were made for the support
of elementary schools. While not made specifically for agriculture, this provision was of
greatest importance to the states that were predominately agricultural and hence was, in
the main, a contribution to rural education. As of 1952, 98,532,000 acres had been so
allotted. U.S. Bureau of the Census, *Statistical Abstract of the United States, 1953,* p. 176.

10. *Budget of the United States Government for Fiscal 1955,* p. 1155.

The importance of the federal action taken, so far as general college instruction is concerned, was in providing stimulus for the creation of such institutions and placing their emphasis on scientific and professional training and research rather than on the classical types of education long maintained in the older colleges and universities. As of now, the land-grant colleges and universities are the principal centers of scientific and professional instruction not only in agriculture but in other fields as well. Except for special projects financed by the federal government in connection with its own programs, they do not depend importantly on the federal government either for funds or guidance, except in the research activities in agriculture, engineering, and home economics. They have been a significant factor in the democratizing of higher education which has been evident in the years since they were established.

Federal Aid for Agricultural Research

Of more direct interest to farmers was the program of federal aid for agricultural research in state experiment stations which was started in 1887. The main body of technical research in agriculture has grown up simultaneously in the state experiment stations and in the Department of Agriculture. The state stations were established under the Hatch Act of 1887, which provided a continuing annual grant of $15,000 to each state for the support of an agricultural experiment station. Federal support was increased from time to time thereafter. The Adams Act (1906) raised the amount to $30,000 annually. The Purnell Act (1925) added another $60,000 per year and opened the way for economic and sociological investigations as part of the program. (The Hatch and Adams Acts provided only for research in the natural sciences.)

Support for research in the state experiment stations was further increased by the Bankhead-Jones Act of 1935 and still more by the Research and Marketing Act of 1946. This latter act, if fully implemented by appropriations, would have more than doubled the amount of money available for agricultural research by 1951.[11] The appropriations made thus far have been much below the amounts authorized.[12] State experiment station expenditures of federal funds under all of these acts combined were at an annual rate of $12,520,000 in fiscal 1953. In addition they were spending $62,500,000 appropriated by the states and territories.[13]

11. Parts of the funds provided under both the Bankhead-Jones Act and the Research and Marketing Act of 1946 are assigned to the Secretary of Agriculture. Those provided under the earlier acts mentioned are exclusively for use in the state agricultural experiment stations.

12. The authorization was for annually increasing amounts which, for both the state experiment stations and the Department of Agriculture, would amount to $61 million of Research and Marketing Act funds by 1951 and would be continued at that level or higher thereafter. This was to be in addition to funds appropriated under other acts.

13. U.S. House Appropriations Committee, *Department of Agriculture Appropriations for 1955*, Hearings, Part 2, p. 310.

During these same years, rapidly increasing appropriations were being made for research in the United States Department of Agriculture and its various substations. By 1953, these were at the rate of $43,590,000 per annum.[14] Thus the total input of federal funds for agricultural research was at an annual rate of $56,110,000. This, added to the funds received by the state and territorial experiment stations from other sources, makes a total of $118,610,000 spent on agricultural research by publicly supported institutions in 1953. This was approximately 0.3 of one per cent of the gross value of farm products sold in that year.

Extension Services Added in 1914

The third main phase of agricultural education and research was provided through the Smith-Lever Act of 1914. This initiated a joint federal-state program for extending to the rural communities the results of the researches carried on in the state experiment stations and the United States Department of Agriculture and for carrying on an extensive program of adult education in rural areas.[15]

The extension services have now become an important and apparently permanent feature of the institutional structure of American agriculture. They conduct demonstrations, provide technical information, supervise and stimulate agricultural youth activities (4-H Clubs), carry on educational work in home economics, and serve as a channel of information between the federal and state agricultural agencies and the farm communities. In addition they provide many incidental services to farmers and other local groups. The greatly increased governmental activity that marked both the depression of the 1930s and the war period of the 1940s emphasized the need for informational contacts with the rural areas, and strengthened the position of the extension services in both farmer and congressional thinking.

These services are now organized in more than 3,100 agricultural counties. Their staffs, including county farm advisers, state extension specialists, administrators and the small staff in the United States Depart-

14. *Ibid.* This figure includes about $5 million assigned for research in forestry which, though administered through the Department of Agriculture, is not, strictly speaking, a part of the farm research program though some of it is used on closely related types of research such as range management, watershed protection and farm forestry operations.

15. This work was started in the South around 1900, through the pioneer efforts of Dr. Seaman A. Knapp. In the beginning it was financed in a small way by the United States Department of Agriculture. Its possibilities soon became so evident that funds for expansion were provided by various private foundations, chambers of commerce, and corporations. Public interest grew rapidly. As a consequence, this type of agricultural education was established more formally through passage of the Smith-Lever Act, which provided for developing the work on a nationwide basis. Though at first received with skepticism by some farmers, the agricultural extension services expanded rapidly during World War I, as a means of furthering the food production and conservation activities of the War Food Administration. Since that time, farmer support has increased markedly, and both federal and state appropriations for extension work have been increased substantially.

ment of Agriculture, number some 12,624 men and women. Financial support by the federal government grew from nothing in 1900 to $32,-150,109 in 1953. During the same period annual appropriations of state funds grew to $30,544,443 and those appropriated by the counties to $19,644,124. Farmers were providing, in 1953, through membership fees in farm organizations, $2,254,598. Thus the total public support of this activity in 1953 (omitting farmer contributions) was $82,338,676.[16]

Support for High School Courses in Agriculture Added in 1916

For many years the rural communities and farmer spokesmen had expressed interest in having special training in agriculture made available at the secondary school level. Some high schools did establish work of this kind and a number of privately financed institutions undertook to provide this type of practical vocational training. There was, in fact, a more definitely expressed farmer interest in this kind of education than in either agricultural college training or the work of the extension services.

Secondary school training in agriculture was put on a national, federal-aid basis through passage of the Smith-Hughes Act of 1916. That act has been supplemented by later laws which provide similar training in a broader range of subject matter. For example, the George-Barden Act of 1946 authorized for 1947 and annually thereafter: (1) $10 million for vocational education in agriculture; (2) $8 million for vocational education in home economics; (3) $8 million for vocational education in trades and industry; and (4) $2.5 million for vocational education in distributive occupations.

The funds thus provided are in addition to those authorized under the Smith-Hughes Act and are distributed in accordance with various criteria specified in the act. Under these acts, federal expenditures for the year ended June 30, 1953 were as follows (in millions): [17]

For agriculture	$10.0
For home economics and trade and industry	14.2
For distributive occupations	0.5
For teacher training (Smith-Hughes)	1.1
Total	$25.8

The federal payments for agricultural instruction were supplemented by $15,335,887 of state funds and $20,011,979 of local funds, making a total input of $45,295,403 for secondary school instruction in agriculture. This is in comparison to about $53 million for similar instruction in trade and industry, $43 million in home economics, and $5 million in the distributive occupations. (Data are for 1952; 1953 data not available as of this writing but the amounts are similar.)

16. *Department of Agriculture Appropriations for 1954,* Hearings, Part 3, pp. 975–77.
17. U.S. Office of Education. Figures rounded to nearest tenth of a million.

Over-All Federal Aid for Research and Education

Federal appropriations for the four types of agricultural aid described above now amount to more than $100 million a year. The over-all input of federal funds for agricultural education and research (including agricultural extension, Smith-Hughes and George-Barden funds) in 1953 was at approximately the following annual rate:

Aid to land-grant colleges and universities	$ 5,030,000 [a]
Provision for agricultural research	56,110,000
Funds for agricultural extension	32,150,109
Aid for secondary school training in agriculture	10,000,000
Total	$103,290,109

a. Does not include income from endowment derived from land grants (Morrill Act of 1862).

These funds were supplemented by $62,500,000 of state expenditures for agricultural research; $50,188,567 of state and county expenditure for agricultural extension; and $35 million (estimated) of state and local funds for agricultural instruction in high schools. This adds up to approximately $250 million [18] in public support for these four types of activity relating to agriculture. While the amount seems large in total, it is only about 0.77 per cent of the $32,373,411,000 received for agricultural products sold in 1952.[19]

INFORMATION SERVICES

In addition to the educational and research activities supported by it, the federal government maintains an extensive program for collecting and disseminating information relating to agriculture. This has grown rapidly in scope and quality. With the increasing complexity of the economy, business and other groups are demanding more and more detailed and comprehensive statistical information for use in their business operations. Almost universally the practice has been for the government to defray the costs of collecting and disseminating data of this kind, not only in agriculture but in other fields as well. Often the government itself is the principal user.

The collection of data relating to agriculture was one of the earliest forms of informational activity undertaken by the government. Small

18. Ignoring state support for the land-grant colleges, which, though large, cannot be segregated as between agricultural and general education and that in the other applied fields. To some extent this reservation applies to the $5 million item of federal support for the land-grant colleges, but any deductions that might be made from that are far more than offset by state appropriations for agricultural instruction.

19. U.S. Department of Agriculture, *Agricultural Statistics, 1953,* p. 614. The cost of research as a percentage of sales for all industries is estimated at 2 per cent. See U.S. Bureau of Labor Statistics and Research and Development Board, Department of Defense, *Industrial Research and Development,* A Preliminary Report, January 1953, p. 38.

beginnings were made as early as 1839, through an appropriation to the Patent Office for the collection of data and dissemination of seeds. In 1840, agricultural items were first included in the schedules used by the census. Coverage in the census has since been greatly expanded, especially from 1880 on. Since 1925, agricultural censuses have been taken at the mid-decennial periods as well as in the regular decennial enumerations.

In 1863, the Department of Agriculture, which was then just getting started, began to publish monthly or bimonthly reports on condition of crops. These reports were later put on a more regular basis. Annual reports on the acreage, yield per acre and production of important crops were initiated in 1866. Reports on December first acreage, prices of important farm products and values per head of major species of live-stock were begun in 1866 and 1867. The Crop Reporting Board was organized in 1905, and in 1912 began to forecast the production of important crops prior to harvest.[20]

The crop and livestock estimating service has now grown to be a large and important part of the work of the Department of Agriculture. It consists of a central office in Washington, a comprehensive array of state and territorial offices, and a large group of reporting farmers who supply field reports on an unpaid, voluntary basis. The estimates issued have become the principal source of current data on agricultural production. They are based on the periodic enumerations made by the Bureau of the Census, these being adjusted annually or oftener in accordance with the current estimates of change as made by the farmer-reporters and other channels of information. As of 1953 the federal funds obligated for crop and livestock estimates amounted to $3,341,256.[21]

The Census of Agriculture, which is a part of the over-all census, requires the expenditure of some $23 million in each five-year period or at the rate of about $4.6 million per annum.[22] It is important not only as a base for current estimates of agricultural production, but also as a principal source of general information about agriculture.

20. For a more complete history of these developments see U.S. Department of Agri-culture, *The Agricultural Estimating and Reporting Services of the United States De-partment of Agriculture*, Miscellaneous Publication No. 703, December 1949, especially p. 2.

21. *Department of Agriculture Appropriations for 1955*, Hearings, Part 3, p. 955. In some states the federal funds are supplemented by sizable inputs of state funds. In the main, however, this is a federal activity supported by federal funds. (The amounts obli-gated do not necessarily coincide exactly with the amounts spent, though usually they do not differ importantly. In this and a few other cases, the data on actual expenditures are not available.)

22. Estimate in U.S. House Committee on Appropriations, *Departments of State, Jus-tice and Commerce Appropriations for 1954* (Dept. of Commerce), Hearings, p. 83. The cost of the Census of Agriculture varies considerably as between the more comprehensive censuses taken at the end of each decade and the limited enumerations made at the middle of each decade. The cost is not a fixed amount but varies with changes in rates of pay for enumerators, cost of travel and supplies and rates paid for clerical help in the Washington office.

Both the agricultural census and the crop and livestock estimating service are probably used more extensively by the government and by various business and other groups than by farmers themselves. However, data based on them are very widely used as a result of interpretations carried to farmers by farm advisors, marketing agencies, the farm press and other media. Farmers have usually supported appropriations to provide these services and regard them as part of the farm program, but the appropriations for them cannot properly be regarded as a subsidy to farmers.[23]

SERVICE ACTIVITIES OF THE DEPARTMENT OF AGRICULTURE

The Department of Agriculture administers a number of regulatory services some of which are of direct benefit to farmers while others are primarily for the protection of consumers. Among those principally for the benefit of consumers are the meat inspection service and the activities of the Food and Drug Administration (now in the Department of Health, Education and Welfare but formerly in the Department of Agriculture).

The research activities in the field of human nutrition and home economics, though not regulatory functions, are likewise of general rather than group interest. Some of the controls and services relating to the marketing of farm products, which are discussed in succeeding chapters, also serve groups other than farmers.[24]

The 1953 expenditure obligated for meat inspection was $14,184,214. Additional funds were available in the form of fees received as reimbursement for special services.[25] Expenditures for the Bureau of Human Nutrition and Home Economics amounted to $1,413,056. (The Bureau of Human Nutrition and Home Economics was abolished as a separate bureau, in the reorganization of 1953. The same work is now carried on as two separate "branches" in the new "Agricultural Research Service.")

Agricultural Regulatory and Protective Services

Most of the regulatory and protective work of the Department of Agriculture is more specifically designed to increase returns to farmers, though a general public interest is apparent as well. The principal activi-

23. The Weather Bureau provides a similar general informational service of which some parts are especially designed to aid agriculture. However, its over-all service is more widely used by society as a whole than specifically by farmers.

24. The principal consumer services of this kind which still appear in the appropriations for the Department of Agriculture are those for meat inspection and the research program in human nutrition and home economics.

25. *Budget of the United States for Fiscal 1955,* p. 329. (Note, the budgeted item for the Bureau of Human Nutrition and Home Economics is also included in the total for agricultural research shown on pp. 58, 60.) Fees collected in connection with the meat inspection program are to cover overtime and travel in providing special service to the industry and hence do not contribute to the basic outlay for the work.

ties of this kind, together with their costs for the fiscal year ending in June 1953, were as follows: [26]

1. Eradication of cattle ticks, scabies, hog cholera, and similar activities — $491,873
2. Eradication of tuberculosis and brucellosis in cattle. (Brucellosis, like tuberculosis, is not only a source of loss to farmers, but a danger to the health of human beings. In humans it appears as undulant fever.) — 5,496,031
3. Control of the manufacture, importation and interstate shipment of viruses, serums, toxins, etc. — 498,474
4. Plant quarantine and related activities to keep out diseases and pests (inspection of airborne traffic, inspection of ships, mail from Hawaii, fumigation, etc.) — 2,692,538
5. Japanese beetle control — 462,971
6. Control and eradication of the sweet potato weevil — 226,106
7. Mexican fruitfly and citrus blackfly control — 240,804
8. Grasshopper and mormon cricket control — 546,859
9. Suppression and prevention of spread of the pink bollworm in cotton — 1,193,369
10. Hall scale control (a stone fruit pest) — 114,175
11. White-fringed beetle control — 654,225
12. Golden nematode control — 316,693
13. Control and eradication of the phony peach and peach mosaic diseases — 150,213
14. Barberry eradication (to control rust in wheat and other small grains) — 628,379
15. Enforcement of Federal Insecticide, Fungicide and Rodenticide Act — 576,763
16. Animal quarantine — 1,281,673
17. Determining existence of disease in the field — 489,373
18. Administration of Butter Process Act — 19,666
19. Insect detection and advisory service — 322,197
20. Emergency outbreaks of insects and plant diseases — 367,700 [a]

a. In addition the Department of Agriculture administers a number of other disease control activities that are not of direct concern to farmers. Among them are Gypsy and Brown-tail Moth Control, White Pine Blister Rust Control, and Forest Pest Control.

These data indicate the scope and magnitude of the federal government's effort to reduce losses from agricultural pests and diseases. They offset to some extent the physical hazards which are peculiar to agricultural operations. Hazards of these kinds are more prevalent and unavoidable in agriculture than in most other industries. More important is the fact that most of them cannot be controlled except through government action.

Here, as in agricultural research, the general public is an indirect beneficiary. Where large losses are prevented the gains from the larger

26. *Department of Agriculture Appropriations for 1955,* Hearings, p. 346. Data on an obligation basis.

output, if sold in a freely competitive market, tend to be passed on to consumers in lower prices. For the major export crops it is doubtful that the quantities saved through control measures of this kind are large enough to affect prices measurably. Hence, in some of the major types of farm production, it is probable that the principal gains from disease and pest control accrue to farmers. Society is also a gainer, however, through such added income as farmers receive and through somewhat larger and more dependable supplies of products.

Other Production Aids—The Farm Labor Program

Other aids to agricultural producers have been provided from time to time. Chief among them are the government expenditures made during the war years for procuring agricultural labor, for aid in supplying fertilizer and as production subsidies. The fertilizer and production subsidy programs are discussed more fully in the chapters dealing with soil conservation and price and income subsidies.

The emergency program for supplying agricultural labor is not a continuing one but has been very important to some areas at some times during the past decade.[27] The intrastate phase of the work was handled by the agricultural extension services, with funds appropriated by the federal government. Interstate and international recruiting and transportation were handled directly by federal agencies, chiefly the War Food Administration.

27. There is in addition a continuing farm placement program which is carried on by the Bureau of Employment Security but is not included in this analysis since similar services are provided in the nonfarm economy as well. The farm labor phase of this more general program was described as follows in recent testimony before the House Committee on Appropriations: "To meet [the] demands for manpower the Bureau will continue its efforts toward full utilization of domestic agricultural workers through (1) recruitment of year-'round farm labor, (2) development and expansion of day-haul programs, (3) expansion of placement service to Indians and Puerto Ricans, (4) promotion in collaboration with State agencies of the movement of underemployed farm families to more productive areas, (5) direction of the movement of migratory and seasonal farm workers, and (6) development of labor supply and demand data and employment conditions by area." See testimony of Robert C. Goodwin, Director of the Bureau, U.S. House Committee on Appropriations, *Department of Labor–Federal Security Agency Appropriations for 1954* (Department of Labor), Hearings, 1953, p. 121.

The federal obligation for this service for the fiscal year ending in June 1953 is put at $467,272 (see *Budget of the United States Government for 1955*, p. 840). This does not include sizable expenditures by the state offices of the Farm Placement Service.

In recent years the Farm Placement Service has turned to Puerto Ricans and American Indians as a source of supply. Because of further unfilled needs, the Congress enacted additional legislation in 1951 (65 *Stat.* 119), which authorized importation of Mexican nationals for work on farms. In 1952, 197,000 Mexican nationals were brought into the United States under this statute. This program has been self-supporting through fees charged the farmers who used the labor. During the fiscal year 1953, the Placement Service expended $2,018,649 from the revolving fund and took in $2,869,776 in fees (*Budget of the United States Government for 1955*, p. 849). In addition to this amount, the Bureau of Employment Security expended $2,497,252 on the Mexican farm labor program in fiscal 1953.

These activities were a phase of the effort to insure maximum production of farm products, but also were, of course, to some extent a direct financial aid to farm operators. Presumably, farmers would have had to bid more for their labor if not so aided. The program consisted mainly of labor recruiting activities both at home and abroad but included expenditures for labor camps and other facilities in some areas. It was supplemented by special concessions in the way of draft deferment for essential agricultural workers.[28] Under this program more than 2.5 million agricultural workers were recruited and placed annually during the years 1943 through 1947.

Over 300,000 foreign workers were recruited and brought into the United States. (See Table 7.) Special programs were also devised for

TABLE 7

FOREIGN FARM WORKERS IMPORTED BY UNITED STATES DEPARTMENT OF AGRICULTURE, 1942–1947

Country of Origin	Total	1942	1943	1944	1945	1946	1947
Total	309,538	4,189	65,657	84,340	73,425	51,152	30,775
Bahama Islands	15,241	—	4,698	3,048	2,100	2,690	2,705
Barbados	3,995	—	—	908	—	3,087	—
Canada	18,423	—	—	1,414	4,055	5,533	7,421
Jamaica	50,598	—	8,828	15,666	17,291	7,796	1,017
Mexico	219,546	4,189	52,131	62,091	49,457	32,046	19,632
Newfoundland	1,735	—	—	1,213	522	—	—

Source: Wayne C. Rasmussen, *A History of the Emergency Farm Labor Supply Program, 1943–47,* U.S. Department of Agriculture, Agriculture Monograph No. 13, 1951, p. 199.

drawing into the farm labor force for short-period tasks considerable numbers of young people and women, through the organizations known as Victory Farm Volunteers and the Women's Land Army. Prisoners of war were also made available, particularly in 1944 and 1945. The numbers of Victory Farm Volunteers, Women's Land Army workers and prisoners of war are reported as follows: [29]

	Victory Farm Volunteers	Women's Land Army	Prisoners of War
1943	834,916	455,049	41,000
1944	903,794	413,083	102,000
1945	741,247	360,536	122,000
1946	600,499	395,472	14,000
1947	529,350	399,595	

28. For fuller comment see Walter W. Wilcox, *The Farmer in the Second World War,* Iowa State College Press, Ames, 1947, Chapter 7.

29. Wayne C. Rasmussen, *A History of the Emergency Farm Labor Supply Program, 1943–47,* U.S. Department of Agriculture, Agriculture Monograph No. 13, 1951, pp. 99, 126–30, 148–50.

These additions to the farm labor force should not be regarded as man-year equivalents. Many were in the labor force only for short periods and the method of reporting undoubtedly involves some double-counting, particularly in the very seasonal types of activity.

Cost of the Farm Labor Program

The over-all cost of the farm labor program for the fiscal years 1943 through 1951 was $113,631,000. This expense was incurred mainly in the war and immediate postwar years. Expenditures in 1949 and 1950 were negligible. In addition $250,000 had been appropriated in 1941 and a fund of $4.5 million was assigned from the President's emergency fund in 1942.

Further subsidization of some parts of the agricultural labor supply has been apparent for many years, especially in the areas where seasonal labor is used extensively. This consists of heavy expenditures for relief in seasons of low employment. Such outlays were very large during the 1930s, but by no means all of them are properly chargeable to agriculture. They consisted, in the main, during that period, of aids to indigents who had congregated in certain rural areas.

In more normal times this type of public aid, mostly supplied locally, provides part of the cost of maintaining a labor supply adequate to carry on the very seasonal work on farms in these areas. Presumably, if such aid were not available, farmers would have to pay more for their seasonal labor and might have to make major changes in their methods of farming in order to keep their labor employed and in the area.

PROGRAMS FOR THE BETTERMENT OF FARM LIVING

The federal government has also undertaken a number of activities designed to make the conditions of life on farms more nearly comparable with those in cities and towns. Most of these have come into being as a result of long-continued efforts on the part of farm organizations and spokesmen for agriculture. One of the earliest was the provision of rural free delivery of mail, established in 1896 in response to widespread agitation on the part of farm people and the rural press. It was followed by a long-sought companion measure, the Parcel Post Law of 1912.

The provision of mail delivery to farms removed one of the most severe handicaps of farm people, and was a long step in relieving the isolation and lack of contact with the outside world that had been so characteristic of many farm families in earlier times.

The principle of making postal services approximately equal in city and country has long been accepted almost universally. The function is one which should, however, be brought under scrutiny from time to time to determine where savings can be made. Most of the rural routes were laid out in the days when they had to be traveled by horse and buggy.

The introduction of the automobile and the widespread development of good roads have opened the way for further consolidations and reorganizations which could apparently reduce costs without creating undue hardships for the personnel used in making deliveries.

Federal Aid for Farm-to-Market Roads

A second important step was that of helping to finance the construction of "farm-to-market" roads. Federal aid has been provided for the construction of through highways since 1916. These, however, have been generally and properly regarded as a service to the public as a whole rather than a special concession to agriculture. The farm organizations began to press strongly for federal aid in the construction and maintenance of "farm-to-market" roads in the early 1920s. More adequate financing for such highways has continued to occupy a prominent place in their legislative programs since then. Small appropriations were made for that purpose in 1933 and much larger ones in a series of subsequent acts, particularly those of 1944, 1948, 1950 and 1952.

Local and rural roads now total about 2.5 million miles. Of these some 202,000 miles had been incorporated into the federal and secondary road system as of June 30, 1949.[30] Local rural road mileage not included in the federal-aid secondary road system, as of June 1949, amounted to approximately 2.3 million miles. For the year ending June 30, 1953, federal aid assigned to the "secondary" road system amounted to $157,-878,511. The comparable amount obligated for primary roads and urban areas was $205,310,182.[31]

It is apparent that the above classifications do not separate in any clean way the federal contributions made specifically for equalizing farm and nonfarm highway facilities. Farmers use the primary highways and such highways constitute a part of the farm-to-market road system. Farmers also help to pay for the primary road system. It may be contended, however, that their relationship to this segment of the highway system is not dissimilar to that of other users.

The federal aid program for secondary highways is in part a subsidy designed to equalize access to improved highways for farm and nonfarm people. Here too the figure is necessarily fuzzy. Urban people also use secondary or feeder roads, but usually not on any large scale. Very large amounts of state funds also go into the construction and maintenance of these roads. It seems not unrealistic to count the $158 million of federal

---

30. U.S. Bureau of Public Roads, *The Local Rural Road Problem,* a Report to the Subcommittee on Roads of the Committee on Public Works, Senate, January 1950, pp. 8 and 9.

31. *Budget of the United States Government for 1955,* p. 455. In addition there was a grant of $154,646,511 for urban arterial routes and $2,347,474 for flood damage restoration. There were also appropriations of $21,073,107 for interstate highways and to cover the expense of administering these programs.

funds assigned to farm-to-market roads as mainly a contribution by society for offsetting the locational disadvantages of farmers. However, the great increase in marketing and production efficiency which results from the improved system of highways contributes markedly to general public welfare as well as to that of farmers.

Electric Power and Telephone Facilities

Having achieved a mail service that was nearly as good as that of the urban areas, and a highway network that was rapidly being improved, farmers turned their interest to obtaining similar access to electric power and telephone service. By 1930, considerable progress had been made in extending telephone service to the rural areas through private and cooperative action. About 34 per cent of the farms had some sort of telephone service though current estimates indicate that only about half of it could be considered "adequate." The more expensive and complex matter of making electric power available had made only modest progress. As of 1935, only 11 per cent of the farms had central station electric power. These farms were mostly those which were close to urban centers or in relatively closely settled farm areas.

In 1935 the President established, by executive order, the Rural Electrification Administration. The agency was given legislative status through the Rural Electrification Act of 1936. The purpose was twofold: to make electric power available to farmers and other unserved rural people, and to provide employment and stimulate sales in the construction and electric equipment industries.

The procedure under the rural electrification program is to make government credit available at approximately the cost to the government.[32] Loans are made through the Rural Electrification Administration

32. The Rural Electrification Act of 1936 provided that interest rates charged by REA would be "the average rate of interest payable by the United States of America on its obligations having a maturity of ten or more years after the dates thereof, issued during the last preceding fiscal year in which any such obligations were issued."

In 1944, this section was amended, by the Department of Agriculture Organic Act of 1944 (58 *Stat.* 734, 739). Loans made thereafter were to bear interest at a rate to be determined by the Secretary of the Treasury but not to be in excess of 2 per cent. In practice, the rate, if under 2 per cent, is set at the rate on *marketable* U.S. securities adjusted to the next lower multiple of $\frac{1}{8}$ of 1 per cent if the rate on marketable securities is not itself a multiple of $\frac{1}{8}$ of 1 per cent. Unmatured and unpaid balances were to be adjusted to 2 per cent per annum if in excess of that rate. In addition, the act lengthened the permissible loan period from 25 to 35 years, with authorization for corresponding adjustments on loans already made.

The Administrator reported in 1952 that the rate REA paid on money borrowed from the Treasury was 1.875 per cent in 1951 and 1952 (U.S. Rural Electrification Administration, *Report of the Administrator, 1952,* p. 10). This rate of cost differs from that given in *Statistical Abstract, 1952,* p. 336, where average interest rate on the interest-bearing debt of the United States is given as 2.270 per cent. The difference is due to the fact that the rate given in the *Statistical Abstract* is for the total public debt, not merely marketable securities. As of June 30, 1952 and June 30, 1953, the computed rate was in excess of 2 per cent so the charge made was 2 per cent, which is the legal maximum.

With the rise in interest costs to the government which has occurred recently, the loan

to finance companies set up to provide electric power to rural areas. Most of the companies thus financed are cooperatives, but loans may be made to other agencies as well. Mainly through this program, some 4.9 million farms were being supplied with electric power as of June 30, 1953.[33] The percentage of farms then electrified was estimated to be 90.8 as compared to 88.1 per cent a year earlier and 10.9 per cent in 1935.[34] The use of power from REA-financed systems continued to increase, reaching 13.1 billion kilowatt-hours in 1953, as compared to 11.4 billion in 1952. Kilowatt-hour consumption per consumer rose from 919 in 1941 to 1,602 in 1946 and to 3,100 in 1953.[35]

As of June 30, 1953, loans approved amounted to $2,730,009,085.[36] These were distributed as follows: for distribution of power, 80.7 per cent; for generation of power, 8.6 per cent; for transmission of power, 10.0 per cent; and for consumer facilities, 0.7 per cent. Borrowing companies numbered 1,079; miles of line built, 1,271,443; and consumers served by these lines, 3,951,940.

Cost to the Government

The major contribution by the government in this program has been that of lending its credit to cooperatives and other agencies for the construction of facilities to provide electric service to rural people not otherwise served. The amount of funds committed is large (nearly 2.7 billion to June 30, 1953). Presumably these loans will be repaid together with interest sufficient to recompense the government for most of its cost on funds borrowed. The principal current cost is for administrative expense and technical assistance to cooperative power distributing and generating companies and to rural telephone companies. Administrative and technical assistance costs borne by government in connection with the electrification program for the year ending June 30, 1953 amounted to $8,005,384.

Payments overdue more than 30 days, as of June 30, 1953, were only $733,450 of principal and interest, a negligible amount considering the size of the lending operation and the high percentage of value of assets

---

rate of 2 per cent to the cooperatives, if continued, will involve some subsidy, the amount depending on the cost of money to the government. Presumably, since these are long-term loans, the most appropriate basis would be the cost to the government for long-term funds rather than on marketable securities of all types.

33. U.S. Rural Electrification Administration, *Report of the Administrator, 1953,* p. 12. This is a total figure which includes places served by private power companies as well as by companies financed through REA. It includes, however, some consumers who are not farmers. REA borrowers were directly responsible for taking service to more than 3,770,000 rural users, or more than half of all rural customers receiving electric power on June 30, 1952 (REA, Press Release of August 28, 1952).

34. Data supplied by REA.

35. *Department of Agriculture Appropriations for 1954,* Hearings, Part 3, p. 1185 and later data.

36. Data supplied by REA.

loaned.[37] The recent period has been one of very high net farm incomes. Should farm prosperity decline appreciably it may be that losses and delinquencies will increase somewhat. Further expansion of the program to more remote and lower-income farms may also contribute to a weaker financial situation. As of now, however, the financial record is excellent. For the majority of farm people, the program has removed one of the major disadvantages of farm life.

Rural Telephone Service

An amendment to the Rural Electrification Act of 1936, approved October 28, 1949, initiated a similar plan for making telephone service more widely available in rural areas. The purpose of the amendment was stated as follows:

. . . it is hereby declared to be the policy of the Congress that adequate telephone service be made generally available in rural areas through the improvement and expansion of existing telephone facilities and the construction and operation of such additional facilities as are required to assure the availability of adequate telephone service to the widest practicable number of rural users of such service.[38]

This further effort to offset the disadvantages of isolation in the rural areas is similar in principle to the rural electrification program and is administered by the same agency. However, it is a more hazardous undertaking and also a more complex problem in that connecting company agreements, supplementation of existing service and many other problems are involved. Hence more safeguards are provided, chief among them being a requirement that the borrowers must provide some of the capital. The equity requirement, for telephone borrowers, may be as much as 25 per cent. Except in unusual situations, it does not exceed 18 per cent of proposed total assets and may be much less. The normal equity requirement for subscriber-owned systems does not average more than $50 for each new subscriber and $25 for each existing subscriber.[39]

37. U.S. Rural Electrification Administration, *Report of the Administrator, 1953,* p. 37. There was also a small amount ($44,478) due on loans that had been foreclosed. Rural electrification loans are normally for 100 per cent of cost, with no requirement of equity capital on the part of the borrowing company except a nominal membership fee. Some assurance of continuing use of the service is provided, however, by the fact that the customers must wire their farms, purchase electrical appliances and convert their farming operations so as to use electric power. The tendency for electric power patrons to increase their use of electric power is considered a further element of safety in the backing for loans. These factors are regarded as a form of equity commitment, and provide a guarantee of continuing use which is not present in the provision for loans to rural telephone companies, which are discussed in the next section. There, the possibility of discontinuance of service in bad times, the lack of substantial investment by the patron, and the absence of prospect for increasing revenue, make necessary the requirement of a borrower equity if loans are to be granted.

38. 63 *Stat.* 948.

39. REA Bulletin 320–6, May 10, 1954, p. 6.

Through June 1953, equity capital amounted to $7 million as compared to $118 million in loans. The interest rate specified is 2 per cent.

Recent estimates indicate that only about 42.5 per cent of the farms have telephone service as compared to 90 per cent supplied with electric power.[40] Census figures indicate that about 39 per cent of the farms had telephones in 1920. By 1935 the number had declined to such an extent that only about one farm in four had telephone service. The number has increased slowly since that time. One of the reasons for the decline was that much of the rural equipment became obsolete and much difficulty arose in maintaining workable connections with the urban systems. An important phase of REA's rural telephone work is that of providing technical assistance to enable the rural lines to keep up with the general progress in the telephone field and to give better service.

As of June 30, 1953, loan allocations had been made in the amount of $118.1 million, though only about $31.7 million had been advanced. Administrative expenses for fiscal 1953 were $2,283,233. These amounts will no doubt be increased as the program gets under way and policies and methods become more fully established. Even after loan funds are allocated much organizational and engineering work is required before construction can be initiated. Much of the work performed by REA in this field during the first years of the program was of this preliminary type but by late 1952 REA-financed telephone systems were going into service at a rate of more than one a week.

Federal Aid for Rural Housing Improvement

The Housing Act of 1949 made special provision for aid in improving rural housing, but in more limited form than for city dwellers. The housing program as a whole is designed primarily for people in the low-income groups. It is a general rather than an agricultural program, the declared objective being to realize "as soon as feasible . . . the goal of a decent house and a suitable living environment for every American family." [41]

The provision for rural housing was less liberal and positive than that for urban housing improvement and financing.[42] The act authorized research and technical assistance in improving the quality of rural housing and reducing building costs. Assistance could also be given in the form of supervision and inspection. These services could be provided with or without charge.[43]

Loans and grants for housing improvement could be made. However, in order to be eligible for a loan of this kind, a farmer had to be one who

40. Data supplied by REA.
41. 63 *Stat.* 413.
42. Federal aid for and active participation in urban housing dates back to 1934 when the Federal Housing Administration was established.
43. The kind of assistance contemplated would be an expansion and intensification of a program already started in a small way through the agricultural extension services.

was without the funds necessary for building or repair work and in a financial situation such that he could not obtain the necessary funds through other lending agencies on terms he was likely to be able to meet. Security could be in such form as the Secretary of Agriculture might prescribe, including income prospects, first mortgages, second mortgages or other assets. Loans could be for periods up to 35 years and at an interest rate of not more than 4 per cent. The borrower was required to agree, however, to endeavor to refinance the loan if directed to do so by the Secretary of Agriculture.

Loans could be obtained for improving the homes of tenants, lessees, and sharecroppers as well as those of farm owners, but only farm owners were eligible to borrow. No specific upper limit on size of loan was provided. Loans made up to June 30, 1952 averaged $4,779 per farmer-borrower. Most were for new construction rather than remodeling.

One of the important reasons for the reluctance of farmers to borrow for home improvement lies in the fact that they cannot separate home financing from business financing. The urban resident can mortgage his home without endangering his source of livelihood. The farmer cannot. His home is an integral part of his business. Consequently, since he is reluctant to jeopardize both his home and his source of income, he tends to defer home improvement until free funds are available for accomplishing it.

This problem was recognized in the act through a provision that the Secretary of Agriculture may grant a moratorium on home loan interest and principal if the borrower can show that his inability to meet them is a result of circumstances beyond his control, and that he cannot make the payments "without unduly impairing his standard of living." During the period of such moratorium, the Secretary may cancel the interest due and payable on the loan. He can also make certain other concessions if he chooses to do so.

For low-income farm families provision was made for grants of up to $500, where there was no prospect of income sufficient to repay the loans. These could be used to repair roofs, install screens, provide sanitary water supplies, improve toilet facilities and so on. They were intended only as a temporary expedient to take care of the situation until something more fundamental could be done.[44]

The scale of operations under this program, to 1952, was recently summarized by a representative of the Farmers Home Administration as follows:

Since the inception of the farm-housing program in October 1949, to June 30, 1952, loans totaling $62,411,165 have been made to 13,059 farm owners

44. For a more extended description of the act and the problems it was designed to solve see Roy J. Burroughs, "Significance to Farmers of Housing Act of 1949," U.S. Bureau of Agricultural Economics, *Agricultural Finance Review*, November 1949, pp. 33–45.

and 667 initial grants have been made in the amount of $308,865. Ninety-nine of these grants were made to farm owners who also received loans; thus 13,627 farm owners have been assisted by the program to this date. The major portion of the building funds, namely $50,715,108, were [*sic*] loaned for dwelling construction and repair. A total of 6,491 new dwellings and repairs to 5,269 additional farm houses have been financed with farm-housing funds.[45]

Farm Housing Authorization Expired in June 1954

The authorization for farm housing, under the Housing Act of 1949, expired in June 1954 and has not thus far been renewed. The program has therefore gone into inactive status, as to new loans. Up to this time, the program has not been carried far enough to warrant conclusions about its appropriateness and prospects of success. For the majority of farm owners, the need is probably greater for technical assistance in planning housing improvements and aid in getting the services of skilled craftsmen than for special types of credit. There is, however, in rural areas as in the cities, a low-income, unstabilized group which should be better housed. In the farm areas this group consists mainly of migratory farm workers and other types of hired farm labor. It is not apparent that a loan program will meet the problems of this group.

The program initiated in 1949 was experimental and tentative. Policies and methods need to be more fully tried out before venturing on any large expansion of this type of lending. Except for meeting the most urgent needs, a program for the betterment of rural housing generally, through loans and grants, might well be limited largely to periods of depression when it could operate as a countercyclical influence. In normal and prosperous times, it probably can best be confined largely to research, education and technical aid, with a view to stimulating action and making the best use of the funds farmers are themselves able to supply or obtain through normal channels. However, even in prosperous times there is need for public action to improve housing for hired farm workers, especially the migrant groups.

SERVICES TO AGRICULTURE AS A PHASE OF GENERAL PUBLIC POLICY

The services described above constitute, in broad terms, an effort to equalize the services and opportunities available to farm people with those of nonfarm people. The justification for providing them at public expense rests basically on three distinctive characteristics of agriculture: (1) its small-unit nature; (2) the fact that it is spread over very large areas and hence does not have practical access to services that are normally available to urban residents through private or municipally owned

45. *Department of Agriculture Appropriations for 1954,* Hearings, Part 3, p. 1084.

suppliers; and (3) its susceptibility to epidemics and other natural hazards that cannot be dealt with effectively by individuals.

The nature of the benefits accruing from these various governmental activities and their significance, both from the standpoint of farmers and as elements of broad social policy, require further explanation. Since their purposes differ somewhat, the relationship to public policy will be clearer if each type of activity is discussed separately.

Education

The establishment of specialized higher education for agriculture was an effort to raise the dignity of the occupation, to provide it with qualified leadership, and to put it in a position to advance in step with the supposedly more favored urban industries. It can be argued that agriculture was, in fact, given a preferred position since even today no other branch of the economy receives comparable educational support and encouragement from the federal government. This, however, does not present any important problem of discrimination. Well over half the graduates of agricultural colleges go into nonfarm occupations or governmental and other public types of agricultural activity. Consequently, the recipients of such training, for the most part, flow into the general pool of scientifically trained manpower and the advantages gained tend to be general rather than occupational.

Undoubtedly the procedure used has tended to stimulate the development of higher education in some of the poorer states, and to equalize to some extent the educational opportunities of young people in all parts of the country. Whether this be true or not, and whether the principle of federal aid for education is sound or unsound, it seems apparent that participation in the support of the land-grant colleges, at least on the scale now in effect, is a settled issue and the policy is not likely to be changed.

Granting acceptance of this conclusion, the question of increasing such aid is less easily disposed of. The colleges of agriculture and mechanic arts are now going concerns. The need for bringing about their creation no longer exists. Question can be raised as to the warrant for additional support from the federal Treasury purely on occupational grounds. The case for or against additional federal aid is similar to that for or against federal contributions to equalize educational costs generally.

It would appear that if further additions to federal support for higher education in the states are to be made they should perhaps be based on a broader conception of equalizing educational opportunities. The availability and quality of educational resources vary more from state to state than as between occupational groups within a given state. At the secondary school level there appears to be now as much reason for providing vocational training in other fields as in agriculture. Agriculture's own interests may in fact be furthered by providing better opportunities for its young people to equip themselves for careers in other occupations.[46]

The Research Programs

In research, there was for a time a differential in favor of agriculture. Few of the nonfarm industries had similar research facilities. Progress in industrial lines was rapid, but it came largely through the work of individual inventors and the owners and employees of small businesses. Recent years have seen a reversal of this balance. Nonfarm industry has come to include many large corporate enterprises. Laboratories and research staffs are being provided both by the government and at private expense on an ever-increasing scale. A recent estimate puts the amount of research expenditures by industrial corporations at $1,783,662,000 for 1951.[47]

This change has given the argument for public support of agricultural research a different emphasis. Industrial corporations now have research staffs and laboratories that are not only more elaborate and more costly than those available to agriculture. They also absorb a larger percentage of the gross value of the products of these industries than does the comparable expenditure on agricultural research. Their expenditure in proportion to output is larger even if we omit the heavy contribution by government which is largely related to military objectives.

The difference in method of financing, for ordinary peacetime research, stems largely from the fact that many industrial corporations are large and can assign private research funds through action by boards of directors. Agriculture, which is a small-unit industry, cannot set up private research facilities comparable to those now available to industrial corporations.[48] Such facilities must therefore be provided largely at public expense or agriculture must fall behind in its rate of technological advance.

The objectives of agricultural research have to some extent been modified in recent years. Since privately financed industrial research is directed primarily to increasing the profits of industry, farmers have felt

46. Recent legislation broadening the scope of vocational aid, such as the George-Barden Act of 1946, seems to imply acceptance of this point of view.

47. U.S. Bureau of Labor Statistics and Research and Development Board, Department of Defense, *Industrial Research and Development*, A Preliminary Report, January 1953, p. 36. The amount of annual research outlay has been greatly increased as a means of strengthening military potential. It is more than four times what it was at the beginning of World War II. Nearly half of the industrial research is financed by the federal government. The figure given above is not directly comparable with the more normal peacetime expenditures for agricultural research which were given earlier.

48. It should be recognized, however, that some of the larger farm cooperatives are moving in the general direction already taken by many of the large nonfarm corporations. Some of them have developed extensive research programs relating both to economic and technical problems. For the most part, however, the individual farmer, like the small-scale urban businessman, is dependent on publicly supported research if he is to make progress comparable to that being made by the large industrial enterprises.

increasingly that agricultural research should place more emphasis on ways to increase the profits from farming. The later authorizing acts reflect this change in attitude. They give more attention to economic research, and, in the Research and Marketing Act of 1946, place heavy emphasis on marketing research. The regional research laboratories which were set up under the Agricultural Adjustment Act of 1938 also are directed specifically to conduct research on new uses for farm products, particularly industrial uses. Nevertheless, the great bulk of the agricultural research continues to be on problems that look to increases in efficiency of agricultural production.

Most of the Benefits Accrue to Society as a Whole

Most of the improved practices, strains and control measures developed by the agricultural research agencies soon come into general use and thus contribute to more ample supplies and lower prices for society as a whole. Nevertheless, the farmers who first adopt them gain significantly and the hazards of farming are to some extent reduced by them.[49] Also, farmers benefit along with the rest of society in the rising standard of living that is thus made possible.

Even in nonfarm industries where the results of research are often retained by the companies supporting the research, as trade secrets or through patents, there is a strong tendency for the benefits to be passed on to the public in better products or lower prices. The process may be slower than in agriculture and the opportunity for private gain is probably greater. Nevertheless, it is not easy to keep a superior method or device under wraps for a very long period.

In agriculture, the greater the range of incomes the higher the average income is likely to be, since an agriculture that is approximately uniform throughout is likely to be made up of farmers who all receive incomes just about large enough to keep them in business. By the same token, powerful machinery for the quick spread of new methods, such as that provided through the agricultural extension service, tends to eliminate the advantages of first adopters and to pass the gains on to society in a relatively short time.[50] Though the competitive advantage from adopting

49. Some farm organizations and a good many individual farmers have at times been very critical of the whole research and extension program, contending that its purpose is to "make two blades of grass grow where one grew before" when production is already so ample as to cause farm prices to be unwarrantedly low. The very evident need for an increasingly efficient agriculture and the high demand of recent years have caused this attitude to recede in the years since 1940.

50. A good example of this is to be seen in the introduction of hybrid seed corn. When it first began to be used, those farmers who planted the higher-yielding strains profited directly from such action, since they got higher yields but did not produce enough to affect the price. As the practice spread so that almost all of the growers in the commercial corn areas were using these high-yielding strains, the result was a lower cost for producing the major portion of the crop. This meant that a lower price would draw into corn production enough resources to meet the demand. However, since demand was increasing

an improved method tends to be temporary (where it is unpatented and information about it is freely disseminated), the same individuals are likely to introduce other new improvements and thus to keep their profits above those of the general run of producers.

Values of Research Widely Accepted

The value to society of a strong research program in agriculture has now come to be so well demonstrated that little question is raised about the desirability of continuing to support it with public funds. The principal policy issue relating to it is not based on a difference in interest between farmers and the public but rather on the question of how much to spend on it and the kinds of research to be carried on. There are also problems of how to organize and administer the funds provided in such a way as to achieve maximum efficiency.

Fully acceptable criteria for gauging the need for increases or decreases in the amounts spent on research are not attainable. Such programs should, however, be kept under continuous and effective scrutiny. Some weaknesses are more or less inherent in publicly supported agricultural research. Among them is the tendency to assign funds on a geographic basis rather than in terms of the availability of qualified staff and appropriate facilities. Another is that the Congress may attempt to prescribe too specifically the nature of the work to be undertaken and where it shall be carried on.

For example, the relative emphases in types of research specified in the Research and Marketing Act of 1946 are probably not the ones that will yield the greatest values, nor the ones that would emerge from wisely directed and more flexible use of these large funds. Also, the tendency to allot funds in equal amounts per state or in accordance with other legislatively prescribed criteria may lead to excessive fragmentation of the work and poor allocation of funds in relation to the importance of the problems to be studied and the availability of qualified research leadership.

This difficulty is offset to a large extent by the fact that the states with larger resources, and presumably more complex problems, supplement the federal grants with larger appropriations of state funds. So long as the federal grants are at or near present levels they probably do not provide more than enough to meet minimum needs even in the states least well equipped to make effective use of them. If they were to be greatly enlarged, efficient administration of them would require more selective allocation.[51]

it actually meant supplying increased quantities without the enlargement of acreage that would otherwise have been necessary. In a similar way the introduction of the production-line process helped to build the Ford fortune. As the process was more generally adopted, the competitive advantage of the Ford Company declined.

51. This problem has been recognized to some extent in the procedures authorized under the Research and Marketing Act of 1946. Regional projects may be undertaken,

In general the record indicates liberal support for agricultural education, research and informational activities in amounts that are perhaps adequate if costs and salaries remain at or near their present levels. The increased support authorized since 1945 has, however, no more than offset the increases in salaries and other costs. Some work is under way on most of the major problems of agriculture. On some of them, research could well be expanded and carried forward at a faster pace. Furthermore, new types of problems are continually arising.

However, progress is not necessarily in direct ratio to the input of funds. It takes time to develop suitably trained and experienced personnel, to plan projects and to design and construct facilities. A too rapid expansion in numbers of workers, if those recruited are not of first-rate ability, may not contribute effectively to genuine progress. For this reason major emphasis should be on wise selection of projects and better use of available leadership rather than on expansion as such.

Differences Between Private and Public Research

One of the important differences between privately supported research and that financed by the federal government in the state experiment stations lies in the tendency to assign public funds on the basis of states, population or some similar mechanistic criterion. Such losses in efficiency as grow out of this procedure are not easy to overcome. Strong political motivations and pressures are involved and the present method of handling funds is supported by precedent and the institutional structure of the research agencies.

Some realignment of federally financed agricultural research might perhaps be achieved by bringing the research activities in each of the major fields under periodic review by small advisory committees of professional research people, drawn from both inside and outside the government and reporting directly to the Secretary of Agriculture, and perhaps to the Congress. This would be a modification of the arrangement provided under the Research and Marketing Act of 1946. That act provides for commodity and general advisory committees drawn from the various branches of agriculture but not, in the main, composed of professional research people.

These nonprofessional committees can be very helpful in highlighting the problems that appear to them to be most significant. The industry members need to be continuously in touch with the kinds of research being carried on and the reasons for them. They cannot be expected to know what problems are currently most promising as fields of research, nor what work is under way. The maintenance of effective pressure on the most significant frontiers of new discovery is a task for professionals,

---

research can be contracted out to either public or private agencies if they are considered especially well equipped to carry it on and the Secretary of Agriculture is given considerable discretion in the allocation of funds.

not for laymen, however good their intentions and general knowledge may be. Certainly close liaison with the prospective users of research results should be maintained, but the type of contribution they are best qualified to make should be recognized and made use of. They should not be expected to be familiar with the details of current research and in most cases should not be expected to assume responsibility for advising on the allocation of funds except as to broad areas of investigation.

Professional advisory committees such as those suggested above could be charged not only with suggesting promising areas for increased research effort, but also with the duty of counseling on types of activity that may have become obsolete or are failing to show promise of significant results. Pressure for the continuance of special kinds of research after their usefulness has become dubious very often comes from outside groups rather than from the research organizations themselves. This is especially true if local stations or installations are involved.

There are many precedents for professional advisory arrangements of the kind suggested above in the far-reaching research programs the government has carried on in other fields during recent years. Some use has been made of similar procedures in agriculture as well. Such committees, if used, should, of course, be advisory rather than administrative.

Protective Services, Disease Control and Similar Activities

The numerous protective and regulatory activities listed above are mostly matters of general public concern. Like those in the fields of research and education, the gains from them tend to accrue at first to farmers but secondarily to society through increased efficiency, smaller losses and lower prices.

Epidemics either of plant or animal disease could, if not checked, destroy wealth on a scale that would far outweigh the costs commonly incurred for their control. Here the expenditure in agriculture is comparable to that in many activities carried on for the benefit of the nonfarm economy, such as the provision of lighthouses and markers for waterborne traffic, control of epidemics and fire prevention.

Supervision of the labeling of pesticides, fertilizers and similar items is not only in accord with general national policy but is particularly important for farmers and other small-scale buyers. The large corporation, with its specialized buying department, and possibly its own laboratories, can protect itself against mislabeling and fraud in production supplies. In a small way similar facilities are becoming available to farmers through the larger cooperative associations. But for most farmers such services are unavailable in practical form, except as they are provided by government.

For nearly all of these types of government activity there is little disagreement in principle. The problem is mainly that of deciding how much expenditure is warranted and how the work can be handled most efficiently. Effective counseling in respect to most of them requires specialized technical knowledge not possessed by the layman.

There is need, however, for further research both technical and economic to throw light on the amounts and kinds of expenditure that can wisely be made. Few generalizations about them are warranted, except the broad one that the interests of both the farmer and the public are furthered by publicly supported protective measures wherever these can be shown to be effective and where competent analysis gives reason to believe that the economic gains will outweigh the costs.

Labor Programs in a Different Category

The recruiting at public expense of parts of the farm labor force is defended on different grounds. The case for it is that, without such aid, farm products already growing may be lost through lack of help to harvest them, and that full-scale or expanded production of farm products may be unattainable if there is no assurance that adequate labor for harvesting will be available. The second of these is undoubtedly the more compelling but the first is by no means inconsequential in times of full employment. Opponents of these programs argue that farmers would pay enough higher wage rates to draw in the labor required to harvest crops already grown if they were unable to get help from the federal government, and that the returns to the whole group of low-paid farm workers would thus be enhanced.

Special programs for the recruiting of farm labor have mostly, in the past, been confined to war periods. At such times and when urban employment is at very high levels, it is not clear that the mere offer of a higher wage scale, within conceivably practical limits, would bring in the amounts of labor required to harvest seasonal crops.[52] If enough workers of the type needed are not in the area, an increase in wage rates will not create them, nor is it likely to bring others in.

In peacetime, except when conditions are abnormal, it seems reasonable to contend that most industries should provide wages and conditions sufficiently attractive to draw the amounts of labor needed, without having to resort to government financial aid and abnormal sources of supply. It must be recognized, however, that some areas have developed labor patterns and institutional structures such that they tend to be chronically short of seasonal help if the urban economy is active.

Government assistance in obtaining foreign labor will undoubtedly continue to be vigorously advocated. It is hard to find warrant for a program of this kind as a permanent feature of American peacetime

---

52. Also, in wartime, it probably would not be socially advantageous to draw labor that is poorly qualified for these tasks out of other essential occupations even if this could be done.

agriculture. As yet no fully satisfactory alternative procedure has been proposed for meeting the problem of seasonality of labor need that is prominent in some areas. There are, however, very strong incentives for meeting part of the problem through increased mechanization of tasks that require large numbers of seasonal workers. Many farmers are turning in that direction. Research on the possibilities of further mechanization might well be intensified and also on ways of modifying production patterns so as to provide more continuous employment and better living conditions for seasonal workers.

Leaving aside the longer-run social problems created by the importation of foreign agricultural labor, the federal expenditure for recruiting and importing such labor is essentially a production subsidy. Its merit from this standpoint depends on the need for the products resulting from the program and on the gain in output as compared to the cost in public funds.

In a longer-run setting, the contentions of the objectors have more validity. There is undoubtedly a larger supply of labor in agriculture than is needed if all of it could be used efficiently. But the reallocation of labor, and the institutional changes required to make effective use of it, are extremely difficult to bring about.[53] The shift should be from other parts of agriculture, not from urban occupations. To bring it about will require institutional and policy changes that will make this kind of work more attractive. In the meantime the subsidized importation of labor should be kept at the lowest level consistent with the social interest in volume of production, since it tends to slow up and preclude the needed long-term readjustments within agriculture itself.

Equalizing Services and Facilities

As in research and education the provision of services to agriculture in forms comparable to those in urban areas presents no major problem in principle. It differs, however, in one important respect. The gains from it flow mainly to farm people and are not, for the most part, passed on to society in general. Presumably a failure to provide such services would continue and increase the disparity in attractiveness of farm life as compared to that in the cities. But the recognized tendency for agriculture to produce and retain more people than can obtain an adequate income from it indicates that society would not suffer from an insufficient number of people in agriculture if these services were not provided. To the

53. The problem is especially acute with respect to West Coast agriculture since, at least in the harvest season, it does not have close at hand any large reservoir of under-employed agricultural labor. The most chronic conditions of overpopulation and under-employment in agriculture are in other regions too distant for practical use on a seasonal basis. The situation is easing, however, and supply and demand are coming more nearly into balance both through a higher level of wage rates in agriculture and a marked increase in the use of machines in performing large-scale, repetitive types of work.

extent that providing them results in a money cost to government they are a non-cash income supplement provided to help equalize farm and city real incomes. Some of them, such as improved highways, rural mail delivery and electric power, do, however, increase the efficiency of agricultural production and thus benefit society as a whole.

Public opinion appears to favor such efforts to equalize real incomes. Here again, however, the problem of how far to go is clearly an issue. For example, how far should government go in providing regular mail services to isolated farms? Is the obligation to provide daily or frequent mail service coextensive with settlement? If not, where is the line to be drawn?

Even more pertinent is the question as to how comprehensive the network of secondary roads should be. Is every farmer entitled to an improved highway regardless of where he may choose to farm? If not, how much public expenditure is warranted, and what portion is the responsibility of the individual? The warrant for some federal expenditure as a means of equalizing access to good highways is clear, but it is a type of expenditure that should be kept under constant and hardheaded scrutiny. It can easily slip into the "pork-barrel" class.

The provision of electric power and telephone service raises issues of a different kind. Is the government's role to be only that of facilitator of private action, or is it to push in aggressively with a public ownership and operation program? The original concept of the Rural Electrification Administration was that it would serve as a banker, supplying funds that were not likely to be available through private channels. Preference was to be given to cooperative companies.[54] It was soon found, however, that engineering assistance was needed, and, to some extent, operating knowhow. As a result the government's role has tended to shift from that of banker to one that is more like that of entrepreneur.[55]

If, as REA officials contend, the privately owned cooperative associations or companies can and will gradually take over both ownership and management, the original plan can be put into effect. If not, the current program may constitute a drift toward public ownership and management. The bitter controversy of recent years over public versus private production and distribution of power, and the growing commitment of REA funds for generating plants and transmission lines, highlight this issue.

The methods prescribed in the legislation, and the announced policies of REA officials, look in the direction of eventual full user ownership and management, with only general supervision and management by the

54. In part the plan was initiated as an anti-depression measure, to stimulate investment, provide work and give an outlet for electrical equipment.

55. Much of the reasoning back of the adoption of the policies under which the Rural Electrification Administration operates is presented in an article by H. S. Person, "The Rural Electrification Administration in Perspective," *Agricultural History*, April 1950, pp. 70–89.

government. This would be roughly in accord with the pattern already established in the federal land banks, which were originally set up with government capital but are now borrower-owned, though supervised by the Governor of the Farm Credit Administration. The question arises, however, as to how far afield cooperative management can be carried successfully. Can it operate generating facilities effectively or will these eventually have to be government owned and managed?

The desirability, or undesirability, of a possible shift to government ownership and operation depends, of course, on the attitude toward public ownership generally. Many people do advocate public ownership and operation of electric power facilities and would favor moving in that direction, both by way of the farm electrification program and the power plants and distribution lines constructed under the reclamation projects of the West. Congressional sentiment appears, however, to favor private action in this realm. In any event the issue needs to be clearly faced rather than to be settled through a gradual and unplanned drift into public ownership and operation through administrative action.

The provision of wider access to rural telephone services presents virtually the same problems. The government's program in this realm has not as yet progressed very far. For the most part it has consisted of financing additions to existing facilities. Extension into new areas will raise the same kinds of questions as those discussed above.

Other Services to Agriculture

The federal government has from time to time initiated other and larger undertakings for the betterment of agriculture or the equalizing of services to it.[56] Chief among them are the price and income support programs, the special credit provisions for agriculture, the crop insurance program, and the efforts to aid low-income farmers. These are given separate treatment in succeeding chapters.

56. Some minor services not here included are also provided. However, those discussed above are the ones that are of principal importance from the standpoint of federal expenditure.

Chapter 4

The Farm Board—First of the "Action" Programs

MOST OF THE activities described in Chapter 3 had become well established by 1920. Others of similar type were being advocated but there was no important agitation for the more aggressive, interventionist types of program that came later.

The depression of the 1920s hit farmers hard and unexpectedly, especially those in the wheat and corn-hog areas. They were suddenly dropped from a peak of prosperity to the most desperate condition they had experienced since the 1890s. There was confusion and controversy about the causes of the depression and what should be done about it. Farmers rather generally attributed it to defects in the marketing system, to the sharp increase in freight rates that occurred in 1920 and to an unwarranted contraction of credit, especially agricultural credit.

Though these were elements in the slump they were not its basic causes. The U.S. position in world markets for farm products had been greatly altered. In addition, American agriculture was going through a sharp reaction from a speculative, inflation-fed boom that got under way in the last years of the war. The freight-rate increases and the credit contractions did, of course, add to the difficulties, and the fact that production was being rapidly expanded in some lines aggravated the price drop still further. So also did the war-reserve stocks of some commodities such as wool.

Some downward adjustments in freight rates were granted in January 1922, and the credit stringency was eased somewhat after the initial period of panic and sharp readjustment. However, credit remained tight in many agricultural areas almost all through the 1920s and thousands of small rural banks went under. Some modifications in credit structure and policies were brought about, but attention centered more and more on price-raising programs and on the possibility of improving the methods used in marketing farm products.

Market Reform Stressed

The emphasis on market reform was strong throughout the 1920s, but few of those advocating it recognized its limitations as a solution for the farm problem. Even such sweeping changes in market structure and functioning as were contemplated by the leaders of the movement could not have overcome the difficulties facing agriculture in these years.

Nevertheless, the idea continued to be prominent in farm organization proposals during most of that period and was repeatedly put forward by the Administration as an alternative to the McNary-Haugen plan, which became the principal objective of the farm groups in the last half of the decade.

During the early 1920s, the emphasis was on large-scale, single-commodity cooperative marketing associations. But successful action in this realm proved much more difficult than the backers of the movement anticipated. Some of the organizations, such as U.S. Grain Growers Inc. and the Grain Marketing Company, never really got under way on a significant scale. Others such as the tobacco and cotton cooperatives operated with some success for a time but most of them proved short-lived.[1] Also, even where moderately successful, these organizations were not able to achieve the results expected by their members.

The hope had been that many of them could maintain higher prices in some uses or markets and divert other portions of the supply to lower-grade uses or other markets.[2] This procedure, which would have required tight control over almost the whole output of the commodity, could not be used effectively unless the cooperative could gain and hold the support of nearly all of the growers of the product. It was the inability of the farmers to achieve such dominance through privately organized cooperatives that led them later to look with more favor on government programs designed to include all growers.

The McNary-Haugen Plan as an Alternative

Partly as a result of the slow progress made in self-organization and partly because of the continuing disparity between farm and nonfarm prices, the proposal shortly to be known as the McNary-Haugen plan, first put forward by George N. Peek and Hugh S. Johnson in the fall of 1921, came under legislative consideration near the middle of the decade.[3] Under this plan a government corporation would have been created to buy up enough of each major export crop to cause the price in the United States to be maintained at a level well above that prevailing in the world market. The products so acquired would have been sold abroad at the lower world market prices, the losses being made up by assessing an "equalization fee" against each unit used domestically.

1. For a fuller account of these developments and of the actions taken by the government in this period, see M. R. Benedict, *Farm Policies of the United States, 1790–1950*, Twentieth Century Fund, New York, 1953, Chapter 9.

2. Most of these plans also included pooling arrangements, binding contracts with growers, novel types of corporate structure and various other features that were different from those of the older cooperatives.

3. Bills designed to implement the plan were introduced in the Senate by Senator Charles McNary and in the House by Representative Gilbert N. Haugen in 1924. Hence the name McNary-Haugen plan. For a fuller description of the movement see Benedict, *op. cit.*, Chapter 10.

The McNary-Haugen bills were introduced and strongly pressed in five successive sessions of the Congress.[4] Finally, in 1927 and 1928, the plan gained sufficient support among the farm groups and in the Congress to achieve congressional approval. Both bills were vetoed by President Coolidge and both failed of passage over his veto. Nevertheless, the backing for them was so strong that the Senate came within four votes of overriding the President's veto of the 1928 bill.[5] This meant that the issue could not be ignored in the election campaign of 1928 which followed shortly after. Both candidates promised early consideration of legislation for the benefit of agriculture.

Mr. Hoover's election marked the death knell of the McNary-Haugen plan, as he was known to be bitterly opposed to it. He had, however, made campaign promises which called for some sort of action on the farm problem. He therefore called a special session of Congress to consider both the farm problem and proposed changes in the tariff laws. On the farm front, a compromise plan known as the Agricultural Marketing Act of 1929 was worked out and passed in June of that year.[6] The new legislation went farther in the direction of government participation in agricultural affairs than the Administration wanted to go but not so far as the farm organizations would have liked. They still favored a program based on the McNary-Haugen plan.

Earlier Types of Government Aid

The new act did not constitute a change of direction in government policy for agriculture. It was rather a stepping up of the tempo of activity relating to cooperation in agriculture, and the adoption of a much more positive approach to the problem. The government had long been committed to the policy of providing services designed to help farmers market their products more efficiently.

Up to that time, the assistance provided by the government was largely regulatory and informational. In earlier periods, farmers had advocated government regulation of some types of market activity and had favored the establishment of official grades and standards for use in the terminal markets. These were services they could not provide for themselves. There had also been a growing demand for improved and more widely disseminated market information and for more liberal credit arrangements. These kinds of assistance, mostly achieved with consider-

---

4. Various other proposals with similar objectives were also put forward during this period. The most important of them was the export-debenture plan which was strongly advocated by the Grange. By 1929, the domestic allotment plan had also been proposed. See *ibid*.

5. Since the motion to override was lost in the Senate, a vote was not taken in the House.

6. It was not actually a new plan. Proposals very much like it had been the Administration alternatives to the McNary-Haugen plan from about 1926 on, though they were not officially presented as such.

able effort, constitute the earlier and more orthodox part of the government program of aid to farmers in marketing.

Though for a time overshadowed by the more spectacular program of the Farm Board, these regulatory and service types of assistance have proved more enduring and still constitute an important part of the government's program relating to the marketing of farm products. The principal activities of this kind, together with their costs to the federal government, are the following: [7]

1. *Administration of the Federal Warehouse Act.*—This act provides for licensing warehousemen and supervising their operations. Licensed warehousers may issue federal warehouse receipts which assure financial responsibility of the warehouseman, proper care of the commodity while in storage and delivery on surrender of the receipt. The system thus provides a sound basis for loans on stored commodities owned by farmers, cooperatives or private traders. The amount appropriated for this activity in 1950 was $652,300.

2. *Administration of the United States Grain Standards Act.*—This act was passed in 1916. It is designed to promote uniform and accurate grading of grain under the official grain standards of the United States. The cost of this service in 1950 was about $1,160,000.

3. *Administration of the Packers and Stockyards Act of 1921.*—This act requires that facilities and services provided to livestock shippers shall be adequate and charges reasonable and nondiscriminatory. All livestock must be sold under competitive bidding, weights must be accurate, and full and correct accounting must be furnished to consignors and buyers. Unfair, deceptive and discriminatory practices are forbidden. The amount appropriated for this service in 1950 was $669,600.

4. *Provision of Market News Service.*—This work dates from 1920 under specific authorization and appropriations, though some start was made on it as early as 1915. Some of the costs are borne by the states. The purpose is to provide accurate and timely information both to growers and the trade on quantities sold, prices paid, receipts at the markets and other information likely to be useful to farmers and others in their selling and buying operations.[8] Its cost to the federal government in 1950 was about $2,000,000.

7. The costs given are from *Research and Related Services in the United States Department of Agriculture,* Vol. III, prepared for the Committee on Agriculture of the House of Representatives, 81st Cong., 2d sess., December 21, 1950. The amounts shown are for appropriations rather than actual expenditures. The two do not differ materially. The report prepared for the Committee on Agriculture gives more detail than the Budget reports and thus provides a more adequate breakdown, though issued before actual expenditures for 1950 could be determined.

8. The Service now maintains approximately 70 market news offices connected by about 10,000 miles of leased wire. These are operated through eight circuits each of which serves a section of the country. More than 1,100 radio stations broadcast market news regularly and 1,200 daily newspapers and 2,000 weekly newspapers carry articles based on the reports.

5. *Supervision of Marketing Agencies by the Commodity Exchange Authority.*—This activity was started under the Grain Futures Act of 1922. The Commodity Exchange Act of 1936 amended the Grain Futures Act, extended the government's regulatory powers, and brought under regulation the exchanges handling cotton, butter, eggs, potatoes, mill-feeds and rice. Wool tops, soybeans, fats and oils and meals were included through legislation passed in 1938 and 1940. The purpose of the Authority is to insure fair practices and honest dealing on the exchanges. Price manipulations and corners are prohibited, and likewise the dissemination of false and misleading information. The Authority also limits the amount of change in price permitted in any given period of trading, thus slowing down sudden breaks or spurts in prices. The cost of this service in 1950 was about $567,000.

6. *Administration of the Produce Agency Act, Perishable Agricultural Commodities Act, Export Apple and Pear Act, and Standard Containers Act.*—These acts were passed at various times from 1916 on. Their principal purposes are to prevent dishonest handling of products shipped to the markets, to standardize containers, and to prevent shipment abroad of low-grade and diseased apples and pears. The funds for carrying on the work, about $350,000 annually, are derived mainly from license fees assessed against the handlers, except for an appropriation of $13,000 for administration of the Standard Containers Act.

The total annual cost of these continuing marketing services provided for the benefit of agriculture by the federal government, as of 1950, was $5,121,922.[9]

Assistance to Cooperatives

In addition to the regulatory and service activities listed above, there has been an increasing tendency to encourage farmer cooperatives. The Capper-Volstead Act of 1922 broadened the definition of cooperative associations, and enabled producers to form associations for processing, preparing for market and handling their products without fear of being in violation of the federal antitrust laws, so long as their associations operate in a normal business way. The Federal Intermediate Credits Act of 1923 included provision for loans on stocks of storable commodities held by cooperatives and thus was expected to aid them in carrying out more orderly programs of selling. This form of market organization was given still more positive encouragement through creation of the Division of Cooperative Marketing in 1926.

Whereas the Capper-Volstead Act merely relaxed somewhat the checks on cooperative action, the Cooperative Marketing Act of 1926 was intended as a means of fostering it. The act created a Division of

9. Some of these services are of considerable value to the trade as well as to farmers. However, their principal purpose is to safeguard the interests of farmers and increase the efficiency of the marketing system. Nearly all of them came into being in response to demands made by the farm groups.

Cooperative Marketing which was placed in the Bureau of Agricultural Economics. The duties assigned to the new division went beyond mere research on the problems of cooperatives.[10] It was directed to "render service to associations of producers of agricultural products, and federations and subsidiaries thereof, engaged in the cooperative marketing of agricultural products, including processing, warehousing, manufacturing, storage, the cooperative purchasing of farm supplies, credit, financing, insurance, and other cooperative activities."

Among the duties listed was that of conferring and advising with committees or groups of producers interested in forming cooperative associations, and making special surveys and analyses to aid in planning for such associations. This action, together with the Capper-Volstead Act, implied full-scale governmental approval of the cooperative form of organization and a policy of giving active support in creating and strengthening agricultural cooperatives.[11]

Farmers Not Satisfied by These Milder Forms of Aid

Though generally favorable to the regulatory, educational and service activities, farmers still did not feel that they were able to bargain on equal terms with the large-scale buyers of their products. This, they believed, could be accomplished only through the creation of larger and stronger cooperative associations.

The strong upsurge of interest in area-wide, single-commodity cooperatives that marked the early 1920s had added a new line of thought as to the functions of cooperative marketing associations. The earlier associations were based mainly on the idea of reducing the cost of selling, thus retaining for the farmer members profits which formerly had gone to private owners of marketing agencies, including those derived from speculating in farm products.

The new philosophy did not stress lowered costs of selling. Instead it contemplated higher costs and more aggressive selling, with a view to inducing or forcing buyers to pay higher prices. Much stress was placed on advertising, on sales at different prices for different uses and in different parts of the market, and on disposal through by-product uses or by sales abroad at less than domestic prices.

10. Some aid to agricultural cooperatives was already being provided by the Department of Agriculture. Work of that kind was started around 1913, on a project basis. It consisted mainly of surveying and describing the work of cooperatives, introducing better methods of accounting, disseminating information on legal problems, and analyzing business methods and organization. The work was given division status in the newly formed Bureau of Agricultural Economics in 1922.

11. The Division of Cooperative Marketing was transferred to the Federal Farm Board (by executive order) in the fall of 1929. It thus became the Board's principal agency for extending general service to agricultural cooperatives. In like manner it was later transferred to the Farm Credit Administration (in 1933) retaining essentially the same functions. Under the Farm Credit Act of 1953 (67 *Stat.* 390), this division was transferred back to the Department of Agriculture and its name was changed to "Cooperative Service."

These, of course, were procedures that could be made effective only by obtaining control of almost all of a given kind of product. They had achieved some degree of success for certain specialty crops grown exclusively in restricted areas.[12] For the major crops they implied nation-wide organization and a measure of control that the cooperatives had not been able to attain. It was for the purpose of assisting farmers in building up stronger, more comprehensive marketing associations that would improve their bargaining position and enable them to sell more aggressively that the Agricultural Marketing Act of 1929 was passed.

Provisions of the Agricultural Marketing Act

The broad objective of the Agricultural Marketing Act, as stated by the Congress, was to place the agricultural industry on a basis of economic equality with other industries. This was to be accomplished through effective merchandising in interstate and foreign commerce, and protecting, controlling and stabilizing the currents of interstate and foreign commerce in the marketing of agricultural commodities and their food products.[13] Four methods of doing this were specifically set forth.

1. Minimizing speculation.

2. Preventing inefficient and wasteful methods of distribution.

3. Encouraging the organization of producers into effective associations or corporations under their own control for greater unity of effort in marketing, and promoting the establishment and financing of a farm marketing system of producer-owned and producer-controlled cooperative associations and other agencies.

4. Aiding in preventing and controlling surpluses in any agricultural commodity, through orderly production and distribution, so as to maintain advantageous domestic markets and prevent such surpluses from causing undue and excessive fluctuations or depressions in prices for the commodity.

The act authorized the creation of a Federal Farm Board consisting of eight members to be appointed by the President. The Board was to

12. Even in those lines where cooperatives had achieved substantial control, the principal gains resulted from more efficient and comprehensive organization, more extensive advertising and more aggressive selling. Activities of that kind had been markedly successful under some conditions, notably where the marketing system was not well organized and where demand could be increased materially through advertising and more vigorous sales effort. The California Fruit Growers Exchange (now Sunkist Growers, Inc.) was a notable example of successful market improvement by these methods. The growers of other specialty crops, such as walnuts, raisins and almonds, had likewise made promising starts, using somewhat similar procedures. There was no evidence that such methods could be applied with equal success in the marketing of the great staple crops such as wheat, cotton, tobacco and livestock. Here the attainment of general control over the product was virtually impossible, except through strong intervention by government, and the prospect of gain through more aggressive selling was not encouraging. Gains, if made, would have to come through improved organization of the marketing mechanism and through lower costs.

13. Federal Farm Board, *First Annual Report, 1930*, p. 1.

give assistance to farmers in organizing and managing cooperative marketing associations and was to make loans to them for the purpose of strengthening and developing a strong, comprehensive system of cooperative marketing organizations. Loans to the cooperatives could be for the following purposes: (1) the merchandising of agricultural commodities; (2) the construction or purchase of marketing facilities; (3) the formation of clearing house associations; (4) enlarging the memberships of existing cooperative associations; and (5) making higher advances to association members than could be made with other types of credit.

The Board was also authorized to recognize and make loans to stabilization corporations set up by the cooperative associations. These corporations were for the purpose of controlling surpluses in times when such oversupplies threatened to depress the markets unduly. They were presumably to deal mainly in storable commodities. Loans were to be repaid out of reserves accumulated by the stabilization corporations but if their reserves were inadequate the Board might lend them money to offset losses.

For perishables, the act contemplated the creation of producer-controlled clearing houses designed to effect economic distribution and minimize waste and losses in the marketing of such commodities. In these, independent dealers as well as cooperative associations were to be eligible for membership.

The Board was also authorized to enter into agreement with cooperative associations for the insurance of the cooperatives against loss through price declines in the agricultural commodities handled by the associations and produced by their members. Such agreements were to be entered into only if (1) coverage was not available from private agencies at reasonable rates; (2) such insurance would further the declared purposes of the act; (3) the commodity was regularly bought and sold in sufficient quantity to establish a recognized basic price for the market grades of the commodity; and (4) there was available an accurate record of the prevailing price for the commodity over a period of years sufficient to serve as a basis for calculating risk and fixing premiums.[14]

As a means of carrying out the authorized functions, a revolving fund of $500 million was provided. This was intended as a source of continuous special banking aid to cooperatives, together with help in getting organized, enlarging their memberships and improving their managements. The act provided that the loans made from the revolving fund would be at less than market rates, and a considerable amount of guidance and service was to be provided at government expense.[15]

14. For full text of the act, see *ibid.*, pp. 64–70. See also 46 *Stat.* 11.

15. This provision, Section 8(a), was that "Loans to any cooperative association or stabilization corporation and advances for insurance purposes shall bear interest at a rate of interest per annum equal to the lowest rate of yield (to the nearest one-eighth of 1 per centum) of any Government obligation bearing a date of issue subsequent to

First Phase of the Board's Program

The Farm Board was set up in July 1929, and undertook immediately the task assigned to it. But the conditions facing it were quite different from those envisioned by the framers of the act. The most devastating stock-market crash in the nation's history occurred within four months of the time the Board took office. The national economy went into a tailspin of catastrophic proportions. The work of the Board had therefore to be carried out under conditions of extreme emergency rather than those of gradual agricultural recovery such as had been anticipated.

The Board tackled first the problem which was its main assignment, that of building up a national system of large-scale cooperative marketing associations. Though the chaos which resulted from the stock-market crash had not yet developed when the first steps were taken, little real progress had been made prior to the onset of the price declines that marked the early stages of the depression.

The first of the national cooperatives set up was that for grain. This was initiated almost immediately, through a conference of representatives of all the various types of grain marketing cooperatives. Out of it grew the Farmers National Grain Corporation, which was incorporated on October 29, 1929, only five days after the great break in the stock market.

The creation of the Grain Corporation was followed quickly by others of somewhat similar character, the National Wool Marketing Corporation (December 1929); the American Cotton Cooperative Association (January 1930); the National Bean Marketing Association (February 1930); the National Livestock Marketing Association (May 1930); the National Pecan Marketing Association (in the spring of 1930); the

---

April 6, 1917 (except postal-savings bonds), and outstanding at the time the loan agreement is entered into or the advance is made by the board, as certified by the Secretary of the Treasury to the board upon its request: *Provided,* That in no case shall the rate exceed 4 per centum per annum on the unpaid principal."

Since the Treasury customarily borrows some of its funds on short-term notes at very low rates of interest, this meant supplying funds at times on an almost interest-free basis. It constituted a rather significant subsidy since the government was paying a much higher rate of interest on its longer-term obligations, which were the real source of the funds advanced by the Farm Board. All interest-bearing securities of the United States during 1930, 1931, 1932 and 1933 were at an average rate of 3.56 per cent. The interest rate charged by the Farm Board, under the terms of the act, varied somewhat depending on what government securities were out at the time the loan was made. During the 1930–31 and 1931–32 seasons, loans to the American Cotton Cooperative Association were at three eighths of one per cent. (See *Investigations of Certain Activities of the American Cotton Cooperative Association,* U.S. Senate Report No. 2030, 75th Cong., 3d sess., p. 4.) During the 1929–30 season the Board reported interest charges ranging from 1⅝ per cent to 3⅝ per cent with an average of 2.9 per cent (Federal Farm Board, *First Annual Report, 1930,* p. 46). These low rates of interest on funds used constituted a significant competitive advantage for the cooperatives, and led to widespread criticism on the part of private operators. It should be noted, however, that concessions were also made to other groups during these years. For example, Section 301(a) of the Merchant Marine Act of 1928 (45 *Stat.* 689 at 691) contained interest rate provisions that were similar to those of the Agricultural Marketing Act.

National Beet Growers Association (August 1930); and the National Fruit and Vegetable Exchange (May 1931). During 1931–32 aid was given in organizing some thirty or forty regional and local cooperatives mostly for the handling of specialty crops.[16] In addition the Board gave assistance to existing cooperatives and made loans to many of them.

The other main feature of the Board's work was of a different kind and constituted the heaviest commitment of funds. It consisted of price stabilization activities carried out both through certain of the cooperatives and through the Grain Stabilization Corporation, set up in February 1930, and the Cotton Stabilization Corporation, set up in June of the same year. The commodities principally involved in stabilization activities were wheat, cotton, butter, wool and mohair and grapes. The butter, wool and grape stabilization efforts were most closely in line with the original plans of the Board. Those relating to wheat and cotton were both of a different character and much more far-reaching and expensive.

The Butter Stabilization Operations

The butter stabilization operation was carried out through Land O' Lakes Creameries, Inc., a federation of cooperative creameries operating mainly in Minnesota and Wisconsin. That organization was granted a loan to enable it to withhold its own product, and, if necessary, to purchase additional butter in the market.

As a means of checking the price decline, which had carried the price of 92-score butter down from 45 cents on November 1, 1929 to 36 cents by mid-January 1930, Land O' Lakes offered to buy 92- and 93-score butter at the market, then about 35 cents.[17] No butter was offered to it at that time. Land O' Lakes later accumulated somewhat over 5 million pounds, by withholding and purchase, and apparently succeeded in checking for the time being the downward trend of butter prices.

During March and April consumption increased and production declined, as compared with a year earlier, and the price stiffened in late March to 38–39 cents per pound, at New York.[18] The cooperative did not attempt to raise prices. It sought merely to keep them from going lower, accumulating stocks when necessary and reducing them whenever it was felt that could be done without breaking the price. The Board comments in regard to this operation as follows:

> The success of this comparatively minor operation in butter may be attributed to a favorable combination of several factors. It rested on a correct appraisal of the facts in the situation. It was undertaken only when

16. For full list see Federal Farm Board, *Third Annual Report, 1932*, pp. 3–4.
17. Federal Farm Board, *First Annual Report, 1930*, pp. 42–43.
18. The average price per pound of butterfat received by farmers stood at 43.5 cents on November 15, 1929. This had declined to 34.9 cents by March 15, 1930. Thereafter it recovered slightly, and, except for June and July, held above 35 cents until December 1930. U.S. Department of Agriculture, *Agricultural Statistics, 1937*, p. 308.

prices had fallen to a low level, and when producers were already adjusting their production to reduced consumption. It was initiated shortly before butter prices normally show a seasonal advance. There was no export surplus of the commodity, and no prolonged holding was contemplated or permitted. The operation was carried out by a strong, experienced and successful cooperative marketing association, in connection with its regular merchandising activities; and the operation was brought to an end when the seasonal strengthening of prices appeared.[19]

During 1931 and 1932 the Board continued its effort to bring about more comprehensive cooperative organization in the marketing of dairy products. It recognized six regional associations: Challenge Cream and Butter Association (Los Angeles), Interstate Associated Creameries Inc. (Portland, Oregon), United Dairymen's Association (Seattle), Land O' Lakes Creameries (Minneapolis), Dairy and Poultry Cooperatives Inc. (Chicago), and the National Cheese Producers Federation (Plymouth, Wisconsin).[20]

Significance of the Operation

There is no clear evidence that the stabilization operation by Land O' Lakes had any lasting effect on the price of butter. The price of butterfat, to farmers, resumed its downward trend in December 1930 and thereafter declined almost continuously, to the low point of 14.4 cents in July 1932, except for minor seasonal recoveries and some strengthening of price which resulted from the drought in the northern dairy areas in the summer of 1931.

From 1932 on, recovery was very slow. Butterfat, at the farm, did not again reach 25 cents until November 1934. The yearly average for 1933 was 18.8 cents, compared with 17.9 cents in 1932. It had recovered only to 28 cents by 1940, except for the years in which production was affected by the drought of 1936. In those years, 1936 and 1937, butterfat prices were 32.2 and 33.3 cents respectively. The changes in price over this period are shown in Table 8.

There are indications that the withholding and purchase program had a useful stabilizing influence, but it apparently did not have any significant price-raising effect. The butter operation did not result in loss to the revolving fund and probably reduced speculative activity somewhat, mainly through assumption by Land O' Lakes, and indirectly by the Farm Board, of functions normally performed by the speculators. The Board's action also put stronger backing behind the supply side of the market, which was then in a weak bargaining position.

19. Federal Farm Board, *First Annual Report, 1930*, p. 44.
20. One additional association of this type was organized in the second year of the Board's operation, Dairy and Poultry Cooperatives Incorporated, a Middle West group. It is reported to have handled 33 million pounds of butter in its first year of operation in addition to eggs and poultry. Federal Farm Board, *Second Annual Report, 1931*, p. 27.

TABLE 8

BUTTERFAT: AVERAGE PRICE PER POUND RECEIVED BY FARMERS, 1929–1934

(*Cents*)

15th of Month	1929	1930	1931	1932	1933	1934
Weighted average	45.2	34.5	24.8	17.9	18.8	22.7
January	47.6	36.7	26.2	22.8	18.9	16.1
February	47.8	35.4	25.0	19.8	15.8	21.6
March	48.3	34.9	27.5	19.5	15.1	23.5
April	46.5	37.3	26.4	17.8	16.5	21.0
May	45.4	36.5	21.2	16.3	20.2	21.5
June	43.6	31.6	20.5	14.6	19.7	22.2
July	43.4	31.6	21.1	14.4	23.0	22.1
August	43.3	35.2	23.9	17.5	18.4	24.3
September	44.6	37.7	26.6	17.6	19.6	24.0
October	45.6	37.0	30.3	17.8	20.1	24.3
November	43.5	35.3	28.2	18.4	20.4	27.2
December	41.9	30.6	27.3	21.1	18.0	28.2

Source: U.S. Department of Agriculture, *Agricultural Statistics, 1937*, p. 308.

Such success as the operation achieved was almost certainly due to placing in strong position two already well organized associations with able management, Land O' Lakes and Challenge Cream and Butter. These had grown up gradually on a foundation of local cooperative experience. The ambitious regional organizations which the Board and the producers attempted to build from the top down were almost universally unsuccessful, not only in the dairy field but in others as well.

Land O' Lakes and Challenge have continued to operate successfully, but many of the new agencies, built up quickly, and largely through Farm Board initiative, disintegrated and have ceased to exist or have been replaced by successor organizations.

Cooperative milk marketing associations were already in existence around most of the larger cities. New ones were formed at Louisville, Denver, Oklahoma City, Portland (Oregon), Lincoln and Omaha (Nebraska), and various other places. In New England and some other areas, efforts were made to coordinate and unify the activities of the various independent associations. Where such action had already been undertaken in a more gradual way, as in the Washington-Baltimore area and in the New York milkshed, coordinated selling was being carried on successfully.

The new organizations sponsored by the Farm Board were mostly too weak and inexperienced to be effective in the badly disorganized and very competitive market situation which then existed. However, in the years since then, successful milk marketing cooperatives have been developed in nearly all of these areas. No doubt there were some gains in experience, interest and know-how from the abortive efforts of the Farm Board period. It must be recognized also that that period was one in which it was very difficult to launch successfully new business ventures of any kind.

The Attempt to Stabilize the Wool Market

The wool program took quite different form from that relating to butter. Growers had had some experience in selling wool cooperatively, but most of it was confined to local and regional organizations that could have little if any effect on the price structure as a whole. The largest of them, the National Wool Warehouse and Storage Company of Chicago, a grower-owned stock corporation, had gone into liquidation in 1924 as a result of crippling overadvances made in 1920. It had been succeeded by the National Wool Exchange, also a grower-controlled stock corporation, with headquarters in Boston. This organization operated conservatively and with relatively small volumes of wool, but developed a skilled selling staff, and operating procedures that were well suited to the cooperative handling of wool.

Near the end of 1929 the Board launched a new and much larger undertaking known as the National Wool Marketing Corporation, made up of 26 member associations, most of them new and most of them organized on a state basis.[21] A National Wool Credit Corporation was set up to handle financing. The principal changes from the practices of the National Wool Exchange were three: (1) the new organization brought in new and inexperienced management; (2) because of this, it hired the services of a private firm engaged in commission selling and speculative buying on its own account to act as selling agency for the cooperative;[22] and (3) it made advances at time of shipment that were at a much higher percentage of market prices than those commonly made in the past. It was here that the Farm Board was mainly involved. The Federal Intermediate Credit Bank of Springfield, Massachusetts, and private banks made loans, through the National Wool Marketing Corporation, to the extent of 65 per cent of the price at Boston. The Farm Board made additional loans to the Corporation, from the revolving fund, in amounts sufficient to enable it to advance about 90 per cent of the current price in 1930 and 80 to 85 per cent in 1931.[23]

This generous advance and other factors enabled the Corporation to gain control of about a third of the 1930 wool clip and around 85 per cent of the mohair clip. In 1931, the amounts so consigned were smaller

21. Five other associations became affiliated during 1929–30 but had insufficient volume to qualify for full membership. As of June 30, 1931, 28 associations were full members.

22. This meant that the cooperative in effect limited its functions to assembling, storing and financing.

23. For many clips the advance in 1930 was actually in excess of 100 per cent of market price since quality variations could not be accurately determined at the time the advances were made.

but still very large (for wool 28 per cent of the clip and for mohair 60 per cent). Many growers looked upon the advance as virtually an outright purchase at full value, but with a chance to participate in gains if the price should rise. In effect, the Board assumed the speculative risk of loss in case prices declined, but transferred to the grower the chance of gain if prices advanced. The revolving fund could lose but could not gain.

The achievement of control over a large portion of the clip was, of course, an important objective of the Corporation and the Board, since it was believed that this would make possible the maintenance of the price of wool at a higher level than would otherwise prevail.

Results of the Wool Program

The results proved disappointing. The Corporation held back on sales during the early part of the 1930–31 selling season, hoping to create strength in the market. However, there was enough wool available from other sources to satisfy the immediate demand, and the size of the National's holding was well known in the trade. It was expected that most, if not all, of these large stocks would be released before the end of the marketing season, and that no pinch on supplies would result.

Wool prices drifted downward throughout the marketing year, from 62 cents in July 1930 to 46 cents in June 1931 (scoured basis, territory 56's at Boston). They remained at about that level until March 1932. Thereafter they declined still further, reaching the low point of the decade at 30 cents, in July 1932, a price less than 30 per cent of that of early 1929 and less than half that prevailing when the operation was initiated. The course of wool prices at Boston, for this class of wools, is shown in Table 9.

The market for mohair collapsed entirely in 1930. Prices dropped from 45 cents a pound to 5 cents. Collins and Aikman, General Motors, Pullman and other manufacturers pulled out of the market entirely and for a time mohair could not be sold at any price despite strenuous efforts to develop new uses and markets for it.

The loss to the revolving fund was heavy considering the size of the operation. The returns from the wool and mohair when sold were much below the advances made to growers plus transportation and costs of handling and selling.[24] The liens held by the Farm Board were junior to those held by the banks, so the claims of the banks were met but those of the Board were not. Since the advances made by the Corporation were undertaken as a stabilization operation, the Board eventually assumed this loss. Otherwise it would have resulted in the failure and liquidation of the Corporation.

24. Such overadvances were legally a charge against the growers, but recovery of such claims was virtually impossible, especially in the depressed conditions then prevailing.

TABLE 9

WOOL:[a] AVERAGE PRICE PER POUND IN BOSTON MARKET, 1929–1934

(*Cents*)

Month	1929	1930	1931	1932	1933	1934
Average	92	63	50	40	61	74
January	104	75	55	49	38	82
February	104	70	52	49	37	82
March	101	67	51	46	38	82
April	95	64	51	42	41	80
May	89	62	48	37	56	78
June	88	62	46	32	63	78
July	88	62	49	30	70	78
August	90	62	51	34	72	67
September	90	62	51	43	76	66
October	89	60	48	42	78	66
November	87	59	48	41	79	66
December	82	58	48	39	82	66

Source: U.S. Department of Agriculture, *Agricultural Statistics, 1937*, p. 285.

a. Scoured basis, territory grade 56's (three-eighths blood combing).

Through compromises effected with the Secretary of the Treasury, charge-offs to December 31, 1936 amounted to $12,349,027.[25] This was by far the largest loss on any of the cooperative ventures except for those incurred in the wheat and cotton stabilization operations. The outcome seems to have been, to all intents and purposes, a transfer to the growers from public funds of some $12 million more than would have been received by them had the government not intervened.[26] There also were no doubt some collateral gains to the industry as a whole, through slowing up the price decline and steadying the situation, especially in 1930.

The National Wool Marketing Corporation organized its own sales force after the 1931 season and thereafter shifted to the management, policies and functions earlier developed by the National Wool Exchange. It has operated successfully since that time, though for the most part over a smaller area and with a smaller volume of wool than in 1930 and 1931. It has not, since 1931, attempted to manage the level of prices in the market as a whole.

The Grape Stabilization Program

A third stabilization effort, also of a different type, was undertaken for grapes grown in California. This involved working out an industry

25. Computed from annual reports of the Farm Credit Administration for 1934, 1935 and 1936.

26. Some part of this, though not a large amount, can be regarded as a cost of getting a new and large organization into operation. Some also can be attributed to unnecessarily high costs of operation under the selling arrangements made.

plan and financing parts of it. The surplus above the amounts considered to be marketable at "adequate" prices was to be purchased and removed from market channels, either by disposal through by-product industries or by leaving the grapes on the vines.

The operation was to be financed through stabilization fees collected from the growers ($1.50 per ton) under contracts by which they agreed to participate in the program for a 10-year period. The Farm Board agreed to help finance the program if a sign-up of 85 per cent or more of the tonnage could be achieved. This minimum was exceeded by July 1930 and the Grape Control Board began operation.

The fresh grape phase broke down almost immediately. The market became demoralized and it proved impossible to collect the fees specified in the contracts. The raisin operation was at first more successful as a price-maintaining device, but at the cost of very heavy abandonment of the crop. Some 337,000 tons of raisin grapes were bought by the Control Board, most of them being left on the vines. About 960,000 tons (240,000 tons of raisins) were sold at a price of $59 per ton of raisins, as compared to $61 for 1929.[27]

Thus about 26 per cent of the crop was abandoned in order to keep the price up. If the entire crop could have been sold for as much as $44 a ton, it would have brought about the same gross return, though, of course, not as much net return since larger harvesting costs would have been incurred. However, in the depressed conditions then existing, it is unlikely that the entire crop could have been sold at any price that would have caused the whole of it to move.

Thus the choice was between a controlled movement designed to hold prices relatively high and an uncontrolled one in which a larger portion of the crop would have been sold at lower prices and some probably would still have gone unharvested. The figures given indicate that marketings may have been curtailed more and prices held higher than was desirable from the standpoint of either the growers or society. It should be recognized, however, that most people still were thinking in terms of the price levels of the late 1920s rather than of the much lower ones that were to come in 1931 and 1932. The actual price net to growers was apparently about $53.75, since stabilization fees amounting to $5.25 per ton were presumably collected from most growers.[28]

The operation was in accord with the views of the more extreme proponents of monopoly techniques for maintaining prices in agriculture. Marketings were held down to what the market would take at relatively high prices.[29] The plan also included a mechanism (the stabilization fee)

27. Federal Farm Board, *Second Annual Report, 1931,* p. 60.
28. The raisin operation appears to have been carried out more nearly in accordance with the original plan than that for fresh grapes. The fresh grape arrangement disintegrated so soon after it was started that the Control Board found itself unable to hold growers to the agreements which had been made under this part of the program.
29. That is, prices that were relatively high in view of the conditions then prevailing in the economy.

which was similar in principle to the equalization fee long advocated by the supporters of the McNary-Haugen plan.

The cost to the public, in this first year's operation, was mainly in the form of waste of some 85,000 tons of raisins which presumably would otherwise have been placed on the market. This, however, was an international public, since around 30 per cent of the raisin crop was normally exported.

There is no evidence that domestic supplies were seriously curtailed or, in fact, that domestic takings would have been markedly larger had the entire crop been made available. The American consumers paid higher prices than they would otherwise have paid. The growers probably would have been about as well off if they had been able to sell more of their crop at a somewhat lower price.

Later Developments

In 1931 there was no surplus of grapes. In 1932, a new pooling arrangement was undertaken. The Control Board then released the Raisin Pool from about half of the $2.5 million obligation owed to the Farm Board. This left the Control Board virtually without assets, and it ceased to function.[30] A principal factor in the collapse was an attack by the Federal Prohibition Administrator on the Control Board's manufacture of grape concentrates. This disrupted a program that involved some $12.5 million in grape processing plants and $3.5 million in Farm Board financing. The Raisin Pool, which succeeded the Control Board, was placed in liquidation in November 1932. The loss to the revolving fund, as of June 30, 1953, was $1,103,525.[31]

The grape control plan was more ambitious than those in butter and wool, and implied both new types of organization and more attempt to manage the market. The results were apparently no more lasting and no more successful than for the wool and dairy undertakings. All three had some price-strengthening effect in their early stages but exerted no sustained influence. As of May 26, 1933, when the Farm Board assets were transferred to the Farm Credit Administration, revolving fund loans on grapes and raisins had amounted to $25,616,460. Repayments of $14,307,898 had been made and loans outstanding amounted to $11,308,562.[32] As of June 30, 1953, the balance outstanding was

30. U.S. Senate Committee on Agriculture and Forestry, *Activities and Operations of the Federal Farm Board*, Senate Report No. 1456, 74th Cong., 1st sess., July 1935, p. 24.

31. From data supplied by the Farm Credit Administration. Fruit Industries Ltd., the processing subsidiary, survived on a reduced scale and, as a result of the repeal of the Volstead Act, was able by December 1933 to pay back $500,000 of its indebtedness. Sun Maid Raisin Growers, the export selling agency of the stabilization organization, was also continued. It was still operating at a loss as of 1935, but has since become a very successful organization.

32. All but about $400,000 of this was for Sun Maid Raisin Growers of California, California Raisin Pool, California Grape Control Board, and Fruit Industries Ltd. (of

$2,257,959. This may be regarded as a close approximation to the loss sustained by the revolving fund as a result of the operation.[33]

THE MARKETING PROGRAM FOR GRAIN

Even before the stock-market break of October 1929, the price of wheat began to slip. World wheat production had been gaining rapidly during the 1920s, moving up from some 3,200 million bushels in 1922–23 to almost 4,000 million in 1928–29. By July 1, 1929, wheat stocks in the United States were about double those of the preceding years. Prices had begun to decline as early as July 1928, but only moderately. Some further weakness appeared in August 1929 and the Board, then just getting under way, urged farmers not to rush their wheat to market.

As a means of encouraging the holding of wheat the Board authorized loans of 10 cents per bushel, in addition to the loans obtainable through regular banking channels. On October 26, the loan offer was changed to a flat $1.18 per bushel at Chicago (for No. 1 hard winter), thus initiating a more positive price-stabilizing activity in place of the former plan, which would have allowed the over-all advances to decline as the market declined. The new rate was approximately the closing price as of October 25. This action seemed for a time to be effective.

Farmers National Grain Corporation Organized

In the meantime the Board had assisted in organizing the Farmers National Grain Corporation. This organization resulted from the conference of thirty-two grain cooperatives which had been held in July. Ten of them became the original stockholders. They were later joined by seventeen others. The Farmers National was not a government agency. It was a private corporation set up under the laws of Delaware, with the regional grain cooperatives as stockholders. The farmer's relation to it was that of a member of a local cooperative, which was a member of a regional federation of cooperatives, which in turn was a member of the Farmers National. The funds used were borrowed from the Farm Board's revolving fund. Stock in the National was sold on the basis of a 10 per cent down payment. Notes were taken for the balance.

The organization and business affairs of the National were badly handled. No clear provision was made for controlling the relative voting strengths of the regional associations and very loose practices were permitted. By the spring of 1931 the Farmers Union Terminal Association of St. Paul owned 28.9 per cent of the stock of the National, though it was providing less than 8 per cent of the grain handled.[34] Four of the

California). Small loans were made to certain associations in New York, but not for the purpose of stabilizing prices.

33. Data from Farm Credit Administration. The balance outstanding as shown in FCA records has not changed since 1943.

34. *Activities and Operations of the Federal Farm Board,* Senate Report No. 1456, p. 7.

regionals held more than 50 per cent of the stock, and could control the Association. The dominant one was the Farmers Union Grain Terminal with some four times as many shares as any other regional association.

Grain Stabilization Corporation Set Up

Almost from the time of its formation, the National was closely inter-related with the Grain Stabilization Corporation, which was set up by the Farm Board in February 1930 for the purpose of pegging prices by buying up and holding grain. The Grain Stabilization Corporation bought from Farmers National and other cooperatives the stocks of wheat they had accumulated. Later, as a result of criticism from elevator owners, and growers not in the cooperative system, it expanded its purchases to include all country-run wheat. Thereafter, Farmers National functioned presumably as a cooperative selling organization and not as a stabilizing agency. Actually it was maintained largely through its close interconnection with the Grain Stabilization Corporation.

In a sharply critical report by Senator McNary, submitted in 1935 for the Senate Committee on Agriculture and Forestry, the defects and mismanagement of Farmers National were outlined at some length.[35] The report points out that:

Though technically separate, Grain Stabilization Corporation and Farmers National were instruments in the same hands. The membership of Grain Stabilization Corporation was composed entirely of cooperatives that were stockholders in Farmers National. Its directors were directors and paid officers of Farmers National. . . . The officers of the one corporation, slightly interchanged, were the officers of the other. The offices of the two were located in the same rooms. . . .

For Farmers National, however, a profit made or an expense saved accrued to the benefit of the stockholders; but a gain or loss to Grain Stabilization Corporation was a gain or loss to the Treasury of the United States. With remarkable accuracy of foresight, transactions that turned out profitably were undertaken by Farmers National, while those that eventuated unprofitably either were relegated to Grain Stabilization Corporation or were undertaken by Farmers National under some special arrangement with the Farm Board which limited the cooperatives' liability for losses.

Some of the transactions were clearly improper. For example, the Farmers National sold some 2 million bushels of wheat to Grain Stabilization Corporation on May 1, 1931, for May 31 delivery, at 80 cents and, without making delivery, repurchased the wheat from Grain Stabilization Corporation at 60–65 cents, thus making a profit to Farmers National of some $365,000 at the expense of Grain Stabilization Corporation, and eventually of the United States Treasury. This illustrates the impropriety of having both a private profit organization and a government stabilization agency operated jointly and by the same individ-

35. *Ibid.,* p. 11.

uals. Numerous other transactions of similar character, both between the two corporations and between them and their officers, are described.[36]

The intermingling of functions as between Grain Stabilization Corporation and Farmers National, and the failure to put them under separate managements, make impossible a clear segregation of losses which can be charged to each one separately. As of May 26, 1933, when the assets of the revolving fund were transferred to the Farm Credit Administration, $46,085,430 had been loaned to Farmers National, $29,856,504.19 had been repaid, and the balance outstanding was $16,498,925.81.[37]

Farmers National Liquidated

Farmers National was liquidated in 1938. At that time the remaining assets were taken over by the revolving fund (then as now administered by the Farm Credit Administration). Farmers National had acquired some 40 million bushels of elevator capacity of which 18 million were owned and 22 million were under lease.[38] These assets, in liquidation since 1938, have now been entirely disposed of. The recoverable values appreciated substantially between 1938 and 1950, thus reducing the net loss to the revolving fund from loans to cooperatives. This gain, however, was a chance accretion not foreseeable at the time liquidation was begun. Hence it is in the nature of a windfall gain to the revolving fund.

The over-all cost of the operation can be presented most realistically as a cost of the price stabilization effort, and is so handled in the later section on wheat stabilization operations. The amount ultimately charged off as loss on loans to Farmers National as a cooperative can be regarded as the cost of an abortive effort to establish a national grain cooperative. The actual charge-off is, however, substantially less than the true cost of that undertaking. Some of the income attributed to Farmers National came as a result of manipulation of its relationship to the Grain Stabilization Corporation, and the venture was subsidized through loans of funds at less than their cost to the government.[39]

The venture into cooperative grain marketing did not bring about either a more efficient or lower-cost system of grain marketing. The

36. There was also implied criticism of the salaries paid to top officials of Farmers National. These ranged from $15,000 per annum to the president, up to $50,000 for the manager and $32,500 for the treasurer. See U.S. Senate Committee on Agriculture and Forestry, *Agricultural Conference and Farm Board Inquiry*, Hearings, 72d Cong., 1st sess., 1931, pp. 215–35. See also Senate Report No. 1456, p. 18.

37. Senate Report No. 1456, p. 34. Balance shown is $270,000 more than the difference between loans and repayments but is presented as given in the report.

38. Ward W. Fetrow and R. H. Elsworth, *Agricultural Cooperation in the United States*, U.S. Farm Credit Administration, Bulletin 54, April 1947, pp. 84–85.

39. The Senate committee put the interest paid by Farmers National in 1932 at $19,794.96 and the cost of these funds to the government at $187,038.66. (Senate Report No. 1456, pp. 17–18.) Much of the obligation to which these interest charges related was, however, a result of stabilization activities not properly chargeable to Farmers National as a cooperative.

results were little more impressive than those of the early 1920s when the farm groups undertook to establish a national cooperative grain marketing organization without government assistance. Such gains as were made were apparently due almost entirely to the help given by the Farm Board in the way of guidance and financial aid. The defects of the undertaking were those which have characterized most efforts to build large-scale cooperatives from the top down. The plans were too ambitious, the management inexperienced, and the underlying farmer membership undeveloped as a cohesive group of loyal supporters. Under the pressures of the emergency situation then existing, facilities were purchased hastily and at excessive cost. Procedures and personnel could not be developed gradually in ways essential for so large an undertaking.

There was, no doubt, some carry-over of experience and know-how. Parts of the personnel and facilities of the Farmers National were taken over in 1938 by the successor regional grain cooperatives. The lessons learned through participation in the earlier undertaking probably contributed to more successful operation in these later, more modest ventures.

COTTON COOPERATIVE ORGANIZED

The American Cotton Cooperative Association (A.C.C.A.), a private corporation, was incorporated under the laws of Delaware in January 1930. It was to operate as a central agency for marketing cotton handled by state cooperatives. Here the foundation structure was more developed than in the grain areas and the growers had had more experience with this type of organization. There was a cotton cooperative in nearly every cotton state. Sixteen state cooperatives had been formed between 1921 and 1924, but some had been reorganized or grouped into regionals during the intervening years. Eleven of the existing organizations were united to form the new association.[40]

The first efforts of the Farm Board to stabilize the price of cotton were undertaken through these various state cooperatives and A.C.C.A. The Board agreed to loan to them amounts sufficient to bring advances to growers up to 16 cents a pound, these loans to be supplemental to those from the commercial banks and the federal intermediate credit banks, which were then recognized as the primary lenders.

During the fall and winter of 1929–30 some $18.5 million was loaned in this way. Though handled as though it were a normal marketing advance to the cooperatives, the action was actually a stabilization operation. Loans were at higher levels than could be justified from a banking standpoint. Since the cooperatives had very limited resources of their own, any losses from sales at less than 16 cents would have to be borne

40. Fetrow and Elsworth, *op. cit.,* p. 39.

by the Board's revolving fund. In this respect the operation was identical with that in wool.

The price of cotton began to slip as early as September and October 1929. The 16-cent level of support was announced on October 21st. In spite of the Board's efforts to retard or prevent the decline, cotton fell below 16 cents at New Orleans in February 1930.[41] The price continued to fall and it soon became evident that the cooperatives could not absorb the losses. When the loans fell due, they were able to repay only $3.2 million of the $18.5 million they had borrowed.

As a means of resolving this difficulty, the Board set up, in June 1930, the Cotton Stabilization Corporation and directed it to take over, at 16 cents, the cotton held by the cooperatives. The Board also advanced to them an additional $2.6 million to clear up liens and back payments to growers, this loan being allowed up to a maximum of $1.50 per bale. There still remained operating deficits of more than $4.1 million which the Board financed in order to avoid throwing the cooperatives into bankruptcy. In so far as this could be covered under the $1.50 per bale of additional credit authorized, it was handled as a loan. The amount in excess of that (about $2.5 million) was absorbed as part of the stabilization operation.[42]

Liquidation of Loans to A.C.C.A.

Thereafter A.C.C.A. ended the practice of pegging prices at a specific level, but continued to borrow heavily for working capital and for making advances to growers. In this way it came to have in hand some 2 million bales of the 1930 crop which it held until the fall of 1932, under an agreement with Cotton Stabilization Corporation and the banks that were carrying loans on cotton.

As of May 27, 1933, loans from the revolving fund to A.C.C.A. had been made in the amount of $182 million, of this $84 million had been repaid and the balance due the revolving fund was $98 million. The amount then due consisted of $20 million in loans for working capital and $78 million in commodity loans. The Stabilization Corporation had absorbed the loss on the 1929–30 operation, except for the $4,337,213 in operating deficits.

The $98 million balance due the revolving fund was liquidated in May 1933, mainly under the terms of the act of May 12, 1933 (the Agricultural Adjustment Act, 48 *Stat.* 31). That act directed the agencies concerned, in this case the Farm Board, to "take such action and to make such settlements as are necessary in order to acquire full legal title to all cotton on which money has been loaned or advanced by any department or agency of the United States, including futures contracts

41. For Middling ⅞-inch, *Agricultural Statistics, 1937*, p. 99.
42. Senate Report No. 1456, p. 20.

for cotton, or which is held as collateral for loans or advances and to make final settlement of such loans and advances."

Such cotton was to be taken over at prices which would cover all amounts loaned or advanced and outstanding and enough additional to pay to growers any sums necessary to make up to them a return equal to 90 per cent of the value of the cotton at the time it was delivered. The purchase price was also to cover accrued carrying charges and operating costs, except such amounts as could be met from assets of the borrowers derived from net income, earnings or profits arising from such cotton or operations relating to it. The cotton so acquired was sold to the Secretary of Agriculture at a price agreed to by him and the officials in charge of the revolving fund.[43]

The obligation of A.C.C.A. to the Farm Board was thus cleared up, except for supplemental loans made to its constituent units when the Cotton Stabilization Corporation took over the losses on their 1929–30 operations.[44]

Interrelation of A.C.C.A. and Cotton Stabilization Corporation

The operations of A.C.C.A. were interrelated with those of the Cotton Stabilization Corporation in much the same way as in the parallel operation in grain. No clear segregation of costs for the two organizations is possible. The over-all loss to the Farm Board's revolving fund from the joint undertaking is shown in a later section in which the cotton stabili-

43. The terms of the liquidation thus worked out with A.C.C.A. were as follows:

Type of Loan	Balance Due Revolving Fund May 27, 1933	Settlement Pursuant to Act of May 12, 1933	Cash Repayments	Refinanced by Central Bank for Cooperatives, Dec. 6, 1933
For reloan to State Associations	$ 130,987.52	$ ——	$130,987.52	$ ——
Working capital for the cotton cooperatives	20,458,313.14	10,422,048.33	36,264.81	10,000,000
For advances on cotton sold through or held by A.C.C.A.	78,238,204.62	78,238,204.62	——	——
Total	$98,827,505.28	$88,660,252.95	$167,252.33	$10,000,000

(From statement by Governor W. I. Myers of the Farm Credit Administration on the history of A.C.C.A., U.S. Senate Committee on Agriculture and Forestry, *Activities of the American Cotton Cooperative Association*, Hearings, 75th Cong., 3d sess., 1938, p. 319.)

44. The status of these obligations, as of May 26, 1933, was as follows:

Repaid by the cooperatives	$ 551,300
Loans renewed	625,000
Assumed by A.C.C.A. and later borrowed by A.C.C.A. from the Farm Board	914,000
Assumed by Cotton Stabilization Corporation	1,056,600
Balance due the Farm Board on May 26, 1933	1,189,913
Total	$4,337,213

(From Senate Report No. 1456, p. 21.)

zation operation is more fully discussed. The loss includes, however, some expenditures properly chargeable to the attempts to build a stronger national cooperative system for marketing cotton.

The A.C.C.A., like the Farmers National Grain Corporation, made little progress during this period and its operations were characterized by many of the same abuses. Here, as in Farmers National Grain Corporation, the Senate Committee charged the organization with extravagance and bad management, including speculation on the part of the Alabama, Texas and Tennessee associations. Here also the Stabilization Corporation activities and those of the cooperative were handled by the same officers, an arrangement that obviously provided inadequate protection for government funds when the interests of the government and of the cooperative were in conflict.

For both organizations the experience during this period supports the view now widely held by leaders in the cooperative movement that large-scale financial support for overambitious plans will not build strong cooperatives. Unlike the Farmers National, A.C.C.A. did survive, but only after a marked tightening up of loose and extravagant management and the establishment of sounder financing arrangements under guidance provided by the Bank for Cooperatives (from 1933 on). Regular banking procedures were established, and the organization divested itself of its price-pegging functions, thus returning to purposes better suited to its capacities.

By 1945, it consisted of six associations, instead of the eleven that composed it in 1930, and had narrowed its functions to (1) providing a hedging service for its members and (2) furnishing a brokerage service for spot cotton.[45]

Farm Board Aid to Other Cooperatives

Though the Farm Board's activities in butter, grapes, wool, wheat and cotton were the only ones that included specific efforts to stabilize prices in large parts of an over-all market, its program included active aid in developing, organizing and financing cooperatives handling other products. The desperate condition of the whole agricultural industry put the Board under severe pressure to do something for almost every type of product, and to do it quickly. Loans were made to many cooperatives, some already established and some newly formed.

As yet, however, no adequate banking structure had been set up, and suitable techniques for appraising and supervising the loans were not available. These were to come later in the system of banks for cooperatives, which may in a sense be looked upon as a product of the experience gained in the period of Farm Board operation.

Except for the efforts to stabilize the prices of wheat, cotton, grapes,

45. Fetrow and Ellsworth, *op. cit.,* p. 39.

butter and wool, the loans to cooperatives were of more orthodox types and in relatively small amounts. The loan repayments, and balances outstanding with respect to the various types of commodities, as of May 26, 1933, are shown in Table 10.

TABLE 10

PRINCIPAL BORROWINGS FROM THE REVOLVING FUND: LOANS, REPAYMENTS AND BALANCE ON MAY 26, 1933

Type of Commodity	Loans	Repayments	Balances
Total	$1,148,906,533.29	$682,663,865.68	$466,242,667.61
Grain [a]	635,554,299.52	430,733,130.25	204,781,169.27
Cotton [a]	409,266,314.69	201,848,068.21	207,418,246.48
Fruits and vegetables [a]	35,869,984.85	18,978,676.60	16,891,308.25
Wool [a]	31,477,898.06	15,302,953.92	16,174,944.14
Dairy products [a]	18,764,989.59	7,215,515.49	11,549,474.10
Poultry products	1,271,299.14	862,452.05	408,847.39
Livestock	7,295,072.39	3,186,558.12	4,108,514.27
Tobacco	5,917,551.57	3,480,196.20	2,437,355.37
Seeds	1,484,869.59	194,306.76	1,280,562.83
Rice	1,379,707.15	697,054.19	682,652.96
Miscellaneous commodities	624,546.44	124,953.89	499,592.55

Source: U.S. Senate Committee on Agriculture and Forestry, *Activities and Operations of the Federal Farm Board,* Senate Report No. 1456, 74th Cong., 1st sess., July 1935, pp. 34–36. Data from Comptroller General of the United States. (Figures as published, not reconciled where inconsistent.)

a. Principally for stabilization of prices.

After establishment of the banks for cooperatives in 1933, the situations of the various cooperatives then obligated to the revolving fund were reviewed. Such parts of their loans as were considered suitable for transfer were taken over by the banks for cooperatives, if the cooperatives chose to make the transfer.[46] The revolving fund (also administered by the Farm Credit Administration) continued to carry the loans which were considered uncollectible or of dubious merit.

46. Loan rates of the banks for cooperatives were prescribed by the Governor of the Farm Credit Administration, but could not be less than 3 per cent or more than 6 per cent. Under the Farm Credit Act of 1933 the rate on merchandising loans was specified as approximately 1 per cent above the federal intermediate credit bank discount rate. The rate on facility loans was to correspond to the land bank rates on farm mortgages. On December 31, 1933, the rate on merchandising loans was 4 per cent; that on facility loans, 4.5 per cent. (*First Annual Report of the Farm Credit Administration, 1933,* p. 40.)

Loans based on storable commodities held by the cooperatives were presumably to be obtained from the federal intermediate credit banks. The rates charged on these loans, which are the ones most nearly comparable to the commodity loans made by the Farm Board, are based on rates paid by the intermediate credit banks on their short-time borrowings. In recent years funds of this kind have been available at rates similar to those charged by the Farm Board. However, the banks for cooperatives have made a good part of their loans out of capital and surplus rather than from funds obtained through the intermediate credit banks. These have been at rates comparable to those charged by the intermediate credit banks.

THE MAJOR STABILIZATION PROGRAMS—WHEAT AND COTTON

The efforts to stabilize prices for both wheat and cotton passed through several stages. In each case the initial step was the attempt to maintain prices by means of high-risk loans to the newly formed national cooperatives. In each case this procedure broke down and was followed by the creation of a stabilization corporation. Each left a tangled array of obligations partly due from the cooperatives and partly due from the stabilization corporation.

The Wheat Program

For wheat the first step taken was in the form of a statement urging farmers to slow up deliveries. This was followed by the offer of a loan to cooperatives at approximately the closing price for October 25, 1929, the day after the big break in the stock market.[47]

During the last two months of 1929, wheat prices recovered but it is not clear that this was due to Farm Board action. The recovery was more pronounced at Liverpool and Winnipeg than in the United States.[48] Beginning in January, Liverpool and Winnipeg moved down more sharply than did Kansas City and the spread between Kansas City and Liverpool was narrowed. The Grain Stabilization Corporation was set up in February when it became apparent that Farmers National could no longer carry the load. During the period February to May 1930, Farmers National and the Grain Stabilization Corporation together bought some 65 million bushels, apparently slowing the decline of Kansas City prices as compared to those at Liverpool.

Between July and October 1930, Liverpool prices declined by a third, largely as a result of further deterioration in business conditions and the dumping of wheat on that market by Russia and Argentina without regard to price. Wheat pledged against loans began to be forced onto the market. Hoping to stem the decline, the Board directed the Grain Stabilization Corporation to step up its purchases sharply. During November and December, additional purchases were made which brought Stabilization Corporation holdings to more than 250 million bushels.

From December 1930 to July 1931, prices at Kansas City were held approximately steady, at around 70 cents. Liverpool prices continued to decline and then held about steady at around 65 cents.[49] The effect of

47. This announcement, dated October 26, offered loans to cooperative associations (those qualifying under the Capper-Volstead Act) in sufficient amount to permit advances as follows: No. 1 Western White, $1.13; basis, Seattle, Portland; No. 1 Northern Spring, $1.25; basis, Minneapolis; No. 1 Durum, $1.12; basis, Duluth; No. 1 Hard Winter, $1.18; basis, Chicago; No. 1 Red Winter, $1.25; basis, St. Louis; No. 1 Hard Winter, $1.15; basis, Kansas City; No. 1 Hard Winter, $1.21; basis, Galveston; and No. 1 Hard Winter, $1.15; basis, Omaha. (Federal Farm Board, *First Annual Report, 1930*, p. 27.)

48. Federal Farm Board, *Third Annual Report, 1932*, chart, p. 65.

49. *Ibid.*

the Board's purchases was apparently to hold Kansas City prices somewhat above those at Liverpool during this period. In the absence of such intervention, they would probably have ranged between 10 and 20 cents below Liverpool.[50]

Farmers who sold wheat between December 1, 1930 and June 30, 1931 apparently received some 20 to 25 cents per bushel more than they would have received had the Farm Board stayed out of the market. However, since much of the wheat had moved to market before December the average gain was much less than this. The Board estimated that Kansas City spot prices for the season averaged 7 cents under Liverpool as compared to a usual spread of around 20 cents.[51] This would indicate a price gain of about 13 cents per bushel.

Not all of the gain went to farmers. The spread between Liverpool and Kansas City was normal or more than normal during August and September when much of the wheat was moving to market and hence was passing out of farmers' hands. Approximately 564 million bushels had been received and graded at inspection points by December 1, 1930, while only 351 million bushels were received between that date and June 30, 1931.[52]

Since these purchases seem not to have affected the over-all wheat market significantly, it would appear that the operation involved transfer of some $35 million to $50 million to farmers and handlers who sold wheat between December 1, 1930 and June 30, 1931. Some of the losses which would otherwise have accrued to those who held wheat purchased between July and December apparently were avoided, since the American price did not decline in harmony with that at Liverpool and other world markets.

To the extent that this loss was avoided, it was largely an advantage to handlers rather than farmers, except for such amounts as were held in grower-owned pools and actually sold during that period. This amount was not large. Some of the pooled wheat was held over and sold later at disastrously low prices. By July 1, 1931, the Grain Stabilization Corporation was holding 257 million bushels of wheat and also was carrying heavy loans on grain held by the cooperatives.

Farm Board Withdraws from the Market

The Board concluded in June 1931 that it could not justify further purchases of wheat and withdrew from the market. The Kansas City price dropped precipitately from about 12 cents above Liverpool to about 15

50. The spread between the two markets varies considerably even when unaffected by governmental intervention. There is no specific relationship that can be regarded as normal.
51. Federal Farm Board, *Third Annual Report, 1932*, p. 67.
52. *Agricultural Statistics, 1937*, p. 21.

cents below it, thus resuming approximately its normal relationship to Liverpool. Thereafter the task of the Farm Board was to liquidate its huge holdings without depressing the American market further. The policy adopted was to limit sales on the domestic market to 60 million bushels for the fiscal year 1931–32, to sell to Germany and China on long-term bonds, and to barter 25 million bushels to Brazil for coffee. By these methods the Farm Board stocks were reduced to approximately 100 million bushels by July 1, 1932.[53]

Partly as a result of a shortage of spring wheats and partly by disposal of some stocks through abnormal channels, together with a cautious sales policy, the Board was able to keep the American market somewhat divorced from Liverpool from July 1931 to June 1932; that is, to hold the spread to somewhat less than its usual amount. This was accomplished by holding down the amounts released on the American markets for ordinary export sale.

Liquidation and Financial Outcome

The remaining stocks were liquidated in 1932–33.[54] As of June 30, 1953, a loss of $65,368,095 had been charged to the grain stabilization operation.[55] However, the actual net loss on the operation was much greater than the $65 million charged to it. The second Red Cross donation involved a write-off of obligations to the revolving fund that was much larger than the cash value of the grain as of the time of transfer. The first donation of 40 million bushels (March to May 1932) was credited to the revolving fund at market value.[56] The second donation

53. Through export sales of 40 million bushels; sales to foreign governments amounting to 47.5 million bushels; sale in domestic markets of 20 million bushels; and transfer to the Red Cross of 40 million bushels, making a total of 147.5 million bushels. Federal Farm Board, *Third Annual Report, 1932*, p. 70.

54. The net outcome of the operation as of December 31, 1933 was as follows:

Total advances to the Grain Stabilization Corporation		$579,687,306
Repayments [a]	$378,735,334	
Credits for first donation to Red Cross (40 million bushels)	21,304,939	
Loans cancelled by statutory authority in connection with second donation to Red Cross (45 million bushels)	97,829,491	497,869,764
Outstanding balance, December 31, 1933		$ 81,817,542
Unrealized assets held		
175,442 bags of coffee		
German Government notes	$3,961,310	
Chinese Government notes	9,212,827	

a. Not including $5,535,518 in interest on loans.

(*First Annual Report of the Farm Credit Administration, 1933*, pp. 56–57.)

55. From data supplied by the Farm Credit Administration.

56. Under terms of the Joint Resolution signed on March 7, 1932. However, the Farm Board was required to pay off loans outstanding on this wheat, and to cancel the amounts due to the revolving fund in connection with it. The Board estimated (*Third Annual Report*, p. 84) that this transaction cost the revolving fund a total of $25 million. This loss accounts for part of the $65 million loss on operations shown above.

of 45 million bushels of wheat and 500,000 bales of cotton, provided under Joint Resolution 418 (47 *Stat.* 741), which was approved on July 5, 1932, was on a different basis. The Congress appropriated not to exceed $40 million for payment of obligations held against this wheat and cotton by commercial or intermediate credit banks and for storage, interest and other carrying charges, but it specified that no payment should be made out of these funds to the Farm Board for its equities and claims.

Under this authority, $97,829,491 of obligations to the Farm Board were cancelled in connection with this second Red Cross donation of wheat. Thus, in this operation as a whole, the federal government cancelled approximately $98 million in obligations to the revolving fund in return for 45 million bushels of wheat which had a cash value, as of July 1932, of approximately $18.7 million.[57]

The difference between $97.8 million and the $18.7 million actual value of the wheat apparently should therefore be regarded as an additional $79.1 million loss on the wheat stabilization operation. This, added to the $65.4 million charged off in 1940, would constitute an over-all loss on the wheat stabilization operation of $144.5 million, in addition to losses on loans to the grain cooperatives for stabilization purposes.

As of December 31, 1936, the grain cooperatives had loans outstanding from the revolving fund amounting to $21,406,033.[58] As of that time $795,099 of their loans had been charged off in recognition of their losses on loans and grants for drought relief which were made at the request of the Farm Board. Loans to grain cooperatives from the revolving fund have since been completely liquidated.

The losses officially allocated to loans to all cooperatives were reduced somewhat during the 1940s, in part through further charge-offs of loans regarded as uncollectible and in part through appreciation of the values of assets taken over. As of December 31, 1940 estimated losses on loans to all cooperatives for cooperative purposes, from the revolving fund, were placed at $16,860,447.[59] As of June 30, 1953 this amount had been reduced to $9,325,506.

57. Based on weighted average price in July 1932 for cash sales at six markets combined, *Agricultural Statistics, 1937*, p. 26. This average price is reduced by the same proportionate amount as that shown to have been actually realized in the sale of the 40 million bushels sold at the market, mostly in April 1932. The reported average price in these markets for April 1932 was 60.1 cents per bushel. Had this price been realized the value of the donation would have been $24,040,000. The value credited to the revolving fund (supposedly for market value at time of delivery) was $21,304,939. This would indicate that the amounts sold in connection with the first donation were either of poorer quality than average or so located that costs of delivery brought the net return below the average on these markets. The assumption made is that the value of the second donation, at the time the authorization was made, bore a comparable relationship to the average price in the six markets reported.

58. *Farm Credit Administration Annual Report, 1936*, p. 178.

59. *Farm Credit Administration Annual Report, 1940*, p. 248.

Economic Effects of the Program

The wheat stabilization operation apparently had no lasting effect on the grain market, and no significant collateral influence on the general economy. The losses incurred, aside from those which resulted from the effort to create a national cooperative grain marketing system, appear to have consisted of a transfer of funds from the United States Treasury to those growers, and others, who sold wheat during the time the price was being supported, that is, the period from October 1929 to June 30, 1931.

The initial effort to check the downward movement of wheat prices in the fall of 1929 seems to have resulted in a narrower than normal spread between Kansas City and Liverpool, from September to December. It was during this period that heavy loans were made to grain cooperatives, loans that later had to be liquidated either through write-off or purchase of grain by the Grain Stabilization Corporation.

It likewise seems evident that the method used in liquidating the stocks held on July 30, 1931 resulted in holding U.S. prices above their normal relationship to Liverpool.[60] This was made possible by what was in effect a major diversion of supply to abnormal outlets, the Red Cross donations and the sales to Germany, China and Brazil. The relationship with Liverpool was also affected by a shortage of spring wheat in the 1931–32 season.

The diversionary program did not increase significantly the total amount of wheat used, except possibly for the small amount that went to China. It did no doubt result in the use of American wheat, in place of that from other sources, in Germany and Brazil. The amounts transferred to Red Cross probably would have been furnished to relief recipients in some other way if not provided from Farm Board stocks. The quantities involved were not large enough to affect significantly either world supplies or world prices. The principal result was apparently a distortion of the U.S. wheat price structure which did not affect very greatly the returns received by farmers.

The wheat growers were obviously in a difficult situation, and good arguments can be made for taking steps to put more buying power into their hands. However, the method chosen did not strike at the root of the problem. Wheat production was overexpanded on a world-wide basis. Loans or grants of a comparable amount of funds could well have been channeled into the wheat areas, especially if so handled as to aid in adjusting wheat acreage, and if such adjustment could have been prevented from causing quick expansion of other types of output. Some type of direct payments or loans to farmers would probably have been more

60. Here as elsewhere, Kansas City price for No. 2 hard winter is taken as representing U.S. price. Kansas City had long been a principal handler of U.S. wheat destined for export to Europe.

effective, and would apparently have resulted in getting to the farmers a larger portion of the public funds put into the venture. However, that is a procedure that had not been discussed or even proposed at that time, except in the readjustment loan program for the spring wheat area which was put forward in the Norbeck-Burtness bill of the early 1920s.

The method chosen was in keeping with the widely prevalent view then held that the principal difficulty was in the marketing system, and hence that a major change in market organization would correct it. The diagnosis was patently wrong. The $1.50 wheat of 1925 and the 40 cent wheat of 1932 were sold through essentially the same marketing mechanism. No mere change in methods and costs of marketing could offset price changes of this magnitude. At best, the gains from more efficient marketing could amount to only a few cents per bushel. It seems clear also that a cooperative system so hastily and loosely constructed as Farmers National could not hope to perform these same functions even as efficiently as the noncooperative system it sought to replace. Experience was gained, and some federal money was donated to the wheat areas, but not enough to affect the situation of the wheat growers significantly.

The Effort to Stabilize the Price of Cotton

The operation in cotton was more complex than that in wheat, but there are many similarities. The first phase of the effort to maintain prices was the offer to the cooperatives of a 10 per cent supplementary loan. This was followed, in October 1929, by the agreement to make supplementary loans sufficient to bring the total advance up to 16 cents a pound. In the bailing-out operation of June 1930 the Cotton Stabilization Corporation took over from the cooperatives about 1.3 million bales, which was virtually all of the 1929–30 crop then held by them. This purchase amounted to $107.5 million, the average net cost to the Stabilization Corporation being 16.3 cents per pound.[61] Stabilization Corporation stocks remained at about that level until August 1932.

In the fall of 1930, the cotton cooperatives acquired about 2.1 million bales of new cotton and thus came to have control of more cotton than had been held by them at the time the Cotton Stabilization Corporation began operation. It became evident in 1931 that the current crop would be exceptionally large. Early season marketings forced prices to record lows. To help in alleviating this situation, the Farm Board, the cooperatives and the banks holding prior liens entered into an agreement (announced on October 12, 1931) whereby the Cotton Stabilization Corporation holdings and those of the cooperatives would be held off the market during 1931 and until August 1932. Together they held about 3.5 million bales.

61. Federal Farm Board, *Second Annual Report, 1931,* p. 50.

The southern banks, on their part, agreed to make or renew loans so as to finance the holding of not less than 3.5 million bales. This agreement as a whole resulted in holding off the market for the 1931 season about 7 million bales of cotton. It strengthened the market moderately at the time it was announced but, of course, did not affect significantly the underlying supply-demand situation in the market. It was a postponement rather than a solution.

In May 1932, the Board decided that it could not make further advances since virtually all of its funds were already committed in the wheat and cotton stabilization operations. It then announced its decision to begin liquidating its holdings in August, but stated that it would limit its sales to about 650,000 bales in the year 1932–33 and would endeavor to feed them onto the market in such a way as to keep the adverse effect on prices at a minimum.[62]

The losses on loans made to A.C.C.A. were mainly on the 1929–30 and 1930–31 operations. For the 1931–32 and 1932–33 seasons the cooperative discontinued its price-pegging activities and adopted a policy of making loans on a conservative credit basis.[63] From June 1931 such price-pegging as was undertaken was nominally a Cotton Stabilization Corporation activity.

The American Cotton Cooperative Association ended the 1930–31 season with a deficit of $52 million, which consisted of advances to state cooperatives in excess of sales and inventories plus some losses in the form of operating deficits.[64] Cotton was then below 10 cents and the loss through reduced valuation of inventories was heavy. Much of the cotton held was not disposed of until after 1933. In the meantime prices had improved somewhat and some cotton had been transferred to the Red Cross.

The A.C.C.A. made a profit of $2.3 million in the 1931–32 season and of $1.5 million in 1932–33. By the end of November 1933 it had reduced its debt to the Farm Credit Administration to $16 million owed to the revolving fund and $7 million owed to the newly formed Central Bank for Cooperatives. However, this favorable showing was, in the main, a result of the settlement provided by the Congress in initiating the Agricultural Adjustment Administration. The settlement made was on the basis of 5 cents per pound from the Secretary of Agriculture plus 4.5 cents a pound from funds assigned by the President out of appro-

62. U.S. mill consumption was then down some 2.2 million bales from the high level of 1928–1929. Foreign consumption had recovered somewhat from its slump of 1930–1931, but was still some three quarters of a million bales under the rate of 1929–1930. This reduced consumption was about offsetting the amount held by the Board and the cooperatives. Meanwhile world production had continued high and was more than a million and a quarter bales above that of 1929–1930.
63. Senate Report No. 1456, p. 22.
64. *Ibid.*, p. 21.

priations made under the National Industrial Recovery Act.[65] This transaction reduced the obligation to the revolving fund by some $58.8 million. It was part of the process of liquidating the Farm Board program and transferring its remaining assets to the successor agencies.

The paucity of published records makes impossible accurate compilation of the losses on cotton stabilization operations. They can be approximated, however, on the basis of the Senate committee's report of 1935, the reports of the Farm Credit Administration and testimony given by the Governor of the Farm Credit Administration in 1938.[66] Governor Meyers' summation, made in 1938, places the figure at $27.3 million, probably as a result of some accretion in the value of assets taken over at the time of transfer to the Farm Credit Administration.

As of 1937, when the bulk of the Farm Board financial activities had been closed out, the Senate Committee on Agriculture and Forestry summarized the over-all results of the operations in cotton as shown in Table 11.

Significance of Farm Board Operations in Cotton

The cotton operations, like those in wheat, seem not to have had any fundamental or lasting effect on prices. There appears to be no way in which they could have done so under the conditions that prevailed during this period. Nevertheless, the operation did soften the blow for a time and undoubtedly enabled many farmers, bankers and businessmen to carry on.

Had the depression been only of short duration, or had the crop of 1931 been poor, the holding operation might have had more of a stabilizing influence, holding prices up in 1929–30 and keeping them down in 1931 and 1932. As it was, the 1930 crop was about average and the 1931 crop was one of the largest on record. Economic conditions grew steadily worse instead of improving.

While the stabilization effort resulted directly in sequestering 3.5 million bales from the fall of 1930 to the fall of 1932 and indirectly in the holding of an additional 3.5 million bales financed by the banks, U.S. mill consumption was off some 4 million bales during this two-year

65. The 1,128,684 bales of spot cotton and 221,100 bales of futures were bought by the Department of Agriculture for $32.4 million (U.S. Senate Committee on Agriculture and Forestry, *Activities of the American Cotton Cooperative Association*, Hearings, 75th Cong., 3d sess., 1938, pp. 318–26.) The supplemental payment from NIRA funds added $26.4 million to this, making a total of $58.8 million which appears to have been not far out from the market value of the cotton as of the date of transfer, assuming that the stocks were of average quality and not in locations where heavy expense for delivery was involved. Crediting this $58.8 million together with the $2.6 million in other assets turned over by A.C.C.A. indicates a net loss to the revolving fund, on this phase of the operation, of approximately $27.5 million. (See Table 11.)

66. *Activities of the American Cotton Cooperative Association*, Hearings, 75th Cong., 3d sess., 1938, pp. 318–26.

TABLE 11

AGRICULTURAL MARKETING ACT REVOLVING FUND: STATEMENT OF DETERMINED LOSS AS OF JUNE 30, 1937, ON PURCHASE AND SALE OF COTTON AUTHORIZED BY THE AGRICULTURAL ADJUSTMENT ACT

	Total	A.C.C.A.	Staple Cotton Cooperative Association	Cotton Stabilization Corporation
Loans canceled May 12, 1933:				
Principal	$115,071,411.39	$88,660,252.95	$7,572,094.74	$18,839,063.70
Interest	668,182.43	287,374.33	5,649.23	375,158.87
Total	115,739,593.82	88,947,627.28	7,577,743.97	19,214,222.57
Deduct:				
Net amount received at 5 cents per pound on cotton	32,390,760.25	32,389,816.40	943.85	—
Net amount received at 4½ cents per pound on cotton	26,400,876.06	26,400,218.29	657.77	—
Adjustment received on futures	221,795.00	182,700.00	39,095.00	—
Realization on notes, accounts, and claims relating to cotton operations	10,356,440.88	2,610,233.65	4,113,581.96	3,632,625.27
Total amount received	69,369,872.19	61,582,968.34	4,154,278.58	3,632,625.27
Unrealized accounts and claims	72,268.03	22,914.67	30.86	49,322.50
Total deductions	69,442,090.22	61,605,833.01	4,154,309.44	3,681,947.77
Determined loss as of June 30, 1937	$46,297,453.60 [a]	$27,341,744.27	$3,423,434.53	$15,532,274.80

Source: U.S. Senate Committee on Agriculture and Forestry, *Activities of the American Cotton Cooperative Association,* Hearings, 75th Cong., 3d sess., 1938, p. 357.

a. The Farm Credit Administration now puts this loss at $46,305,669.

period, as compared to the rate of consumption prevailing in 1928–29, and foreign consumption was down about 1.5 million bales in 1930–31.[67] Hence there was abundant cotton available to supply all effective demand and there is little reason to think that withholding 7 million bales from the market could have had much price-raising effect.

The lending and purchasing activities of the Board evidently kept cotton prices higher than they would otherwise have been during the fall of 1929. They also held prices up in 1930–31. It seems probable that the leveling off of cotton prices in 1932 was due mainly to the fact that the 1932 crop was 4 million bales smaller than that of 1931. It was somewhat smaller than the outputs that were customary in the late 1920s.

However, this slowing of the decline in cotton price was carried out at considerable loss to the revolving fund and was thus, in effect, a transfer of public funds to the growers, the cooperatives and the trade. Its influence was mainly on the timing of the price decline rather than on levels ultimately reached. Here, as in wheat, the outlays by the government did not add corresponding amounts to the incomes of cotton growers. There was much leakage in the process.

OVER-ALL RESULTS OF THE FARM BOARD EXPERIMENT

On the whole, the Farm Board's efforts to maintain prices were not successful. They did slow down somewhat the rate of decline, but merely by providing temporary price subsidies. The subsidies went partly to farmers and partly to the trade. Price stabilization was apparently accomplished in a minor way in butter but the operation had no large or lasting effect.

The attempt to create a more comprehensive system of cooperatives for the marketing of farm products was not successful. The principal efforts to create new national or industry-wide cooperatives were in grain, cotton, livestock, wool, beans, beet sugar, and pecans. The grain cooperative did not survive, and left little residue either in the way of organization or experience. The cotton cooperative survived but has been reorganized and its functions have been greatly reduced. The bean, sugar beet, and pecan cooperatives either did not get under way or disintegrated in a short time.

The livestock association, organized along lines fairly well established by precedent, is operating successfully. The National Wool Marketing Corporation is in good shape, and probably is operating on a larger scale than if the Farm Board stimulus had not been given. However, its basic organization and procedure are essentially those developed by the National Wool Exchange in the 1920s. The heavy losses from overadvances in 1930 and 1931 were charged off as stabilization expenditures.

67. *Agricultural Statistics, 1937,* p. 94.

The Board loaned money to many other cooperatives, most of which were already established. These loans helped them through a difficult period and the aid given them by the Board probably enabled some of them to survive whereas they might otherwise have gone under.

As of May 26, 1933 loans to all cooperatives, other than those handling grain and cotton, totaled $104,085,919. Repayments of $50,082,-667 had been made, leaving a balance outstanding of $54,003,252.[68] As of December 31, 1936, the balance still due the revolving fund was $16,790,267. The remainder had been repaid, charged off or transferred to other lending agencies, principally the banks for cooperatives. As of that date, the amount charged off, with respect to cooperatives other than those handling wheat and cotton, was $13,468,960. The bulk of this, more than $12 million, was the charge-off relating to wool stabilization operations.

It is apparent from the data shown that the great bulk of the loss suffered by the revolving fund resulted from the attempt to maintain the prices of wheat, cotton and wool in a period when all other prices were declining rapidly.

Total Losses Sustained

As of September 7, 1943, the Governor of the Farm Credit Administration reported the status of the revolving fund as follows: [69]

Original appropriation	$500,000,000
Interest received	23,315,572
Total	$523,315,572
Credits allowed by Congress for donations of wheat and cotton to Red Cross	$197,385,144
Loss on assets acquired under the Agricultural Adjustment Act	46,298,337
Losses on loans to cooperatives	18,623,865
Probable future losses (as estimated by FCA)	78,224,629
Total	$340,531,975
Estimated return to the government	$182,783,597 [a]

a. This figure is $1,726,645 greater than the estimate of two years earlier because of improved collections and appreciation in value of assets taken over.

This method of stating the outcome of the Board's operations conceals a sizable part of the losses incurred. The Red Cross donations involved transfer of approximately $40 million worth of wheat and $29.7 million worth of cotton against a cancellation of $197.4 million in obli-

68. Senate Report No. 1456, pp. 34–36.
69. U.S. Senate, *Activities and Operations of the Federal Farm Board,* Senate Report No. 416, 78th Cong., 1st sess., September 24, 1943, pp. 2–3.

gations to the revolving fund. The total loss appears therefore to have been, as of 1943, approximately as follows:

Loss accepted in connection with Red Cross donations	$127,700,000
Loss on A.A.A. transaction	46,300,000 [a]
Losses then estimated on loans to cooperatives	18,600,000
Probable future losses	78,200,000
Total loss	$270,800,000
Assets acquired by the government through purchase for the Red Cross	69,700,000
Approximate recovery of funds by the government	183,000,000
Total	$523,500,000

a. This was a loss to the revolving fund though the cotton later appreciated in value thus resulting in some eventual gain to the government.

The undertaking involved two other items of expense, the cost for salaries and expense in administering the act and the interest subsidy which resulted from the terms of the act whereby money was loaned at less than its cost to the government.

The salary and expense item is available through 1933. This, however, does not include later expenses for administration and liquidation. Salaries and expense through 1933 amounted to $4,130,202. All interest-bearing U.S. securities during 1930, 1931, 1932 and 1933 averaged 3.56 per cent.[70] If it be assumed that the full $500 million was in use for the equivalent of three years, interest cost to the government would have amounted to $53,250,000, which is in effect an additional government outlay since the interest received has already been credited to the revolving fund in the summation given above.[71] Thus the total cost to the government was approximately $557,380,290, made up as follows:

Amount appropriated for revolving fund	$500,000,000
Net cost to the government for interest on funds used	53,250,000
Administrative expense	4,130,290
Total	$557,380,290

As of 1943, when the operations were last brought under study by the Congress, the estimated recovery by the government had been as follows:

Value of commodities turned over by the Farm Board	$69,700,000
Funds recovered by the government	183,000,000
Total	$252,700,000
Approximate net loss on the undertaking	$304,680,290

70. U.S. Bureau of the Census, *Statistical Abstract of the United States, 1950*, p. 340.
71. This is obviously a very crude approximation. Not all of the fund was in use throughout the period. On the other hand, substantial portions of it were tied up for some years after the close of Farm Board activities. The assumption of three years' use of the entire fund probably does not involve serious distortion.

Conclusions to Be Drawn

The Farm Board program constituted a major and rather costly experiment in which views widely held prior to that time were put to the test. The expense of carrying through a large-scale experiment is justified only if valid conclusions can be drawn from it and if society can profit by them. Results from any given experiment may be negative as well as positive. Positive results naturally are hoped for and usually are expected. Nevertheless, progress often must be made by trying one procedure after another and eliminating those which do not prove effective. The knowledge gained is a social asset if understood and used.

The Farm Board program as a whole cannot be considered a success. It is only fair to say, however, that, had the Board operated under the kinds of conditions that were visualized at the time the act was passed, its record would have looked much better and some of the weaknesses of the plan might not have become evident for a number of years. Also, had 1930, 1931 or 1932 turned out to be a very bad crop year, the stabilization activities might have appeared wise and constructive. Only two years later the "nonrecourse loan" program on corn, which was based on essentially the same principle, was regarded as highly successful. Its success was due, however, to the chance occurrence of a disastrous drought in the year immediately following that in which the stocks were accumulated.

The chance onset of the worst depression of modern times within the first year of Farm Board operations, in conjunction with continuing high farm production, emphasized the weaknesses of the Farm Board plan and made it appear much worse than it was. However, after full weight has been given to these factors, the following conclusions seem warranted:

1. Changes in marketing organization alone cannot make large changes in the prices received by farmers. High prices and low prices may occur whether the marketing system is cooperative or of the private profit type. This is not to say that improved methods of marketing cannot or should not be introduced. It does mean that results in the way of higher prices from successful innovations will be small in percentage terms as compared to price changes resulting from other factors.[72]

2. Successful large-scale farmer cooperatives cannot be organized quickly or from the top down. Virtually all of the experience in developing the existing, and in many respects highly successful, cooperative marketing system we now have tends to bear out this conclusion. Almost without exception the quickly formed, overambitious cooperative ventures have fallen apart before they could get well under way.[73]

72. Assuming that there is already in existence some fairly well developed system of marketing whether of the private profit or cooperative type.

73. Some few exceptions may be noted, but almost invariably they were built on a groundwork of successful smaller-scale cooperation and were able to draw on a body of management experience not usually available in a farmer board that has not previously managed ventures of that kind.

3. Cooperatives operating with only their own resources cannot do much toward maintaining prices in a falling market. They may be able to exert some stabilizing influence provided *stabilization* is the real objective and not price-raising. Their principal gains must be sought through efficient selling. They will be modest in amount. In some few cases monopoly gains can be achieved, but such a monopoly is difficult to perpetuate, unless supported by government, and is usually destroyed in one way or another if attempts are made to achieve large monopoly gains.

4. If government is to aid cooperatives and at the same time protect the interests of the public, the functions of the two must be clearly identified and carried out by different managements. Intermingling of the two functions contributes to loose management and questionable practices, and is not likely to contribute to the building of strong, vigorous, well-managed cooperatives. Government aid must be given cautiously and on a hard-headed business basis if it is not to prove an element of weakness rather than one of strength in the long run.

5. Loans to cooperatives should be handled on a banking basis. If aid is to be given, other than that of making available suitable types of credit on appropriate terms, it should consist of educational and service work rather than direct government action in creating new organizations, or unbusinesslike loans to those already in existence. The "borrowing" of funds that obviously cannot be repaid is demoralizing and tends to foster poor management.

6. The mere acquisition of stocks of commodities cannot be effective in raising prices continuously over a period of time. Under favorable circumstances, it can exert a stabilizing influence, but only if very large funds are available, and if liquidation of stocks is carried out courageously and at appropriate times. Short-term accumulations are likely to distort the market rather than to stabilize it. Their ultimate effect may even be a lower average price than would have resulted from freer operation of the market.

7. The Farm Board program marked probably as high a degree of government intervention as the Congress and the Administration were willing to accept at that time. It seems likely that neither farmers nor the public would have been willing to undertake at that time programs that involved as much intervention by government as they did accept in the procedures later adopted by the Agricultural Adjustment Administration. At the time the Agricultural Marketing Act was passed, conditions were by no means so desperate as those of 1933 when the agricultural adjustment program was launched. Agriculture had made a substantial recovery from the severely depressed conditions of the early 1920s. It seems evident therefore that, at that time, the practical alternatives were not a choice between the Farm Board type of program and the kinds of action

undertaken in 1933 but rather one of trying out the Farm Board approach or turning to the McNary-Haugen plan. The McNary-Haugen plan was not tried out; but there is little evidence that it would have been more successful under the conditions prevailing in 1930–1932 than was that of the Farm Board. The foreign markets were by then so weak and demoralized that they would not have offered much promise of gains from export dumping.

8. It is probable that the experience of the Farm Board with loans to cooperatives contributed to the establishment of the more soundly conceived banks for cooperatives that grew out of it.

9. The Farm Board experience contributed to a far greater interest in efforts to raise prices through controlling amounts produced, and probably cleared the way for the production control program initiated under the Agricultural Adjustment Administration. In fact the members of the Board themselves became strong advocates of production adjustment in the latter part of this period.

Chapter 5

Government Credit Aids—The Cooperative System

WERE IT NOT for the peculiarities of the agricultural industry, some of which have been described in Chapter 2, there would be little reason to provide government assistance in creating a special set of credit agencies for farmers. A vast, complex and relatively efficient private credit system has grown up in the United States and most parts of the economy are well served by it, except in acute depressions or inflationary periods when it tends to contract or expand credit too violently.[1]

However, this system has grown up largely in response to the needs of urban industries and commercial enterprises. Its traditional procedures as to length of loan and source of loan funds are not well suited to the needs of agriculture. In recent years, partly under the stimulus of competition from the federally sponsored agencies, it has made adjustments which enable it to give much better service to farmers than was customary twenty or thirty years ago.

Agriculture is a widely scattered, small-unit industry. Yet the amounts of capital needed are usually in excess of the owned resources of the farm operators. For land-mortgage loans, the period of repayment must extend over a long span of years and there is need for a lending procedure that calls for regular amortized payments, if the loan is to be reduced or repaid in an orderly way.

Large business enterprises using a corporate form of organization can handle this problem by issuing common and preferred stocks, by selling bonds and by building up corporate reserves. These devices are not generally available to farmers, except as they can pool their credit resources in such a way that risks can be spread and distant sources of loan funds can be tapped.

The individual lender cannot afford to buy a mortgage on a farm halfway across the continent, which he probably has never seen and whose owner he does not know. Even where he does know the farmer and his security, the risk of something going wrong on a single farm is too great. As a consequence, loan funds have often been very inadequate in many

1. The private credit system as a whole includes much more than the commercial banking organizations. It consists in part of the great network of life insurance companies and other savings institutions, of the mechanisms for issuing, servicing and exchanging corporation bonds and common stocks and of great numbers of individual lenders and stockholders.

rural, capital-deficit areas, even when savings accumulated in other sections of the country were seeking an outlet.

It was to overcome this difficulty, and to provide an orderly and safe channel for the transfer of such funds, that the federal land bank system was created. By means of these banks, the credit bases of many farmers could be combined in such a way that bonds based on them could be sold in the money markets in convenient denominations and with the risks so spread as to make their purchase comparatively safe for the investor.

Under this system risks have been reduced, spread and absorbed not only through basing the bonds on large numbers of individual farm mortgages but by building up reserves in the land banks and providing machinery for careful appraisal of the properties, and for supervision of the loans after they are made. The amortization plan of repayment required under the authorizing legislation also increases the likelihood of repayment and provides an orderly method of receiving the payments and servicing the bonds.

In recent years, the life insurance companies, and even some of the larger private banks, have found that they too can handle farm loans in this way. However, until 1930 and after, when the land banks had demonstrated the feasibility of such procedures, almost none of the private lending agencies, except the joint-stock land banks, offered anything but short-term farm mortgage loans, usually on a three- to five-year basis.

With such a loan the borrower was in a precarious position if a severe depression occurred, as he might not be able to renew his loan and thus ran a serious risk of losing his farm through foreclosure. Furthermore, the opportunities for orderly reduction of principal were lacking since he usually could not make small regular payments for that purpose.

Origins of the Federal Land Bank System

During the nineteenth century, farmer interest in money and banking centered mainly on monetary issues such as specie versus paper money, the issuance of greenbacks, and free coinage of silver. The farm groups also opposed central banks and the national bank system. But credit as such did not bulk large in their legislative programs.

Shortly after 1900, the credit problem assumed a larger place in their thinking. Demands for special banking arrangements for agriculture became frequent and vigorous. The movement for a new approach to the farm credit problem began to take organized form around 1908, when President Theodore Roosevelt appointed a Country Life Commission to explore the problems of agriculture and suggest things needed to improve its condition. That Commission stressed the inadequacy of agricultural credit as one of the principal causes of unsatisfactory conditions in the rural areas. Shortly thereafter, the American Bankers Association and the Southern Commercial Congress became interested in the problem, giving particular attention to the possibility of developing a cooperative credit system patterned after those which had long been used in some of the European countries.

The movement became strong enough by 1912 so that all three major political parties pledged action to provide improved credit for agriculture, if their candidates were elected. President Taft had already taken steps looking in that direction and President Wilson followed up almost immediately by appointing a commission to study the methods and organization of the European cooperative credit associations. Shortly thereafter various bills providing for the establishment of a system of federally sponsored land banks were introduced. Though there was a good deal of controversy as to the plan of organization, there was general agreement on the need for some kind of improved mortgage credit organization for agriculture. The outcome, after a considerable period of hearings and debate, was the Federal Farm Loan Act of 1916.[2]

System Based on Conservative Principles

Under the Farm Loan Act, twelve regional federal land banks were established as cooperative loan agencies to be owned eventually by the borrowing farmers, though they were to continue to be supervised and serviced by a Federal Farm Loan Board which was created by the act. The act also authorized the creation of a privately owned system of joint-stock land banks. These, too, were to be supervised by the Federal Farm Loan Board.

The system thus set up was designed to operate on a very conservative basis and to provide only land-mortgage loans. Its principal purposes were to provide funds at lower rates of interest, to introduce more orderly, long-term methods of repayment and, presumably, to encourage the acquisition of farms by tenants. It was not intended as a way of dealing with emergency situations such as those which were to come shortly thereafter.

The later and much more extensive development of federally sponsored credit arrangements for agriculture was largely a response to emergency needs, though it continued to have a strong central core of basic organization designed for conservative, business-type loans. After assisting farmers in meeting the acute emergency situation of the 1930s, the system has reverted more and more to the relatively conservative, cooperative principles which characterized the original land bank legislation.

This system, now known as the Farm Credit Administration, provides a comprehensive, federally sponsored but in the main privately owned, set of organizations for supplying various types of credit to American

2. For a fuller description of this development see M. R. Benedict, *Farm Policies of the United States, 1790–1950*, Twentieth Century Fund, New York, 1953, pp. 145–48.

agriculture. These organizations and their place in the credit structure as a whole are more fully described in later sections.

The Need for Intermediate Credit

Though the federal land bank legislation laid the groundwork for an improved system of farm mortgage credit, it did not touch in any significant way the short-term credit problem. A criticism commonly made by farmers was that the loans made by commercial banks for many types of farm operation were not for long enough periods to make possible the repayment of the loans out of the income resulting from them. Many farm production operations require at least six to nine months for completion and for sale of the product. Some require two to three years, or even more, especially some of the livestock operations. Banks were in the habit of making loans for three to six months and, in ordinary times, renewing them until such time as repayment could be made out of the proceeds of the undertaking.

If no squeeze in loan funds occurred, this system worked reasonably well. But if bank depositors chose suddenly to withdraw their deposits, or if the price outlook became bad, the farmer was likely to be faced with a demand for repayment of his loan before he was able or willing to dispose of his crop or livestock. He resented this situation, not only because he might be unable to make payment when his loan fell due but because he frequently felt he was being forced to sell at a time when the market was glutted, whereas if he could hold his crop longer he might be able to sell to better advantage.

Part of this difficulty stemmed from the nature of the loan funds used by the banks. Since the banks depended partly on deposits, which could be withdrawn suddenly and without notice, they were apt to find themselves faced with demands from their depositors for funds which they had loaned to farmers on paper that could not be liquidated quickly. Some of the agricultural paper could be rediscounted with the Federal Reserve Banks, but they, too, were designed mainly for handling the short-term, highly liquid types of paper customarily used in urban business operations.

It was to overcome this difficulty that the federal intermediate credit banks were established in 1923. Their loans were not to be made out of deposit funds but rather from the proceeds of fixed-term debentures sold in the open market. They were to provide loans of one to three years duration and also to make advances on warehoused farm commodities held by farmer-owned cooperatives. Thus it was expected that both farmers and cooperatives would be under less pressure to sell in a weak and declining market and that farmers would be able to get loans better suited to their needs.

The intermediate credit banks were not to become borrower owned. They were, and still are, government-owned corporations designed to serve as discount banks, not as original lenders. That is, the loans, except those to cooperative associations, would first be made by local agricultural finance corporations, livestock-loan companies or banks and then rediscounted with the federal intermediate credit banks.

Later Additions to the Farm Credit System

The farm credit system was later to be broadened by setting up the banks for cooperatives (with capital supplied from the remaining assets of the Farm Board) and the production credit corporations and associations. The production credit system, which came in 1933 and after, consisted in the main of a rounding out of the local part of the intermediate credit system.

Farmers had not been able to use the intermediate credit banks effectively because they did not have local finance corporations through which to borrow. The production credit corporations were a means whereby the government could give assistance in organizing and financing local production credit associations until they could become strong enough to operate without government assistance and capital. The principle was very similar to that under which the federal land banks had been capitalized by the government until they could develop into borrower-owned cooperatives.

These various types of farm credit agency constitute the main body of the federally sponsored cooperative farm credit organization now in existence. During the period prior to 1933, they were supplemented to some extent by emergency credit organizations, notably seed and feed loans, the revived War Finance Corporation and the regional agricultural credit corporations set up under the Reconstruction Finance Corporation. Discussion of most of these is deferred to Chapter 6, though some emergency activities were included under the Farm Credit Administration during its early years of operation.

The Farm Credit Administration was set up in 1933, using some of the authorizations of the Agricultural Marketing Act of 1929. It was a means of bringing together and coordinating most of the agricultural credit activities then being carried on and of adding several new ones. As the emergency lending activities have receded in importance, the Farm Credit Administration has become more and more the focus of the continuing, conservative phase of government-sponsored farm credit. It is mainly cooperative and mostly privately owned. The less orthodox types of lending have been gradually transferred to the special types of credit agency described in Chapter 6.

Emergency Financing Limited Until After 1930

Up to the time of the depression of 1930, there was little effort by the government to provide emergency credit on any large scale. Until then, the policy was mainly to create a more orderly and efficient credit system for agriculture but still one that would be conservative and would for the most part be organized and operated on orthodox lines. The plans did not imply large inputs of federal funds.

The seed and feed loans, begun in 1918 to aid farmers suffering from drought, and the revived War Finance Corporation, which was a means of carrying frozen assets until they could be liquidated, were exceptions to this general plan.

None of the plans discussed in this period contemplated vigorous and widespread emergency credit to farmers in a period of serious general depression. Yet it was emergency credit on a large scale that was to be needed by farmers in the 1920s and on a much wider scale in the 1930s. For the most part, the depression of the 1920s was weathered through without emergency credit aid from the government. The situation in the 1930s was much more desperate and the government stepped in on a much larger scale.

CREDIT PROBLEMS OF THE 1920s

As a result of the abrupt decline in farm prices that began in the summer of 1920, the availability of credit for agriculture became immediately a matter of prime importance. The need was for renewal or even enlargement of loans, to enable farmers to carry on until conditions would improve or until some plan of aid could be devised and agreed on.

Hundreds of thousands of farmers whose loans were falling due or who were unable, for the time being, to make incomes cover cash outlays were seeking new sources of credit. Most of the borrowing was through private lending agencies, chiefly life insurance companies, commercial banks, farm mortgage corporations and individuals. Banks in particular were under heavy pressure to reduce their loans and gain liquidity at the earliest possible time, but the insurance companies, joint-stock land banks and individual lenders also undertook to reduce their loans and get into more liquid condition.

The trouble stemmed in part from overoptimistic lending and borrowing in the period just preceding. For some borrowers, the only way out was through bankruptcy or forced sale. But for many others a quick expansion of alternative loan funds would have provided relief and would have given them a chance to save their farms and possibly even, eventually, to regain some of their lost equities.

Credit alone could not solve their problems. It could only serve as a shock absorber which could give time for the slower process of price recovery and cost adjustment to come about. But in times of panic, the amount of private credit is inevitably reduced sharply. In such times, the government is the only agency that can step in effectively to replace credit thus suddenly destroyed through contraction of private lending.

The warrant for such action depends, of course, on the amount of indebtedness and the prospect of a return to levels of prices and costs somewhat in keeping with those in which the debts were incurred. The uncertainty about future prices is a major stumbling block in such periods. At the time, no one knows what the price level will be over the years ahead. It is a safe bet, however, that it will be higher than in the depths of depression and that many farmers who cannot meet their obligations currently will be able to do so later. The values to be conserved are so important that the government is warranted in taking some risks.

Farm Debts Too High in the 1920s

In the early 1920s, there was little prospect that farm incomes would return to or near the levels that had prevailed during the war years. Hence refinancing of heavily mortgaged farmers on the basis of inflated valuations gave little promise of affording them genuine and lasting help. It might only prolong the agony, and at the same time assure heavy loss to the lending agencies.

An attempt to expand credit generally at that time would have been likely to inhibit needed readjustments in the nonfarm economy. In fact, that type of credit expansion apparently was not greatly needed once the urban activities were again on the upgrade, as they were by the end of 1922. If a freer flow of credit was to benefit agriculture it would have to be channeled directly into agriculture, thus operating as a selective expansion of credit rather than a general one.

Though the prospect for farm earnings was not such as to warrant a full-scale rescue operation, an easing of the tight credit situation in respect to loans for current operations would have been helpful. However, there was not much effort to provide help of that kind. Most groups, both in and out of agriculture, still held strongly to the conservative banking mores of an earlier period and few proposals were put forward or discussed that would have looked to any large-scale action to provide emergency credit for agriculture.

In the main, the debtors worked their way out or defaulted in much the same way as in previous depressions. Thousands of farms were lost and many banks were closed. Many farmers were too heavily involved to be able to meet their obligations even if given more time. Only an improvement in prices, a squeezing down of inflated land values and a reduction of costs could bring full recovery. All of these adjustments did occur gradually during the 1920s but the situation had not yet come fully into balance when the depression of the 1930s brought on a new and more serious crisis.

Sources of Loan Funds and Amount of Debt in the 1920s

As of 1920, about 95 per cent of the farm mortgage debt was held by noninstitutional lenders, life insurance companies and commercial banks. Nearly all of this was in short-term mortgages with no provision for gradual reduction through amortization, and no assurance of renewal when due. The newly formed federal land banks and joint-stock land banks were almost the only lenders making long-term, amortized loans. Together they held less than $360 million in farm mortgage loans out of a total of some $8.5 billion. Nearly 70 per cent of the total mortgage debt was held by individual lenders, many of them, no doubt, former owners of farms which had been sold. Commercial banks held a somewhat larger volume of loans than the insurance companies but only about one fifth as much as the individual lender group. The sources and amounts of farm mortgage debt in this and the preceding and following years are shown in Table 12.

Though mortgage foreclosures, bankruptcies, and involuntary transfers were heavy, the total volume of outstanding farm mortgage debt did not begin to decline until 1923. This was due in part to the shift of overdue short-term loans to mortgage form as a protection to lenders.[3] When the depression was at its worst, temporary accommodation for current operating expenses or for interest and taxes was virtually impossible to obtain since nearly every country bank was striving desperately to get money to pay depositors or reduce bills payable. Consequently, the borrower who was unable to pay off his short-term loans often had to increase his real estate mortgage to obtain money for paying off chattel mortgages or as a means of putting additional security back of the short-term loans he was unable to pay.

Even with adjustments of this kind, many farmers were in desperate circumstances. Interest rates were high, taxes were rising, and cash costs still were inflated. Farm incomes in many areas were less than half what they had been during the war years.

The need for emergency credit was more urgent than for some specific level of prices or for any long-term plan for improving farm incomes. Farmers could weather a period of hardship and low prices, as they often had done in the past, but only if they could retain possession of their farms. It was the lack of credit suited to this process of "hanging on" that was their most serious handicap in the 1920s, so far as credit was concerned.

3. For the years before 1925 the information is sketchy on numbers of involuntary transfers of farms, that is, transfers resulting from bankruptcy, foreclosure, or forced sale. It is common knowledge, however, that such transfers were heavy in the early 1920s.

TABLE 12

SOURCES OF FARM MORTGAGE DEBT, 1910–1930

(Thousands)

Beginning of Year	Estimated Total	Federal Land Banks [a]	Life Insurance Companies [b]	Joint-stock Land Banks [c]	Commercial Banks [d]	Individuals and Others [e]
1910	$3,207,863	———	$386,961	———	$406,248	$2,414,654
1911	3,522,131	———	423,454	———	477,568	2,621,099
1912	3,929,758	———	479,653	———	580,300	2,869,805
1913	4,347,679	———	550,158	———	673,752	3,123,769
1914	4,707,358	———	597,462	———	723,787	3,386,109
1915	4,990,785	———	669,984	———	746,111	3,574,690
1916	5,256,425	———	765,571	———	776,269	3,714,585
1917	5,825,851	———	861,144	———	933,990	4,030,717
1918	6,536,860	$39,112	955,591	$1,888	1,008,492	4,531,777
1919	7,137,365	157,021	1,018,163	8,384	1,030,240	4,923,557
1920	8,448,772	296,386	974,826	60,038	1,204,383	5,913,139
1921	10,221,126	356,010	1,205,778	77,959	1,447,483	7,133,896
1922	10,702,257	443,062	1,432,367	85,017	1,540,005	7,201,806
1923	10,785,621	655,681	1,556,203	218,775	1,506,467	6,848,495
1924	10,664,919	822,161	1,792,145	392,639	1,388,106	6,269,868
1925	9,912,650	923,077	1,942,624	446,429	1,200,456	5,400,064
1926	9,713,213	998,552	2,030,301	545,559	1,178,460	4,960,341
1927	9,658,422	1,068,642	2,123,664	632,574	1,143,595	4,689,947
1928	9,756,957	1,144,984	2,172,863	667,314	1,097,085	4,674,711
1929	9,756,559	1,182,813	2,138,980	656,516	1,046,624	4,731,626
1930	9,630,768	1,201,732	2,118,439	637,789	997,468	4,695,340

Source: U.S. Department of Agriculture, *Farm-Mortgage Credit Facilities in the United States*, Miscellaneous Publication No. 478, 1942, p. 12. Data for 1930 revised to accord with later estimates.

a. Excluding Puerto Rico.
b. Partially estimated.
c. Including banks in receivership.
d. Open state and national banks (estimated).
e. Residual of estimated total not accounted for by designated lending agencies.

Federal Land Bank Operations to 1933

The Federal Farm Loan Act of 1916 had authorized the Treasury to purchase stock in the twelve federal land banks to the extent of such part of $9 million as would not be subscribed privately. In accordance with this directive, the Treasury advanced $8,892,130 to put the banks into operation. The stock thus purchased was to be gradually replaced by stock acquired by the borrowers in connection with their loans.[4]

By the end of 1931, the government-owned stock had virtually all been retired (only $204,698 was still owned by the Treasury at that time). The total capital of the banks, almost entirely owned by the borrowers, had grown to $65,676,130. The land banks were then providing $1,167,898,205 [5] in farm mortgage loans.

Interest rates on these loans in 1931 were about .6 of 1 per cent lower than the average for all farm mortgage lenders. The principal competing institutional lenders were the life insurance companies and the commercial banks. Interest rates charged by the insurance companies were about .4 per cent lower than the average for all lenders and about .2 per cent above those of the land banks. Commercial bank rates were approximately 1.2 per cent above those of the land banks and 1 per cent higher than those charged by the insurance companies. Noninstitutional lenders, mostly individuals lending their own funds directly to borrowers, were making loans at rates that were, on the average, above those of the land banks and insurance companies and below those charged by the commercial banks.[6]

There is no clear evidence that the federal land banks had much influence on the level of farm mortgage interest rates charged by other lenders in this first period.[7] After 1933, when they came to play a much

4. Each borrower was required to purchase stock in his local farm loan association in the amount of 5 per cent of his loan. The local farm loan association in turn purchased a corresponding amount of stock in the federal land bank of its district. There was also a provision for individual borrowing through agents, where local farm loan associations were not available. Until 1933, this procedure was used principally in Puerto Rico.

5. Data given here and below are end of year figures.

6. Data on interest rates from U.S. Department of Agriculture, *Farm-Mortgage Facilities in the United States,* Miscellaneous Publication No. 478, 1942, p. 232. The estimates of average rates charged by the various types of lenders in 1931 were as follows:

	Percentage
All lenders (average)	6.0
Federal land banks	5.4
Joint-stock land banks	5.9
Insurance companies	5.6
Individuals	6.2
Banks	6.6
Others	6.2

7. This comment probably understates the significance of land bank competition, especially for high-risk areas. In the Corn Belt and other low-risk areas, which were attractive to private lenders, the observable effect on rates charged is negligible. The most significant effects were in the high-risk, capital-deficit regions such as the South and the Plains and Mountain states. Here the land bank competition apparently did reduce rates, especially those charged by local banks. However, these were not the areas in which the

larger part in mortgage lending operations, their influence on the level of interest rates apparently was more significant. The interest rates charged by the various lending agencies remained nearly constant from 1910 to 1933 except for a small increase of less than ½ of 1 per cent in the years 1922–1926.[8] Those who borrowed through the land banks were apparently benefiting to the extent of some $5 to $7 million annually as compared to what they would have paid if their rates of interest had been as high as the average rate charged by all lenders.[9]

Possibly a more logical comparison is with the rates charged by the insurance companies, since these types of loans are most directly comparable. On this basis, the annual saving was in the order of $2.3 million per year. The land bank loans were, to be sure, conservative, but probably little if any more conservative than those of the insurance companies.

As a means of strengthening the credit situation in agriculture, the introduction of the long-term, amortized loan was of much greater importance than the modest reduction in the rate of interest charged. The land banks and joint-stock land banks were the pioneers in bringing into use this fundamental improvement in farm mortgage lending operations.[10] For the first time in the history of American agriculture, the indebted farmer could obtain a long-term, amortized loan and go about retiring it in an orderly way.

Furthermore, he could protect himself against the threat of foreclosure in time of acute depression, provided he could keep up his interest and amortization payments. The arrangement still was not sufficiently flexible to meet his needs in times of acute depression, but it was vastly better than any that had preceded it. However, less than one fifth of the total farm mortgage debt was held by the land banks and joint-stock land banks when the depression of the 1930s again plunged American agriculture into a major credit crisis.

Intermediate Credit Operations to 1933

The federal intermediate credit banks did not become important lenders for agriculture during the 1920s. This was partly because the farmers had few local finance corporations or other agencies through which their loans could be channeled into these rediscount banks.[11] It

---

land banks and joint-stock land banks made the bulk of their loans in the early period, and the insurance companies and other general lenders tended to stay out of such areas. Consequently, direct comparisons of rates charged are somewhat inconclusive. The land banks did make funds available in some areas at much lower rates than had been customary, but the volume of such business, especially in the period prior to 1933, was not large.

8. *Farm-Mortgage Credit Facilities in the United States,* p. 232.

9. On the basis of the loan volume of 1929.

10. Most of the insurance companies and some of the other lenders have since shifted over to long-term loans and an amortization plan of repayment.

11. Most country banks did not turn to the federal intermediate credit banks as a source of loan funds, partly because of the very narrow spread between the interest rate charged them and the rate they were allowed to charge their borrowers on notes redis-

was also due to the fact that, once the credit stringency of the early 1920s had eased off, the intermediate credit system had little to offer that could not be as well supplied through the more convenient and familiar mechanism of the commercial banks, so long as the banks were seeking new loans instead of trying to contract their operations.

Government stock in the intermediate credit banks was increased gradually from $20 million in 1923 to $32 million in 1932 and then sharply to the $60 million originally authorized. Franchise taxes on these funds were to be paid out of earnings. These taxes apparently were intended at first as a means of reimbursing the government for the capital invested in the banks but have since come to be looked upon as a type of payment somewhat comparable to a dividend on stocks owned. The amount of such taxes was about $500,000 per year for 1924 through 1926. Thereafter it dwindled off to negligible amounts in 1930 and 1931 and to nothing in the years 1932 through 1936.[12]

During the 1920s, federal intermediate credit bank loans and discounts reached a peak of $177 million in 1926 and then receded to $138 million in 1929. Loans outstanding at year end showed a similar pattern, with a peak of $92 million in 1926 and a recession to $76 million in 1929. There was a new upsurge in 1930 and 1931. For 1931, loans made amounted to $268 million and loans outstanding at the end of the year to $120 million, but volume again fell off in 1932.

This failure to achieve an important volume of loans in the 1920s, or in the years 1930–1932, affords clear evidence that the intermediate credit system, as organized in the years prior to 1933, was not likely to play a large role in times when commercial banks were willing and able to make the same types of loans, or even in times when loans were desperately needed.[13]

Until 1933, the principal achievements were that the banks had been launched and some experience had been gained. They had provided a modest amount of credit but not enough to affect the agricultural situa-

---

counted with the intermediate credit banks. Since only a few agricultural finance corporations and livestock loan companies had been created, most farmers therefore had no practical channel through which intermediate credit bank loans could be obtained. They lacked both the capital and the operating experience that would have been needed for setting up and operating successfully any considerable number of finance corporations of their own.

12. For the years 1923 through 1931, the total amount of franchise taxes paid was $2,496,779. The law was amended in 1932 (47 *Stat.* 159) in such a way as to provide that after July 1, 1932, the intermediate credit banks would pay a franchise tax only after their earned surpluses had reached 100 per cent of paid-in capital. On the earnings in excess of this amount they were to pay 50 per cent as a franchise tax. Previously all of the remaining amount had to be turned over to the Treasury. A later amendment, passed in 1937, made some changes in these provisions such that the banks had to resume payment of franchise taxes.

13. The federal intermediate credit banks did, however, close loans and discounts from 1923 through 1932 in the amount of $1,634,652,648, or an average of about $160 million per year.

tion importantly. The volume had been declining until the depression struck and even then was expanded only moderately.

Except in the period between 1929 and 1933, borrowers probably could have obtained funds on about as good terms if the intermediate credit banks had not been in existence. The trouble did not lie in the idea of production and marketing loans based on investment funds, instead of credit supplied by deposit banks, but rather in the lack of adequate organization to reach through to the farmer borrower. After 1933, the provisions made for organizing and financing local production credit associations were to give the intermediate credit banks a much larger and more significant place in the farm credit system (see pp. 156 ff.).

Emergency Credit—The War Finance Corporation

Aside from seed loans provided for drought-stricken areas, the only significant emergency credit relief given to agriculture prior to 1930 was that which resulted from reactivation of the War Finance Corporation, which had been set up in 1918 to assist in financing industries essential to the prosecution of the war. After the armistice, emphasis shifted to the financing of exports to the allied nations. The Corporation was intended only as a war agency, and its lending operations were suspended in May 1920. When the sharp break in the prices of farm products occurred shortly thereafter, agitation developed for a revival of its activities.

Both Secretary Houston (of the Treasury) and President Wilson opposed such action, contending that the ordinary banking facilities available to exporters were adequate to take care of the needs. However, congressional sentiment for renewal of lending operations through the Corporation continued strong and a Senate Joint Resolution (41 *Stat.* 1084) was passed over the President's veto, in January 1921. It directed the Secretary of the Treasury to "rehabilitate" the Corporation with a view to assisting in the exportation of agricultural and other products.

In accordance with this directive, the Corporation granted loans for the export of American farm products but the amount was not large. The total amount loaned for this purpose was $38.6 million, of which all but some $342 was repaid. The bulk of the operation (some $26.6 million) was in cotton. Loans on grain amounted to $3.3 million and those on tobacco to $2.4 million.

While these transactions were entirely successful from a banking standpoint, they had little significance as a means of aiding agriculture. The smallness of the demand for such credit bore out the contention of the President and the Secretary of the Treasury that, for loans of this type, the regular private lending facilities were sufficient. The action taken did apparently strengthen the cotton market, because of the assurance afforded that financing would be available if needed. The Corporation agreed to finance about one million bales in the amount of $40.7 million, but not all of this commitment was taken up. This was about one sixth of the total volume of exports. The availability of such credit probably also helped somewhat in restoring confidence and inducing commercial banking institutions to resume lending operations of this kind, thus reducing the need for financing through the War Finance Corporation.

The Agricultural Credits Act of 1921

The act authorizing the War Finance Corporation was amended in August 1921, by the Agricultural Credits Act of 1921. The amendment provided that advances might be made to dealers in and handlers of agricultural products to carry them until the commodities financed could be sold for export. It also permitted the Corporation to lend to banks and trust companies that had made advances for agricultural purposes.

Under this provision, the most important work of the revived War Finance Corporation was carried out. It was the most significant emergency credit action taken by the government during the 1920s. Advances could be made, until July 1, 1922, for periods not exceeding one year, but the time could be extended at the discretion of the Corporation for periods not exceeding three years from the time of granting the loan.

The Corporation advanced in this way approximately $298.6 million, thereby easing the pressure on rural banks and indirectly on farmer borrowers. Some banks were relieved of slow paper to an extent that enabled them to resume the making of new loans to farmers for production purposes. In the livestock areas, where the credit stringency was especially acute, the action taken relieved many of the country banks of slow or frozen loans and helped to restore confidence. It also gave farmers more time to work out of their difficulties.

Repayments on these loans amounted to $296.8 million, about 99.4 per cent of the amount loaned. The Corporation also collected about $52 million in interest. Operating expense for the agricultural loan agencies amounted to $2.2 million plus an unsegregated portion of the total administrative expense of the Corporation from 1918 to June 30, 1939, which amounted to about $5.2 million.[14]

The action taken was appropriate for emergency relief in a period of acute agricultural depression though the program was so conservatively administered that it did not provide as much help as could well have been given. Many would contend that the seriousness of the depression and the need for easing credit in the farm areas were warrant for taking larger risks at that time, even though at some loss to the government. Had this been done, more banks and more farmers could probably have been saved at rather moderate public expense.

14. For more detail, see *Liquidation of the War Finance Corporation,* Letter from the Acting Secretary of the Treasury to the Speaker of the House transmitting the Final Report of the Secretary of the Treasury with regard to the Liquidation of the War Finance Corporation, October 26, 1942.

It must be admitted, however, that some contraction of agricultural credit was in order and that many banks and farmers were so seriously overextended that it would have been impractical and unwarranted to bail them out. Furthermore, the accepted view, both of the public and of the Congress, was that activities of this kind should be self-supporting. From a banking standpoint the operation was well handled and the help given was timely and significant, though undoubtedly smaller in amount than would now be considered appropriate in such a situation.[15]

THE EARLY 1930s: CREDIT CONDITIONS AND THE STEPS TAKEN

The blow to agriculture in the early 1930s was far more devastating than that of the 1920s. The drop in prices and incomes was more severe and recovery slower in starting. Furthermore, the decline began from what was considered a low level of prices and incomes. Land values had worked down gradually from 170 in 1920 to 115 in 1930 (1912–14 = 100). Thus, they were only moderately above those of the period just before World War I. This meant that there was little in the way of inflation-created values to be liquidated.

By 1933, the value of all farm land and buildings was down to $30.7 billion, a drop of more than half from the $66.3 billion valuation of 1920.[16] Thus, the mortgage credit base of agriculture had shrunk by more than $35 billion, and the value of farm lands and buildings was less than it had been in 1910. About half of this shrinkage, $17.1 billion, occurred between 1929 and 1933.

Forced sales, mortgage foreclosures, bankruptcies, and delinquent tax sales were estimated at 54 per thousand farms in 1933.[17] This would indicate that, in that year alone, more than 350,000 farmers lost their farms through distress transfers of one kind or another. In the years 1930–1935, it is probable that more than one sixth of all farms in the United States were lost to their owners through these various types of forced sales.[18] In the early 1920s, the number of forced sales ranged only

15. From 1918 on, the government also provided emergency credit in the form of seed loans. These were not "business-type" loans since they were available only to borrowers whose assets were such that they could not borrow from the usual types of credit agencies. The loans were made from funds appropriated by the government, were limited to specific areas, usually those where crops had failed because of drought, and were only in amounts sufficient to enable the drought-stricken farmers to put in a new crop. These, together with the other "welfare" types of credit, are discussed in Chapter 6.

16. U.S. Bureau of the Census, *Historical Statistics of the United States, 1789–1945*, 1949, p. 95.

17. *Ibid.*

18. These data must be taken with some reservation as it is obvious that the borderline between forced and voluntary sale is often a vague one. Nevertheless, the statement given above appears to be approximately in accord with the facts. Undoubtedly, the proportion of real farms, that is, those producing significant amounts of commercial farm products, was higher than that here indicated. The census figures for total numbers of farms include many small units of little agricultural significance which, however, tend to

from an annual rate of about 7 per thousand farms to 16 per thousand. This was less than one third of the rate of such turnover in 1933.

Such wholesale dispossession of farm families with its accompanying loss of work opportunity, home, and community position could not be allowed to go unchecked. By 1932, resentment over foreclosures and forced sales was leading to a virtual breakdown of ordinary legal processes in some of the farm communities. Judges attempting to carry out foreclosure proceedings were threatened with mob violence, and radical movements such as the Farmers' Holiday Association were taking shape, even in some of the normally conservative farming areas.

The need for some type of credit relief was soon recognized, but the actions taken in the early years of the depression were far too mild and limited in scope to offset the tremendous shrinkage in private credit that was occurring. Few recognized as early as 1930 and 1931 what an extensive refinancing job was needed in agriculture. Foreclosures and forced sales did not reach their peak until 1932 and 1933.

Contraction of Mortgage Loans

At the beginning of the depression of the 1930s, about 2.5 million farms were mortgaged, and the total farm mortgage debt amounted to nearly $10 billion. Farmers owed, in addition, around $2.5 billion in shorter-term loans.[19] Farm prices stood at 143 in 1929 (1909–14 = 100), an increase over those of the prewar years but certainly not one that was out of line with other prices or a reflection of wartime inflation.

Those farmers who were in debt were in a very vulnerable position. Less than one fifth of all mortgagors had loans that were not subject to call within from one to four or five years. Many others were shortly to be forced to borrow when farm incomes shrank to levels that would not cover cash expenses, and many of those with amortized loans were to find themselves unable to meet the current payments required under their contracts.

Following the stock market crash of 1929, most private lenders found it desirable to cut down on farm mortgage loans, some because of the need for cash funds, others because of concern over the income prospects of the agricultural industry. Between 1930 and 1936, the insurance companies reduced their holdings from $2.1 billion to $1.05 billion. Commercial bank holdings were reduced from approximately $1 billion to

---

be less vulnerable financially in times of depression than are the larger, commercial farms, and hence are less commonly forced into bankruptcy in periods of severe depression.

19. Number of farms mortgaged from *Farm Mortgage Debt in the United States,* cooperative report by Bureau of Agricultural Economics and Bureau of the Census, 1945. Amount of debt owed is from Bureau of Agricultural Economics, *Agricultural Finance Review,* November 1951, p. 94. The $2.5 billion in short-term debts includes only those owed to institutional lenders. Other large amounts were owed to merchants, dealers, and individual lenders. For these there are no estimates.

less than $.5 billion. Noninstitutional lenders, who had held about $4.7 billion of such loans in 1930, had reduced them to $3 billion by 1936 and were continuing this rapid rate of liquidation.[20] Joint-stock land bank loans were also being reduced. The only offsetting loan changes were Land Bank Commissioner loans (after 1933) amounting to about $800 million and an increase in loans by the federal land banks of a little under $1 billion.

Much of the $2 billion reduction in the net amount of farm mortgage debt that occurred between 1930 and 1936 came through transfer of mortgaged farms to creditors, thus wiping out the equities of several hundred thousand farm families and reducing them to tenant status or forcing them into other employment or onto relief.[21] When creditors took over the farms, they became the owners, usually on a debt-free basis. From 1930 through 1934, it is estimated that around 45 per cent of the *mortgaged* farms changed hands through distress transfers.[22]

Here was a situation in which almost every logical consideration pointed to the need for a quick and large expansion of government lending to prevent foreclosures and release private funds, as an aid in the effort to restore buying power. Much hardship in the farm areas could thus have been prevented, and a significant stimulus to general recovery could have been provided. However, until 1933 neither the Administration nor the Congress advocated such drastic action. Some aid was given but on a modest basis and in the traditional pattern.

Weak Market for Land Bank Bonds

As early as 1928, the land banks began to encounter difficulty in selling their bonds. The yields on outstanding federal land bank bonds rose from 3.95 per cent in January 1928 to 5.96 per cent in September 1931, this advance being a reflection of the tightening of the money market and of decreased confidence in the earning power of agriculture.[23]

20. Data from *Farm-Mortgage Credit Facilities in the United States*, p. 12 (as later revised).

21. Part of the reduction came about through voluntary readjustments made by creditors. However, the organized efforts to bring about voluntary downward adjustment of debts did not get under way on a significant scale until 1934. Such adjustments were made more generally by individual holders of junior obligations than by the institutional lenders. Holders of second mortgages, many of them taken as part of the purchase price for land, often were in a position where foreclosure would wipe out their equities. Hence, it was to their advantage to make adjustments in interest rate or face of mortgage so the farmer could continue in possession of his farm and have a chance to work his way out. Adjustments in the face amounts or interest rates on first mortgages also were made in some cases, especially if the mortgages were for high percentages of the values of the farms.

22. *Farm-Mortgage Credit Facilities in the United States*, p. 39. Based on estimate of 9.5 per cent per year.

23. To some extent also it was a result of the efforts made by the Federal Reserve Board to check speculation in the security markets in the late 1920s. Banks were then

To relieve the stringency, the Federal Reserve Banks bought about $24 million in land bank bonds between the fall of 1929 and the summer of 1931. These, however, were held for only short periods.

In a further effort to strengthen the market for land bank bonds, Congress authorized the Treasury to buy an additional $125 million in stock of the land banks at the beginning of 1932. This was to increase the financial strength of the banks and thus, presumably, to make their bonds more salable. However, the market for their bonds remained stagnant and few were sold, even though yields were above 5 per cent, which was a practical upper limit if the banks were to keep within the 6 per cent upper limit on loans to borrowers provided by law. The amount of federal land bank loans outstanding actually decreased by $70 million between December 31, 1929 and December 31, 1932. Those of the joint-stock land banks declined by about $120 million.

During 1932, there were no public offerings of federal land bank bonds. Such lending as was done was mostly out of the $125 million of new capital subscribed by the government.[24] By the fall of 1933, some funds were being obtained through short-term borrowing from the Reconstruction Finance Corporation.

The transactions of this period, including the purchase of additional stock in the land banks, did not result in any significant direct loss to the federal government. The stock purchased was eventually retired at par, and the only cost to the government was for the interest foregone on the funds thus used. The major loss was a social cost not a fiscal one, namely, the loss of an opportunity to check the disastrous liquidation of mortgaged farms that was occurring.[25]

The Regional Agricultural Credit Corporations

Beginning in the fall of 1932, a semi-emergency type of credit was provided through the twelve regional agricultural credit corporations (RACC's) established under the auspices of the Reconstruction Finance

---

under pressure to put their portfolios in a stronger position and to cut down on speculative loans. With a very strong demand for funds for stock market operations in 1928 and 1929, liquid funds could be loaned to very good advantage in the call-money market.

24. The ability of the land banks to lend in this period was also hampered by the fact that the financial situation of many of the local farm loan associations had deteriorated to such an extent that new loans could not legally be made through them.

25. The amount of capital stock owned by the government at the end of 1932 was just over $125 million. In subsequent years, the government contributed $139 million to paid-in surplus and subscribed additional amounts out of money previously paid back to the Treasury through retirement of government-owned stock. Thus, the total input of capital stock and paid-in surplus by the government amounted to $314 million. This was retired rapidly from 1939 on and was entirely paid off by 1947. The cost to the government of the funds used for purchase of land bank stock and subscriptions to surplus, from 1918 through 1947 when the last of the funds so advanced were retired, was about $82 million.

Corporation. These were designed to relieve the credit stringency in respect to relatively conservative ("sound") agricultural and livestock loans, not to provide high-risk or relief-type credit. The Reconstruction Finance Corporation subscribed $44.5 million to the capital stock of the RACC's, this being paid in as needed. The regional corporations discounted borrowers' notes with the Reconstruction Finance Corporation and the federal intermediate credit banks.[26] This meant that their loans had to be sufficiently conservative to meet the requirements of these regular banking agencies.

The operation was started at a time when the condition of most banks was deteriorating alarmingly. Few of them were making new loans, and nearly all were striving to make collections on loans then outstanding. Thus, the purpose of the RACC's was to make available a type of loan that would normally have been accepted readily by the commercial banks. Interest was set originally at 7 per cent but was reduced to 6.5 per cent on the 1st of January, 1933.

The broader and more varied attack on the farm credit problem which was initiated in the spring of 1933 caused the regional agricultural credit corporations to be de-emphasized, since the production credit system was being developed to serve approximately the same purpose. However, the regional corporations were not entirely eliminated. They were transferred to the Farm Credit Administration on May 27, 1933 (by executive order).[27] On April 30, 1934, they were placed in liquidation, it being assumed that the production credit system would thereafter be the appropriate permanent agency for handling this type of loan.[28]

Under authority provided in the Farm Credit Act of 1937 (50 *Stat.* 703), a new corporation, known as the Regional Agricultural Credit Corporation of Washington, D. C., was established to take over the assets and liabilities of the 12 regional corporations and to carry out the further liquidation of them.[29] No new loans were made from then until 1941, except such minor ones as were required in protecting the assets of the Corporation and facilitating liquidation.

26. The RACC's were authorized to discount with the Federal Reserve Banks as well but did not make use of this source of funds.

27. The executive order transferred to FCA all administrative functions of the corporations, except that of providing expenses of operation. The RFC continued to own the stock of the corporations until 1938, when it was transferred to the Treasury. However, RFC continued to pay their costs of operation until 1947.

28. As of that date, the regional corporations had made $261 million in loans, exclusive of renewals amounting to $57.6 million.

29. This meant, in effect, taking over the six regional offices and four branches still in operation west of the Mississippi River. The operations of the six offices east of the Mississippi had already been combined and transferred to the Washington office of the Farm Credit Administration. See *Fifth Annual Report of the Farm Credit Administration, 1937*, pp. 79–80.

Reactivation of RACC of Washington, D. C.

This Corporation was revived in 1942, as a war measure, and was authorized to make loans for a limited period in the Wenatchee (state of Washington) apple area. In 1943, the Secretary of Agriculture directed it to make loans to aid farmers in meeting the production goals that had been set up by the Department.[30] It returned to the Treasury, on December 31, 1944, $39.5 million of its capital stock and an additional $4.9 million on May 31, 1945.[31]

This left it with only $100,000 in capital stock, but the remainder was to be held in a revolving fund in the Treasury to be returned if requested by the Governor of the Farm Credit Administration. Under an act of April 6, 1949 (69 *Stat.* 43), the Corporation was dissolved and its functions, assets and funds were transferred to the Secretary of Agriculture. They were subsequently reassigned to the Farmers Home Administration.

Activities of the Regional Agricultural Credit Corporations

The corporations had $87 million in loans outstanding at the end of 1934. Thereafter, their lending activities dropped off rapidly, to $43 million in 1935 and to less than $4 million in 1942. As part of the production program of the war years, loans were increased but they declined rapidly thereafter and amounted to less than $1.5 million in 1949. This was a special program, unrelated to the original purpose of the regional corporations.

In the earlier period, the need for this type of relief from credit stringency was greatly reduced by the re-establishment of confidence in the commercial banks in the spring of 1933, through the provision of federal deposit insurance and in other ways, and also by the development of the production credit system, which had similar functions. The production credit associations took over about $40 million of RACC loans between 1934 and 1937.

Charge-offs on RACC loans were modest but amounted in all to just under $4 million.[32] The largest amounts were in the years 1935–1938, when they ranged from $287,000 to $492,000. At that time, many western livestockmen had suffered severe losses from droughts. These losses were absorbed out of the operating incomes of the corporations, except for the over-all cost shown below.

30. Since the Farm Credit Administration had, in the meantime, been transferred to the Department of Agriculture, the RACC was then under the supervision of the Secretary of Agriculture.

31. The $39.5 million retired in 1944 had previously been returned to the revolving fund in the Treasury but had been reissued to enable RACC to aid in the food production program of 1943.

32. There were, in addition, cancellations of special war crop advances in the amount of $3,539,380, making a total of $7,485,048.

The costs involved in the operation were approximately as follows (figures in millions):

Net interest cost to the government for funds supplied as capital	$4.2 [a]
Net RFC payments for operating expenses	9.2
Total expenses	$13.4
Less assets other than capital stock	1.4
Approximate net cost to the government	$12.0

a. Farm Credit Administration estimate. Interest cost on the total amount of government funds supplied was about $7 million. However, the RACC's maintained sizable deposits with the Treasury. These were available for other uses and are estimated to have reduced the cost by about $3 million.

The RACC's were not of major importance either as an emergency or long-term feature of the farm credit program. In principle, the action taken had merit as a means of easing the acute credit stringency in some agricultural areas, but the policy governing loans was so conservative and the volume of lending so small that it had no large effect. However, it was important to some farmers and ranchers, especially in the range areas, and no doubt saved many of them from being forced out of business.

The drastic action taken in the spring of 1933 to revive confidence in the banks was the step most needed, but it is doubtful that the country was ready for such a step at the time the regional credit corporations were set up. Had the banking situation not been stabilized, and if the production credit system had not been established, it is likely that these corporations would have come to play a more important role as suppliers of conservative credit aid to farmers who were reasonably well able to carry on, though perhaps with some forced liquidation of their crops and livestock.[33]

THE EXPANDED PROGRAM OF 1933 AND THEREAFTER

A greatly enlarged program of credit aid to agriculture was launched in the spring of 1933 and further supplemented in 1934. It included several different types of activity, some designed to meet the emergency then facing farmers, others to provide a more effective and comprehensive long-term program of government-sponsored farm credit.[34] The principal actions taken were:

33. It is possible, also, that more aggressive action to organize agricultural finance corporations to channel loans into the federal intermediate credit banks would have been taken if the banking situation had not improved.

34. The reorganization carried out at this time was in three steps. Executive Order No. 6084, issued on March 27, 1933 (effective May 27) abolished the Federal Farm Board and established the Farm Credit Administration. Title II of the Agricultural Adjustment Act of May 12, 1933 provided emergency relief by authorizing the Farm Loan Commissioner to issue $2 billion in bonds on which the government guaranteed the

1. The combining of the existing federal farm credit activities in one agency operating under a governor rather than a board. This included the abolition of the Federal Farm Loan Board and the Federal Farm Board and transfer of all or parts of their functions to the Governor of the newly created Farm Credit Administration.

2. The creation of twelve production credit corporations to help establish, finance and supervise local production credit associations so as to provide a connecting link that would enable farmers to be financed through the intermediate credit banks.

3. The creation of thirteen banks for cooperatives to provide to cooperatives, in a more orderly and businesslike way, much the same kind of credit and guidance as had been given by the Federal Farm Board.

4. The creation, in 1934, of a Federal Farm Mortgage Corporation, a wholly government-owned emergency credit agency designed to provide a market for federal land bank bonds and to serve as a source for land-mortgage loans at higher percentages of value than could be obtained through regular land bank loans. The federal land banks could loan up to 50 per cent of appraised value of the land and 20 per cent of the value of improvements, though they did not always do so. The Land Bank Commissioner, using Federal Farm Mortgage Corporation funds, could loan up to 75 per cent of appraised normal agricultural value, either as a first mortgage loan or on a second mortgage supplementing a land bank or other first mortgage loan. Where combined, the two loans could not exceed 75 per cent of appraised value, and individual Land Bank Commissioner loans could not be for larger amounts than $7,500.[35]

In addition, the seed and feed loan activities of the Department of Agriculture and the Division of Cooperative Marketing, formerly in the Federal Farm Board, were transferred to the Farm Credit Administra-

---

interest. Certain other emergency features were included in that act, which is known as the Emergency Farm Mortgage Act of 1933. It was followed by the Farm Credit Act of June 16, 1933, which authorized the creation of the banks for cooperatives and the production credit corporations.

The Emergency Farm Mortgage Act also provided for liquidation of the joint-stock land banks. These banks were not capitalized by the government though they were included in the land bank system and were under the control of the Federal Land Bank Board. They were established and owned by private investors. They had authority to issue tax-exempt bonds similar to those of the federal land banks. The joint-stock banks made loans directly to individuals, rather than through local farm loan associations, and were operated for private profit. By 1933, many of them were in serious financial difficulty and only 50 of the 88 that had been established were in operation.

The Emergency Farm Mortgage Act of 1933 withdrew from them both the privilege of issuing tax-exempt bonds and authority for making new loans. They were gradually liquidated thereafter, the process being completed in April 1951 when the last of the banks surrendered its charter to the Farm Credit Administration. For a short history of these operations, see Farm Credit Administration, *Annual Report, 1950–51*, pp. 86–88.

35. The limit established in the Emergency Farm Mortgage Act of 1933 was $5,000. It was increased to $7,500 in 1934 when the Federal Farm Mortgage Corporation was established.

tion.[36] The remaining assets of the Farm Board were made available for capitalizing the banks for cooperatives.[37]

The reorganized farm credit system had four principal parts: the twelve federal land banks, now under a Land Bank Commissioner (he also had charge of the "commissioner loan" program, that is, the program of second mortgage and other mortgage loans not handled by the land banks); the twelve intermediate credit banks, now under an Intermediate Credit Bank Commissioner; the twelve production credit corporations under a Production Credit Commissioner; and the twelve district banks for cooperatives, and one central bank, under a Cooperative Bank Commissioner. In charge of the whole system was the Governor of the Farm Credit Administration.[38]

REFINANCING FARM MORTGAGES

By 1933 there had already been a drastic reduction in the amount of farm mortgage debt. Liquidations amounting to around $1 billion had occurred between January 1, 1930 and January 1, 1933. This was in addition to the contraction of nearly $1.25 billion that had been brought about between 1923 and 1930. Much of this decrease in the over-all volume of mortgage debt had come about through foreclosure of mortgages rather than by actual repayment of loans.

The federal land banks had done little to prevent or offset this shrinkage, partly because of difficulty in selling their bonds and partly because the conservative loans to which they were limited by law were not large enough to enable a heavily indebted farmer to pay off his current mortgage with the amount he could borrow from the land bank. Land values had shrunk so severely that many farm mortgages made previously, even where the percentage of value was relatively conservative at the time the loan was made, now amounted to very high percentages of the reduced values of the farms. The borrowers who already had land bank loans

36. The Division of Cooperative Marketing became, in FCA, a part of the Cooperative Division. It was later renamed the Cooperative Research and Service Division. (This division has since been transferred back to the Department of Agriculture, under the Farm Credit Act of 1953, which took the Farm Credit Administration out of the Department of Agriculture and made it an independent agency in the executive branch of the government.)

37. These various steps were not all taken at the same time or through a single legislative act. However, all of them were parts of the general reorganization which was begun in the spring and summer of 1933.

38. Technically, the setup was a revamped Federal Farm Board. The name of the position known as Chairman of the Federal Farm Board was changed to Governor of the Farm Credit Administration. The land banks and intermediate credit banks were transferred into the Farm Credit Administration, and the Federal Farm Loan Board was abolished, as were the positions of the Federal Farm Board members, other than that of the Chairman. The legal authorizations and assets of the Federal Farm Board were continued under FCA except as abolished by order of the president. As actually worked out, this resulted in transfer of the remaining assets of the Farm Board for use in capitalizing the banks for cooperatives and for transfer of the Division of Cooperation to FCA. The other powers were discontinued.

were better off than those who did not, but the much larger number who were borrowing from private lenders could not turn to the land banks as a way out.

The failure of the land banks to supply adequately the unexpected and unprecedented need for mortgage credit in the early 1930s was not due to poor administration of the banks themselves. It stemmed from the lack of suitable provision for supplementing the land bank system with an appropriate mechanism for assuring salability of its bonds in time of depression, and also from the absence of any provision for emergency credit which could be used in refinancing mortgages where there was reasonable prospect that the farmer could eventually work his way out. It was to overcome these defects that the Federal Farm Mortgage Corporation was established.

While the action taken in 1933 was appropriate and undoubtedly too long delayed, it should not be assumed that similar steps could have been taken in 1920 and 1921. As of that time, such an approach was so out of keeping with principles on which the land bank system had been based, and with the general philosophy of nearly all groups, that it would have had little chance of acceptance even if it had been proposed.

With the precedents now available, it is probable that more prompt and effective action would be taken if such a crisis should arise again. There still would remain, of course, the crucial problem of how high a level of land prices and mortgage debt should be supported. While such support should be moderately conservative, there appears to be warrant for the government to take some risk in the creation and use of new credit in crises as severe as that of the early 1930s. Such action has ramifications that extend beyond the farmers directly concerned. It helps in the general process of reflation that is so much needed in such times.

The Federal Farm Mortgage Corporation provided a market for federal land bank bonds such that the land banks were able to increase their first mortgage loans by nearly a billion dollars between 1933 and 1936.[39] In addition, the government made available through the Corporation about $800 million in the form of "commissioner loans." [40]

Thus, the farm credit agencies injected about $1.8 billion of government-created credit into the farm mortgage field during this three-year period. This checked the disastrous liquidation that was occurring, though even this very sizable input of new funds did not fully offset the shrinkage in mortgage loans from other sources.

39. Including the loans made in 1933 before the FFMC was created. The increase in land bank loans between 1933 and 1936 was from $1,147,014,000 to $2,113,502,000 (revised data supplied by the Farm Credit Administration).

40. Not all of this was by direct appropriation, though the effect was much the same as though it had been. A fund of $200 million was appropriated in 1933 for use in making loans of this type. In 1934, the Federal Farm Mortgage Corporation was created, with the $200 million previously appropriated serving as capital. FFMC then obtained funds by issuing its own bonds secured by federal land bank bonds and "commissioner" mortgages. These bonds were fully guaranteed by the federal government.

Some shrinkage was no doubt inevitable. Many farms were so heavily mortgaged that even a 75 per cent of "normal value" loan would not enable them to refinance, unless the mortgagee was willing to agree to some reduction in his claim.[41]

Reduction of Interest on Land Bank Loans

The Emergency Farm Mortgage Act of 1933 provided that interest on land bank loans outstanding be reduced to 4.5 per cent, with the government reimbursing the land banks for the losses incurred as a result of this action. In 1935, the rate was reduced to 3.5 per cent and that level of rates was continued until January 1945. The rate was then raised to 4 per cent. In August 1948, FCA adopted a policy of letting rates in some of the regions go to higher percentages. For the Columbia district the rate reached 5 per cent in 1951, but in most districts it remained at 4 per cent. The interest loss thus absorbed constituted a subsidy from the federal Treasury to the borrowers from federal land banks and to those who had borrowed from the joint-stock land banks on mortgages later taken over by the federal land banks. It was not a subsidy to all farmers whose farms were mortgaged.

In addition, the Emergency Farm Mortgage Act of 1933 authorized the Treasury to subscribe to the paid-in surplus of the land banks in amounts sufficient to enable them to defer payments on principal until July 11, 1938, if the loans were in good standing otherwise. This was, in effect, a further subscription to bank capital, later to be repaid but in the meantime used without charge.

The interest subsidy on land bank loans was the heaviest of all drains on the Treasury in connection with the regular farm credit agencies. Total payments from 1933 to 1946 amounted to $277,123,225.[42] Similar payments made to the Federal Farm Mortgage Corporation amounted to $57,026,639.

Land Bank Loans from 1936 On

By 1937 the crisis in farm credit was about over, except in the areas where the credit base had been seriously damaged by the droughts of 1934 and 1936 and the accompanying dust storms. These disasters made many farms virtually worthless for the time being. Some, of course, were ruined permanently.

41. Appraisal on the basis of so-called "normal" values, that is values based on average prices of farm products between 1910 and 1914, was provided by the laws relating to Land Bank Commissioner loans. Appraisals by the land banks were also put on this basis, but by administrative decision rather than by law. These also were required by law to be on a "normal value" basis from 1945 on. Using this basis, the 50 per cent land bank loan plus a 25 per cent commissioner loan could in many cases make possible refinancing at something near the full market value of the farm in the depressed and demoralized land market that then existed.

42. Farm Credit Administration, *Thirteenth Annual Report, 1945–46*, p. 93.

Outstanding loans of the federal land banks reached their peak in 1935 at $2,072 million. The amount had declined moderately, to about $1,851 million, by 1940 and was reduced rapidly thereafter. Loans outstanding in 1950 amounted to only $931 million.[43]

FCA Put on Self-Supporting Basis in 1943

Since 1943 the administrative expenses of the Farm Credit Administration have been derived from the operating incomes of the various lending agencies of which it is composed, that is, the land banks, the intermediate credit banks, the banks for cooperatives and the production credit corporations, except for minor amounts provided for carrying on certain service and miscellaneous activities.[44]

From 1943 on, the budget provided for the Cooperative Research and Service Division was the principal contribution of government funds to FCA.[45] This amounted to around a half million dollars per year, but from 1946 on about a third of this budget was provided through transfer of funds appropriated under the Research and Marketing Act of 1946.[46]

This does not mean, of course, that no government subsidy has been provided from 1943 on. The government still owns the capital stock of the intermediate credit banks and production credit corporations, and the major portion of that of the banks for cooperatives. The last of the government's paid-in capital and surplus of the land banks was retired in 1947.[47] The retired capital was, for a time, retained in the Treasury

43. End-of-year figures to 1943, June 30 thereafter. *Annual Report of the Farm Credit Administration, 1950–51,* p. 134. Land bank loans reached a low of $864 million in 1948 but increased to $880 million in 1949 and to $931 million in 1950. By 1952, a further increase had brought the loan volume to $1,046 million. On June 30, 1953, it reached $1,136 million.

44. Principally those of the Cooperative Research and Service Division. Until 1946, the expense of administering crop and feed loans was provided through appropriations to the Department of Agriculture and FCA. This activity was transferred to the Farmers Home Administration in 1946, and the expenditures and income relating to such loans now are handled by that agency.

45. As noted earlier, this unit has now been transferred to the Department of Agriculture.

46. The funds made available to the Farm Credit Administration through appropriation acts are not contributions of Treasury funds (except those which were made for the Cooperative Research and Service Division and some other small items). The cost of operating the Washington office is met by advance assessments against the institutions examined and supervised. The funds are deposited in the United States Treasury and disbursements are made from the Treasury.

47. The Farm Credit Act of 1953 (67 *Stat.* 39) puts the Farm Credit Administration under a Federal Farm Credit Board of thirteen members, one to be appointed by the President from each of the farm credit districts and one to be appointed by the Secretary of Agriculture. The act also provides for the payment of a franchise tax by the land banks, the banks for cooperatives and the production credit corporations. For the first two, the tax is to be 25 per cent of net earnings or an amount equal to the interest cost of the money invested in them, whichever is smaller. For the PCC's it is to be equal to 25 per cent of net earnings after authorized deductions have been made. The district boards were retained with little change except that as the borrower institutions come to own a larger share of the stock they will elect a larger portion of the directors.

as a revolving fund that could be drawn upon in the event of recurrence of need for increased capital. This provision has since been eliminated.

Thus, in the course of three decades, 1917 to 1947, the federal land banks and their network of local farm loan associations have been established on a self-supporting and apparently permanent basis. Between 1933 and 1937 they channeled into the farm mortgage credit pool about a billion dollars at a time when other farm mortgage credit agencies were reducing their loans by more than $2 billion.

During these five years the land banks made approximately 330,000 farm mortgage loans, not counting the commissioner loans which were handled through the land banks though not with funds obtained from the sale of federal land bank bonds.[48] Not only were many of these farms saved to their owners through the combined land bank and commissioner loans but considerable amounts of money were thus made available to other lenders, through the repayment of mortgages held by them. Also, the refinancing of these mortgages resulted in the payment of considerable amounts of back taxes owed to state and local governments.

Cost of the Land Bank Program

Until 1932, the cost of the aid given the land banks was nominal. It consisted of funds provided as capital stock ranging from about $9 million in 1917 down to some $200,000 in 1931. At the prevailing rate on government borrowings, the cost of this item for the 14-year period was approximately $1.9 million. There was an additional cost for expenses of the Federal Farm Loan Board during part of this time. Published data on these costs are not available. However, the amount was relatively inconsequential.[49]

From 1931 on, the subsidy provided through the land banks took other forms and was much larger, though still modest as compared to the subsidies provided in some of the other programs. An additional $125 million of capital was subscribed in 1932 and was used virtually in full

48. The magnitude of this operation as an administrative as well as a financing job is indicated by the fact that the number of land bank appraisers was only 210 at the time the Emergency Farm Mortgage Act of 1933 became effective. By December 7, 1933, it had been built up to 5,141, which was the peak number employed. Had the operation been started earlier, and if more trained appraisers had been available, a larger number of farmers could have been aided and many foreclosures could no doubt have been prevented. Nevertheless, the record of performance, once the emergency operation was started, is a very creditable one.

49. From 1923 to 1930, the expenses of the Farm Loan Bureau were charged to the land banks and the federal intermediate credit banks. After 1930, such charges were limited to the salaries and expenses of employees in the Division of Examinations. See *Fourteenth Annual Report of the Federal Farm Loan Board (1930)*, p. 59. Later, the applicable laws were again amended so that from July 1, 1942, the costs of both examination and supervision of the intermediate credit banks and production credit corporations were borne by them. This provision was extended to the land banks and banks for cooperatives as of July 1, 1943.

until 1939, after which it was retired rapidly. The government also supplied $189 million in the form of paid-in surplus during this period. The interest cost to the government from 1932 through 1940 was about $53 million, and that from 1941 to the completion of stock retirement in 1947 about $27 million. From July 1, 1930 to June 30, 1943, the costs of supervising the banks were paid out of appropriated funds.

The other and larger type of subsidy provided through the land banks was that resulting from congressional action reducing the rates of interest on land bank loans to less than the contract rates based on the yields of bonds issued. This subsidy was initiated in 1933 and was continued until June 30, 1944. Its over-all cost to the Treasury was about $277 million.[50]

This was in no way connected with the cost of establishing and operating the banks. It was, in effect, a direct grant of supplemental income to a selected group of recipients, namely, the borrowers from the federal land banks. The subsidy thus granted was more than three times the total amount required to establish the banks and operate them over a period of some thirty years. Yet it resulted in no continuing asset such as the land banks, and established no orderly or fundamental policy. Its merit is dubious.

The land bank borrowers were, to be sure, hard pressed and glad to have some easing of their interest load. But so also were the borrowers from life insurance companies and those whose loans were held by banks and individuals. In fact, by the nature of the lending policies followed, the land bank borrowers were presumably among the best risks. Also, the rates charged on land bank loans were already significantly lower than those charged by most other lenders.

Furthermore, the interest subsidy was continued long after there was any justification for it. By 1942, the Department of Agriculture and the state colleges were putting on educational campaigns designed to forestall a speculative upsurge in land prices. Even if the earlier action placing land bank interest rates at subsidy levels was justified, the $56 million spent in this way after 1941 was worse than a waste. It was running counter to the policy then being advocated by most of the government's own educational agencies.

The Land Banks as an Investment

The conclusion seems warranted that the creation and development of the land bank system was a well considered and very useful form of aid to agriculture. Its cost, aside from the subsidization of interest rates, was modest, about $82 million over a thirty-year period which included one of the worst depressions in our history. The expenditure has resulted in a well-established going concern that is now virtually self-supporting

50. For land bank loans only. This does not include the $57 million supplied in a similar way through the Federal Farm Mortgage Corporation.

and largely self-directed. The land bank system was undoubtedly a major factor in putting American farm mortgage financing onto a sounder basis than in any previous period, through long-term, amortized loans. This gain alone is worth far more to American agriculture than the costs which have been incurred. It is a continuing benefit such that further expenditures of similar character do not appear to be required.

The amount of saving in interest to farmer borrowers as a result of the development of the federal land bank system cannot be estimated with any assurance. It seems conservative, however, to assume that farm mortgage interest rates on loans made by the land banks, joint-stock land banks, and insurance companies are at least a half per cent lower than the borrowers from them would have been able to obtain had the land banks not been in existence.[51] If this assumption is warranted, the saving in interest to land bank borrowers, since the inception of the system, may well be as much as $200 million.[52] In addition, it has been demonstrated that the land bank system provides an exceedingly important and efficient mechanism for channeling credit into agriculture in a time of severe depression.

FEDERAL FARM MORTGAGE CORPORATION LOANS AND COSTS

Although the land banks provided the mechanism through which emergency mortgage credit could be channeled into agriculture, they were not themselves emergency credit agencies, and would have been inviting destruction had they attempted to make high-risk, emergency

51. Average rates charged by insurance companies, the principal institutional competitors of the land banks, declined from 6.11 per cent in 1915 to 5.61 per cent in 1917. They rose again in the period 1918 to 1922, but thereafter settled down to a level closely comparable to that on land bank loans. *Farm-Mortgage Credit Facilities in the United States,* p. 229. There is little indication that the rates charged by banks and individuals were reduced significantly except in some of the high-risk areas.

52. This estimate hinges on the rather arbitrary assumption that land bank borrowers did benefit by a half per cent. Using end-of-year loans outstanding, 1917 through 1950, and the assumed .5 per cent lower rate, the saving would amount to approximately $196 million. The comparative contract rates of interest charged by the various agencies for 1935 and 1949 were as follows:

	Percentage	
	1935	1949
Commercial banks	6.28	5.25
Insurance companies	5.53	4.39
Individuals	5.74	4.75
Federal land banks and Land Bank Commissioner	4.73	4.05
All others	6.01	4.92

Data for 1935 are from *Farm-Mortgage Credit Facilities in the United States;* 1949 data are from later supplemental releases. It will be noted that the spread between the land bank rate and the insurance company rate was more than a half per cent in 1935 and less than that amount in 1949. However, it should also be recognized that the competition provided by the land banks probably had some tendency to reduce or hold down the rates charged by the insurance companies and other lenders. Also, the insurance companies tend to confine their loans to low-risk areas whereas land bank loans are made in all parts of the United States.

loans without supplemental facilities. Their function was best performed by expanding their activities in the established pattern and keeping themselves in a solvent condition, but at the same time attempting to keep appraisals realistically oriented to probable long-term values rather than to inflationary upswings and the distress values resulting from extreme depression.

The device chosen for providing emergency mortgage loans was logical and practical. The Federal Farm Mortgage Corporation, with its initial capital of $200 million, was authorized to issue up to $2 billion in bonds fully guaranteed by the government. These constituted, in effect, government-created credit. They were to be absorbed by the Treasury if not salable in the security markets.[53]

By the end of 1934, outstanding commissioner loans financed by the Federal Farm Mortgage Corporation amounted to $617 million. During the next two years, this amount was increased to $837 million. Thereafter it declined gradually to 1942. From 1942 on, repayment of these loans was rapid, and the amount outstanding on June 30, 1953 was only $20 million.[54]

Financially the operation was unexpectedly successful. The cost to the government of the capital used is estimated at about $44 million.[55] In addition, the government subsidized a reduction in interest charges to these borrowers, from 1937 to 1944, in a manner similar to that used in assisting borrowers from the federal land banks. This involved a direct subsidy, paid by the Treasury, which amounted to about $57 million. The Corporation returned to the government about $122 million in divi-

53. For a time, the payments to both land bank and commissioner loan borrowers were made in the form of Federal Farm Mortgage Corporation bonds, except for fractional amounts above multiples of $100. Beginning in May 1934, claims amounting to less than $500 were paid in cash. This practice of making payments in bonds was discontinued in August 1935.

54. About three fifths of the amount loaned was on second mortgages and two fifths on first mortgages. For farm properties not considered eligible for land bank loans, the full amount was loaned from Land Bank Commissioner funds, usually on what was referred to as a "prudent investment" basis. This was especially helpful to part-time farmers who derived a sizable portion of their incomes from off-the-farm sources. If there was prospect of farm and nonfarm income sufficient to carry and pay off the loan, the borrower became eligible for aid though he could not qualify for a regular land bank loan.

Until the passage of the Farm Credit Act of 1937, most commissioner loans were for a 13-year period with requirement that only the interest be paid in the first 3 years and thereafter 10 per cent of the principal each year. This proved too rapid a retirement of principal for some borrowers. The act of 1937 authorized the directors of the Corporation to accept payments of 5 per cent per annum if in their judgment such action was warranted.

55. Since the government was borrowing heavily, it seems reasonable to regard the cost of the funds used as equivalent to the average rate paid on government securities. Most of the money loaned was obtained through sale of bonds though some came from collections on loans made earlier. However, the Corporation maintained sizable balances in the Treasury which, of course, were available for other purposes. This factor resulted in a credit, estimated at $6 million, against the $50 million of estimated cost to the government for the total amounts allocated to the Corporation.

dends and, as of June 30, 1953, had an earned surplus of $23 million. Thus, there was an apparent gain to the government on the Farm Mortgage Corporation operation itself of approximately $101 million, if the $57 million paid out for reduction of interest on loans held is regarded as a direct subsidy to borrowers as in the summary of land bank costs presented earlier.[56]

Liquidation of Loans and Assets

The Farm Mortgage Corporation has been gradually liquidated from 1940 on. By an amendment of June 25, 1940, the Congress directed that capital in excess of $100 million be retired by June 30, 1941. The amount so retired was to be held available for resubscription if needed. Further liquidation was provided in an act of June 30, 1945 (59 *Stat.* 265). The Corporation was authorized to sell and assign to the land banks such of its notes and mortgages as the banks would accept, provided the amount due the bank and the Corporation did not exceed 65 per cent of the normal agricultural value of the security and provided the borrower was willing to buy the required amount of stock in the local farm loan association that would service the loan.

In 1948 (62 *Stat.* 1183), the Corporation was directed to declare dividends and pay into the Treasury $68 million and all additional cash funds in excess of operating expenses for the fiscal year. The total of bonds that might be outstanding was reduced to $500 million. The statutory power to make new loans expired on July 1, 1947, and was not renewed. Previously it had been renewed from time to time so as to keep the Corporation in operation. From 1947 on, its loans have been in process of liquidation. By June 30, 1953, $122 million in dividends had been repaid to the Treasury.

Significance of the Operation

The Federal Farm Mortgage Corporation was one of the most appropriate and effective emergency measures of the farm program of the 1930s. Earlier action of similar character would have saved many farms and avoided much hardship. When the Corporation was set up, it brought quick and vital financial relief to many thousands of farmers, and to their creditors as well. It was so designed as to supplement and strengthen the established long-term farm credit agencies rather than to replace them, compete with them or continue in operation after the emergency was over.

Various changes that have been made since 1933 make it unlikely that so significant a contribution could be made in the same way in the

56. The two situations are not entirely comparable since in the Farm Mortgage Corporation, the government itself was the supplier of the funds, whereas in the land banks the funds were derived from the sale of bonds. The Farm Mortgage Corporation arrangement was in essence a granting of direct government loans at less than the market rate.

event of a recurrence of such acute distress as that of the 1930s. The most serious feature of the farm credit situation in that period was the fact that very large numbers of farm mortgages were falling due and could not be renewed. A much larger portion of the farm mortgage lending is now on a long-term, amortized basis. Hence a severe depression would not at once place so large a number of farmers in jeopardy.

Since July 1, 1945, the land banks have been authorized to lend up to 65 per cent of the appraised normal value of farm properties (as compared to 50 per cent of the value of land and 20 per cent of the value of improvements, which was the limit prior to that time). This higher loan limit would make possible a greater measure of relief than the land banks could provide in the 1930s, though it would not be adequate in the event of a major depression. In such times an emergency operation with government funds has definite advantages. Loans can be made to higher percentages of value, and justifiable risks can be taken that would not be appropriate for the land banks with their heavy reliance on public confidence in their bonds.

Furthermore, in the event of serious depression there would almost certainly be need for an emergency outlet for land bank bonds in order that the land banks not be prevented from expanding their loans because of inability to dispose of their bonds.[57] The Farm Mortgage Corporation was admirably suited for meeting that need, and the way was left open for a prompt return to selling land bank bonds in the regular security markets as soon as those markets were able to absorb them.

Results Partly Due to Price Increases

While the record of the Farm Mortgage Corporation is a good one and the mechanism very well suited to the kind of problem for which it was devised, it should be kept in mind that this favorable result was partly fortuitous. The onset of war in 1939 and the later United States involvement in it, together with the long run of good crop years that followed the making of the loans, created an extremely favorable opportunity for quick retirement of these high-risk loans. Under more usual conditions, the time required for repayment would have been longer and the losses heavier. The government assumed a risk cost which it did not have to pay for.

Nevertheless, the operation would have been eminently suitable and warranted even if the government had suffered sizable losses as a result of it. Its purpose was to preserve the pre-existing structure of agriculture and to save the homes and livelihoods of many thousands of farm families. It did not constitute a continuing drain on the Treasury as many other programs tended to do.

Even had the high incomes of the war years not occurred, there is

57. The Farm Mortgage Corporation still has authority to purchase land bank bonds.

reason to think that the ultimate loss would not have been large, though the program might have had to be continued for a longer time. Farm prices remained relatively low until 1941, but commissioner loans had already been reduced by about $150 million from their January 1937 peak of $837 million. Partly as a result of the more orderly repayment arrangements introduced during that period, the total mortgage debt declined by about $1 billion between 1935 and 1940.

THE PRODUCTION CREDIT SYSTEM

Until the twelve production credit corporations were set up, under the reorganization of 1933, the intermediate credit system was not in a position to carry out effectively the role which was planned for it. For the most part, the essential local link between the farmer borrowers and these discount banks was lacking. For production loans, farmers still were heavily dependent on the local commercial banks. Since the commercial banks tended to contract credit sharply in times of depression, there had long been a widespread desire on the part of farmers for a production credit system which would be less closely related to deposit banking and which would make loans on a time schedule better suited to the cycles of agricultural production. In addition, there was need for less emphasis on chattel security and for more consideration of prospective ability to pay.

Farmers did not have funds with which to capitalize local finance corporations, and even if funds had been available for establishing such corporations, there was need for guidance in organizing and operating them. The production credit corporations were assigned the task of providing a system of local cooperative credit associations to fill this gap and were provided with funds for carrying it out. The procedure was for the borrower to take class B stock in the local production credit association to the extent of 5 per cent of his loan. As a supplement to the stock thus provided, the production credit corporation of the district in which the association was to be located could subscribe for an amount of class A stock sufficient to bring the total capital up to about 20 per cent of the actual or expected volume of loans.[58]

The voting privilege was confined to the class B stock, owned by the borrowers. As the volume of business grew, the government-owned stock was to be gradually retired, leaving the association entirely in the hands of the borrowers except for general supervision. The principle was similar to that under which the federal land banks had been established.[59]

58. The Governor of the Farm Credit Administration could authorize purchase of additional amounts of class A stock where conditions seemed to warrant such action.

59. The distinction between production credit associations and production credit corporations should be noted. The PCA's are local associations of farmers, somewhat comparable to the local farm loan associations in the land bank system, which are designated officially as national farm loan associations though they are not national. The PCC's are

At the end of 1934, the government's subscription to stock of the production credit corporations amounted to $112 million. It was increased to $120 million in 1935 and remained at that level through 1939. It was reduced to $105 million in 1940, but was re-expanded to $120 million for the years 1941 through 1943. Thereafter, the amount was gradually decreased and was down to $36 million on June 30, 1953.[60]

The production credit corporation investment in class A stock of the production credit associations was $90 million in 1934. It declined gradually to 1940 when it stood at $61 million. It was re-expanded to $81 million in 1941 and 1942, as a means of aiding in the wartime food production program. Thereafter, the growing prosperity of agriculture enabled the borrowers to take over more and more of the capital stock. By June 30, 1953, the government investment in class A stock was down to $6 million.[61] Loan volume has increased almost continuously from the beginning. The amount of loans closed during the fiscal year ending June 30, 1953 was $1,290 million.

By 1947, some of the PCA's were wholly owned by the farmer borrowers. Between 1947 and June 30, 1953, the number so owned grew from 31 to 283, out of a total of 499. Thus by 1953, over half of the associations had ceased to be dependent on capital supplied by the government and many others were well on their way to achieving that status.[62]

Significance of the Production Credit System

If the need for a more stable source of agricultural production credit is granted, the production credit program initiated in 1933 was a logical way of making the intermediate credit system effective. Without a net-

---

regional, government-owned corporations set up to aid the production credit associations in getting started. It was not intended that the production credit corporations would become borrower-owned. The PCA's, on the other hand, are presumably to be eventually owned by the borrowers and to become permanent units in a cooperative production credit system.

60. Sizable amounts of the capital supplied to the production credit corporations were invested in government securities and used as a source of income to cover operating expenses of the corporations. The amount of capital assigned to the corporations appears to have been somewhat larger than was really needed. However, if such an excess existed, a good part of the unbalance has been overcome by the reductions made in recent years.

61. Figures rounded to nearest million. Nongovernment stock ownership was very limited in the early years, being only $8.4 million in 1935, all of it class B, that is, borrower-owned, voting stock. By June 30, 1953, this class of stock had increased to just under $68.8 million, and farmer borrowers also owned $23.4 million in class A stock. If the owner of class B stock ceases to borrow for 2 years, and retains his stock, it is automatically converted to nonvoting class A stock. If he later becomes a borrower again, this can be reconverted to class B stock. Some of the ownership of class A stock by farmer members resulted from direct subscriptions by them rather than from conversions of class B stock left in.

62. In 1934 there were 597 production credit associations. The number declined to 499 by June 30, 1953. This change was due mainly to consolidations, though some of the decrease resulted from liquidation of unsuccessful or unneeded associations.

work of local, farmer-controlled finance corporations there was little prospect that the intermediate credit banks would become an important source for production credit. There was almost no prospect that the commercial banks would use the intermediate credit banks extensively as a rediscounting agency or would change their loan practices significantly. Hence, the bulk of the lending for agricultural production would continue to be on a short-term basis and subject to sudden contraction in times of depression.

The danger of such sharp and severe credit restriction as occurred in the 1920s and in 1930 was, to be sure, somewhat lessened by the introduction of federal deposit insurance and other related banking changes. Nevertheless, bankers would have strong incentives to cut back on loans if prosperity declined. The intermediate credit banks, on the other hand, would not be under pressure to reduce lending so long as their debentures could be marketed, either privately or to the government, except that depressed conditions would naturally lead to a more conservative lending policy.[63]

Many would argue that, with the banking improvements of the 1930s, such a system is not needed. Nevertheless, farmers have felt strongly that an alternative source of production credit should be available, as a stimulus to better service from the banks if nothing more.

Certain it is that the production credit associations have pioneered in developing types of loans better suited to agricultural needs than those previously available, and that the commercial banks have tended to follow this lead, thus improving the services they provide. Loans both from the PCA's and the commercial banks have come to be more carefully analyzed and programmed, and are now based more on income prospects and less on chattel security. Interest charges have been reduced somewhat and farmers have been able to proceed with more assurance in their production plans. In the fiscal year 1953, they borrowed more than $1.2 billion through the PCA's even though bank credit was notably easy and plentiful.

Capital and Earnings of the Production Credit Corporations

In the years since 1934 (to June 30, 1953) the production credit corporations have had available to them government-supplied capital

63. It is not clear that authorizations now exist for either direct or indirect purchase of intermediate credit bank debentures by the government. However, such action might well be considered in the event of another severe and prolonged depression. It would be almost directly comparable to the purchase of land bank bonds by the Federal Farm Mortgage Corporation and there would be similar reasons for undertaking such purchases. Such a procedure would be a logical mechanism for channeling government-created credit into a loan market where other forms of credit would probably be contracting sharply.

of $120 million through 1943,[64] and declining amounts thereafter ranging down to $36 million in 1953. If this is figured at the average cost of government borrowings, the government's contribution would be $46.2 million. As of June 30, 1953, these corporations had an earned surplus of $14.8 million. Thus the net cost to the government, to June 30, 1953, may be considered to be approximately $31 million. As of that date, the corporations owned $5.5 million worth of class A stock in PCA's and $44.6 million in government securities.[65] They had combined earnings in the fiscal year ending June 30, 1953 of $1,172,539.

Almost all of the earnings consisted of income on investment, that is, on funds supplied by the government but not invested in class A stock of PCA's. Assessments against PCA's for credit examinations and other services amounted to $87,894. Operating expenses, including payment of a portion of the general overhead of the Farm Credit Administration, amounted to $1,652,679. The net loss for the year was $778,931.

In earlier years, earnings were larger because of the large amounts of government-supplied capital still held but not needed for investment in class A stock of the PCA's. This was, in effect, an endowment used in supporting the PCC's but one which was gradually reduced from 1943 on.[66]

Self-Support Not Expected

It was not expected that the production credit corporations would be self-supporting in the early years of their existence. They had no significant income except that from interest on government securities held. The return from these was essentially a direct government subsidy, probably a larger one than was really needed. Other income could come only from payment of dividends by the PCA's on the class A stock held by the corporations or from fees collected for services.

The original plan did not contemplate that dividends would be a source of income to the corporations in the early years, or a continuing one in later years. The law required that the PCA's build up rather substantial reserves before beginning to pay dividends. Dividends were paid by a few of the associations in the period 1940 through 1950

64. Except for smaller amounts in two of the years, $112 million in 1934 and $105 million in 1940.

65. *Annual Report of the Farm Credit Administration, 1952–53*, p. 101.

66. As of June 1948, the production credit corporations still held some $81.5 million in government capital and had income somewhat in excess of their outgo. Since 1949, expenses have exceeded income. The profit in 1948 amounted to $634,052. By 1951, the corporations showed a loss of $600,621. From here on, they will apparently have to reduce expenses, obtain more return from the capital invested in class A stock of PCA's or experience a gradual reduction in their earned surplus, unless the government returns to them some of the capital that has been retired. Since the PCA's have been rapidly building up their assets, it would seem logical for the expenditures and activities of the PCC's to be reduced gradually, with most of the PCA's becoming going concerns for which subsidy will not be needed.

(except in 1941) but in small amounts. Their policy has been to build up reserves through retention of net earnings.[67] Obviously, as the government-owned class A stock is retired, this source of income to the production credit corporations will disappear, even if the PCA's become profitable enough so they can pay dividends regularly. In the meantime, the PCA's have built up reserves and unapplied earnings which amounted to $86.2 million as of June 30, 1953.

Future Financing of PCC's

The question now is what the future role of the production credit corporations should be and how they should be financed. The system of production credit associations appears to be well established. The prospect seems good for all or most of them to become wholly borrower owned. The organizing and financing function which was a primary purpose for setting up the production credit corporations has largely been accomplished. There will, of course, be need for continuing supervision and servicing of the PCA's if an effective and consistent cooperative production credit system is to be maintained throughout the country. Whether the corporate form of organization now in effect is the best way of providing such supervision and service is a matter on which opinions differ. In view of the well-known tendency for emergency organizations to be continued after the urgent need for them has disappeared, the possibility of simplifying organization and effecting economies obviously should be explored from time to time.

There are apparently three ways in which needed supervision could be provided from here on:

1. The production credit corporations might be liquidated and such amount of general supervision, auditing and so on as may be needed could be handled as a part of the general supervisory function of the Farm Credit Administration, probably under a production credit division. If this is done, and if the most logical precedent is followed, namely, that of the land banks and farm loan associations, the cost of this supervision would be assessed against the PCA's.

2. The production credit corporations might be continued, but with provision for their support by the production credit associations.

3. The production credit corporations might be continued and allowed to retain a sizable amount of government capital as an endowment, that is, as a continuing subsidy. This appears not to be in keeping with government policy in respect to business corporations, and would seem to have little to recommend it.[68]

67. For example, only 78 associations paid any dividends out of 1952 earnings. That was the largest number in any one year up to that time.

68. Officials of the Farm Credit Administration apparently, as of the present at least, feel that the corporate form of organization should be retained since it fits in well with the activities of the other FCA units which function as corporations. It is contended

A fourth possibility would be for the government to make direct appropriations for supervising the production credit associations through an administrative division of the Farm Credit Administration. There would seem to be little justification, however, for handling the PCA's in this way if proportionate shares of the general Farm Credit Administration supervisory cost are to be assessed against the land banks, the intermediate credit banks and other units of the system.

The policy most nearly in keeping with that under which the land bank system has been established would be that given as number 1 above. This would mean looking upon the building of a cooperative production credit system as an accomplished task, subsidized in its formative stages but thereafter put on a self-supporting basis with continuing supervision by the Farm Credit Administration.

THE BANKS FOR COOPERATIVES

The attempt of the Farm Board to create large-scale farmer cooperatives through government sponsorship and financing encountered numerous difficulties stemming largely from the effort to combine price-supporting activities with the longer-term objectives for which the Board was created. There was some residue of increased cooperative activity after the Board's dissolution in the spring of 1933, but the main strength of the cooperative movement was still, as in earlier years, in the more slowly developed, less ambitious cooperatives that had grown up with little or no assistance from the government.

A continuing strong desire to enlarge and strengthen the cooperative movement was apparent, however, and there remained in the assets of the Farm Board a sizable amount of money appropriated for that purpose. It was decided therefore to put the loans to cooperatives on a banking basis, and to eliminate efforts to use the cooperatives as a means of stabilizing prices. The Farm Credit Act of 1933 authorized the creation of thirteen banks for cooperatives, one for each land bank district and a central bank which would handle unusually large loans and those required by cooperatives that overlap district lines. It could also participate with the district banks on loans within the districts.

The capital stock of these banks was to be supplied mainly by the government, out of the fund of about $180 million derived from the remaining assets of the Farm Board's revolving fund. The Central Bank for Cooperatives was capitalized at $50 million and each of the district

---

that this permits decentralized supervision and authority in the field through the district boards of directors as part of a coordinated credit service adapted to each district in accordance with its needs. That form of organization could, of course, be retained under either alternative 2 or alternative 3. It should be recognized, however, that the Farm Credit Administration has a relatively complex corporate structure and that some simplifications and economies in operation might be feasible now that the pioneering period is over. Further study of this type of problem both within and outside the Farm Credit Administration would seem to be warranted.

banks at $5 million. The law directed the Governor of the Farm Credit Administration to readjust the amounts of capital stock as needed to meet the needs of eligible associations.

The borrowing associations were required to own capital stock in the bank making the loan, in the amount of $100 for each $2,000 in operating and facility loans obtained and $100 for each $10,000 in commodity loans. The general plan was that the banks would eventually come to be owned, and in large part managed, by the borrowing cooperatives. The provision for such transfer of ownership and management was less definite, however, than for the land banks and production credit associations. The government funds put in were much larger and the prospect of early liquidation much less evident.

Types of Loans Provided

The banks were to provide to the cooperatives three types of loans— facility loans, operating loans and commodity loans. The first two were needed and not available through other government credit agencies. The third was a type of loan already provided for in the intermediate credit bank system. The justification for using the banks for cooperatives for this kind of loan, if there was such justification, lay in the closer working relationship between the banks for cooperatives and the cooperative associations, and the need for a fair volume of business if the overhead expense of the banks for cooperatives was to be justified. There was also more flexibility in the kinds of commodity loans that could be made.

The most important need in putting many of the cooperative associations on a sound basis was a refinancing of the debts owed on their facilities, together with technical help and guidance in developing improved business practices. For this the banks were admirably suited, as soon as their staffs had been built up and had gained experience. The banks could make the necessary analyses and could help in working out financial plans, and then were in an excellent position to make the program attractive through the fact that they could lend the money with which to put it into effect.

The situation was similar in respect to operating loans. If business methods were poor, membership relations bad, book credit too loose, or management inadequate, the banks could agree to make operating loans, but on condition that the defects be corrected. These types of help naturally were more important to the small struggling cooperatives than to the large and strong ones.

Capitalization and Lending Operations

The banks for cooperatives were started in a small way in 1933, and by 1934 had been assigned government capital of $110 million. This was gradually increased to $149 million in 1939, but was then reduced by $40 million ($30 million being returned from the Central Bank). This was in accordance with a suggestion in the President's budget message.[69] Government capital was increased again in 1941, 1942 and 1943, reaching $178.5 million in 1945, at which level it has remained through 1953.

In the meantime capital stock owned by the cooperative associations has been built up from $942,000 at the end of 1933 to about $18 million as of June 30, 1953. Loans outstanding have grown from $28 million in 1934 to $319 million in 1953 (as of June 30).

There are some features of the financial structure of the banks for cooperatives that appear to be uneconomical from a public standpoint. Most of these could apparently be corrected without damaging seriously the essential functions of the banks, though certain alternative arrangements would be necessary. The capital stock available to the banks is undoubtedly larger than is needed for a straight banking business with a loan volume comparable to that handled by them. This has led to direct lending out of capital funds, which is not a normal banking practice.

Such funds, in a bank that is not intended as a means of creating or contracting credit, are usually obtained by rediscounting notes with a bank of issue or by selling debentures in the security markets. That practice has not been used extensively, partly because of the large amount of capital available to the banks for cooperatives and partly because of the unfavorable conditions under which rediscounting arrangements would have to be carried out with the federal intermediate credit banks.

Rediscount Problems of Banks for Cooperatives

The banks for cooperatives are at a disadvantage in rediscounting with the federal intermediate credit banks, because the cooperative associations have the privilege of turning directly to the intermediate credit banks if they wish to do so. Thus, if the banks for cooperatives charged any margin over the intermediate credit bank rate it would be to the advantage of the associations to go directly to the intermediate credit banks for such of their commodity loans as are acceptable to those banks. They would still have to turn to the banks for cooperatives for facility and operating loans and for some types of commodity loans. The volume of operating and facility loans may become smaller as the financial situation of the cooperatives improves though at present the trend seems to be the other way.[70]

69. The President's recommendation and the plans developed contemplated a reduction of $60 million but the reduction actually made was $40 million.

70. Outstanding loans of the three types as of June 30, 1950 and three years later were as follows:

	June 30, 1950	June 30, 1953
Commodity loans	$ 15,183,174	$ 26,779,951
Operating loans	127,072,052	159,932,617
Facility loans	102,350,354	132,395,980
Total	$244,605,580	$319,108,548

It should be noted that commodity loans tend to be near their lowest level at the end of June. Ordinarily the old crop has been mostly liquidated by that time and the new one has not yet come on.

For a time (1935–1948) the intermediate credit banks returned to the banks for cooperatives, as compensation for their work and assumption of risk in making the loans, a portion of the spread between the rate paid on debentures and the rates charged by the intermediate credit banks. For these loans, a good part of the servicing had already been done by the banks for cooperatives and such loans also had back of them the financial resources of the banks for cooperatives as well as those of the cooperatives to whom the loans were made. Thus, they were virtually riskless and very low-cost loans for the intermediate credit banks.

This practice was discontinued in 1948, partly because of congressional criticism (which the above analysis would indicate was not well conceived) and partly because of the narrowing spread between rates paid on debentures and those which the intermediate credit banks could charge in the highly competitive loan market that existed at that time. Without this concession, the banks for cooperatives were placed in a difficult position. They needed the commodity loans, as well as facility and operating loans, in order to have a volume of business adequate to carry their overhead without relying heavily on the subsidy provided in the form of government-owned capital.

The Central Bank for Cooperatives has authority to market its own debentures and has done so in the period 1950–1953.[71] This, however, does not appear to be a satisfactory way of solving the difficulty. It involves having two government agencies selling securities of very similar type, that is, debentures based on commodity loans. The situation is also complicated by the fact that the banks for cooperatives make loans based on other types of security, for example, facility and operating loans and commodity loans ineligible for discount with the intermediate credit banks. Furthermore, if the banks for cooperatives were to turn to direct sale of their own debentures in the money market that would reduce the loan volume handled by the intermediate credit banks and thus affect their profit-making possibilities. However, there are advantages both to the cooperative associations and to the banks for cooperatives in having the full line of credit to a borrowing cooperative handled through one agency. No easy solution of this problem is apparent as of this writing, short of continuance of some type of subsidy to or through the banks for cooperatives, unless arrangements can be worked out whereby the intermediate credit banks can and will make loans to or through the banks for cooperatives at interest rates that are lower than those charged on loans made directly to the cooperative associations.

71. The issues to date have been as follows:

Date of Issue	Interest Rate	Maturity Date	Amount Issued
2–1–50	$1\frac{5}{8}\%$	2–1–53	$30,000,000
10–1–51	$2\frac{1}{2}\%$	2–1–54	40,000,000
6–2–52	$2\frac{1}{4}\%$	6–1–53	40,000,000
2–2–53	$2\frac{5}{8}\%$	6–1–54	30,000,000
6–1–53	$2\frac{3}{4}\%$	6–1–54	40,000,000

For the banks for cooperatives to discontinue the practice of lending capital funds and use their capital mainly as a margin of safety in connection with borrowings from other sources would, of course, constitute a drastic change in their operations and present many problems. The profits to be derived from making loans out of funds borrowed in the open market probably would be inadequate to maintain the amount of service the banks now give. It seems reasonable to expect, however, that the amount of service required may decrease as the cooperatives become more soundly financed and the initial examinations for most of them have been made. If not it would appear to be sounder policy for the government to provide, as a direct subsidy, the amounts needed, as determined by Budget Bureau review and congressional scrutiny, rather than to maintain the banks with what is, in effect, a very large endowment.

It does not follow that aid should be withdrawn, or that the banks for cooperatives should necessarily be on a wholly self-supporting basis, though this would seem to be a desirable long-run objective. It has become settled policy for the government to provide special assistance in organizing and strengthening farmer cooperatives. Much of the service provided by the banks for cooperatives is essentially educational in character rather than mere continuing free service. Its worth has been well demonstrated and the close tie-in of such educational work with the lending operation is certainly the best way to make it effective.

Cost of the Banks for Cooperatives to 1953

The fact that the capital stock and reserves of the banks for cooperatives constitute the major portion of the loan fund used by them, not a margin of safety to assure repayment of loan funds derived from other sources, stems from their origin as a revised mechanism for handling the revolving fund assigned to the Federal Farm Board. The government provided, through the Federal Farm Board, a revolving fund of $500 million for making loans to cooperatives and for stabilization activities. About $320 million of this was lost or used in the various activities carried on by the Farm Board. The amounts derived from the liquidation of that operation were made available to the Farm Credit Administration for establishing the banks for cooperatives. They were thus financed in terms of the size of an available fund rather than on the basis of straight banking needs.

The capital turned over to the thirteen banks, $178.5 million, together with about $18 million in capital stock supplied by the borrowing cooperatives, makes a total capitalization of about $197 million. In addition, the banks have about $73 million in earned surplus, reserves for contingencies and legal reserves.[72]

72. As of June 30, 1953. See *Annual Report of the Farm Credit Administration, 1952–53*, p. 117.

Outstanding loans at the end of June 1953 amounted to $319 million, and at the end of the year to $372 million. It is apparent that the banks could carry more than half the loans outstanding at any one time out of their owned capital and surplus, with only limited resort to rediscounts with the federal intermediate credit banks or sale of their own securities. A good part of the "earned surplus" has apparently been derived from interest on owned capital invested in government securities rather than from actual earnings through banking operations.

The provision of this large fund on an interest-free basis has consti- tuted a sizable continuing subsidy if valued at the average cost to the government for funds made available. This cost has amounted in recent years to just under $4 million per annum, and for the whole period, to 1953, to about $75 million, if no allowance is made for portions of it retained in the Treasury and presumably used by it. Credits assignable to funds used by the Treasury are estimated at about $4 million, making the net cost to the government about $71 million. The amount of gov- ernment capital supplied appears unnecessarily high, and the extent of subsidy greater than is needed to assure healthy functioning of the banks.

As a theoretical offset to this $71 million in interest foregone, the government presumably owns a share (proportional to its share of the total capital stock of the banks) in the earned surplus and reserves of the banks, roughly $64 million. Actually, the significance of this as a government asset is dubious. If the management should become less care- ful and efficient, or if heavy losses should be incurred through a sharp decline in farm prices, it could be dissipated. Also, if the government- owned capital were to be gradually retired, this fund probably would pass gradually into ownership by the cooperatives owning stock in the banks. It seems more realistic to regard the cost in the form of interest- free capital as representing approximately the amount of subsidy.

Ratio of Capital to Loans in Other Banks

In 1953, the ratio of capital to loans in the banks for cooperatives was about 1 to 1.2 (total capital $196 million, surplus $73 million and loan volume $319 million). In contrast, the intermediate credit banks, as of June 30, 1953, had $60 million in capital, a surplus of $51 million and a loan volume of $830 million, a ratio of capital and surplus to loans outstanding of 1 to 7.5. The land banks, at their peak, had owned capital and surplus of about $358 million as a margin on outstanding loans of a little over $2 billion,[73] a ratio of about 1 to 5.8. As of June 30, 1953, the ratio was much narrower, about 1 to 3.5, but in the meantime all of the government-owned capital had been retired.[74]

73. In 1935. As of December 31, 1935, federal land bank mortgage loans outstanding amounted to approximately $2,072 million and capital stock and reserves to $358,152,944. See *Third Annual Report of the Farm Credit Administration, 1935,* pp. 128–29.
74. As of December 31, 1935, government-owned capital amounted to $123,097,895.

There are, to be sure, certain differences in the problems faced by these various types of banks. The individual loans of the banks for cooperatives may be large, though not so large as to require anything like the capitalization now maintained. These banks find it convenient and desirable to maintain a full line of credit, and to integrate the commodity loans with the facility and operating loans made to a given cooperative association. If they must rediscount the commodity loans with the intermediate credit banks, and pay them the regular rate, they cannot offer the loan on terms as favorable as those which the cooperatives could obtain by dealing directly with the intermediate credit banks. Consequently, they are faced with the alternative of handling such loans for nothing or losing the business and having the package of loans to a given cooperative split up.

Though these are very real problems, they hardly seem to warrant the maintenance of an unduly expensive cooperative banking structure duplicating in part the functions of the intermediate credit banks. The problem could be met in part if the intermediate credit banks could compensate the banks for cooperatives for servicing and supervising loans supplied by the intermediate credit banks but channeled through the banks for cooperatives.

This, for reasons already given, has not appeared to be a practical solution in recent years when the intermediate credit banks were operating on very narrow margins because of keen competition in a very easy money market. In a tighter credit situation with more normal spreads between the costs and returns on funds, it would appear to offer more possibilities. However, if the banks for cooperatives are to continue to give as much service as they have been doing it cannot be expected that they will be wholly self-supporting.

Government Capital Could Be Reduced

Even after taking account of the problems and difficulties discussed above, the government-owned capital in the banks for cooperatives apparently could be reduced rather substantially without destroying their usefulness. They might in fact be strengthened in the long run, since this would constitute a long step in the direction of a borrower-owned and borrower-managed system of banks for cooperatives. With interest rates at the levels of recent years and the financial condition of cooperatives improving, there appears to be no important reason for continuous subsidy in supplying credit to farmer cooperatives. They should have available to them loans suited to their needs at a cost commensurate with the expense of channeling funds to them through an efficient system of banks. This would be in keeping with the underlying principle of the federal land bank system and the intermediate credit system.

To the extent that the banks for cooperatives provide educational and service aids to cooperatives, in excess of those required for normal lending activities, government aid may well be warranted. If granted, however, the amount of such aid should be determined on a showing of amounts needed rather than by making available the use of whatever funds may happen to remain from a past operation now closed.

THE PROBLEM OF FUTURE FARM CREDIT POLICIES

Though the record of the Farm Credit Administration is excellent, various problems will require continuing consideration, and adjustments may be advisable as conditions change. As of 1953, the federal government had incurred costs of about $177 million in creating and maintaining the system as a whole. This does not include the investment in stock still held by the government. All of this is presumably balanced by assets of equivalent value and part of it, that in the intermediate credit banks, is providing a return to the federal Treasury.

The constituent elements of the cost figure given above are as follows (figures in millions): [75]

Interest cost on funds supplied to the federal land banks, 1918–1948		$82
Cost of funds supplied to the intermediate credit banks, 1923–1953	$47	
Less franchise taxes paid and earned surplus and reserves	54	
	(profit)	$7
Cost of funds supplied to the production credit corporations, 1933–1953		31
Cost of funds supplied to the banks for cooperatives, 1933–1953		71 [a]
Total cost (net)		$177

a. For reasons given earlier, this does not take account of the $73 million in surplus and reserves now held by the banks for cooperatives.

The system of farm credit agencies is now a going concern and large segments of it are owned by the borrowers. The federal land banks and the intermediate credit banks are virtually self-supporting. The production credit system is moving toward full borrower ownership for the local associations but not for the regional production credit corporations. The banks for cooperatives are likewise becoming more largely borrower-owned but still involve a subsidy of something in the order of $4 million per year.[76]

75. Cost of the regional agricultural credit corporations, the Cooperative Research and Service Division and some of the general overhead are not included. The $277 million supplied for reduction of interest rates on federal land bank loans and the $57 million for reducing interest rates on Land Bank Commissioner loans, between 1933 and 1944, are also omitted as being a direct subsidy to the borrowers concerned rather than a part of the cost of establishing the farm credit system. The Federal Farm Mortgage Corporation is likewise omitted since it was an emergency operation now largely liquidated. Figures are rounded to nearest million.

76. If the increase in reserves, which is unlikely to revert to the government, is ignored.

It does not seem likely that government support of the production credit associations could be entirely withdrawn now or for some time to come. Continuance of the current policy of supplying capital, where actually needed, until the associations not now borrower-owned can become independent seems to be warranted, but with continuing strong encouragement for retirement of government capital. Where particular associations prove unable to achieve independent status in a reasonable length of time, or to make significant progress toward it, their liquidation may well be considered.

Such a policy would look to the eventual development of a wholly borrower-owned, cooperatively managed network of production credit associations covering all areas in which the volume of business and competitive conditions are such that they have reasonable prospect of successful and useful operation.

Supervision and Stand-by Aid Needed

Supervision and educational aid, such as is now provided by the production credit corporations, seems necessary, but may taper off gradually. Thus the PCA's would come to have their principal contact with the federal intermediate credit banks, which are their chief source of funds and their logical channel for reaching the money market. Eventually, if that should be the device chosen, it would be feasible to retire most of the government funds now invested in the capital stock of the production credit corporations and to reduce them to the status of supervisory divisions in the district offices of the Farm Credit Administration, supported either by contributions from the PCA's or by government appropriations.[77]

In times of severe credit stringency, provision could well be made whereby the sale of intermediate credit bank debentures would be assured on a scale sufficient to enable the production credit associations to expand loans enough to meet the legitimate needs of borrowers if private credit should be contracted suddenly or severely.

Commercial banks could, and undoubtedly would, supply in most periods a good part of the production credit needed. This, however, need not be a cause of concern provided there is in existence an alternative source of production credit which can be expanded in the event of panic withdrawal of bank deposits or a sharp contraction of credit through protective action on the part of commercial bank managements.[78]

77. There would apparently be warrant, however, for retaining a modest fund that could be used in helping new PCA's to get started, in localities not now served, and as a stand-by arrangement capable of being expanded quickly if any sudden catastrophe should cause considerable numbers of the PCA's to be unable to meet legitimate demands for credit in their localities.

78. If the PCA's can maintain efficiency and keep costs down sufficiently to enable them to survive in competition with the deposit banks, and if the safeguards suggested are provided, agriculture could not be subjected to so severe a contraction of credit as that which occurred in the early 1920s or in the 1930s.

Land Loan System Well Developed

For land-mortgage loans, agriculture is now relatively well equipped. Both the land bank and insurance company loans are on a basis such that acute distress, like that of the 1920s and 1930s, would be unlikely to occur, especially if the government stands ready to assure the salability of land bank bonds and to offset unreasonably severe contractions of farm mortgage credit.

The problems now are of a different kind. Among them is that of minimizing overhead and simplifying organization. This is largely an internal problem for agriculture itself, though the government may need to assist in its solution. The farm credit system of the United States is a relatively expensive and complex one—as compared to those of other countries. It is possible that it can be simplified, streamlined and made more efficient. Since it is now largely farmer-owned, such progress as can be made in that direction would benefit farmer borrowers rather than the federal Treasury. These are matters that merit separate and continuing study.

More important is the necessity for keeping costs at such a level that the land banks can meet the competition from other lending agencies and continue as a significant factor in the farm mortgage field. They constitute the anchor to windward in the event of a credit crisis or severe depression. If they do not have a substantial volume of business, and an adequate and well-qualified staff, they cannot be used effectively as a channel for injecting new credit into agriculture in times of depression.

The Problem of Changing Price Level

The price level changes of recent years have raised credit policy problems of at least three types. These are: (1) how much adjustment should be made in appraisal policy as a result of the increase in price level that has occurred during and after World War II; (2) what policy should be followed if there is a continuing general rise in prices; and (3) what policy should be followed in a time when prices are declining, particularly if the price decline is severe and sudden as it would be in the event of a serious depression?

During the depression of the 1930s, appraisals based on 1910–14 price levels were taken as a rough practical norm. This device had merit both for that period and for the war years that followed. It implied a justifiably liberal lending policy in the 1930s, which gave some support to a badly depressed land market, and operated as a mildly restraining influence in the period following. The private lending agencies tended to follow a similarly conservative policy during the 1940s.

The 1910–14 income criterion was sufficiently realistic to be workable and useful during those two decades. This criterion was replaced in April 1951 by one based on higher levels of prices. Any standard of that kind is bound to present problems in times of rapidly changing price levels. Apparently, the only feasible alternative is some kind of long-term price forecast. Obviously such a forecast involves many difficulties and lies outside the scope of this study. Yet some sort of forecast of prices is implied in any appraisal policy.

The basic policy followed since 1933, or earlier, appears to be sound and useful, namely to avoid following the extreme downswings of land prices in a severe depression and to refrain from basing appraisals on the high values that may result from a period of inflation, especially if the inflation is accompanied by active speculation in farm lands.

Policy in Periods of Severe Depression

If farm earnings should decline moderately or even continue to have a mild downward trend for rather long periods, there is little likelihood of a severe credit crisis, with farm mortgages written as a good portion of them now are. Farmers would find the going tough, but most of those with long-term, amortized mortgages would not be in serious danger of losing their farms. Furthermore, the basic situation of American agriculture appears to be much stronger than it was in the early 1930s. Our population has grown enormously, the period of most rapid and revolutionary mechanization seems to have passed its peak and the farmers of the United States are somewhat less dependent on foreign outlets than in the past. So sudden and severe a contraction as that of the early 1930s seems unlikely.[79]

If there should be a general depression in agriculture, or in the economy as a whole, the land bank system and the government should be prepared to expand operations quickly, taking over soundly based loans that cannot be refinanced elsewhere and channeling government credit into agriculture to take the place of that withdrawn. A very difficult problem of what levels of mortgage debt to support would be presented, but it is safe to assume that some level above that which would come about naturally could safely be maintained. Prices are not likely to remain for long periods at extreme depression levels.

It should be recognized, however, that so far-reaching a rescue operation as that of the 1930s would not now be possible. Interest rates on farm loans are now more in line with those in other industries than they were in 1930, much of the farm mortgage debt does not require refinancing within a short period and the general level of debt is lower. Payments on principal could be deferred and probably should be. Under extreme conditions, even interest payments might properly be deferred,

79. It should be recognized, however, that severe readjustments may occur in some lines and may affect regional conditions in very important ways. Such products as wheat are easily overproduced and markets can be seriously depressed even when the national economy is in a healthy and prosperous condition. In the event of a severe general depression, it is likely that both general and specific antideflation devices would now be used more quickly and effectively than in the 1930s.

but, on the whole, agriculture can best place its reliance on the fact that it now has a much more depression-proof mortgage system than it had in the early 1930s. If land values should shrink severely, a revival of the commissioner loan program probably would be warranted.

Abnormal Types of Loans

The preceding discussion relates principally to usual and relatively conservative types of farm credit. It does not touch significantly the problem of the young farmer wanting to buy a farm and therefore needing a loan that will cover a very high percentage of the value of the farm. Neither does it meet the needs of the borrower whose land value rests heavily upon prospective future or non-cash income, such as residential values, mineral rights and so on; or those of the part-time farmer whose income is derived largely from nonfarm sources.

These, for the most part, fall in the category of welfare and high-risk loans, which are discussed in Chapter 6. There appears to be little warrant for extending the activities of the major, conservative credit agencies into these realms. To do so might jeopardize their possibilities for greatest usefulness in the lending activities for which they are specifically designed. Speculative loans can probably best be left to the private credit agencies. Secondary loans, to permit purchase of farms by young farmers, and loans to facilitate or save part-time farming ventures, can best be made from special funds obtained on some other basis than that of land bank bonds and intermediate credit or cooperative bank debentures.

However, there might well be continuing effort to achieve better co-ordination of such lending with that of the agencies now in the Farm Credit Administration. The inclusion within the Farm Credit Administration of the welfare types of credit, but as a separate agency, merits consideration. The two types of credit operation should be supplemental, not competing.

A third and very important type of credit, namely that provided by the Commodity Credit Corporation, is not discussed here. Some of the Commodity Credit Corporation loans are merely the means of implementing price-supporting programs and can hardly be regarded as genuine credit operations. However, there are other aspects of CCC operations which constitute very important supplements to the more orthodox lending activities and can be of great importance to agriculture if not misused. These and the price-supporting activities of CCC are discussed more fully in Chapter 10.

Chapter 6

"Emergency" and "Supervised" Credit

THE CREDIT AGENCIES described in Chapter 5 are the oldest and best known parts of the government-sponsored credit system for agriculture. Their organization and operations are in keeping with conservative banking principles. The chief purpose in establishing them was to reduce interest rates and provide a more orderly plan of repayment. Government aid has been given to all of them, but mainly with a view to getting them established on a self-supporting basis. In large part, that aim has been accomplished.[1]

These agencies do not touch significantly the credit problems of high-risk borrowers. The kinds of loans not provided are chiefly of two types, those needed as a result of droughts, or other physical disasters, and those needed by farmers who are chronically undersupplied with working capital, know-how and land resources. The problems of these higher-risk borrowers are so different from those of the farmers served by the more conventional credit agencies that two quite separate types of credit programs have emerged.

Generally speaking, the farmer whose crop has been destroyed by droughts or floods will presumably be able to resume normal operations if he can get funds to carry through until a new crop can be made. He is, in most cases, a commercial farmer, that is, a farmer who produces mainly for the market. More often than not he is in a one-crop area largely concerned with cash-crop production.

The other group, a much larger and more scattered one, is not in difficulty because of some specific local catastrophe. Instead it is made up of farmers who operate continuously at low levels of output and income. The earning prospects of these farmers even in good years are not such as to make them good credit risks for ordinary lending agencies. In many cases they do not have the skill to use credit in lifting themselves to a higher economic level, even if it can be obtained.[2] Often their farms are too small, too poorly organized or on land too poor for profitable

1. Emergency financing through the land banks in the 1930s was a deviation from this principle but not an important change in it. The steps taken were, in fact, designed to enable the land banks to aid in meeting a major disaster without being wrecked in the process or having their basic structure changed.

The loans made by the revived War Finance Corporation in the 1920s, described in Chapter 5, were also emergency loans, but on such a conservative basis that they were in keeping with orthodox banking principles rather than with those of "soft" or "welfare" credit.

2. This does not necessarily mean that such farmers are inherently inefficient. Some are. Others are in trouble as a result of conditions beyond their control and of such a nature that they cannot overcome them without outside guidance and financial assistance.

operation. Some of these farmers, of course, have also suffered droughts or other catastrophes, but these are not the principal causes of their need for special types of credit.

Banks Unable to Meet These Needs

Neither the land banks nor the intermediate credit banks can make the kinds of loans needed by these low-income farmers. The commercial banks are likewise unsuited for making such loans on any considerable scale. They often do carry drought-stricken farmers until a new crop can be made, but are likely themselves to be in desperate circumstances if located in areas severely damaged by droughts or floods. Even less is the local bank equipped to extend credit constructively to the chronically unproductive, low-income farmer. Here there is need for technical aid in replanning the farm business, improving methods of farming and deciding where credit can be used to advantage. Most of the banks do not have the personnel, the know-how or the inclination to meet problems of that kind.[3]

Yet without active assistance of some such kind nearly a third of the farmers of the United States are apparently destined to continue on a bare subsistence basis in ordinary times and many of them will inevitably be in need of publicly supplied relief funds if a severe depression occurs. Their plight was little recognized until the depression of the 1930s put hundreds of thousands of them on the relief rolls and brought sharp realization that they constitute a major problem in American rural life. Though these chronically poor, low-producing farmers were more numerous and widely distributed than the victims of droughts and floods, they were not the ones first given consideration by the Congress.

The credit needs of farmers in areas severely afflicted by drought were much more apparent and the members of Congress were much more sympathetic to them. Consequently, the first steps taken were for the purpose of aiding victims of droughts and other hazards rather than to meet the needs of those who were handicapped in other ways. Action in respect to the chronically impoverished group did not come until the 1930s.

DISASTER-TYPE LOANS

Seed Loans and Crop and Feed Loans

Special loans to assist farmers severely affected by drought were first made in 1918, as a means of enabling those in the affected areas to get

3. There has been a significant change in recent years in the operation and attitudes of local commercial banks. Partly as a result of the competition and example of the government agencies, many of these banks are now employing agents or consultants to advise them on loan terms, criteria and methods of programing loans to farmers. In some cases, local committees are used. Changes of this kind are making the commercial banks more responsive to agricultural needs but they still are not in a position to supply on any large scale the "welfare" types of loans here discussed or the amount of education and guidance needed by chronically impoverished farmers.

going again, especially in the production of wheat, which was then in critically short supply because of high war demand and poor yields. From then on, such loans were authorized at frequent intervals. They were granted only to those in desperate need and only in specified areas outlined in the acts making the appropriations.

No important change in method of farming or kind of product was implied. The aim was to restore or maintain the kind of farming that existed before the disaster occurred. No supervision of the borrowers was contemplated, and even the lending and collecting activities were on a minimum and temporary basis.

Though nominally provided for the purchase of seed for putting in new crops, or for feed to maintain livestock, many of the loans were used, partly at least, for living expenses of the farm families during the ensuing production period. Such loans had some tendency to keep in production areas in which the hazards of crop loss were too great to warrant their retention as crop-producing lands. Droughts and floods, for example, are likely to recur at frequent intervals in the same localities. It was in part an increasing awareness of this defect in the stopgap seed and feed loan activities that led eventually to the initiation of a land retirement program and the development of types of loans designed to change and improve farms rather than merely to keep them in operation.

The widespread distress in agriculture in 1930 and 1931, and the inability of many farmers to get loans from the hard-pressed banks, led to a broadening of the authorization for making emergency loans. Farmers who were unable to get necessary credit for continuing their farm operations were made eligible to receive loans whether afflicted by natural disaster or not.[4] The area of lending was thus enlarged to include the whole United States, instead of being confined to specified counties. Also, the loans were called "crop and feed" loans rather than "seed" loans, a change in designation which implied more emphasis on maintaining the farm business as a whole rather than merely putting in a new crop.

The seed and crop and feed loans were recognized as high-risk, relief-type credit on which losses might be large. Hence they could not be financed by the sale of bonds and debentures, as the land bank and intermediate credit bank loans were. If they were to be made, the government must supply the money through direct appropriations and must be prepared to accept the losses incurred. Nevertheless, congressional sentiment has almost invariably been friendly to the provision of such aid whenever any large number of farmers have been suddenly and unexpectedly reduced to a condition of dire need.[5]

Until the latter part of the 1930s, specific appropriations were made to meet each emergency as it arose. This practice was changed in 1938.

4. Under the Reconstruction Finance Corporation Act of January 22, 1932, 47 *Stat.* 5.
5. Until 1933 the seed and crop and feed loans were administered by the Secretary of Agriculture, through agencies and individuals selected by him. From 1933 to 1946 they were administered by the Farm Credit Administration. In 1946 this activity was transferred to the Farmers Home Administration (to be described later).

In February of that year the Congress, by joint resolution (52 *Stat.* 26), authorized the making of loans (after June 30, 1938) from the unexpended balance of a $50 million fund that had been appropriated, and from all past and future collections on 1937 and 1938 loans. These funds were to be available until June 30, 1939, for making loans under the act of January 29, 1937.

Since the authorization was extended in subsequent appropriation acts, in effect a revolving fund was created for crop and feed loans. New appropriations for such loans virtually ceased except for one of $15 million in fiscal 1940, one of $5 million in fiscal 1944 and another of $5 million in 1947.

Amounts Loaned

Until 1931 the number of farmers assisted by loans of this type was not large. It never exceeded 50,000 in any one year and usually was much less. The desperate condition of agriculture in 1930 and 1931 led to a greatly expanded program in 1931 which affected about 439,000 farmers. During 1932 such aid was given to more than 500,000 farmers, and in 1933 the number reached 634,000 or about one farmer in ten for the entire United States. Until 1931 the total amount loaned never exceeded $6 million. In that year it jumped to nearly $56 million. It was even larger in the four succeeding years. Though the amounts loaned were smaller from 1935 on than in the years 1931 to 1935, they continued to be much larger than in the 1920s. (See Table 13.)

Special Drought Relief Fund, 1934 and 1935

In 1934 and 1935, funds were assigned from a special drought relief fund which provided for a much broader range of activities than any of the earlier appropriations. The catastrophic drought of 1934 came at a time when the country was in a major economic depression. The President requested, in June 1934, a special drought relief fund of unprecedented size: $525 million. He outlined the purposes of this fund as follows (figures in millions):

1. For special work programs and human relief $125
2. For livestock purchase in addition to funds under the Jones-Connally Act   75
3. For shipping, processing and relief distribution of purebred cattle   100
4. For loans to farmers to finance emergency feed purchases and shipments   100
5. For emergency acquisition of submarginal farms and assistance in relocating destitute farm families   50
6. For work camps to afford employment in the drought area for young men principally from cities and towns   50
7. For purchase of seed for 1935 plantings and for loans to get seeds into farmers' hands   25

TABLE 13

DISASTER-TYPE LOANS BY YEARS, 1918–1947

Year	Number of Loans	Amount Loaned	Maximum Size of Loan Authorized	Average Size of Loan Made
1918⎫ 1919⎭	15,973	$4,200,833	$—	$263
1920	—	—	—	—
1921	13,935	1,957,407	200	140
1922	11,968	1,480,107	300	124
1923	—	—	—	—
1924	3,152	413,983	500	131
1925	—	—	—	—
1926	908	244,205	500	269
1927	—	—	—	—
1928	—	—	—	—
1929	46,067	5,758,650	2,000	125
1930	45,311	5,340,727	2,000	118
1931	438,727	55,770,721	600	141
1932	507,631	64,204,503	400	127
1933	633,586	57,375,940	300	91
1934–35 [a]	300,614	72,008,540	—	240
1934 [b]	445,198	37,891,586	250	84
1935	424,441	57,419,915	500	132
1936	188,944	16,629,190	250	88
1937	252,894	32,503,280	250	129
1938	174,557	19,647,535	—	113
1939	139,452	15,079,509	—	108
1940	157,443	19,453,680	—	124
1941	146,740	18,345,912	—	125
1942	141,405	19,823,951	—	140
1943 [c]	104,695	16,650,519	—	159
1944 [d]	100,571	18,801,174	—	187
1945 [d]	81,653	16,748,114		205
1946 [d]	80,381	17,543,430	—	218
1947 [d]	2,765	711,485	—	257

Sources: Compiled from Annual Reports of the Farm Credit Administration and from Norman J. Wall, *Federal Seed-Loan Financing and Its Relation to Agricultural Rehabilitation and Land Use,* Department of Agriculture, Technical Bulletin No. 539, 1936, pp. 4, 16. No disaster loans of this type were made after 1947. From then on, the disaster loan program was operated on a different basis and under the Farmers Home Administration.

a. Drought relief loans under separate appropriation.
b. Other loans.
c. January through June.
d. Fiscal year.

The Congress authorized the $525 million requested, making it available, until June 30, 1935, for allocation by the President in supplementing appropriations made previously for emergency purposes, including those to farmers. The act stipulated that the fund was to be used for relief in stricken agricultural areas. However, the relief provided was not confined entirely to farmers. Crop and feed loans amounting to some $72 million were made, but in the main the fund was used for meeting the human relief problem, which was especially serious in rural areas at that time.[6]

Classes of Farmers Served

The individual seed and crop and feed loans made were small and cannot have affected very significantly the farming activities or general welfare of the borrowers. Nevertheless, some small amount of emergency credit was essential to many of them.[7] The borrowers fell roughly into three groups: (1) those who could not get credit because their usual sources, particularly country banks, were unable to supply them; (2) those whose resources had been seriously impaired by drought, hail or floods; and (3) those whose land or type of farming was such that their returns were too low for them to build up resources that would warrant ordinary commercial loans.

The first group clearly is not one that would require special emergency credit if adequate commercial or cooperative credit institutions were available. Much of the problem of these farmers has since been met by strengthening the banking structure and by the growth of the system of production credit associations. The needs of the second group should also be met, in the main, by an adequate system of local credit facilities.[8]

For the third group, and some of those in the second group, the problem is of a different kind. Here the need is for improvement in the methods of farming or in the character of the farm, or abandonment of crop farming and reversion to grazing, if weather hazards are too great to give prospect of success in crop farming.

There is a marked tendency for certain areas to be more or less con-

6. It has been estimated that out of 5.2 million households receiving emergency relief under the general relief program in February 1935, 1.9 million or 36 per cent were located in rural areas and 188,000 or 4 per cent in small towns of 2,500 to 5,000. As of that date 39 per cent of all rural and town families in the cut-over areas of the Lake states were on relief, 34 per cent in the spring wheat area, 21 per cent in the Appalachian and Ozark sections, 21 per cent in the western cotton region, 17 per cent in the winter wheat region and 16 per cent in the ranching areas. See *The Rural Relief Population, February 1935,* Federal Emergency Relief Administration, Research Bulletin H-1, August 13, 1935, pp. 1 and 7. The report is based on sample studies rather than on complete counts.

7. The marginal significance of even small amounts of actual money is often very large, especially for farmers who obtain most of their income in non-cash form.

8. Provided the local credit facilities are developed sufficiently in all areas to meet the legitimate needs of farmers who are reasonably good credit risks.

tinuous candidates for relief of the crop and feed loan type because of especially uncertain rainfall or other physical hazards.[9] The type of program then in use afforded no lasting solution for problems of that kind. In fact, it tended to perpetuate farming in areas where the farmers concerned would perhaps have been better off if forced to seek work or business opportunities elsewhere or to change radically their types of farming. For either solution they usually were in need either of help in getting relocated or of technical aid and credit for changing their types and scales of operation.[10]

To the extent that the program supplied credit otherwise unavailable because of inadequate local lending facilities, it can be regarded as having bridged a gap pending more fundamental long-term solutions. The need for continuing such a program on this basis does not seem pressing. Where aid was given in recovering from a serious and probably nonrepetitive disaster, it appears to have been justified. The more questionable part of the program is that relating to areas where production is very uncertain and to farmers who are chronically unprosperous and unproductive.[11]

Cost of Disaster and Relief Loans to 1953

Through 1931, disaster and relief loans totaled about $75 million. By the close of 1940, repayments had amounted to about $55.8 million. Thus, the accrued loss on principal was about $19 million. After 1931, with a broadened area of coverage, a changed criterion for making loans and much more general depression in agriculture, the scale of operation increased materially.[12] The status of this loan program in summary for the years 1918 through 1953 is shown in Table 14.

9. Prior to 1936, Montana, North Dakota and Florida received aid in almost every year during which seed and crop and feed loans were made available. Wall states, "In general, there seems to be a close correlation between counties having a high ratio of loans and the frequency with which such counties have received Federal aid." Norman J. Wall, *Federal Seed-Loan Financing and Its Relation to Agricultural Rehabilitation and Land Use*, Department of Agriculture, Technical Bulletin No. 539, 1936, p. 5.

10. Approximately half the loans made between the beginning of the seed loan program and October 31, 1946 were in seven states—Arkansas, Georgia, North Carolina, North Dakota, South Carolina, South Dakota and Texas. See *Report of the Administrator of the Farmers Home Administration, 1950*, pp. 36–37.

In the western states the most common cause of continuing reliance on emergency loans is drought. In the states farther east, floods, agricultural depression and chronic poverty are more commonly the causes of need for special types of credit. Where drought is a primary cause of distress, it tends to recur in certain parts of the states affected rather than over their entire areas, except in general droughts such as those of 1934 and 1936.

11. As interest shifted from the local disaster problem to the broader problem of chronic poverty in agriculture, efforts were made to devise and initiate a more fundamental and constructive attack on these problems. This took shape in the programs of the Resettlement Administration, the Farm Security Administration and, later, the Farmers Home Administration.

12. From 1931 to 1937, loans of this kind were made in nearly all parts of the United States on the basis of inability to get credit for continuing farm operations, even where

For the period as a whole, the average expense to the government for disaster loans of various kinds was about $5.5 million per year for capital losses, administration and cost of funds. Much the largest part of this expense was incurred during the 16 years 1931 through 1946. For the loans made prior to that time, both administrative expenses and losses were modest, amounting to some $4 to $5 million for the 12-year period. From 1931 through 1946, the period of major activity, the total cost of the program was about $10.5 million per year.

Evaluation of the Program

In evaluating the program, the principal question is not how much it cost, but rather whether this was the best way of using a given amount of disaster relief funds. The Congress has shown little reluctance to come to the aid of limited numbers of farmers who are in acute distress because of some disaster which they were powerless to foresee or prevent. Presumably this attitude will continue. Such catastrophes occur from time to time in almost every part of the United States, not only from drought but from floods, tornadoes, hurricanes and other natural causes. Where they occur unexpectedly and with devastating severity, there may be great need for temporary aid both to help the farm families themselves and to get production going again.

Local lending agencies are likely to be unable to provide such aid on a sufficiently liberal and general basis. Here the government, or relief agencies such as the Red Cross and other humanitarian organizations, are almost the only sources of aid that can provide quick relief. The Red Cross can and usually does undertake to supply the immediate needs of the people affected. It is not equipped to aid significantly in restoring production activities.

The principal defect of the program in earlier periods was the lack of a suitable stand-by agency qualified to step in quickly and with funds already authorized, thus avoiding the slow process of obtaining appropriations and congressional directives.[13] Furthermore, there was need for continuing study of criteria to be used in delimiting areas of application, determining loan policy and handling collections. The facilities for such a continuing stand-by arrangement have now been provided through the

---

physical loss of crops was not involved, though there still was emphasis on drought loans. From 1937 to 1946, the loans based on economic distress unrelated to drought tended to be taken over by the Farm Security Administration under its rural rehabilitation program. From 1946 on, this responsibility was assigned to the Farmers Home Administration, with certain exceptions to be noted later.

13. A procedure that requires specific authorizing legislation with respect to each disaster is likely to be wasteful and poorly timed. Such legislation often is hastily drawn and may include areas not really in need of special assistance. Needs of this kind arise frequently enough to warrant maintaining stand-by arrangements under general guiding directives from the Congress and a modest revolving fund which can be used without specific appropriation. For more serious and widespread disasters, the Congress should, of course, retain the function of making special appropriations.

TABLE 14

Crop and Feed Loan [a] Activities to December 31, 1953

(*Summary*)

Total loans made (all matured)	$575,934,022
Repayments of principal	475,084,932
Loans outstanding	19,976,010
Loans written off or reduced to judgment	80,873,080
Status of loans outstanding	
Total amount	19,976,010
Estimated future losses	17,000,000
Over-all cost of the seed and crop and feed loan programs, 1918–1953	
Write-offs and judgments	80,873,080
Estimated future losses	17,000,000
Cost of administration to 1947 [b]	61,000,000
Cost of funds used [c]	63,000,000
Total cost	221,873,080
Less interest received [d]	57,288,278
Net cost of crop and feed loan operations	164,584,802

Source: Based on data supplied by the Farmers Home Administration. (Under the Farmers Home Administration Act of 1946, the crop and feed loan and rehabilitation loan programs were discontinued, at least in terms of those designations. However, from 1949 on, the Farmers Home Administration was authorized to make "disaster" loans from the $45 million revolving fund derived from the capital released by the Regional Agricultural Credit Corporation.)

a. Includes "seed" loans made between 1918 and 1932.

b. Figure rounded to nearest million. Administrative costs are not available for the loans made in 1918, 1919 and 1920. Hence they are not included in these tabulations. The loans still unpaid were transferred to the Farmers Home Administration in 1946. Administrative expenses of the Farmers Home Administration (1946–1953), on loans of this type made prior to 1946, are included in Farmers Home Administration expenses and do not appear in this tabulation. Thus the figure given is somewhat smaller than the actual cost of administering these loans.

c. Rounded to nearest million. On basis of average rate paid on government securities outstanding as given in *Statistical Abstract* for years after 1932. For 1921–1932 the amount loaned is multiplied by the average annual cost of money to the government (3.98 per cent). It is assumed that the money was used for one year. Some loans were repaid in less than a year while others remained unpaid for much more than a year.

d. For the years 1930–1934 the prevailing practice was to deduct interest at time of making the loan. Consequently the interest received in these years is included in the amounts shown as principal repaid. This practice was discontinued by an act of June 19, 1934, but was used in administering the act of February 1937. (See Norman J. Wall, *Federal Seed-Loan Financing and Its Relation to Agricultural Rehabilitation and Land Use*, Department of Agriculture, Technical Bulletin No. 539, 1936, p. 18.) The interest rate charged was 5 per cent until 1932, except for 1918 when it was 6 per cent. Beginning in 1932, it was set at 5.5 per cent. The rate was further reduced, to 4 per cent, in 1940.

Farmers Home Administration and should result both in more prompt and effective aid and in better use of government funds.

No large-scale economics on this phase of the credit program are to be expected. However, a sharper distinction should be made between farmers needing only temporary aid to re-establish customary types of agriculture and those who should be transferred to longer-term improvement programs. Crop and feed loans made because of economic depression, and drought loans in areas that appear to be chronically in the problem class, call for other policies and treatment.

The older type of crop and feed loan, as a means of aiding farmers not affected by physical disaster, probably should not be revived even in times of severe depression.[14] This device was used in the early 1930s because of a recognized need and before the more adequate and suitable procedure now available had been developed. For low-income farmers and those whose credit rating is too poor to enable them to get adequate loans even when times are not bad, a combination of technical guidance and loans affords the most practical means of providing help in the form most needed and most likely to be effective.

Some Lands Should Be Put to Other Uses

Where farmers are operating on lands subject to such frequent recurrence of drought, flood or other disaster as to make them uneconomic for the existing type of agriculture, no loan program alone can be anything more than a palliative which constitutes a continuing drain on national resources. Even with frequent aid in the way of disaster loans, farmers in such areas almost inevitably find themselves in a continuously precarious position economically, and most of them eventually give up and drift into other areas or other occupations. Thus the palliative supplied has served only to prolong their hardships and delay a new start under more promising conditions. If the lands are unsuited for profitable continuing operation, even with improved organization and better farm management, some procedure for making more drastic changes in land use should be devised.[15] Lands unsuited for crop production should not be allowed to become a continuing drain on the federal Treasury and a cause of chronic hardship to their operators.

REHABILITATION IN THE 1930s

The depression of the 1930s, and the devastating droughts of that period, focused attention on a number of agricultural problems that had been almost unrecognized up to that time. Among them was the situation of the chronically impoverished small farmer who lived at a bare subsistence level even in ordinary times.

Farmers of this kind had shown great powers of survival in most depression periods. They produced little for the market and bought little. However, they had for some generations been falling farther and farther

14. However, in the event of such an all-inclusive and severe depression as that of the early 1930s some provision of outright grants-in-aid to certain classes of needy farmers might well be considered. Even then, aid should be administered by a qualified staff of the Farmers Home Administration or relief agency type rather than in the haphazard fashion of many of the early seed and crop and feed loan activities.

15. As, for example, transfer to grazing districts, forest reserves or other extensive types of use.

behind the more progressive farmers in their standards of living and levels of income. Until the 1930s neither the farm organizations nor the Congress gave much attention to this problem. Most of the low-income farmers were not members of the general farm organizations and their troubles did not stem from some sudden, highly publicized catastrophe such as a drought or flood which would be likely to arouse congressional interest.

Relief Costs Shifted to Federal Agencies

From 1930 to 1934 the financing of relief activities, both urban and rural, was shifted gradually from local and state agencies to the federal government. Many of the state and local units of government, and the voluntary agencies, had virtually exhausted their resources and were no longer able to carry the load. By the late winter of 1935 nearly one million farm families were being partially supported by relief grants or rehabilitation loans from the federal government.[16]

Efforts were being made in both urban and rural areas to find ways of enabling recipients of relief to become self-supporting. For urban workers this meant, in most cases, finding or creating new jobs, retraining workers or providing work through publicly financed projects. In the rural areas the problem was different. The principal need was for increased efficiency, more home production of foodstuffs and better management generally.

With unemployment at high levels in the urban areas, there was little merit in trying to move families off the farms, even though their prospects in agriculture were far from good. Instead, the policy adopted looked, in the main, to providing loans, and in some cases grants, which would enable destitute farm families to become self-supporting without a shift to a new job or a new location. In some areas, off-farm employment was provided through federally financed make-work projects.

The rural relief problem was greatly intensified by the severe and widespread drought of 1934 and the one which followed it in 1936. Thousands of farmers, particularly in the southern plains area, had to abandon their farms and seek employment elsewhere. In addition, many commercial farmers, in their effort to cut costs, turned to tractor farming, thus displacing croppers and wage workers who depended on field work for their livings. Great numbers of farm families came to be without settled residence and were on the move seeking work, mostly in the Pacific Coast states.

As a result, the western states were flooded with agricultural job seekers who far outnumbered the jobs and the housing available. Local

16. Berta Asch and A. R. Mangus, *Farmers on Relief and Rehabilitation,* Works Progress Administration, Research Monograph VIII, 1937, p. xviii. The rural relief load was at its peak in February 1935. Only 42 per cent of the agricultural relief cases were carried through June.

relief agencies were unable to cope with the situation and most of the communities to which the migrants moved felt that the problem was not one of their making. Some form of federal action appeared to be the only solution. The task was assigned to the Federal Emergency Relief Administration, which set up a rehabilitation program designed specifically to aid people in the rural areas.

The rural rehabilitation program of the Federal Emergency Relief Administration was set up at first on a decentralized basis, and was to be handled through state rural rehabilitation corporations financed by the Relief Administration. A ruling by the office of the Comptroller General that funds made available through the Emergency Relief Appropriations Act of 1935 could not be disbursed through the state rural rehabilitation corporations caused the program to be transferred back to the federal government. It thus became a centralized rather than a decentralized activity.

Creation of Resettlement Administration

With a view to putting the work on a more orderly basis and also as a means of carrying out a program of submarginal land retirement, a new agency, the Resettlement Administration, was created by presidential order in April 1935. Executive Order 7027 (May 1935) under which the agency was set up directed it to (1) administer approved projects involving resettlement of destitute or low-income families, (2) initiate and administer a program with respect to soil erosion, stream pollution, seacoast erosion, reforestation and flood control,[17] and (3) make loans to finance in whole or in part the purchase of farm lands and necessary farm equipment by farmers, farm tenants, croppers and farm laborers.

The Division of Subsistence Homesteads of the Department of the Interior and the Rural Rehabilitation Division of the Federal Emergency Relief Administration were transferred to the Resettlement Administration, as were the Land Program of the Federal Emergency Relief Administration and the Land Policy Section of the Agricultural Adjustment Administration.[18] Funds were assigned to it from those appropriated to the Relief Administration.

17. The Soil Erosion Service had already been established and had functions very similar to the conservation activities assigned to the Resettlement Administration. The Forest Service and other agencies also had responsibility for carrying on conservation programs of various kinds. To avoid duplication of function and inter-agency conflicts, the conservation efforts of the Resettlement Administration were limited to a specific type of problem not included in the other programs, namely, the purchase of privately owned farm lands considered unsuitable for crop farming and their assignment to other uses.

18. The submarginal land program had originated earlier, in the Federal Emergency Relief Administration and the Land Program Section of the Agricultural Adjustment Administration.

The Federal Emergency Relief Administration had also initiated a program for making advances of capital goods to farm relief "clients" instead of cash, with a view to making

The most direct tie of the Resettlement Administration was with the Department of Agriculture rather than with the Relief Administration, since Rexford G. Tugwell, its Administrator, continued to serve as Under Secretary of Agriculture. It was formally transferred to the Department of Agriculture on December 31, 1936 (Executive Order 7530).

The name of the organization was changed to Farm Security Administration in September 1937 (by order of the Secretary of Agriculture). The Bankhead-Jones Farm Tenant Act of July 1937 (50 *Stat.* 522) provided congressional authorization for most of the activities then being carried on under the Resettlement Administration and for some additional functions.[19] Those retained and the ones added by the new act became the continuing program of the Farm Security Administration.

Though the land retirement phase of the Resettlement Administration was much discussed in the early years of its existence, its program included many other activities relating to low-income farmers, displaced farmers and farm wage workers. The farm families aided were mainly of the following types: (1) those that were chronically impoverished; (2) families in need of help because their crops had been ruined by drought; (3) displaced farm families and single workers who had neither homes nor jobs; and (4) families on land considered too poor to warrant keeping it in crop production.

The program devised by the Resettlement Administration for meeting these problems had four principal parts: rural rehabilitation, land use, rural resettlement and suburban resettlement. Since the land-use program pertained mainly to devising better uses of land and bringing about conservation of land resources, discussion of it is deferred to a succeeding chapter on conservation. The suburban resettlement efforts were mainly intended as a means of aiding urban workers and hence are omitted from consideration here. The principal agricultural activities, aside from those pertaining to land use, were the rehabilitation efforts, rural resettlement and the programs designed to aid migrant farm workers.

Since the activities of the Farm Security Administration, until it was abolished in 1946, were essentially a continuation of those of the Resettlement Administration, the two are combined in the following analysis. There were, however, changes in emphasis and scope during the period covered. The resettlement activities were de-emphasized, both as a result

---

them self-supporting. The program included both rehabilitation in place and relocation on new lands. By April 1935 the rural rehabilitation program included 209,830 cases involving 1,028,362 persons. While most of the early effort was in the South, many drought victims were brought into the program in March 1935.

The Subsistence Homesteads Division was part of the "back-to-the-land" movement and had been authorized in the National Industrial Recovery Act (Section 208, Title II). It sought to combine part-time wage work with subsistence farming and to encourage industrial decentralization into rural or semirural areas.

19. The provisions included were in part based on the recommendations of the President's Farm Tenancy Committee, which brought out its report in 1937, and in part on the activities which had been carried on by the Resettlement Administration.

of congressional opposition and of difficulties encountered within the programs themselves. During the war years both rural rehabilitation and tenant-purchase expenditures were reduced.

Rural Rehabilitation

The rural rehabilitation loan program constituted the most significant change in lending practice and general philosophy. It was an approach designed to bring about a positive and guided change rather than merely to preserve existing farm structure and methods of operation. Though often criticized in respect to individual cases, and even in principle, the procedure appears to have widespread public and congressional support, and has apparently become a rather settled feature of the farm program.

The first step in making a loan of this kind is the preparation of a plan for increasing the productivity, income and level of living of a farm family whose financial status is such that it cannot borrow through ordinary credit channels. Such a plan may call for increased use of fertilizer, more or better livestock, a change in kind of product, enlargement of the farm, the use of more machinery or some combination of these. For some families, the need is for more productive land resources to be acquired either through rental or purchase.

These changes usually require both additional capital and guidance in the effective use of borrowed funds. The fact that loans can be made for carrying out such improvements provides a powerful incentive for accepting the guidance that goes with them. The later supervision not only helps to bring about the improvements agreed on but makes it more likely that the loans will be repaid when due.

Changing Emphasis in the Rehabilitation Program

During the 1930s the emphasis in rural rehabilitation was largely on getting destitute farm families onto a self-supporting basis, or at least onto a basis where less public aid would be required. The first requirement was to enable them to continue operation on what was virtually a subsistence basis. Increased production for home use was strongly stressed.

This effort to help the families achieve self-support was gradually merged with that of increasing their ability to obtain credit from other sources. During World War II the emphasis shifted to increased production of food for the market, and thus toward a commercial rather than a subsistence type of agriculture. In the postwar years a further change has occurred. The principal effort now is in the direction of correcting chronic difficulties which keep many low-income farm families poor and inefficient.

The methods in the current program are similar to those originally devised under the Emergency Relief Administration and the Resettlement Administration, though some restrictions have been imposed by the Congress and some improvements have been made on the basis of experience. Better trained personnel has been developed and the emphasis now is more on upgrading inefficient and underfinanced farmers and less on procedures designed to keep farmers off the relief rolls. The principal legislative changes, after 1937, are those contained in the Farmers Home Administration Act of 1946 (60 *Stat.* 1062) and in the supplementary act passed in 1951.[20] These resulted in part from the very critical attitude which marked the congressional investigation of the Farm Security Administration in 1943 and 1944.[21]

Criticisms of the Rehabilitation Program

Critics of the rural rehabilitation program objected to it as being unduly paternalistic, and some of the borrowers objected to the amount of supervision and direction they were required to accept. Farmers eligible to obtain credit through the regular credit agencies, in general the larger and more successful farmers, tended to be skeptical of the merits of the "soft credit" programs and in some areas the farm organizations opposed them. However, in recent years most of the farm groups have come to have a more tolerant attitude toward them, provided the recipients are "graduated" into the use of regular commercial types of credit and are not permitted to continue to use loans of the subsidized type after they have become eligible to obtain credit through the more orthodox agencies. One group, the Farmers' Union, has expressed strong approval of loans of this type and urges that they be given a larger place in the government's program of aid to agriculture.

Such loans and the supervision associated with them undoubtedly involve more paternalism than has been customary in American agriculture. However, some such type of action appears to be the only alternative to a continuing state of poverty for a large group of low-income farm families, with its concomitant low productivity and waste of manpower. It is not so much a provision of more assistance to this group than to others as the granting of aid in a different form.

The larger, better established and more successful farmers tend much more generally to use the agricultural extension services, the facilities of the Farm Credit Administration and the various other agricultural services provided partly or wholly at government expense. In addition, considerable aid is given to them through price-supporting activities, help

20. 65 *Stat.* 197.
21. The criticisms were aimed principally, however, at the resettlement activities rather than at the rehabilitation loan program or the tenant-purchase feature. The rehabilitation loans were less at variance with past policies and methods. When first initiated, they were similar to the drought relief loans of the 1920s and the crop and feed loans of the early 1930s, but with longer-run objectives, more supervision and more effort to improve farming rather than merely to carry it through a period of acute emergency.

in recruiting labor, soil conservation payments and so on. The low-income group reached by the rehabilitation loan program does not use or profit from the activities mentioned above to the same extent as do the larger, commercial farmers. Hence, if a comparable amount of assistance is to be given them, it must be through a different kind of service which is especially suited to the needs of this group.

Resettlement Activities

The resettlement phase of the program, which was the focus of the major attack on Farm Security Administration policies in 1943 and 1944, broke much more sharply with traditional policy than did the rehabilitation activities. It was basically a carry-over from the years of extreme depression when all sorts of experiments were being tried in an effort to stabilize and rehabilitate destitute farm families.

The program took a number of forms. In part it was an effort to relocate families moved off the submarginal lands bought up by the Resettlement Administration for conversion to other uses. More generally, however, the aim was to establish landless farmers and farm wage workers in permanent homes on the land. A secondary objective was to provide temporary or permanent housing for such families. The procedures used included the establishment of cooperative farm communities, land-leasing associations, camps for migrants, and a number of other unfamiliar corporate and cooperative undertakings.

Such experiments had been undertaken in the United States at various times before, mostly on a private basis and by idealistic or religious groups. A similar plan was tried by California in the early 1920s, in its Durham and Delhi colonies, and some minor ventures of this kind had been undertaken by the federal government in its efforts to rehabilitate partly disabled veterans after World War I. Almost without exception, the effort to establish group living and production of this type in American agriculture has been a failure.

In these projects, as elsewhere, there was a nearly universal desire on the part of the participants to own or at least to control the land they worked, and to be free of group or governmental supervision.[22] The advantages of access to larger-scale mechanical equipment and better housing were not sufficient to offset this desire for independence and self-direction. Furthermore, some of the project managers were inexpe-

22. The reasons for failure were complex and included many psychological factors as well as economic ones. Edward C. Banfield, on the basis of a study of the Casa Grande project in Arizona, concluded that attempting to bring about change by forming new institutions instead of using old ones requires much too great an investment in leadership, an asset the projects did not have and probably could not get at the pay scales available. The settlers were unable to adapt themselves to cooperative living (except in one Indian settlement) and continually struggled among themselves to gain power and status. See Edward C. Banfield, *Government Project*, The Free Press, Glencoe, Illinois, 1951, especially Chapter 15.

rienced and lacked business judgment. Costs of construction were high and a great deal of development work had to be done, much of it with relief help, which was high in cost per unit of output.

Generally speaking, the efforts to rehabilitate families in place and in accordance with traditional American patterns of operation were much more successful than the resettlement undertakings. Some of the resettlement projects would no doubt have appeared more successful had they had more time to become established and to increase their efficiency, especially with the upsurge of farm prices which occurred in the 1940s. However, there is little evidence that such a plan of production and living would have been continuously satisfying to American farm families, even with better incomes and a more successful financial showing for the projects themselves. Many congressmen and farmers were hostile to the projects almost from the beginning, and many of the families settled on them chose to leave and seek other opportunities as soon as conditions permitted.

Congressional and Farmer Opposition

Congressional opposition to the group farming activities began to appear shortly after the first projects were initiated. This phase of the Resettlement Administration program was criticized sharply in the congressional committee hearings of 1937, when the Bankhead-Jones bill was under consideration, but that act, when passed, authorized the Secretary of Agriculture to continue such of these activities as might be necessary for the completion of projects already under way and within the limits of funds already provided. Much stronger criticism developed later.

During the late 1930s the Congress continued to exert pressure to eliminate the cooperative farming projects, or at least to prevent the creation of new ones. This pressure appeared chiefly in the hearings and in directives in the appropriation acts. It brought about some changes in the program but did not bring it to a halt as many of the congressional representatives and farm organization leaders desired. An interim type of organization known as a land-leasing association was tried out.

Land-Leasing Associations

The Farm Security Administration began experimenting with land-leasing associations in 1939. These were cooperatives which leased land in relatively large tracts from owners and in turn leased small units to the members of the cooperatives. Some involved the 99-year leases which were later sharply criticized. The operating capital needed was obtained by borrowing from the Farm Security Administration.

The land-leasing associations, mainly in the South, were operated under a manager and usually had also a full-time home supervisor. They supplied many of the services customarily provided by plantation owners.

In all, 52 land-leasing associations were formed with about 2,000 members and 136,000 acres of land. They were mostly in Arkansas and Louisiana but some were established in Mississippi, Virginia, North Dakota, Utah, New Mexico and Texas.

The Select Committee set up by the Congress in 1943 to investigate the Farm Security Administration held that these associations were established as substitutes for the resettlement projects and that they were "created and financed in violation of law." [23] The appropriation act of 1944 forbade the formation of additional land-leasing associations and required discontinuance of those already established.[24]

At the conclusion of its hearings in 1944, the Select Committee presented a very critical report in which it commented as follows on the resettlement phase of the Farm Security program:

> They established, maintained and operated communities and villages in rural and suburban areas, built and maintained streets, roads and highways, shops, stores and warehouses, hotels and inns, recreational halls and community houses and playgrounds, and other places of amusement. They built power plants and water systems. They built hospitals and rest homes, sewage-disposal plants and irrigation systems, creameries and canneries, packing plants, and factories for the manufacturing of numerous articles, including pants for men and full-fashioned hosiery for women. They built and financed dairies and grain elevators, cotton gins, potato houses, and other storage facilities. They provided modernly equipped homes, with all conveniences and facilities. They made loans and grants of Federal funds according to their own wishes and desires and for just about everything from marriage licenses to burial expenses. They provided funds for the payment of lodge dues and poll taxes, for work stock, tractors and plows, and for farm implements of every kind and description. They furnished money with which to buy cows and sows, and bulls and boars, and with which to pay for family subsistence and for feed, seed, and fertilizer, and for the harvesting and marketing of crops. They provided funds for the purchase of stock in corporations and for the payment of dues in cooperatives.[25]

By 1946, when the Farmers Home Administration Act was passed, opposition had become so vigorous and general that a requirement that

23. FSA did not rely on the Bankhead-Jones Act for authority but instead cited a number of appropriation acts. The Comptroller General found that the expenditures were not authorized by law. The Attorney General, in an opinion on the matter, asserted that the Comptroller General was in error. The principal controversy was over the meaning of "rural rehabilitation" as used in the relevant appropriation acts. Since the case was never adjudicated in the courts, no final determination was made. However, the Congress eventually clarified the matter by directing that the land-leasing associations be discontinued.

For opinions of the Comptroller General, see Ops. Comp. Gen. No. B23881, March 5, 1942, pp. 90–99. The Attorney General's opinion is given in U.S. House Committee on Agriculture, Select Committee to Investigate the Activities of the Farm Security Administration, *Activities of the Farm Security Administration*, Hearings, 1944, Part 1, pp. 72–76.

24. For a fuller account of the activities of these associations see Olaf F. Larson and Associates, *Ten Years of Rural Rehabilitation in the United States*, Bureau of Agricultural Economics, July 1947, pp. 218–23.

25. *Activities of the Farm Security Administration*, p. 7.

all community projects and others of similar character be liquidated was included in the legislation. This provision not only required that the group farming ventures be liquidated but also directed the Secretary of Agriculture to dispose of farm labor camps.

Number and Kinds of Cooperatives Set Up

In 1941 the Farm Security Administration reported 78 community-type farm projects, planned for about 6,000 families. Facilities for about 5,000 families were then completed and in use. The capital investment as of June 30, 1941 was given as $43,780,582.74 or about $7,300 per family of planned capacity.[26] In addition $36.3 million had been invested in "scattered-farms-type" projects, $6.9 million in "subsistence-home-stead-type" projects, $36.2 million in suburban projects and $15.5 million in "stranded group" projects.[27]

The Farm Security Administration also made loans to various other types of cooperatives. These were reported in 1944 as having amounted to $25,740,771.[28] Of these loans, $4,954,190 were transferred to the Federal Public Housing Authority, apparently under authority contained in Executive Order 9070, dated February 24, 1942. Only $146,035 or about 3 per cent of this amount had been repaid at the time of transfer. On the other $20,786,581, repayments as of December 31, 1943 amounted to $2,749,438 or 13 per cent.[29]

Most of these cooperatives were small; they were mainly associations for buying bulls, machinery, feed and so on. The loans made to them, though numerous, were not of large size. The Farm Security Administration was frequently criticized for creating a multiplicity of small insignificant cooperatives, each to perform a specific function, when apparently a smaller number of more general cooperatives would have served equally well or better. As of the end of June 1943 there were about 4,000 such small cooperatives, financed in part through loans and partly by

26. *Report of the Administrator of the Farm Security Administration, 1941,* p. 34. As of June 30, 1943, 4,647 of the 9,223 units in the farm projects had been sold. All farms on 19 of the projects were sold to residents. Sixteen projects were being sold as surplus land (some of them undeveloped). Eight of the projects were being transferred to other federal agencies and one had been leased to the War Relocation Authority as a relocation center for Japanese internees. *Annual Report of the Farm Security Administration, 1942–1943,* p. 22. Liquidation of the projects was continued over the succeeding years and by June 30, 1946 more than 8,700 of the units had been sold or transferred.

27. *Report of the Administrator* (1941), p. 33.

28. *Activities of the Farm Security Administration,* pp. 15–16.

29. The Farmers Home Administration reported in 1947 that it had continued to work with these cooperatives and that by June 30, 1947, 212 of the associations (out of 446) had repaid their loans in full. One hundred fifteen were meeting their payments satisfactorily and 119 had been liquidated or were in process of liquidation. These figures do not include land-leasing and purchasing associations or water facilities associations. The making of new direct loans had been discontinued as of June 30, 1943. See U.S. Farmers Home Administration, *Strengthening the Family Farm,* Report on Activities of the Farmers Home Administration in the 1946–47 Fiscal Year, 1947, p. 9.

means of grants.[30] Some apparently received only supervisory assistance, not loans.

Medical Care Provided

Administrators of the rural rehabilitation programs soon became convinced that poor health was one of the causes of the inability of many of the low-income farmers to make progress. Medical surveys rather generally supported that view. Few of the families were able to pay for corrective medical service at customary prices. Efforts were made to overcome this handicap by setting up cooperative arrangements with county medical associations.[31] These provided that families would pay $15 to $45 per year into the hands of a trustee. Medical service was provided by cooperating doctors and the funds received were prorated among them on the basis of services performed. The arrangement provided a modest level of medical service at less than standard rates of compensation to the doctors. The number of such associations, in 1942, was 787 and the number of families served 109,000. Thereafter both the number of units and the number of families served declined.[32]

The public expense involved was not large, but the plan did, of course, depend on the willingness of the doctors to participate on this basis. Such cooperation was given rather freely during the depression years but became more difficult to obtain as prosperity returned and the shortage of doctors became more acute.

Migratory-Labor Camps and Labor Homes

The migratory-labor camp program was initiated in 1936, as a means of providing shelter and better sanitary conditions for some of the large number of agricultural workers and displaced farm families then on the move. Many of the residents of these camps were from the "dust-bowl" areas and from localities where rapid mechanization was reducing the opportunities and need for croppers and hired farm workers. Others were migratory workers for whom on-farm housing was not available in the cash-crop areas. The influx of families of these types in some areas greatly exceeded both the available housing facilities and the labor needs of the farms. As a result many migrants were living in temporary shelters of the most primitive kind and under conditions that constituted a health threat not only to the migrants themselves but to the community.

The activities relating to this group were primarily a phase of the relief program, though the facilities provided did supplement to some extent those maintained on the farms and in the farm communities. They

30. Larson, *op. cit.*, pp. 213–14.
31. During 1933 and 1934 medical service was provided by FERA at public expense, to families on relief. Beginning in 1934 the attempt was made to shift rural rehabilitation "clients" to the cooperative arrangement. Actually, however, much of this cost continued to be supplied from public funds by way of the loan and grant programs.
32. For a more detailed explanation see Larson, *op. cit.*, pp. 230–53.

consisted principally of minimum-standard camp facilities with supplementary aids in the form of recreation halls and medical services.[33] The program was primarily a means of meeting a desperate emergency rather than part of a long-term solution of the problem.

In the early period the camps were viewed with considerable disfavor by many farmers in the communities in which they were established, partly because they were regarded as "hotbeds of radicalism" and "havens for loafers." However, the main body of migrant farm families, that which moved from the dust-bowl areas to the Pacific Coast states, was absorbed in the receiving economies at an unexpectedly rapid rate. Even as early as 1940, this group of migrants had ceased to be a major problem. As war activity quickened, the situation in most farming areas, especially those in the West, changed from one of excess labor supply to one of labor shortages.

Financial Results of the Resettlement Program

The financial outcome of the cooperative farming and related ventures as summarized by the Farm Security Administration in 1946 was as follows:

Returns under liquidation (farm units sold)
Investment in farm units sold	$53,067,803
Return on farm units sold	31,700,498
Loss	$21,367,305 [a]

Returns under liquidation (community facilities sold)
Investment in facilities sold (as of June 30, 1946)	$ 5,793,845
Return on facilities sold	3,511,424
Loss on facilities sold	$ 2,282,421
Assets still to be liquidated	$12,055,756
Estimated loss on assets still to be liquidated	$ 4,843,821 [b]

a. As of June 30, 1946, the number of unsold farm units had been reduced to 630 consisting of 39,444 acres. Eighty-five of the 152 projects had been completely liquidated, including disposition of community facilities. Project property costing $3,761,882 had been transferred to other agencies. (Data from U.S. Department of Agriculture, *Explanatory Statements of Work under Appropriations and Supplemental Funds, Fiscal Year 1948*, Vol. II, p. 271 and Tables XX, XXI and XXII.)

b. On basis of same percentage loss as for assets sold earlier. This is probably low since the best units would naturally be sold first. However, values of real property were rising rapidly in this period and this strengthening of the market may have offset the poorer quality of the remaining assets.

33. As of 1941 the facilities provided under this program consisted of 6,911 shelters, 5,975 tent platforms and 2,183 labor homes located in some fifty camps in Arizona, Arkansas, California, Colorado, Florida, Idaho, Michigan, Missouri, Oregon, Texas and Washington. As of that time, they involved a capital investment of about $15 million. (*Report of the Administrator of the Farm Security Administration, 1941*, pp. 38–39.) Later expenditures, partly associated with war activities, brought the total outlay up to more than $22 million.

A small start had been made in providing "labor homes" for farm workers, that is, small separate houses for rental, together with garden plots for some production of food.

The over-all figures on investment and realization are:

Investment as of June 30, 1946	$70,917,404
Returns from assets sold	35,211,922
Total loss on the projects (as of June 30, 1946)	33,079,659
Loss on assets sold	23,649,726
Estimated loss on remaining assets	4,843,821
Operating loss	4,586,112 [34]

Most of the funds used for these projects, except for administrative expenses and technical assistance, were committed before the Farm Security Administration was created. Its function in respect to them was therefore largely that of administering projects launched before it came into existence. The funds used came mainly from allocations made by the President from Federal Emergency Relief Administration appropriations. After 1937, and more especially from 1943 on, the projects were in process of liquidation.[35]

Cost of Migratory-Labor Camps

The camps-for-migrants program involved expenditures of about $22 million distributed over a period of eight years as follows:[36]

1935–36	$ 577,262
1937	342,097
1938	1,060,738
1939	5,077,303
1940	4,926,720
1941	4,417,693
1942	4,214,266
1943	1,389,085
Total	$22,005,165

In 1943 the camps were transferred to the Office of Labor under the War Food Administration. They were used during the war in the federal program for increasing the supply of farm labor, including foreign

34. Operating costs and returns to June 30, 1946 were:

Cumulative operating expense	$12,916,935
Operating income	8,330,823
Loss on operations	$ 4,586,112

35. Technical assistance apparently was supplied from general administrative and technical assistance funds shown as costs in the summaries of Resettlement and Farm Security Administration expenditures.

36. U.S. Senate Committee on Appropriations, *Agricultural Appropriation Bill for 1947*, Hearings, p. 400.

workers brought in and prisoners of war. At the close of the war the Secretary of Agriculture was directed to transfer these camps to state or local units of government or sell them to cooperative associations of farmers established for the purpose of taking them over and operating them.

In general, the states and counties were reluctant to take on this responsibility, and the farm employer groups did not choose to take them over. The camps, for the most part, had not been built as permanent structures. After ten years or more of hard use, considerable expenditure would have been required to rehabilitate them. Most farmers preferred to put such funds as they were prepared to spend on labor housing into structures on their own farms.

The status of the camps remained indefinite until 1950, when, under the terms of the Housing Act of 1950, they were transferred to the Public Housing Administration. This transfer, made on June 19, 1950, included 39 labor camps—20 in California, 8 in Florida, 3 in Arizona, 3 in Texas, 2 in Oregon and one each in Colorado, Idaho and Washington.[37]

State Rural Rehabilitation Corporations

Though virtually inactive as separate entities from 1935 on, the state rural rehabilitation corporations continued through 1950 to have title to certain assets previously transferred to them by the Federal Emergency Relief Administration. The Comptroller General's ruling that funds made available under the Relief Appropriation Act of 1935 could not be disbursed through these state corporations placed them in an anomalous position. When the Resettlement Administration set up its own program it became responsible for the expenditure of all federal funds made available for rural rehabilitation except those already assigned to the state corporations.

The President requested that the states enter into agreements whereby the assets of the state corporations would be transferred in trust to the federal government for administration by the Resettlement Administration. Under this arrangement, though the loans and grants made from state rural rehabilitation corporation funds were of the same general

37. At the time of transfer the 39 camps contained 9,606 units. They were all being operated under revocable use permits by county agencies, nonprofit associations of farmers or local housing authorities. The Public Housing Administration has had difficulty in disposing of these camps and still holds many of them. The properties were in need of extensive repair. As of 1950 it was estimated that $2.5 million of government expenditure would be required to rehabilitate them.

Under the Housing Act of 1950 the Public Housing Administration has responsibility for improvement of nonfarm housing in rural as well as urban areas, while the Secretary of Agriculture is charged with administering the provisions of the act relating to on-farm housing. There is apparently no currently active public housing program for rural nonfarm people.

nature as those made directly by the Resettlement Administration and the Farm Security Administration, they were kept in separate accounts as revolving funds. The total amount of loans made with funds of the state corporations to June 30, 1953 was $181,752,527. As of that date, the status of repayments and interest collections was as follows:[38]

Collections	$121,436,262
Write-offs and judgments	28,230,510
Interest due	24,766,752
Interest collected	16,495,132

This operation was part of the relief program initiated in the worst stages of the depression and does not constitute a significant phase of the longer-term agricultural program. The functions for which it was intended have now been take over by other agencies. Under an act of 1950 (64 *Stat.* 98) the Secretary of Agriculture was authorized to liquidate the corporations within a period of three years from May 3, 1950. The states might apply for return of the funds, under an agreement to use them for rehabilitation purposes. In that event, the Secretary may accept and administer the funds in such states (in effect, continue the present arrangement). Otherwise the funds are to be returned to the United States Treasury. There does not appear to be any strong case for continuing this cumbersome arrangement. The retention of separate fund status and/or administration by the states involves extra administrative costs, unnecessary bookkeeping and confusion in records.[39]

Farm Debt Adjustment

Efforts to bring about the adjustment of farm debts were begun informally in 1933.[40] In the fall of that year, the Governor of the Farm Credit Administration suggested to the governors of the various states that they appoint state farm debt adjustment committees which in turn would nominate and organize county debt adjustment committees. The work was on an informal basis until 1937, when it became official under the re-enacted Frazier-Lemke Amendment to the Federal Bankruptcy Act.[41]

38. Data from FHA budget officer. Administrative costs are not included as these are not reported separately. They are included elsewhere in the costs for the rural rehabilitation program as a whole.

39. The principal reason for not terminating the arrangement is the reluctance of the states to turn the funds back to the federal Treasury. Though the Farmers Home Administration has arrangements for administering them and is doing so, there appears to be little if any advantage either to the states or to the federal government in continuing them as separate funds.

40. Beginnings were made locally in some states even before that time.

41. The first Frazier-Lemke Amendment, passed on June 28, 1934, was declared unconstitutional in *Louisville Joint Stock Land Bank* v. *Radford*, 295 U.S. 555 (1935). It was later repassed in modified form, and was upheld in *Wright* v. *Vinton Branch of Mountain Trust Bank of Roanoke*, 300 U.S. 440 (1937).

In the early years, the procedure was to try, through the good offices of a "neutral" committee, to bring into conference farmers faced with foreclosure and the creditors to whom their debts were owed. Efforts were then made to work out a plan whereby the farmer would pay equitably to his various creditors as much as appeared reasonably possible. The creditors would in turn extend the loan, reduce the rate of interest, forego interest for a time, or adjust the principal amount of the debt to the size of refinancing loan that could be obtained from the federal credit agencies. The aim was to enable the creditors to get about as much as they were likely to get anyway, and at the same time permit the farmer to retain his farm.

Farm Credit Administration loans to the extent of 75 per cent of appraised "normal value" of the farm were available. These often amounted to nearly 100 per cent of what the farm could be sold for in the very depressed land market then existing. In many cases, liquid funds were more useful to the creditor than a foreclosed farm of potentially greater value. Many creditors were therefore willing to make some adjustment of principal in order to get cash in place of the frozen loans.

The Frazier-Lemke Amendment substituted a plan whereby a farmer threatened with foreclosure could apply to the courts and, if the court approved, obtain a stay of up to five years. During this period the farm would be operated by the farmer under supervision of the court, only the net return above costs of operation being paid to the creditors.[42]

Under this arrangement, paid county conciliators, responsible to the courts, gradually took over most of the functions of the unofficial farm debt adjustment committees, though the state and county committees rather generally remained in existence until about 1940. The Resettlement Administration and the Farm Security Administration, from about 1935 on, supplied funds for the expenses of the farm debt adjustment committees and for employment of county conciliators.[43]

Between 1936 and 1943, cases officially reported as adjusted under the program numbered 187,272 with a downward adjustment in principal of $109,477,777 on a face amount of $505,202,861. In the early years, much of the action taken was informal and consisted of voluntary concessions in respect to time of payments and rate of interest rather than reductions of principal.

The first annual report of the Resettlement Administration gives an estimate that the cost of this work was then running at a rate of about $1.6 million per year. A staff equivalent to 600 to 900 full-time employees was assigned to the debt adjustment work in the late 1930s, in

42. For a fuller explanation of the program and its results see Larson, op. cit., pp. 253–62.

43. Responsibility for aiding with farm debt adjustment work was transferred from the Farm Credit Administration to the Resettlement Administration on August 31, 1935. After June 30, 1943, debt adjustment activity under the Farm Security Administration was restricted to borrowers from that agency.

addition to the approximately 500 state and 12,500 county committeemen who served without compensation.

The over-all cost to the government of the farm debt adjustment program was in the order of $12 to $15 million. Like many of the other depression-born activities, it was continued beyond the time when there was significant need for it. The major refinancing job in agriculture had been carried through by about 1938. These heavy expenditures for farm debt adjustment could probably have been tapered off at about that time without serious hardship to really meritorious debtors.

Tenant-Purchase Loans

The tenant-purchase loan program, initiated under Title I of the Bankhead-Jones Act of 1937, constitutes the major effort of recent years to increase the number of owner-operators and reduce the amount of tenancy. Concern over the increase in tenancy had been evident from the time suitable lands ceased to be available for homesteading.

The first attempt to increase owner-operation by government action, the Federal Land Bank Act of 1916, did not prove effective as a means to that end. The land banks became useful agencies in providing better credit facilities to borrowing farmers, but they had no important effect in converting tenants into owners. With the relatively high values placed on commercial farming units and the very conservative loans provided by the land banks, most tenant farmers did not have sufficient resources to make the necessary down payments for the purchase of farms.

The Farm Tenant Act was designed to overcome this difficulty by providing, to a selected group of tenants, loans amounting to 100 per cent of the value of the farm. The interest rate on these loans was 3 per cent and repayments were amortized over a period of forty years. The act authorized appropriations of $10 million for the fiscal year ending June 30, 1938, $25 million for 1939 and $50 million for each year thereafter.[44]

This feature of the program has been popular with the Congress and, in the main, has been successful financially. The percentage loaned exceeded the accepted standards of safe loan limits, but the recipients were so carefully selected and the conditions so favorable that nearly all factors have combined to make possible orderly progress in repaying the loans. Repayment was also presumably facilitated by the flexible payment plan authorized in the act. Under this provision, the borrower was expected to pay more than the scheduled amount if his income was above normal but might defer or reduce the payment if his income was unusually low because of low prices or low yields.

Since the applications for these loans have run at times as high as 20 or 30 for each loan that could be granted, the county committees charged

44. During the war years, expenditures were cut back sharply, amounting to only $30 million in 1943, $24 million in 1944 and $13 million in 1945.

with making the selections have tended to choose those with best prospects of success. These were the tenants who in all probability would be successful and probably would eventually become owners anyway. The situation of the great bulk of tenants could not be improved in this way, at least with the volume of funds likely to be provided. If funds were available on a much larger scale, so as to enable the majority of tenants to become owners, the prospect of loss would obviously become greater and the program would be almost certain to have an inflationary influence on land prices.[45]

During the early years of the program there was some tendency for these loans to cause young tenants to associate themselves with farm units that were too small for efficient operation. Though the original act did not place an upper limit on the size of loan that could be made, the agency found it advisable to place such limits in order to spread the benefits of the act as widely as possible and to avoid unwarranted favoring of a few individuals.[46] From 1941 to 1946 the appropriation acts limited the size of farms financed to the average value of farms in the county.[47]

The act of 1946 specified that the farm on which the loan is made should not when acquired or improved exceed "the average value of efficient, family-type farm-management units . . . in the county, parish, or locality where the farm is located." The agency continued to apply its own administratively established upper limits but the tendency has been to handle this in a more flexible and realistic way in recent years. Local administrators cannot authorize loans in excess of $12,000. State offices may go to $15,000. The national office has no specific upper limit, except the general legislative requirement that loans may not exceed the average value of an efficient family-type farm in the area.

Farmers Home Administration

The Farmers Home Administration Act of 1946 marked the end of the pioneering and experimental stage in providing aid for low-income farmers and gave recognition to this as an accepted and continuing part of the over-all national farm program. It did away with the more controversial activities, and at the same time recognized that the price sup-

45. The Farmers Home Administration does not, of course, contend or assume that the tenant-purchase program is a complete answer to the tenancy problem. However, the Congress has tended to ignore other approaches to the problem, apparently on the assumption that the tenant-purchase program will eventually solve it.

46. The 1937 act specified that the farms purchased must be large enough "to constitute an efficient farm-management unit and to enable a diligent farm family to carry on successful farming of a type which the Secretary deems can be successfully carried on in the locality in which the farm is situated." Bankhead-Jones Farm Tenant Act, Section 1(c).

47. In determining the average value of farms in the county, only farms of 30 acres or more were to be included.

port programs, which were of principal interest to the larger-scale, commercial farmers, could not, even if wholly acceptable and successful, contribute much to the well-being of some two million farmers whose earnings and levels of living would not thereby be improved materially.

Changes Made

The new act abolished the Farm Security Administration and provided the legislative authorization under which the Farmers Home Administration was created. The feed and seed, drought relief and crop and feed loans that had been administered by the Farm Credit Administration were transferred to the Farmers Home Administration for supervision and liquidation.

Later, under Public Law 38, 81st Congress, 1949 (63 *Stat*. 49), the assets and revolving fund of the Regional Agricultural Credit Corporation of Washington were transferred to the Secretary of Agriculture, who in turn assigned them to the Farmers Home Administration for use in making disaster loans. This action provided, in effect, a continuing stand-by arrangement whereby emergency loans can be made promptly to meet needs arising from specific, localized disasters such as severe droughts or floods.

These transfers removed from the Farm Credit Administration virtually all emergency features. That agency thus became more clearly and unequivocally a supplier of conservative, business-type farm credit. The action marked the culmination of a trend observable over a period of nearly twenty years during which the conservative lending activities were brought together and coordinated in one agency and the emergency and "welfare" credit operations were similarly grouped and coordinated in another agency.

The 1946 act directed that all labor supply centers, labor homes, labor camps and facilities formerly under the supervision of the Farm Security Administration or transferred to the War Food Administrator were to be liquidated.[48] Trust agreements relating to the state rural rehabilitation corporations were to be liquidated as soon as practical.[49]

Regional offices of the Farm Security Administration were to be liquidated by June 30, 1947 and the Secretary of Agriculture was specifically directed to liquidate "as expeditiously as possible" all resettlement projects. Lands suitable for farming were to be sold to individuals eligible to purchase them under the Bankhead-Jones Farm Tenant Act. The Secretary was prohibited from making any further loans to corporations

48. Their liquidation has been postponed from time to time by subsequent acts. Under the Public Housing Act of 1950 facilities still owned by the government were to be transferred to the Public Housing Administration for disposal.

49. As previously stated, an act of 1950 (64 *Stat*. 98) provided that the assets of these corporations might either be returned to the states or administered by the Secretary of Agriculture in behalf of the states.

or cooperatives or for any land-purchase or land-leasing program or for any collective or cooperative farming venture.

Major Programs Retained

On the positive side, the new act reaffirmed and continued the rehabilitation and tenant-purchase loan programs, but with some tightening of the requirements.[50] Initial rehabilitation loans, which under the new act are designated as "production and subsistence" loans, could not exceed $3,500 and could not be extended so as to total more than $5,000. They could not run for more than five years.[51] The interest rate was set at 5 per cent.

The provision for flexible payments on tenant-purchase loans was retained, but only for accumulations in advance of due dates, not for smaller payments than those due if funds had not been accumulated to offset them. That is, under the earlier plan a farmer was expected to pay more than the scheduled amount on principal and interest if income was above normal, but he could keep his loan in good standing by a payment of less than the scheduled amount if his income was below normal. Under the revised plan, he must accumulate excess credits before being allowed to carry his loan for a given year with a payment smaller than the amount scheduled.

The interest concession to this selected group of borrowers was also curtailed. Whereas under the earlier legislation the tenant-purchase borrower could continue to receive credit at less than the going rate on farm mortgage loans, the later act provides that when he has achieved an equity status such that he can borrow from the regular farm credit agencies, he is to transfer his loan to them.[52] For land-mortgage loans, this means that when the borrower has paid off principal to where he has an equity amounting to 35 per cent of the appraised value of the farm, he must apply for a loan from a federal land bank or some other established, conventional lender in his community. Recipients of production and subsistence loans are also expected to shift from this source of credit to regular loans from production credit associations or private banks as soon as they are eligible for these more normal types of credit.

Farm Enlargement Loans

The act of 1946 took a very important step forward in authorizing loans for farm enlargement and improvement. This implied a different

50. Under the Farmers Home Administration the tenant-purchase loans are called farm-ownership loans.

51. A later act, 65 *Stat.* 197 (August 23, 1951), raised these limits to $7,000 and $10,000, and increased the maximum repayment period to seven years.

52. Borrowers who received their loans under the earlier legislation cannot be required to change them to the terms and provisions prescribed in the later legislation. New loans must be written in accordance with the law as it now stands.

objective from that of the older-type tenant-purchase loan. The tenant-purchase and farm-ownership loans are intended to make owners out of tenants, whereas the farm enlargement or improvement loans are designed to raise the productivity and income of farmers who are already owners, but on such a small and poor scale that their economic situation may well be worse than that of tenant farmers.

This addition to the program was probably potentially the most important farm credit development of the 1940s. It not only has possibilities for helping to bring about the most needed types of change on several hundred thousand small farms, but makes it possible to aid large numbers of farmers at relatively small cost. When accompanied, if necessary, by a production and subsistence loan and some supervision and help in planning, this type of loan opens the way for a permanent improvement in the economic status of the farm family and lessens the likelihood of need for continuing assistance. At the same time the loan itself is likely to be more secure than the regular tenant-purchase loan since the equity margin is larger. Furthermore, these farmers are already established in their communities. Hence loans to them may involve less risk than those to farmers who have yet to establish themselves as owner-operators.

Provision for Insured Loans

The second major change was a provision for making insured loans through banks and other private lending agencies. This looked in the direction of using insured private funds for the bulk of the farm-ownership loans and supplementing them by a limited amount of direct lending of government funds. The plan is somewhat similar to that which the Federal Housing Administration uses in financing the purchase of urban homes. An interest rate of 2.5 per cent (3 per cent since June 1948) was allowed to the lending agency, while the borrower paid an additional one per cent for insurance and administration. An appropriation of $25 million was authorized for setting up an insurance fund,[53] and the amount of loans that could be insured during any one fiscal year was limited to $100 million.

Loans under this plan were limited to 90 per cent of appraised value. In this, too, the Federal Housing Administration precedent was followed rather than that of the Farm Security Administration. In order to make such loans more attractive to lenders, the Secretary of Agriculture is authorized to purchase the notes, on request of the lender, after a one-year period if the loan is in default, and after a period of not less than five years if the loan is not in default. After purchasing insured mortgages the Secretary may resell them.

53. Under this authorization only $1 million was appropriated in the Department of Agriculture Appropriation Act of 1948. As of June 30, 1953 the estimated assets of the fund were $2,563,000. See statement by the Department in U.S. Senate Committee on Appropriations, *Agricultural Appropriations for 1954*, Hearings, p. 737.

TABLE 15

Direct Loans [a] for Farm Purchase and Farm Enlargement and
Development, 1938–1953

Fiscal Year	Total Amount Loaned	Initial Loans		Subsequent Loans	
		Number	Amount	Number	Amount
Total	$391,152,296	56,576	$372,487,623	11,153	$18,664,673
1938	8,914,209	1,815	8,914,209	0	0
1939	23,248,713	4,131	23,087,791	293	160,922
1940	36,006,648	5,947	35,800,241	376	206,407
1941	45,673,795	8,139	45,508,944	243	164,851
1942	45,236,635	7,843	44,644,814	869	591,821
1943	27,464,524	4,556	25,608,149	1,861	1,856,375
1944	19,938,634	3,004	18,347,753	1,307	1,590,881
1945	11,181,240	1,763	10,559,314	552	621,926
1946	26,825,753	3,505	26,587,752	138	238,001
1947	43,492,461	5,489	41,682,243	1,082	1,810,218
1948	14,053,888	1,829	13,422,448	291	631,440
1949	14,755,530	1,867	13,739,182	491	1,016,348
1950	14,793,198	1,706	13,534,927	546	1,258,271
1951	21,724,155	2,017	18,717,598	1,366	3,006,557
1952	18,849,044	1,534	16,177,980	882	2,671,064
1953	18,993,869	1,431	16,154,278	856	2,839,591

Source: Farmers Home Administration.

a. Loans made under Title I, that is, appropriated funds. Excludes Farm Development loans made from "Loans, Grants and Rural Rehabilitation" funds and non-cash Project Liquidation loans.

Tenant-Purchase and Farm-Ownership Loans Through 1950

Loans made under Title I of the Bankhead-Jones Farm Tenant Act of 1937, as amended, for purchase of farms by tenants, croppers and farm workers (and also, since 1946, for farm enlargement and development), reached a peak of $45.5 million loaned to 8,139 farmers in 1941. Thereafter, the number of new loans made declined during the war years and was down to 1,763 in 1945. Lending increased in 1946 and 1947, to $41.7 million, but declined sharply thereafter.[54] Between 1948 and 1953 the range has been $13.4–$18.7 million. (See Table 15.)

54. Since 1946 most of the direct farm-purchase loans have been made to veterans but only a small portion of the insured loans has gone to them. Veterans usually are less able than other borrowers to make the 10 per cent down payment. The percentages of direct and insured loans distributed to veterans were as follows:

Direct Loans [a]		Insured Loans	
1947	55		
1948	79	1948	17
1949	78	1949	28
1950	99	1950	32
1951	97	1951	30
1952	98	1952	22

a. U.S. House Committee on Appropriations, *Department of Agriculture Appropriations for 1954,* Hearings, Part 3, p. 1082.

Status of Tenant-Purchase "Direct Loan" Programs

The number of loans (initial only) made under the "direct loan" program through June 30, 1953 was 60,639. As of December 31, 1953 the status of the program was as follows (figures in millions): [55]

Total amount loaned	$437.6 [a]
Repayments of principal	244.6
Amounts written off or reduced to judgment	1.5
Loans outstanding	191.6
Cost of program (direct loans only)	
Cost of funds used	50.0
Administrative expenses [b]	34.0
Write-offs and judgments	1.5
Expected future losses on loans then outstanding [c]	1.9
Total	$ 87.4
Less interest received	67.3
Net cost	$ 20.1 [d]

a. Includes supplemental as well as initial loans.

b. Administrative expenses from 1938 to 1947 from U.S. Budget. From 1947 to 1953 expenses estimated as 10 per cent of the total expense on all loans administered by FHA.

c. Loans cannot be written off until they have been delinquent five years. Thus the actual write-offs as of a given date are smaller than the amount of loss recognized as probable.

d. This does not take account of risk costs assumed which may not yet be evident, though the $1.9 million item covers this in part. However, the repayment record to date has been good. Loan maturities and delinquencies are not given in the published reports, but available information indicates that repayments as a whole are about 23 per cent greater than maturities. These include excess payments made by borrowers who are ahead of schedule, but this does not mean that there are no delinquencies.

Experience with Insured Farm-Ownership Loans

Since there was no provision for insured loans until this feature was included in the Farmers Home Administration Act of 1946, experience under this plan has been limited. The amount loaned under it was increasing at a moderate rate until the stiffening of interest rates in 1951 made this outlet for funds less attractive to banks than it had been. As of this writing, lending under this provision is in very limited amounts even though the interest rate to lenders has been increased from 2.5 to 3 per cent and more liberal arrangements have been made whereby the Secretary of Agriculture may take over nondelinquent loans at the request of the lender after the expiration of a five-year period.

The plan contemplates a gradual de-emphasis of direct lending from appropriated funds and an increasing use of private funds for the purchase of farms. The requirement of a 10 per cent down payment also

55. Based on data supplied by the Farmers Home Administration.

implies a more conservative loan policy. The shift toward reliance on private funds, if successfully carried out, presumably will mean that a larger volume of lending will be possible than if sole reliance must be on the amounts the Congress is willing to appropriate for direct loans. The number of loans increased from 338 in 1948 to 2,191 in 1950 and amounts loaned, from $2.4 million in 1948 to $17.6 million in 1951 under the insured loan program. Thereafter there was a marked decrease in both numbers and amounts of such loans. (See Table 16.)

TABLE 16

INSURED FARM-OWNERSHIP LOANS, 1948–1953

Fiscal Year	Total Amount Loaned	Initial Loans		Subsequent Loans	
		Number	Amount	Number	Amount
Total	$65,785,891	7,982	$65,446,736	105	$339,155
1948	2,412,837	338	2,412,837	0	0
1949	7,937,241	1,149	7,937,241	0	0
1950	16,586,859	2,191	16,579,689	2	7,170
1951	17,596,050	2,150	17,555,650	16	40,400
1952	10,563,677	1,105	10,448,554	39	115,123
1953	10,689,227	1,049	10,512,765	48	176,462

Source: Farmers Home Administration.

The one half of one per cent allowed for administration of the insured loan program has not thus far been sufficient to cover the expense of making these loans. Income from this charge was estimated at about $230,000 for 1952 and total expense at $980,000. The difference has been made up out of general administrative funds of the Farmers Home Administration.[56]

As of 1953 the insurance fund, to which one half of one per cent is assigned, had taken in more than had been disbursed in payments on delinquent installments. However, the program was still too new to afford dependable information about the probable experience over a longer period or in times when farm incomes are less favorable.

MINOR PROGRAMS UNDER FSA AND FHA

Both under the Farm Security Administration and under the Farmers Home Administration there have been a number of smaller programs, some continuing, others carried on only in certain periods.

A water facilities program, applicable to the 17 western states, was begun in 1938, under an act passed in 1937 (50 *Stat.* 869). Loans are made at 3 per cent to farmers "who are unable to get the credit they

56. See *Department of Agriculture Appropriations for 1952*, Hearings, Part 2, pp. 846–47.

TABLE 17

WATER FACILITY LOANS OBLIGATED, 1939–1953

Fiscal Year	Total Amount Loaned	Initial Loans		Subsequent Loans	
		Number	Amount	Number	Amount
Total	$28,089,440	14,424	$25,930,923	2,481	$2,158,517
1939	276,658	311	276,658	0	0
1940	472,218	911	472,218	0	0
1941	806,413	805	659,438	379	146,975
1942	978,442	1,376	883,013	293	95,429
1943	792,843	900	593,569	468	199,274
1944	755,332	646	548,840	335	206,492
1945	778,470	1,016	716,102	91	62,368
1946	1,040,399	1,062	971,350	105	69,049
1947	1,435,738	912	1,296,741	156	138,997
1948	1,484,237	782	1,392,160	92	92,077
1949	1,497,891	759	1,342,011	90	155,880
1950	2,950,150	1,207	2,777,379	92	172,771
1951	3,854,695	1,350	3,672,414	109	182,281
1952	4,966,015	1,174	4,658,985	142	307,030
1953	5,999,939	1,213	5,670,045	129	329,894

Source: Farmers Home Administration.

need from other sources." Two kinds of loans are made, loans for farmstead facilities and loans for irrigation facilities. Engineering, legal and other technical services are provided to the borrowers. Administrative expenses and costs of technical assistance are not reported separately, but are included in over-all administrative costs of the agencies in charge of the program. The amounts loaned initially have been small, rising from $276,658 in 1939 to about $5.7 million in 1953. (See Table 17.)

The status of the water facilities loan program as of December 31, 1953 was as follows: [57]

Total loans made, 1939–1953	$30,977,983
Matured loans	12,370,918
Repayments	12,322,094
Write-offs	13,494
Estimated future losses	435,000
Interest received	1,795,303

Flood restoration assistance was provided in 1943 and early 1944 under a special appropriation of $15 million made in the summer of

57. Data from the Farmers Home Administration.

1943 (57 *Stat.* 537, 542). Loans and grants were made to farmers who could not get credit from other sources, in order that their properties might be brought back into production. The 1943 act applied only to fiscal 1944 (except that the unspent balance was made available for the following year). Two kinds of loans were made, production loans, for periods up to ten years, and real estate loans, which might run for twenty years. By the end of 1946 some 4,000 farmers had received loans amounting to $2,762,415 for production purposes. Twenty real estate loans amounting to $41,360 had been made, and grants had been provided in the amount of $34,000. By the end of June 1946, $1,281,886 of principal had been repaid and interest payments amounting to $106,-314 had been made. The principal payments amounted to 87 per cent of maturities.[58]

Disaster Loan Revolving Fund

The act of April 6, 1949 (63 *Stat.* 43) which dissolved the Regional Agricultural Credit Corporation of Washington, D.C., gave the Secretary of Agriculture authority to make disaster loans to farmers and stockmen "where he finds that a production disaster has caused a need for agricultural credit not readily available from commercial banks, cooperative lending agencies or other responsible sources." The revolving fund and other assets of the Corporation were made available for this purpose.[59] Loans made from the fund under this authorization for the years 1949–1953 have ranged between $1.2 million and $43 million. As of December 31, 1953, collections amounted to about $74.5 million of the $118 million in matured loans. (See Table 18.)

58. *Annual Report of the Farm Security Administration for 1945–46*, p. 16. From 1946 on, the unpaid loans have been administered by the Farmers Home Administration along with other claims from programs no longer active.

59. The act was amended in 1953 (67 *Stat.* 149). The amendment authorized the Secretary of Agriculture to make loans to established farmers and stockmen affected by *economic* disasters as well as natural ones. Such loans may be made in areas designated by the President, but only on the basis of a finding by the Secretary of Agriculture that the economic disaster has caused a need for credit which cannot be met "for a temporary period from commercial banks, cooperative lending agencies, the Farmers Home Administration under its regular loan programs, or other responsible sources." The Secretary may prescribe rates of interest and terms for such loans.

In addition, the amendment authorizes for a period of two years special livestock loans which may be made to "established producers and feeders of cattle, sheep and goats (not including commercial feed lots)" if they have a good record of operations, have a reasonable prospect of working out their difficulties with supplemental financing and are temporarily unable to get credit. Such loans, if they exceed $50,000, must be approved by the Secretary. The legislation thus appears to contemplate relatively large loans to farmers and ranchers who operate on a considerable scale. The Secretary is also authorized, in areas designated by the President as eligible for disaster loans, to make available for seed and for livestock feeding commodities held by the Commodity Credit Corporation and to reimburse the Corporation for them to the extent that collections on such loans do not cover the cost of the commodities supplied.

TABLE 18

Disaster Loans, 1949–1953

Fiscal Year	Amount Loaned	Collections [a]	Administrative Expense
1949	$ 1,214,390	$ —	$ 22,402
1950	31,580,777	1,630,227	485,579
1951	20,394,180	23,030,675	1,034,288
1952	31,675,160	20,173,390	1,358,880
1953	43,099,739	29,703,909	1,920,765

Status of Loan Funds as of December 31, 1953

Principal advanced	$133,525,674
Principal matured	118,135,994
Write-offs and judgments	140,865
Estimated future losses	5,000,000
Interest collected	2,847,171

Sources: U.S. House Committee on Appropriations, *Department of Agriculture Appropriations for 1953,* Hearings, Part 2, p. 1161; data on status of loan funds from U.S. House Committee on Appropriations, *Department of Agriculture Appropriations for 1954,* Hearings, p. 1124, and FHA sources.

a. Interest included.

Status of Resettlement Administration and FSA Loans

The rural rehabilitation loan program was terminated as of October 31, 1946, when the assets and most of the activities of the Farm Security Administration were taken over by the newly created Farmers Home Administration. A similar program has been carried on under the Farmers Home Administration but under a different name and a different set of conditions, and with policies and objectives differing somewhat from those of the earlier period.

The loans now are referred to as "production and subsistence" loans, or, in shorter form, as "operating" loans, to distinguish them from the longer-term mortgage loans under the farm-ownership loan program. The data here shown pertain to rural rehabilitation loans made before November 1946 but they include repayments, interest collected and costs through 1953 (except costs of administration from November 1, 1946).[60]

This is to distinguish them from the later loans which are more representative of present policies and operating conditions. The financial results of the rehabilitation loan program carried on between 1935 and 1946 were, of course, adversely affected by the very depressed conditions of the 1930s. On the other hand, the repayment record was undoubtedly improved by the great increase in prices during the 1940s. The produc-

60. Administrative expenses relating to these loans are not reported separately by the Farmers Home Administration and are therefore included with the other costs of administering that agency. This, however, does not distort seriously the realities of the situation since loans of similar type are now being made by the Farmers Home Administration and will require expenditures for supervision and collection in later years.

tion and subsistence loan program of the Farmers Home Administration is discussed in a later section. Loans made by the Resettlement Administration and the Farm Security Administration, 1934–1947, totaled more than $1 billion. Nearly $889 million of the principal had been repaid by 1953. Of the remainder, $75 million had been written off or reduced to judgment, and estimated future losses amounted to $35 million. The net cost of the program, after deducting interest received, was about $300 million. (See Table 19.)

TABLE 19

FINANCIAL DATA [a] ON RESETTLEMENT ADMINISTRATION AND FARM SECURITY
ADMINISTRATION REHABILITATION LOANS, 1934–1953

(*Millions*)

Loans and repayments	
Matured principal	$1,004.4
Unmatured principal	.4
Total loans made	$1,004.8
Repayments of principal	$888.8
Loans outstanding	41.3
Loans written off or reduced to judgment	74.7
Total	$1,004.8
Approximate cost of program	
Write-offs and judgments [b]	$ 74.7
Estimated future losses	35.0
Cost of administration and technical assistance to	
borrowers [c]	237.0
Cost of funds used [d]	77.0
Total [e]	$423.7
Interest received	123.8
Net cost of program	$299.9

Source: Based on data supplied by the Farmers Home Administration.

a. It should be noted that the data here given do not include either feed and seed loans or loans made under the Federal Emergency Relief Administration. They pertain wholly to the types of loans officially classed as rehabilitation loans, that is, loans accompanied by planning and supervision.

b. Judgments are included with write-offs since most of them are probably not collectible.

c. To June 30, 1946. Administrative expenses for later years are included in Farmers Home Administration budget.

d. Includes cost of money used for water facilities, construction, flood and windstorm and wartime-adjustment loans handled by FSA and loans by State Corporation trust funds, but only to end of 1951.

e. There was in addition an unmeasurable but significant risk cost that was assumed by the government but did not have to be paid. The unexpected increase in farm prices and incomes that occurred after most of these loans were made probably caused repayments to be larger than they would have been otherwise. Had farm prices and incomes remained at about the level of 1940, or if they had returned to that level after 1946, the losses would no doubt have been greater than they were.

Supplementing the rehabilitation loan program was a sizable outlay for grants to borrowers, over and above the amounts of their loans, especially in the early years of the program. These grants were made ordinarily as a means of carrying out a plan of rehabilitation which involved expenditures that apparently could not be fully repaid out of the prospective earnings of the farm. During the depression years many of the grants were essentially relief payments to supplement family incomes while planned improvements were being put into effect. The amounts of such grants declined from $50 million in 1936–1937 to $42,000 in 1947. (See Table 20.)

TABLE 20

Grants Made to Rehabilitation Clients, 1936–1947

For Fiscal Year Ending June 30	Amounts [a]
Total	$152,757,052
1936 and 1937	50,259,191
1938	23,142,905
1939	22,718,939
1940	24,015,591
1941	16,993,464
1942	13,125,994
1943	1,735,557
1944	277,043
1945	196,898
1946	249,146
1947	42,324

Source: Farmers Home Administration.

a. These totals do not include grants made under the water facilities program in the years 1939–1943. These amounted to $390,962, of which $342,057 was from rural rehabilitation funds and $48,905 from appropriations made under the Pope-Jones Act (50 Stat. 869).

These grants were in part incentive or enabling payments somewhat comparable to the soil conservation payments discussed in Chapter 9. They were discontinued in 1947.[61]

Production and Subsistence Loans and Expenditures, 1947–1953

The act of 1946 did not change importantly the main features of either the rehabilitation loan program or that relating to the purchase of farms. However, the loans made from 1946 on can be looked upon as a new

61. More than $44 million, or about 28.5 per cent, of the total amount of grants went to North Dakota and South Dakota and about 8 per cent to California. Most of the remainder was about evenly divided among seven states: Nebraska, Kansas, Missouri, Alabama, Montana, Texas and Oklahoma. Some small amounts went to other states.

start in which the losses that had accrued as a result of the very abnormal depression and war years and the early experiments with new types of programs could be segregated and put in liquidation. Also, the policies relating to such loans were modified both by congressional directive and by administrative decision. Since 1946, loans have been made more cautiously and only to farm families believed to have reasonable prospect of developing successful, family-type farms that will make effective use of the family labor available.

The costs of administering the Farmers Home Administration include expenditures for servicing, collecting and supervising loans carried over from the older organizations. However, since these expenses are not reported separately, the over-all cost of administering the Farmers Home Administration program, including the servicing of old loans, is given as a single figure.

These old loan programs should, of course, be liquidated. Administrative costs for continuing them will soon run to more than the prospective recovery from them. Such of the borrowers as are eligible for refinancing under the current, more orderly loan programs should be transferred to them as soon as they reach a stage where that can be done legally. Loans that are definitely uncollectible should be written off or compromised, and the remnants of agencies now obsolete should be fully liquidated.

The total of new loans of the production and subsistence type made by the Farmers Home Administration from its inauguration to December 31, 1953 was $667,862,125. Repayments of principal had been made in the amount of $430,750,400 and write-offs and judgments totaled $1,909,152. Anticipated additional losses of principal have been estimated at about $22 million. The amount of interest collected through 1953 was $38,780,005.

Administrative costs of the agency for handling all loans, other than real estate loans but including technical aid and supervision, are as follows for the years since its inception:

1947 [a]	$23,045,878
1948	18,971,334
1949	21,260,134
1950	23,946,592
1951	26,238,990
1952	30,633,281
1953	29,536,942
Total	$173,633,154
Average per year	$ 24,804,736

a. Figures include expenses of administering the disaster loan fund.

Special Loans Made from the Disaster Loan Fund

The act of 1949 made special provision for loans to fur farmers. These, though not of the "disaster" type, were made from the revolving fund set up with Regional Agricultural Credit Corporation funds. Fur farm loans made to the end of June 1953 were as follows:

Amount loaned	$4,843,878
Principal matured	3,837,811
Principal collected	3,605,146
Interest collected	172,245

In addition, there was a small volume of lending on orchard properties as authorized in 1950 under Public Law 665 (64 *Stat.* 414). Advances under this act to June 30, 1953 amounted to $207,800, collections to $172,245 (practically 100 per cent of maturities) and interest payments to $3,501. For both fur and orchard loans the number of borrowers is very small, less than 350 in all.

COMMENTS AND CONCLUSIONS

The Rehabilitation Loan Program

Of the various loan programs initiated in recent years, the provision for rehabilitation loans constitutes probably the most significant change of policy. As compared with the earlier emergency lending operations, this new approach added three principal features: (1) a specific effort to diagnose the problems of the particular farm and farmer; (2) a recommended plan for overcoming the difficulties; and (3) continuing educational assistance of a more intensive and specialized kind than that provided by the agricultural extension services.

The approach is in terms of the farm as a whole rather than merely of some one enterprise on it. Because of this, the prospects of profit to the borrower, and of repayment of the loan, are better than if the loan were made only on a single activity, without considering other weaknesses and potential strengths in the farm business.

Students of the problem of improving farm efficiency and incomes are coming more and more to believe that significant improvement in farm organization and management can be made quickly only if it is based on intensive, whole-farm analyses of this type, even where credit needs are supplied through regular commercial channels. Not only the credit agencies sponsored by the government but many private lending agencies as well are showing increased interest in carefully made farm plans as a basis for loans.

If the loans made during the depression period are omitted, the repayment record on loans of this type has been creditable, considering the nature of the program and the classes of borrowers served. The largest expense is for technical aid and supervision. It is here that the higher cost of this type of program, as compared both with that of the Farm Credit Administration and with crop and feed loans, is most apparent.

For rehabilitation loans, public expenditures for administration and technical aid were at the rate of about 23.6 cents per dollar loaned as compared with around 10.6 cents for the crop and feed loans. However, the loss of principal was much greater on crop and feed loans than on rehabilitation loans. The total costs for the two are not greatly different, but the lasting improvement brought about by the rehabilitation type of loan is clearly more impressive.

Under the current program administered by the Farmers Home Administration, administrative costs and technical aid were running at the rate of about $29.2 million per year as of 1953.[62] The cost to the government of funds used in 1953 was about $17.2 million. Thus the total cost of the FHA loan program was approximately $46.4 million. Interest received amounted to $22.1 million. The government was putting into the program about $25 million a year, aside from losses on capital.

There is no dependable basis for computing risk cost (prospective loss of capital), but it may be assumed that there will be losses of this kind. On rehabilitation loans, such losses have averaged in the past about 9.4 per cent of the amounts loaned but they will undoubtedly be much lower under present conditions and with the type of program now in effect.

It is reasonable to expect annual losses of $5 to $10 million on the $642 million loan fund now outstanding (for both farm ownership and production and subsistence loans).[63] Thus as a rough approximation it may be concluded that the government is now putting into this program something in the order of $30 to $35 million per year in the form of special aid to about 300,000 farmers in the low-income group. The outlay per farmer served is apparently less than that given to the larger-scale, commercial farmers by means of the great variety of programs which are carried on primarily for their benefit.[64] The soil conservation payments alone, mostly paid to the larger farmers, have in recent years amounted to nearly as much per farmer aided.

Relation to Other Lending Agencies

If subsidized loans of the kind here under discussion are made available to borrowers who can obtain loans from the regular lending agencies, they will, of course, constitute a competitive lending program that could

62. However, this figure includes costs for servicing and collecting loans made before the Farmers Home Administration took over.

63. Omitting rehabilitation loans made under the Resettlement Administration and the Farm Security Administration.

64. These more general aids to agriculture are not confined to the larger farmers, but the farmers who operate relatively large acreages and produce mainly for the market are the ones who can and do profit most from the programs of these types.

be criticized as putting undue pressure on other credit agencies, and also as affording special privileges to a comparatively small group of borrowers. This emphasizes the importance of limiting such loans to those unable to obtain credit from other sources, and of requiring borrowers to turn to other agencies as soon as their credit rating makes them eligible to do so.

If that principle is followed, Farmers Home Administration borrowers will consist largely of farmers who are marginal as credit risks. The aim will be to graduate them out of that class. To the extent that that is not done, the program fails of its purpose and becomes continuing relief.[65]

The need for supervisory and technical personnel and its distribution should be reappraised from time to time to see whether the agency is retaining an unnecessarily large bureaucracy in areas where the problem has largely been solved. However, the field staff handling production and subsistence loans apparently constitutes the most appropriate mechanism for making, supervising and collecting loans of the disaster type, when it is found advisable to make such loans. Hence these workers may handle some activities not specifically related to production and subsistence loans, though many, perhaps most, of the borrowers who have in the past been aided by means of disaster loans probably can be given assistance under the more developed procedures of the production and subsistence loan program.

Aside from outright relief, handled through other agencies, it would appear that adequate development of the production and subsistence loan program and appropriate use of the disaster loan revolving fund should virtually eliminate the need for special drought and flood loans. Special appropriations may at times be needed to provide localized expansion of the loan program to meet needs growing out of specific disasters.

Liquidation or Transfer of Obsolete Programs

The whole process of legislative hearings, supervision and accounting could be simplified and made less costly by reducing the complexity of legislative authorizations and administrative organization. Progress in this direction has been made, especially under the Farmers Home Administration, but the Congress itself tends to add from time to time unnecessary and undesirable new features.

For example, there seems to be little need for a special and separate water facilities loan program. This was an outgrowth of depression conditions when it was considered desirable to provide make-work

65. This is not intended as a criticism of the present policies of the Farmers Home Administration. The agency is endeavoring to carry out the policy here suggested and relies heavily on its county committees to assure that only borrowers unable to obtain adequate funds from other sources are certified. These committees also are expected to review the situations of FHA borrowers from time to time to determine whether they have achieved a financial status such that they should be expected to seek credit elsewhere.

projects as a means of channeling funds into agriculture. Many of these borrowers could now obtain funds for such improvements through regular commercial channels if they chose to do so. Where they cannot, the regular production and subsistence loan or a production credit association loan would seem to be appropriate so far as most of the individual farm projects are concerned. For the larger group loans, cooperative action is feasible and funds are available through other lending agencies.[66] Education and technical counsel, where needed, might well be supplied through the regular service facilities of the Farmers Home Administration or the agricultural extension services.

In like manner the special orchard loans made in 1941 and the fur loans authorized in 1948 seem not to warrant special legislation and funds.[67] If sound and probably collectible, they should be entirely suitable either as regular commercial loans or as production and subsistence loans. If not reasonably sound and collectible, they probably are not appropriate for special loan categories.

There is little merit in providing such loans at an abnormally low rate of interest. With interest rates at the levels now prevailing, a difference of two or three per cent on small loans will not make the difference between ability or inability to survive. The crucial issue will be the ability to repay principal. In view of the fact that American agriculture now has a highly developed and comprehensive farm loan system, the Congress might well use great reserve in authorizing new special types of lending and no doubt could eliminate some of those now in existence. There may, however, be need for special programs to help bring about major adjustments in some areas that are chronically in the problem class.

Conversion of Land to Other Uses Appropriate in Some Areas

There appears to be need for a modest but continuing program for shifting land to other types of use in areas that are more or less continuous candidates for aid, because of droughts, floods or other disasters. These would be brought under study to determine whether it would be better to undertake a reorganization of the area as a whole so as to make it less vulnerable, or for the government to reacquire the land for inclusion in some more extensive type of land use.

66. However, at least some of the members of Congress are apparently favorable to the expansion of such loans rather than to their elimination. A bill introduced in March 1954 by the Chairman of the House Committee on Agriculture calls for the extension of this program to the entire United States (it applies now only to the 17 western states) and for increasing the size of loan authorized from $100,000 to $250,000, for loans made to organizations such as water districts.

In times of serious depression, loan and grant programs of this kind may well be warranted as a means of enabling recipients to make constructive improvements and use effectively the labor resources available. The need for them in times when the economy is relatively active is much less clear, particularly since other credit agencies, both governmental and private, could apparently supply the needed capital.

67. The orchard loan program has been revived under legislation recently passed. Up to June 30, 1952 only 22 borrowers had been assisted by loans of this kind.

This is primarily a phase of the more general conservation program described later. It should include effective cooperation among the agencies concerned. Experience indicates that where a land-use change of this kind is undertaken, the government need not take responsibility for resettling the farmers displaced. The land can be acquired on an equitable basis and usually over a considerable period of time, leaving the farmers to relocate in accordance with their own individual judgments rather than on the basis of recommendations made by government agencies.

Farm-Ownership Loans Do Not Reach Main Body of Tenants

The farm-ownership loan program has had strong support in the Congress from the beginning. It accords with the traditional American view that the best solution of the farm-tenant problem is to convert tenants into owners. Also, the repayment record has been good. These facts have tended to obscure the inadequacies of this method of solving the tenancy problem.

The program has now been in operation since 1938. To June 30, 1953, 60,639 initial tenant-purchase and farm-ownership loans had been made, in the amount of $437,619,053 (including supplementary loans). This number, however, is only 2.6 per cent of the number of farm tenants in 1940 and only 4.2 per cent of the much reduced number in 1950. The principal factor in the sharply reduced percentage of tenancy in American agriculture during the past decade has been prosperity in agriculture and a reduction in the number of farms, not the farm-purchase program.[68]

68. The reduction in amount of tenancy that has occurred between 1940 and 1950 has been striking and significant. The percentage of tenancy declined from 38.7 in 1940 to 26.8 in 1950, thus bringing it to a lower level than at any time since 1900. It had reached a peak of 42.4 per cent in 1930 and was about as high (42.1 per cent) in 1935. (These figures must be considered very rough approximations since they are affected by the completeness of coverage of small rural units, mostly owner-operated, by the method of handling cropper units in the South and by employment practices with respect to cotton workers.) The percentage of tenancy undoubtedly was enlarged in the 1920s and 1930s by the heavy loss of farms through foreclosure and reversion of many owner-operators to tenant status. Thus the 1930, 1935 and 1940 figures are abnormally high.

The 1950 figure unquestionably marks a very significant change in trend, though it may well be a lower percentage than will be maintained in later years. The upsurge in owner-operation cannot be attributed to any one factor alone. By far the most important one was the great increase in net returns from farming that occurred in the 1940s. The tenant-purchase and farm-ownership loan programs also had some effect, and the improved credit facilities of the Farm Credit Administration and the private lenders have also facilitated the purchase of farms.

However, the marked change in percentage of tenancy was due mainly to a reduction in the number of tenants (and of farms) rather than to a phenomenal increase in the number of owners. The number of farms declined from 6,096,799 in 1940 to 5,382,162 in 1950. The number of full and part owners increased by 215,329. If we assume that none of the tenant-purchase borrowers would have bought farms without this special type of credit, the tenant-purchase program would account for about 28 per cent of the increase in number of farms owner-operated. (Data from *Statistical Abstract*, various years.)

The purchase program has provided special aid to a relatively small group, many of whom possibly would have achieved ownership eventually even if not so aided.[69] There is need for some method by which young farmers can get a start as owner-operators, but the program as now set up is inevitably a very selective one. There are usually many more applicants for loans of this type than can be given assistance with the loan funds available. Under these conditions, the county committee-men naturally tend to approve loans to a select group of the most promising candidates. For this reason, and because of the small amount of funds available, the program bypasses the great majority of farm tenants, especially those most in need of help.[70]

Ownership status is generally accepted as a suitable national and individual objective by most tenants and by the Congress and the public as well. However, a program of the type now in effect cannot be expected to result in nearly universal owner-operation of farms in the foreseeable future. If enough money to enable large numbers of tenants to become owners quickly were to be appropriated, the result would almost certainly be a marked inflationary upsurge in the prices of farm lands, thus to some extent defeating the purposes for which the funds were made available. Furthermore, lands acquired by one generation of farmers do not thereby become permanently owner-operated farms. They easily revert in a single generation to much the same status as they had before.

Efficient, commercial farms now involve so large an investment that they cannot be made readily purchasable by operators with no capital. This is true also of most other businesses. More and more generally in urban lines of business, the people in charge do not own the businesses they operate, though they may own a share in them.

Way to Farm Ownership Should Be Kept Open

Unquestionably the way to farm ownership should be kept open so far as is reasonably possible without undue favoritism. But other more widely applicable approaches to the problem should not be ignored on the assumption that the tenant-purchase program, with its limited scope, will solve the farm tenancy problem of the United States. Part of the desirable attributes of farm ownership could be achieved generally, and with little cost to the government, by an improved body of laws governing tenancy relationships. That action has long since been taken by many

69. Except for the veteran group, which has been given preferred status since the close of World War II.

70. This does not mean that there have been no collateral benefits from the farm-purchase loan program. It has, no doubt, given hope to many tenants who could not be accommodated under the program and has served to some extent as a demonstration of the conditions under which the purchase of land with only small initial capital can be carried out successfully. It is not apparent, however, that the program can or should be enlarged to a scale such that most of the competent tenants can expect to become owners through loans of this kind.

of the more advanced countries of the world. Such a solution has been retarded in the United States both by the recency of our emergence from pioneer conditions and by the nature of our Constitution, which reserves to the states the right to legislate on internal matters of this kind.

The things farmers seek through ownership are continuity of tenure, the right to retain for themselves the benefits of improvements made, the opportunity to profit from gains in the value of the land, and the satisfactions and status that result from ownership. The last two of these cannot be acquired without ownership. The first two could be provided to most tenants by appropriate legislation and at little or no cost to the public.

Such legislation would limit the power of the owner to displace a tenant without official sanction and appropriate cause, and would assure to the tenant the gains from improvements made by him. He would thus be in a position to build up a constructive, long-term type of agriculture on the land and to take his place in the community as a settled and reasonably permanent resident. Speculation in farm lands by nonresidents would to some extent be discouraged.

Legislation of this kind has been in effect for three quarters of a century in England and for long periods in various other countries. Many tenants, where protected in this manner, prefer not to be burdened with the expense and risk of a large investment in land, and feel that they can use their limited financial resources to better advantage as operating capital than by having their money sunk in land while they operate with too little equipment and livestock. Such a plan is not a substitute for owner-operation but could provide some of the advantages of ownership. It might well be considered as a supplement to the farm-ownership loan program, not as a substitute for it.

Farm Enlargement Loans May Offer More Promise

Potentially more important than the farm-purchase program is the provision for farm development and enlargement loans initiated under the Farmers Home Administration. This, however, is designed for a different group of borrowers from that served by the farm-purchase loan program. A farm tenant, if operating on a reasonably large scale, and with an appropriate lease, may make a good income and be in a position to improve his situation in the course of time. The farm owner whose farm is too small or too poorly equipped may, on the other hand, be so situated that his labor resource is chronically underemployed and his prospect of advancement very limited. Such farms are numerous and constitute at least as much of a problem as do the tenant farms.

A given amount of appropriated funds can reach and help far more farm families if used for farm enlargement and farm development loans than if confined to purchase loans for units large enough to be efficient. Probably it can also add more to productive efficiency and rural welfare.

The development and enlargement loan program means making available a marginal amount that will enable the small-scale, low-income farmer to get off dead center and become a productive member of society, whereas if he cannot or does not break out of his static situation, he is unlikely to do so or to achieve a status satisfying to himself. He maintains himself but produces little and consumes little.

Most such farmers cannot make effective use of additional funds without technical aid and guidance. This the Farmers Home Administration is now equipped to provide. Since the Congress is understandably unwilling to make funds available on a scale that would convert large numbers of tenants into owners under the farm-ownership program, it might consider placing more emphasis on farm enlargement and farm development loans. Here a smaller input of funds per person can probably accomplish comparable results.

Insured Loans Warrant Further Trial

The insured loan program for farm purchase appears to warrant further study and trial. If successful, it could largely replace the direct lending of federal funds for this purpose, and would have potentialities for wider usefulness, since it could be made available to a much larger number of eligible candidates without increasing the burden on the Treasury. This procedure is not being used extensively at the present time, because lending agencies are not eager to make funds available at 3 per cent. It may be, however, that lending and purchasing of this kind should be somewhat countercyclical, expanding when funds and lands are available and contracting in times like the present when the demand for both funds and lands is active.

If emphasis is shifted to insured loans as compared to direct loans, certain realities will have to be faced. The one half of one per cent now allowed for administration is not sufficient for the kinds of supervision and technical assistance required if these high-percentage-of-value loans are to be made successfully. Therefore, either a higher interest rate will have to be charged or the government will have to continue to subsidize a considerable part of the overhead cost. This expense is incurred, however, even in the direct loan program.

It is unlikely that loans approaching so closely the full value of the farm can be carried at a rate of interest materially higher than that now charged. It would seem warrantable, however, to carry the technical aid and educational phase of the program at public expense, in view of the evident public interest in facilitating the transition from tenant to owner status. The program might then be expected to carry the interest payments to lenders, the cost of maintaining the insurance fund and the costs of the ordinary business transactions involved. This might require a moderate increase in the rate paid by the borrower as compared with that now charged, in order to make such loans attractive to lenders and to keep the insurance fund solvent. It is too early to draw conclusions as to the adequacy of the one half per cent insurance charge for meeting losses.

A successful evolution along the lines indicated above would make the farm-ownership program comparable to the federal home loan program for urban residents, which is also on a 90 per cent basis supplemented by an insurance fund. It would meet a need not filled at present by the more conservative lending agencies. Promising young farmers would be enabled to make an earlier start as owners, but would be required to give evidence of ability to accumulate savings before being aided in launching such a venture.

Such a plan would avoid the high selectivity and inherent favoritism that go with the current limited program of direct loans at 100 per cent of value and at heavily subsidized rates of interest. It would also lessen the size of appropriations needed and would constitute a move in the direction of less lending of government funds and more reliance on the private capital market. Most farm groups have repeatedly expressed preference for a loan system based principally on private funds efficiently channeled into the agricultural industry.

Group Farming Unsuited to U.S. Agriculture

The cooperative and community farming ventures can be regarded as an expensive and unsuccessful experiment that should not be repeated. Not only the experience of the Resettlement Administration but that of virtually all other agencies, both state and private, supports the conclusion that group farming does not meet the needs or wishes of most American farm families.

Even in countries where such schemes are in operation, it has often been found necessary to create and maintain them by force, often after most drastic liquidation of farm groups opposed to the change. There is little evidence anywhere in the world that farmers choose voluntarily to operate under the restrictions imposed by group management, unless forced to it by conditions that make individual management virtually impossible. While some technological advantages may be gained, they apparently are not sufficiently important to compensate for the loss of freedom of action, and they may even be nonexistent unless the management of the project is unusually able and effective.

Significance and Magnitude of the "Welfare Credit" Programs

During the past thirty years the government has loaned under these "welfare credit" programs some $3 billion. It has recovered through repayments and interest about $2.5 billion. There is a loan fund now outstanding, most of which presumably will be repaid, of approximately

$706 million. Costs to the government for the period as a whole, but chiefly for the past two decades, were about $600 million (if we include administrative costs for the postwar years). A very large part of this can be regarded as an outlay for depression and drought relief.[71]

The rehabilitation loan program was started at about the time agriculture was beginning to recover. The higher incomes of the late 1930s and especially those of the 1940s gave this program a better record on repayments than could have been expected if incomes and prices had continued at depression levels. Under comparable conditions, it can be taken for granted that the rehabilitation type of loan will cost more than loans of the crop and feed type. However, the results lend support to the view that the extra expense is more than offset by the improvement in farming and the prospect that requirements for loans and grants of the relief type will be smaller in the future.

The farm-purchase loan program has so far been relatively successful in respect to repayment of loans. It appears to have sufficient popular support to warrant its retention, but might well be brought more fully into harmony with customary credit mechanisms. With interest rates at the levels prevailing in recent years, success or failure will not ordinarily depend on a difference of one or two per cent in the rate of interest but rather on prospective ability to repay principal. For loans running to very high percentages of value, that prospect will be heavily dependent on continued prosperity in agriculture as a whole.

Continuing Study of the Low-Income Farm Group Needed

There is some tendency for proponents of these programs to be over-optimistic about the possibility of improving the efficiency, productivity and level of living of farmers in the "low-income" group. That many of them can be aided permanently has been demonstrated. It is equally evident that a great many of them cannot be converted into successful farm operators by these methods. Whether the decision is to expand,

71. Expenditures for the program as a whole during the fiscal year 1953 were as follows:

Farm ownership loans [a]	$ 18,993,868
Production and subsistence loans	119,999,931
Water facilities loans	5,999,939
Farm housing loans	19,294,817
Disaster loans [b]	44,124,520
Total loans	$208,413,075
Grants (farm housing)	$ 55,310
Salaries and expenses [c]	32,218,355
Total	$ 32,273,665
Total expenditures	$240,686,740

a. Not including insured loan program.
b. Includes loans to fur farmers.
c. Including expenses in connection with the disaster loan fund.

contract or maintain the amounts loaned, the program needs to be kept under continuous and realistic study.[72] To be effective and, in the long run, successful, it must continue to be selective, with the major effort directed to those groups that are found to respond to this type of aid. Others may be equally needy, or more so, but none should be included merely because of need.

If too large a portion of unsuccessful borrowers is included, the result may be a reaction against the program as a whole, thus depriving many deserving would-be borrowers of an opportunity to better their situation. The program is likely to remain controversial and vulnerable to attack or to underemphasis. The larger, commercial farmers are better organized, more vocal and more influential. They are likely therefore to continue to receive more consideration in the granting of aid for agriculture than are the farmers in the low-income group.

The increase of incomes which has occurred on the farms assisted by the Farmers Home Administration, though partly due to price increases, is sufficiently striking to warrant the conclusion that a modest input of funds and technical aid for this group may be one of the most profitable

72. Public and congressional confidence and interest in these programs would apparently be strengthened if the agency administering them could provide more suitable, informative and objective reports. FHA is moving in that direction and the current reports are more adequate and informative than those issued earlier by the Farm Security Administration and the Resettlement Administration but they still do not provide the amounts and kinds of information needed by the Congress and the public in supervising and appraising these new and rather controversial activities. Too much of the information required by congressional committees has to be elicited by the laborious and expensive process of congressional committee hearings and investigations, at times in an unfriendly atmosphere, when it could well be readily available to the Congress and the public in published reports.

More information is needed, by categories, on amounts loaned, loans matured, interest collected, delinquency, number of borrowers served and costs of administration. Though one of the justifications for these programs is obviously the need of these borrowers for special educational and technical aid, which might well be regarded as an appropriate public expenditure, costs of this kind are not separated in such a way that they can be distinguished from the normal costs of administering loans. Neither is there an adequate showing of the sizes and kinds of loans made and of the kinds of problems encountered. The reports from year to year do not give comparable data so that trends in results can be effectively shown and analyzed. There is a tendency to bury the rather meager summary figures in narrative statements without adequate presentation of the underlying data.

A thorough review of accounting and reporting procedures by a competent outside technical committee would seem to be a constructive move from the standpoint of both the Farmers Home Administration and the public. A system of data collecting and reporting which would be better suited to the internal needs of the organization and to those of the users of its reports could undoubtedly be devised. It is not the intention here to single out the Farmers Home Administration as a special case. Similar comments might be made with respect to some of the other government agencies, especially those which were set up hurriedly in the depression years when there was heavy emphasis on getting quick action, and little time for developing adequate accounting procedures. Many of the depression-born agencies were brought under more rigorous control as a result of the Government Corporation Control Act of 1948. However, the agencies which were not in corporate form were not included though some of them carry on extensive business-type activities which are similar to those usually handled through government corporations.

of the public expenditures in behalf of agriculture. Recent data collected by the Farmers Home Administration indicate that the average operating-loan borrower, in 4.7 years under the program, has increased his gross cash income from $1,803 to $2,958 and his net worth from $2,667 to $5,029. While these data may not be entirely dependable and the price changes that have occurred make the gains appear larger than they really were, the results nevertheless reflect significant benefits from this type of program.

Chapter 7

Production Adjustment and Price Supports
Methods, Objectives and Legislative Authorizations

THE PRODUCTION ADJUSTMENT and price-support programs initiated in 1933 differed markedly from any that had been proposed or put into effect in earlier periods. The activities of the Farm Board, which were described in Chapter 4, involved more government participation in agricultural affairs than any previously undertaken but the philosophy on which they were based was still that of helping farmers to help themselves, not direct government action.

The unexpected and severe depression that began almost immediately after the Board was established did cause it to intervene on a scale that was not contemplated at the time the legislation was passed. Even the stabilization corporations, which became the instruments of direct price-supporting activities, were originally conceived as secondary aids rather than as instrumentalities for the over-all management of agricultural production and prices. The Agricultural Marketing Act was in fact put forward as an alternative to the McNary-Haugen plan, which called for more government participation than the Administration then in power was willing to sponsor. However, even the McNary-Haugen plan did not imply governmental control over amounts produced.

The farm credit programs, described in Chapters 5 and 6, though greatly expanded and changed from 1933 on, had their origins in the earlier, more conservative period. They are based on a general philosophy more like that of the 1920s than that of 1933 and after. The depression caused important modifications in the farm credit programs but did not change their underlying purposes materially. The cooperative credit system has reverted almost wholly to the principles laid down in the Federal Land Bank Act of 1916 and in the Intermediate Credits Act of 1923, though with broader coverage and more developed organization. The emergency and supervised credit activities have undergone more drastic change but still have their roots in the emergency assistance given from 1918 on, and in the original purpose of the federal land banks, which was in part to make owners out of tenants.

So that the reader may have in mind the nature of the price and production programs authorized and used in the period from March 1933

224

onward, their main features are described here in general terms. The activities undertaken in respect to specific groups of commodities are more fully discussed in the companion volume of this study, *The Agricultural Commodity Programs: Two Decades of Experience*. Many of the techniques provided were used for more than one commodity. To discuss them in connection with each commodity program would be repetitive and confusing. The aim here is therefore to make clear the kinds of programs which could be or were used and the crops and products to which they could be applied. There were, of course, modifications and special applications of nearly all of them, but in broad outline and general purposes they were approximately in accord with the procedures described in the following pages.

The new programs did not take the place of the research, educational and service activities built up in the earlier years. They were added to them. Most of the older lines of work were in fact expanded and strengthened. However, the new programs were so novel and sensational that public attention has been focused on them, and much of the current discussion of farm policy centers around them. This has led to a general tendency to overestimate their role in bringing about the striking changes in American agriculture that have occurred in the past two decades.

Changes in Agriculture Due to Many Factors

During this period, other less publicized but very important influences have been at work. American agriculture has been going through an industrial revolution which has increased its power resources enormously. The rapid change-over from horse and man power to tractor and electric power has constituted, for agriculture, a change in amounts and kinds of power used that is somewhat comparable to the one which affected industrial production so profoundly shortly after 1800, though it has not resulted in such fundamental changes in the structure of the industry. In addition, a vast program of soil improvement has been undertaken and great strides have been made in the introduction of better methods of farming, improved varieties and more effective control over pests and diseases. The agricultural credit system has been made much more effective and comprehensive than it was before 1933. Industry has moved into the rural areas on an increasing scale, especially in the Old South, and agriculture, which has traditionally had a surplus of labor, has reached a stage where, in some areas, it is feeling the pinch of labor shortage.

The agricultural price programs have been a factor in many of these changes, but not a dominant one. Some of the changes are the results of influences that were emerging even before the farm programs of the 1930s were launched. Others are the consequences of more general changes in which the agricultural price programs had little part. For example, the massive upsurge in demand that was the dominant feature of the 1940s constituted an influence so powerful that it would have brought prosperity to American agriculture even if there had been no farm price legislation at all.

It is impossible to distinguish clearly the changes which came about as a result of the government's efforts to aid agriculture from those which were due to other causes. However, even these more basic types of change were modified, and to some extent speeded or retarded, by the agricultural programs put into effect in the 1930s. For example, even without a soil conservation program, farmers would undoubtedly have become more aware of the soil erosion problem, especially after the disastrous droughts of 1934 to 1936, and would have made some progress in meeting it. But the vast new program of governmental participation in conservation activities stepped up interest in it, gave much needed technical assistance and provided funds with which to carry out the kinds of improvement that were most needed.

The agricultural economy of the cotton states of the Old South would have moved in the direction it did, but it cannot be doubted that the acreage controls, and related programs, carried out by the Agricultural Adjustment Administration enlarged the scope of the change and hastened and facilitated it. Many other trends and developments were affected in similar ways. Nevertheless, it would be erroneous to assume that American agriculture would have continued to be the same as it was in 1932 if the government had not stepped in.[1]

The gradual drift toward reliance on government aid in solving production problems and improving marketing organization has been traced in earlier chapters. Nevertheless, by 1933 both farmers and the Congress had become disillusioned about the adequacy of the types of agricultural aid then being provided. Led by the Administration, they embarked on a series of programs which implied acceptance of the view that agricultural production should be controlled in ways similar to those used by large industrial organizations, that government should take a much larger part in the management of agricultural affairs and that the old idea of maintaining a freely competitive economy was to some extent outmoded.

Except for the limited shift in this direction in the Agricultural Marketing Act of 1929, the first important effort to apply this new attitude came in the Agricultural Adjustment Act of 1933.

1. While the specific effects of legislation and financial aid can be identified and measured only in broad terms, it is this general summarization of results that is most needed in the efforts now under way to reappraise the farm program and chart a course for the years ahead. The war-engendered enlargements of market outlets are rapidly becoming less significant. If there is no new upsurge of war activity, farmers will be in a less favorable position in the 1950s than in the 1940s, but there is little reason to expect a situation so desperate as that of the 1930s.

The Agricultural Adjustment Act of 1933

The stated objective of the program launched in 1933 was both broader and more specific than that of 1929. It was declared to be the policy of the Congress "to establish and maintain such balance between the production and consumption of agricultural commodities, and such marketing conditions therefor, as will re-establish prices to farmers at a level that will give agricultural commodities a purchasing power with respect to articles that farmers buy, equivalent to the purchasing power of agricultural commodities in the base period." [2] For all agricultural commodities except tobacco, the base period specified was August 1909 to July 1914. For tobacco it was designated as August 1919 to July 1929. The approach to this equality of purchasing power was to be "by gradual correction of the present inequalities therein at as rapid a rate as is deemed feasible in view of the current consumptive demand and foreign markets."

The consumer's interest was to be protected by limiting the readjustment of production to "such level as will not increase the percentage of the consumer's retail expenditures for agricultural commodities, or [the] products derived therefrom, which is returned to the farmer, above the percentage which was returned to the farmer in the prewar period, August 1909–July 1914."

This price relationship, now referred to as "parity," has come to be regarded by the Congress, and by many farmers, as the appropriate goal of agricultural price-raising activities. While parity has become a well-established term and appears frequently in the legislation passed from 1933 on, the formula according to which it is computed has been changed from time to time both by action of the Congress and by changes made in the weightings given to different items in computing parity. "Parity price" as used now does not mean precisely the same thing as when the term first came into use.

In the amendments of 1935, 1938 and 1949 the formula was modified to take into account increases in taxes, interest payments and wages paid by farmers, as well as the prices paid for *commodities* purchased by them. These changes, particularly the inclusion of wages paid to farm workers, which was provided in the act of 1949, resulted in a parity index which was higher in the early postwar years than it would have been if computed by the old formula. Farm prices, accordingly, had to be higher to be considered at parity than they would have had to be under the formula used in earlier years. The changes made prior to 1949, that is, the inclusion of interest payments and taxes in the formula, made less significant changes in the level of parity prices. [3] The interest item

2. 48 *Stat.* 32.
3. Changes in the cost of transportation, which were added to the formula in the act of 1938, were omitted in the act of 1949 as it had not been found practical or logical to include them. For comparisons of parity indexes with and without the changes in

has, in fact, operated to lower the index in recent years rather than to raise it.

This type of change in the goal of farm price policy is not well understood, because the term parity price is applied whether the figure was obtained by the old or the new formula. In some years, as for example in 1953, the difference between the two series is negligible. In 1946, parity as computed by the new formula was 16 points or about 8 per cent higher than if computed by the old formula. Usually the difference has been much less.[4]

Methods Authorized for Raising Farm Prices and Incomes

The procedures authorized in the Agricultural Adjustment Act of 1933 were very diverse and far-reaching. The Secretary of Agriculture was given the following powers:[5]

1. To reduce acreage or production for market, or both, of any "basic" agricultural commodity through voluntary agreements with producers, or by other methods. To this end he could make rental or benefit payments in such amounts as he deemed "fair and reasonable." He could also make advance payments on nonperishable commodities stored and sealed on farms, under regulations prescribed by him.

2. To enter into marketing agreements with processors, associations of producers and others for the purpose of controlling the prices paid to producers and the margins allowed to handlers and processors. "The making of any such agreement shall not be held to be in violation of

---

formula mentioned above see U.S. Department of Agriculture, *Parity Handbook*, 1952, p. 22.

For the years 1946–1953, the indexes of prices paid by farmers under the old and new formulas have been as follows:

	Old Formula	New Formula
1946	191	207
1947	230	239
1948	248	259
1949	242	250
1950	250	255
1951	272	281
1952	280	287
1953	278	279

4. For an explanation of the concept and its origins and implications see Appendix A.

5. The procedures and authorizations described in this chapter are only those applying specifically to agriculture. The Administration was attempting in many other ways to raise prices generally, including those of farm products. The NRA included price-raising features. The Federal Reserve Board was endeavoring to enlarge the use of credit, and the President initiated, in the summer and fall of 1933, measures for reducing the gold value of the dollar. Authority for the revaluation of the dollar was contained in Title III of the Agricultural Adjustment Act, along with authorizations for several other unorthodox actions on the monetary front. Among them were the authorization to issue $3 billion in fiat currency, the relaxation of reserve requirements of the Federal Reserve Banks and large-scale purchases of silver, as well as the powers relating to the manipulation of the gold value of the dollar. Other broad powers affecting agriculture stemmed from the acts appropriating funds for the Federal Emergency Relief Administration and other nonagricultural agencies.

any of the antitrust laws of the United States, and any such agreement shall be deemed to be lawful." The parties to such agreements were made eligible for loans from the Reconstruction Finance Corporation.[6]

3. "To issue licenses permitting processors, associations of producers, and others to engage in the handling, in the current of interstate or foreign commerce, of any agricultural commodity or product thereof, or any competing commodity or product thereof." Such licenses were to be for the purpose of eliminating "unfair practices or charges that prevent or tend to prevent the effectuation of the declared policy and the restoration of normal economic conditions in the marketing of such commodities or products and the financing thereof." The Secretary could suspend or revoke any such license, after due notice and opportunity for hearing.[7]

In addition, the Secretary was given authority to levy processing taxes on farm products up to the amount of "the difference between the current average farm price for the commodity and the fair exchange value of the commodity." This was to be the principal method of financing the rental and benefit payment programs. An appropriation of $100 million was made, however, for administrative expenses and to finance the program in its initial stages.[8]

The Secretary was also authorized to establish state and local committees to aid in administering the functions vested in him, and to permit cooperative associations to act as agents for their members and patrons in the distribution of rental and benefit payments.

The basic agricultural commodities, that is, the ones for which rental and benefit payment programs might be used, were defined as wheat, cotton, field corn, hogs, rice, tobacco, and milk and its products. Others were added later and the make-up of the list varied somewhat during succeeding years as new acts and amendments were passed.

METHODS USED BY THE AGRICULTURAL ADJUSTMENT ADMINISTRATION

The principal powers granted to the Agricultural Adjustment Administration fell roughly into two groups, those designed to regulate production and transfer income to farmers, and those designed to regulate

6. By an executive order signed on June 26, 1933, the President assigned to the Secretary of Agriculture the functions vested in him by Title I of the National Industrial Recovery Act in respect to trades and industries engaged principally in handling foodstuffs and tobacco, except those parts relating to hours of labor, rates of pay and other conditions of employment. These provisions were modified somewhat by later executive orders.

7. Other minor authorizations and directives were included in this and the preceding section, but are omitted from this summary in the interest of brevity and clarity. They included provision for taking over stocks of cotton from the Federal Farm Board and other agencies, for inspection of the books of licensees and for control of warehousing practices.

8. The Secretary was also authorized to levy processing taxes on competing products if the processors of the "basic" products were found to be placed at a disadvantage because of the taxes placed on them. Processing taxes were not to apply on goods exported, on those sold to charitable institutions or on those used by farmers.

marketing methods, prices and margins by means of agreements, licenses and orders. However, the broad discretionary power granted to the Secretary of Agriculture in both types of program made it possible to develop a great variety of techniques based on administrative decisions. As the program developed, it included most of the kinds of action advocated by various groups over the preceding ten or twelve years.

The First Period, 1933–1936

Since the government agencies and the cooperative marketing associations were heavily loaded with stocks of farm products carried over from previous years, emphasis was first placed on the reduction of output. A closely related objective was to get money into the hands of farmers as quickly as possible so as to relieve acute financial distress in the farm areas. Some adjustment of the output of certain crops, particularly wheat and cotton, was needed even granting that the basic causes of economic disturbance, whether in agriculture or in the nation as a whole, were shattered morale, unemployment and low buying power. Even with the most vigorous efforts to enable consumers to buy, the huge stocks of cotton and wheat would not have moved quickly.

Funds for initiating the program were made available by authorizing transfer of up to $100 million from funds appropriated for the National Recovery Administration and through Treasury advances against future collections of processing taxes. From the beginning of the program on August 1, 1933 to December 31, 1935, shortly before this source of revenue was eliminated, the revenue from processing and related taxes amounted to $966,136,739.[9] The amount made available through direct appropriation and transfer from NRA was $137 million.

For cotton, the plan adopted was to offer payments to farmers for plowing up part of the acreage already planted and growing. These payments ranged from $7 to $20 for each acre thus taken out of production. As an alternative to the cash payment, growers were offered options, at 6 cents a pound, on an amount of government-owned cotton equivalent to the estimated production on the cotton acres plowed up. Those accepting this offer were also to receive cash payments, but these were to be smaller than those paid to farmers who did not choose to accept options on cotton held by the government. These smaller cash payments ranged from $6 to $12 an acre. When the cotton options held by cooperating farmers were later sold, at 10 cents a pound, the total return on each

9. U.S. Agricultural Adjustment Administration, *Agricultural Adjustment, 1933–1935,* "A Report of Administration of the Agricultural Adjustment Act, May 12, 1933 to December 31, 1935," 1936, p. 291. The Supreme Court decision which eliminated these taxes was issued on January 6, 1936. The figure given above is therefore slightly less than the total amount collected up to the time authority for such collections was terminated. (Later figures compiled by the Department of Agriculture put the total at $970.1 million for the period 1933 to January 6, 1936.)

acre plowed up ranged from about $10 to $24, depending on customary yields of the specific acres plowed up.[10]

A similar plan of acreage reduction and plowing up was contemplated for wheat, but as the 1933 season developed it became evident that adverse weather would reduce the crop materially. Consequently, a different plan was adopted. The procedure chosen was a form of the domestic allotment plan. Each producer was offered a payment of 28 cents a bushel for 1933–34, on the normal yield of that portion of his acreage needed to supply domestic requirements. This was in return for his agreement to reduce acreage of the 1934 and 1935 crops by such amounts, not exceeding 20 per cent, as the Secretary might direct. Additional payments were to be made in 1934 and 1935 but not necessarily in the same amount. The Secretary determined that the portion of the crop normally consumed domestically was 54 per cent of the total. Thus the 1933–34 payment worked out to about 15 cents a bushel on total normal production.[11]

Tobacco Program More Complex

For tobacco growers, a different kind of program was required. Tobacco is grown in a number of noncontiguous areas, and the regional types differ markedly in their characteristics and the uses to which they are put. Also, the market structure is quite different from that for cotton and wheat. The crop is bought by a comparatively small number of large manufacturing and exporting firms. Some areas heavily dependent on tobacco were extremely poor even in more normal times. In others the crop was produced only as a side line in connection with more general types of farming.

The arrangements differed for the various types of tobacco because each presented special problems. However, in all of them the primary purpose was to hold down production and raise prices. It was found that there would not be any shortage in the cigar types if no crop at all was grown in 1933 and 1934.[12] Consequently, the reduction sought was a drastic one. Growers were asked to agree to reduce the acreages of these kinds of tobacco by 50 per cent in 1933, and by amounts to be specified by the Secretary (but not to exceed 50 per cent) in 1934 and 1935. In

10. The realized net cost of the cotton program for the period 1933–1936, under the Agricultural Adjustment Act of 1933 and related acts, was $167.7 million. Program expenses of $416.7 million were partially offset by processing taxes collected on cotton, which amounted to $247.2 million, and miscellaneous receipts amounting to $1.8 million. Part of the expense relating to this program resulted from the taking over of stocks previously held by the Farm Board. U.S. Department of Agriculture, *Realized Cost of Agricultural and Related Programs, by Function or Purpose, Fiscal Years 1932–1953,* 1954, Appendix.

11. The wheat program of these years involved program expenses of $354.6 million and processing tax collections of $244.9 million. *Ibid.*

12. Since tobacco manufacturers normally carry large stocks of the raw product, usually well over a year's supply, a change in the amount produced is not quickly reflected in the output of manufactured tobacco products.

return for such reductions, payments were to be made which, for 1933, were set at $15 to $47 per acre plus 40 per cent of the average value of the tobacco grown on the farm in 1933. Acreage thus eliminated from tobacco production could not be used for any other commercial crop and not more than half of it could be used to grow crops for home use.

The wide variation in amounts paid reflected differences in customary values for the different types of tobacco. The low figure of $15, for the first payment, was for Miami Valley tobacco while the high of $47 was for New England tobacco. The 40 per cent of the 1933 value per acre was paid as a second installment. These payments represented a very high per acre rental on tobacco lands. As the program developed over succeeding years, some of the tobacco lands on which production was permitted came to have greatly inflated valuations which were based on the allotments associated with them.

For the flue-cured tobaccos, a marketing agreement with the processors was entered into, after a good deal of negotiating and considerable pressure on the part of the Adjustment Administration. Growers were asked to sign agreements limiting their production to 70 per cent of that of the base period, unless authorized later to produce more.[13] In return, they were to receive a rental of $17.50 per acre for the land kept out of production plus 12.5 per cent of the net value of the tobacco produced under the contract. Some $16.5 million was to be distributed on this basis. In certain areas, price equalizing payments were provided for growers who had sold their 1933 crop before the adjustment program was initiated. In somewhat similar manner, special programs were developed for the Burley tobacco areas and for fire-cured tobacco, dark air-cured tobacco and Maryland tobacco.[14]

The Corn-Hog Program

The corn-hog program also took a special form, because of the nature of the product and the uses to which it is put. Corn may be sold as corn or in the form of meat animals to which it has been fed. Much the largest part of it is sold "on the hoof." Consequently corn and hogs, and to some extent beef cattle, can be regarded as alternative forms of the same commodity. This relationship was recognized and the program set up included both the corn produced and marketed and the hogs to which most of it was fed.

The most novel feature of this program was the decision to buy brood sows and small pigs at premium prices and to slaughter them in order to reduce the quantities of pork coming on the market in the following

13. The base period specified was the average of the acreages grown in 1931, 1932 and 1933.

14. For the program as a whole, processing taxes collected and other receipts amounted to $70.6 million (for tobacco). Benefit payments and other program expenses (for tobacco) totaled approximately $62 million. *Realized Cost of Agricultural and Related Programs* (see Appendix B).

autumn. The principle was not different from that of plowing up growing cotton to reduce output, but the general public reacted much more vigorously against it. The corn-hog program was one of the most unpopular steps taken by the Agricultural Adjustment Administration.

For corn, the program adopted was like that used for wheat, but with modifications. It was recognized that even though processing taxes were to be collected on both corn and hogs the bulk of the revenue would have to be derived from the tax on hogs. Only a small portion of the corn grown is processed in ways other than through feeding to livestock. The plan eventually arrived at, and put into effect in 1934, was to pay 30 cents a bushel on the estimated normal yield of the corn land taken out of production, and $5 a head on 75 per cent of the number of hogs produced for market from the 1932–1933 litters. In return, farmers taking part in the program and thus eligible for these benefits were required to reduce corn acreage by at least 20 per cent and to hold hog numbers to 75 per cent of the numbers produced in the base period.[15]

Processing taxes collected in the fiscal year ending in June 1934 amounted to nearly $98.7 million on hogs and $11 million on corn, or a total of some $109.6 million. Expenditures were much larger, amounting to a total of $227.5 million. By 1935, collections and expenditures were about in balance. The latest figures on the program as a whole, as compiled by the Department of Agriculture, put the processing taxes collected at $261.4 million, miscellaneous receipts at $.6 million and program expenses (for corn and hogs) at $488.7 million.[16]

Better Balance Between Supply and Demand Needed

These and various other steps designed to bring production and stocks into better balance with market demand were the most prominent features of the farm program during the first years of the Roosevelt administration. There was real need for bringing about a better balance between supplies available to the market and the effective demand for them. The stocks of wheat, cotton and tobacco in particular were so large and the markets so demoralized that no mere price adjustment could cause them to be absorbed quickly. There still was need for about the usual flow of foodstuffs, but the buying power of consumers was so low that these amounts could be taken only at ruinously low prices. For nonfood commodities, such as cotton and wool, further price concessions on the raw material were unlikely to stimulate mill purchases until goods already manufactured could be moved into consumption and until prospects for sales improved.

World wheat production had been running above normal market demand for some years. There was little prospect of moving increased

15. They could if they wished reduce acreage as much as 30 per cent and still be paid in proportion.
16. *Realized Cost of Agricultural and Related Programs.*

amounts of wheat, cotton or tobacco into foreign outlets even at bargain prices. Consequently, some reduction in the output of these important commodities seemed logical and likely to create a healthier tone in the markets for them. Though many consumers were in need of greater quantities than they were able to buy, continuing accumulation of stocks that could not be absorbed did not seem to be in the interest either of farmers or consumers.

Defects in the Program

Unfortunately, the method of financing chosen, that is, the use of processing taxes, tended to aggravate the situation since it kept prices to consumers higher than they would otherwise have been. For some products, the problem was as much underconsumption as oversupply. Holding prices above the free-market level therefore tended to restrict consumption, especially for high-value products such as meats, vegetables and milk. Millions of consumers were as much in distress as were the farmers. It was therefore illogical to collect funds from consumers in the form of sales taxes to transfer to farmers as a supplement to their incomes.

There was great need to reflate the whole economy. That could best be done by deficit financing. Since a better adjustment of agricultural production to effective demand was needed, a program designed to accomplish that might well have been financed with borrowed funds rather than by means of processing taxes, since in that way the incomes of farmers could have been increased without placing an added burden on an already hard-pressed consumer group.[17]

It soon became evident that curtailment of production could not in itself raise farm prices and incomes quickly. The stocks of wheat, cotton and tobacco were so ample that no immediate reduction in the supplies available for manufacture could result from the acreage reductions then being initiated. The adjustment program itself therefore could not be expected to exert an important influence on prices until stocks were substantially reduced.

The crop adjustment procedure appeared more effective than it was because the droughts that began in 1933 and became very severe in 1934 reduced current output so sharply that carry-overs of wheat and corn were quickly brought down to levels where they were no longer burdensome. The wheat situation changed so drastically that imports were required in 1934, 1935 and 1936 to make up for the deficits in United States production. However, cotton and tobacco would have continued

17. Farm spokesmen pointed out that those nonfarm workers who were still employed had not suffered as much reduction in income as had those employed in agriculture. This was true, but it ignored the fact that many millions of nonfarm workers who were unemployed had suffered even more drastic reductions in their incomes than had the farmers.

in excess supply had it not been for the drastic reductions which resulted from the rigorous restraints provided later in the Bankhead and Kerr-Smith Acts.

The administrators of the program soon recognized both the inevitable time lag in raising prices by reducing supplies, and the probability that a satisfactory level of prices could not be achieved in that way. They therefore devised a number of procedures designed to act more quickly and positively in raising farm prices and incomes. Among them were Commodity Credit Corporation loans, relief purchases and benefit payments.[18]

The Commodity Credit Corporation

In October 1933 the Secretary of Agriculture and the Governor of the Farm Credit Administration, acting under instructions from the President, incorporated the Commodity Credit Corporation.[19] The Corporation has since become the principal agency for making price-support loans and for buying and selling agricultural commodities under the various agricultural price-support programs of the federal government. During the early years of the program, most of the funds used by CCC were obtained from the Reconstruction Finance Corporation, though its $3 million capital was supplied by the Secretary of Agriculture and the Governor of the Farm Credit Administration out of funds made available by the President. Until July 1, 1939 the Corporation was operated virtually as an affiliate of RFC. At that time it was transferred to the Department of Agriculture, under President's Reorganization Plan No. 1. The Corporation was later given permanent status through the Commodity Credit Corporation Charter Act (62 *Stat.* 1070), approved on June 29, 1948.

The first major operation of the Corporation was the cotton loan of 1933. This consisted of an offer to lend 10 cents a pound on the unsold portion of the crop, which was to be held in storage as security, in return for an agreement to participate in the 1934 acreage reduction program. Banks, factors, brokers, merchants, warehousemen and cooperative marketing associations were invited to make loans in accordance with this plan, under assurance that the Commodity Credit Corporation would purchase the notes at par, with accrued interest, at any time up to June 30, 1934. This meant establishing a price floor for the commodity and set a pattern which has come to be one of the principal methods used in the support of agricultural prices.

18. The Administration was, of course, trying out many other plans for stimulating economic activity and increasing buying power. Large-scale make-work projects were initiated, the National Recovery Administration program was launched, monetary manipulation was tried and large sums were spent on relief.

19. Though owned by the government, the Corporation was set up under the laws of Delaware, which have long been widely used as a means of creating corporations for unusual kinds of operation or especially diverse types of activity.

A more radical departure from past practices was initiated in the corn loan program. Under this plan, corn might be stored under seal on the farm as well as in licensed warehouses. The advance made was about 10 cents per bushel above the market price at the time the plan was put into effect. If the price went higher than the amount of the loan, the borrower could pay off the loan and release the corn. If it remained below the amount loaned he could, if he chose, surrender the corn to the government and be absolved from any responsibility to repay the loss thereby sustained by the government. These were "nonrecourse" loans in which the government took the risk of a decline in price, or of failure of the price to reach the loan level, while the farmer could profit from price increases above the loan level.[20]

The administrators justified this procedure on two grounds: that it put money into the farm areas much sooner than if the growers had to wait until their corn was sold, and that the anticipated reduction in acreage would bring the price above the low level that prevailed in the fall of 1933. Since the farmers receiving such loans were required to participate in the corn acreage reduction program, this favorable loan provision was in part a payment for participating in the control program.

Both the cotton and the corn loan programs worked out better than most observers expected they would.[21] For the corn loans, this was not so much a result of the production adjustment program as of the extremely severe drought of 1934 and the short crop of 1933. The 1933 crop was smaller than those of the two preceding years and the crop of 1934 was nearly 900 million bushels below that of 1933. Most borrowers paid off their loans and repossessed the corn, as it was needed in carrying out their own feeding operations. The government lost no money on these loans. The growers received much needed cash in the fall of 1933 and feed supplies were stabilized to some extent.

CCC loans on cotton, for the 1933 season, amounted to $99 million; those on corn amounted to $120.5 million. The cotton loans were supplemented by $21 million in bank loans guaranteed by the Commodity Credit Corporation. A similar procedure was used for corn but bank loans on farm-stored corn amounted to only $1.3 million.

The guaranteed bank loan was to come into much wider use in later years. In 1934 this method of financing became the dominant one for cotton, with some $208 million derived from this source and only about

20. Under the bylaws of the Commodity Credit Corporation, nonrecourse loans could be made only on commodities designated by the President of the United States as eligible for such loans. In 1934 the commodities on which such loans were made were cotton, corn, and gum turpentine and rosin.

21. The principle involved was much like that of the overadvances of the Federal Farm Board in 1929 and 1930 which resulted in heavy losses. There the Board encountered a rapidly falling market, whereas these first Commodity Credit Corporation loans were made just ahead of an advance in the market. Both the cotton and the corn loans are discussed more fully in Chapters 1 and 5 of the companion volume of this study, *The Agricultural Commodity Programs: Two Decades of Experience.*

$15 million from the Commodity Credit Corporation. The 1934 drought was so severe in the Corn Belt that there was little demand for non-recourse loans in that year. Only about $3.5 million was borrowed from CCC and $6 million from the banks.

The general reaction to the nonrecourse loan program was favorable and it came to be used much more widely in later years. It served much the same purpose as was contemplated under the plan which was put forward shortly thereafter as the "ever-normal granary." That is, it provided for advancing money to enable farmers to hold stocks over from good crop years to years of low production. The marked success of the corn operation was due, however, to the fact that the very lean year came immediately after the program was started. A series of good years would have caused the administrators of the plan to be faced with much the same kind of dilemma as that which caused trouble for the Farm Board in 1931 and 1932.

The Bankhead and Kerr-Smith Acts

The voluntary acreage reduction programs initiated in 1933 provided substantial financial incentives for farmers to agree to make reductions in output and to abide by the agreements entered into. However, there was nothing to prevent farmers who chose not to participate from enlarging their acreages and presumably profiting by the reductions made by others. This was the old problem of the noncooperator which has been such a frequent cause of complaint on the part of members of cooperative associations and labor unions. If enough producers stayed out, and increased instead of reducing their acreages and output, they obviously could wreck the program.

The payments authorized were liberal and the prospect of large-scale abstention from participation for individual gain seemed remote. Nevertheless, results in the first year demonstrated that all growers would not participate in the programs voluntarily. Some were not reached in the sign-up campaigns, some were opposed to the basic idea of the "adjustment" program and some felt they could profit more by staying out than by going in. Also, some accepted the payments but evaded the obligations assumed. Furthermore, there was a tendency to eliminate or plow up only the poorest acres and to intensify production on the better land. The result was a percentage reduction in output that was smaller than the percentage reduction in acreage.

Sentiment for rigorous controls on output was stronger in the cotton and tobacco areas than in the wheat and corn regions. Also, the amounts marketed could be more easily checked. Cotton had to be ginned. Hence quantities marketed could be supervised at the gins. Tobacco had to be processed and the number of processors was small. But for wheat and corn the opportunities for evasion were much greater.

As a result of strong demand for more rigorous controls on the part of cotton and tobacco growers, the Bankhead Act (48 *Stat.* 598) for control of cotton marketings was passed on April 21, 1934 and the Kerr-Smith Act (48 *Stat.* 1275) for control of tobacco on June 28. Under the Bankhead Act, the number of bales of cotton that could be ginned and marketed without penalty was set at 10 million for the 1934–35 season. Tax-exemption certificates were issued to growers covering the amounts they were permitted to sell under the quotas assigned to them. Cotton sold without such certificates was to be taxed at a rate of 50 per cent of the average central market price of lint of cotton. The Kerr-Smith Act provided similar controls on sales of tobacco.[22]

These acts introduced two principal changes. First, participation in the program was no longer a voluntary matter, unless more than a third of the growers voting voted against imposing controls. Second, the control now was over output as well as acreage. The principle involved was similar to the union shop provision in labor contracts. There, every worker must join the union if he wishes to work. Here, every grower had to come into the program if he wished to sell without paying a prohibitive tax.

The Jones-Costigan Sugar Act

Another important feature of the 1934 legislation was the Jones-Costigan sugar amendment of May 9, 1934 (48 *Stat.* 670), which established a special program for sugar producers. The adjustment problems in sugar differed from those for the other crops in that more than two thirds of the supply was derived from offshore areas, principally Cuba, the Philippines, Hawaii, Puerto Rico and the Virgin Islands. Also, the product of a given grower does not flow directly into a general market. Usually he can sell only to certain processors whose plants are near. Consequently, the acreage to be grown is, in many cases, a matter of agreement between the growers and the processor before planting time.

The supply situation for sugar was similar to that for wheat and cotton. Prospective supplies, for 1934, amounted to about 7.9 million tons. Consumption was estimated at about 6.5 million tons. It was felt desirable, therefore, to place quotas on the amounts that could be sold in continental United States. Quotas were assigned to each area and also, in the U.S.-controlled areas, to each processor of beets or cane.[23] The quotas assigned to these processors were in turn divided among the

22. The tax rate for sales of tobacco in excess of allotments was placed by the Secretary at 25 per cent of value instead of 50 per cent. He was authorized to put it at 33.3 per cent if he chose to do so.

23. The quotas to be prescribed for sugar produced in continental United States were specified in the act. Those applying to U.S. offshore and foreign areas (principally Cuba) were to be determined by the Secretary of Agriculture. They were to be in proportion to actual shipments from those areas in the three most representative years between 1925 and 1933, the years to be chosen at the discretion of the Secretary of Agriculture. Those actually used were the years 1931, 1932 and 1933.

growers who had previously supplied their plants. The allotments were designed to give each grower his equitable share of the total U.S. acreage allotment. He could, however, base his allotment on his average acreage in the preceding 5-, 4-, 3- or 2-year period as he might choose.

The program provided for adjustment payments to bring the price up to parity for the years 1934 and 1935, such payment to be not less than $1.25 a ton on sugar beets of the 1934 crop. Somewhat similar arrangements were made in the cane-sugar areas. These payments were to be provided on condition that the grower agreed to comply with the acreage allotments to be promulgated for the years 1935 and 1936. The cane-sugar arrangement for 1935 included some measure of crop insurance, in that the growers were to receive $1.50 per ton on the estimated production of acres abandoned through causes not under their control.

The program was financed by a processing tax of one half cent per pound on raw sugar. This, however, might not exceed the amount by which the President lowered the tariff on sugar, the idea being to prevent an increase in the price to the consumer. Processing taxes collected on sugar from the insular possessions of the United States were to be kept in separate funds for use in production adjustment and benefit payment programs in those areas.[24]

The program thus set up was designed as a substitute for the traditional policy of seeking to maintain prices to domestic growers by means of a protective tariff. The plan, however, was more positive in that the quotas on shipments from offshore areas could be restricted to specified amounts so that supplies from these areas could not flood the domestic market in a time of surplus such as then existed. Furthermore, the total return to growers was placed at a higher level than would have been likely to result from the protection afforded by the tariff.

The quotas allotted to growers in continental United States were comparatively liberal and did not imply any drastic reduction in acreage. The plan was therefore highly favorable to producers in the continental areas. It included, however, a feature not contained in the arrangements pertaining to any of the other crops, namely, a provision requiring payment of minimum wages to field workers and a ban on child labor in the sugar beet fields. Growers were not eligible for benefit payments unless these conditions were met.

List of "Basic" Commodities Enlarged

The act of 1933 had classified as basic commodities wheat, cotton, corn, hogs, rice, milk and tobacco. These were regarded as commodities

24. The Department of Agriculture compilation of the cost of this program for the period 1933–1936 gives a figure of $91.0 million for program expenses and processing taxes collected in the amount of $76.2 million. For this program, the computation of costs and returns is more complex than in most of the other programs. *Realized Cost of Agricultural and Related Programs.* For a fuller explanation, see Chapter 7 of *The Agricultural Commodity Programs: Two Decades of Experience.*

of sufficient importance that increased prices for them might have significant effects on the agricultural economy as a whole. It was argued that, if the producers of these commodities could be made more prosperous, this in turn would set a better tone for the markets into which the minor commodities moved. These were also the commodities which were considered to be in excess supply and therefore appropriate candidates for production control programs. Furthermore, it was hoped that by this means the scope of the program could be kept down to manageable proportions.

It is apparent, of course, that political considerations entered into the decisions to include or exclude particular crops. That is, most of these crops or products were grown over wide areas. Programs relating to them could affect large numbers of farmers and thus were important politically. The single exception in the first list was rice.

Inclusion of some commodities and exclusion of others naturally led to insistent demands by legislators that other commodities be included, whether of similar importance in the economy or not. This tendency to widen the list of commodities constitutes one of the economic weaknesses of such programs, but is the foundation of their political strength. It is difficult to make them selective and to concentrate effort on the crops and areas where the need is greatest and where the funds expended will accomplish most. In some cases the storability of the crop was a factor in deciding whether to include or exclude it.

The areas and crops in which major adjustments were most needed were cotton, wheat, tobacco and possibly corn. Prices for most of the others were depressed, but there were few major maladjustments in supply as compared to normal demand. Nevertheless, if programs involving large grants of federal funds are to be continued, they must reach directly large numbers of voters. Hence every such program, whether it be a farm subsidy, an appropriation for river and harbor improvement, a shipping subsidy or a plan for reclamation and power development, tends to spread, partly as a means of gaining support for the program as a whole and partly as a result of efforts by legislators to get into it federally financed activities that are important to some of their constituents.

As a result of pressures and incentives of this kind, seven additional commodities were added to the list of basics in 1934. These were cattle, sugar beets and sugar cane, peanuts, rye, flax, barley and grain sorghums. This meant that processing taxes could be levied on these commodities and production adjustment programs could be undertaken for them. However, some of them did not lend themselves as well to these procedures as others.

The Jones-Connally Act and the Cattle Program

The cattle producers were not receptive to the idea of a processing tax or a production control plan. There was, however, some discussion of a marketing agreement with the packers. As a means of providing a different kind of program for the cattle industry, the Jones-Connally Cattle Act (48 *Stat.* 528) was passed on April 7, 1934. The act included some provisions relating to crops but was intended primarily as a means of providing relief in the western range areas.[25]

As a result of the serious and widespread drought which developed in the summer of 1934 such plans as had been under discussion for the range livestock areas were dropped. The feed supply on the western ranges declined so severely that hundreds of thousands of cattle, sheep and goats were starving. As a consequence the relief program for these areas took the form of extensive purchase and slaughter, or removal, of range livestock with money appropriated by the Congress, whereas most of the major basic crop programs were financed out of processing taxes collected on the commodity concerned. The livestock purchases were financed, in the main, out of funds made available under the $525 million drought relief appropriation assigned to the President. Through such government purchases and as a result of drought losses, supplies were reduced to such an extent that the initiation of a special marketing program seemed less urgent.[26]

The Jones-Connally Cattle Act authorized expenditure of $200 million for surplus reduction and production adjustment in the dairy and beef cattle industries. Part of the money used in the drought relief program came from this source. In addition, the legislation authorized the use of $50 million for relief purchases and for eliminating diseased dairy and beef cattle, including those suffering from tuberculosis and Bang's disease. Additional amounts were appropriated in later years.[27]

These programs were in part a concession to a group of producers not much concerned with the basic crop program. They came about largely as a result of the desperate situation prevailing in the drought-stricken

25. This act added cattle, peanuts, rye, flax, barley and grain sorghums to the list of basic crops. Sugar beets and sugar cane were designated as basic crops in the Jones-Costigan Act, which was passed at about the same time.

26. Through December 31, 1935, the Agricultural Adjustment Administration spent $119,356,056 for the purchase of cattle, sheep and goats under its drought relief program. Most of this amount was used for the purchase of cattle, many of them of little or no value. Some were in the last stages of starvation and were destroyed. Payments ranged from $1 to $14 per head. The total number purchased was 8,280,148 and the total cost $111,546,104. This was around 30 per cent of the cattle inventories on the farms affected. In a similar way 3,609,654 sheep and 350,460 goats were purchased at a total cost of $7,709,952. *Agricultural Adjustment, 1933–1935*, pp. 66–67.

27. Most of the cattle purchased under the drought relief program, if not slaughtered on the ranches, were turned over to the Federal Surplus Relief Corporation. Those animals not condemned as unfit for food were slaughtered, canned and distributed to needy families. Some, however, were shipped to areas where pasturage was still available. Some sheep and goats were also moved.

The tuberculosis elimination program supplemented the federal-state work of this kind which had been under way since 1917. The Bang's disease phase was a new addition. Bang's disease, otherwise known as contagious abortion, is also considered a cause of undulant fever in human beings. The program involved both the testing of cattle and the payment of indemnities for destroying infected cattle.

areas. The effect was to reduce rather substantially the number of cattle and sheep on the ranges and to eliminate considerable numbers of diseased cattle in other regions. These were the principal steps taken to aid the livestock industry, especially that of the West.

The Dairy Program

Milk (together with the products made from it) was designated as a basic commodity in the Agricultural Adjustment Act of 1933. However, it presented very different problems from those involved in the crop programs herein described.

Milk is a highly perishable commodity. The amounts produced vary considerably from season to season, but consumer demand for milk in fluid form is relatively stable throughout the year. To assure an adequate supply of milk in short seasons, it is necessary to maintain a volume of production that will result in surpluses above fluid milk requirements during flush seasons. This surplus is converted into manufactured products such as butter and cheese. There are also alternative uses for the fluid product, notably cream and ice cream. In addition, there are large areas in which virtually all of the milk produced is converted into relatively nonperishable products, particularly butter, cheese and condensed or evaporated milk. The price relationships in such a market are very complex and controls are difficult to set up and administer.

In the milksheds supplying fluid milk to the urban areas, complex organizations had already grown up, usually in the form of cooperative organizations of producers set up to bargain with distributors and, in some cases, to handle and process milk for their members. Class prices for milk used in different outlets, that is, as fluid milk for direct consumption or as raw material for butter and cheese manufacture, were widely prevalent in the industry. Thus these markets already had many group controls and monopolistic types of pricing.

In such a setting, the relatively simple device of restricting acreage, or even numbers of animals, could not be used effectively. The price of dairy products had fallen to about half what it had been in 1929, but still many people were unable to buy adequate amounts of fluid milk. There were lengthy conferences about procedures to be used in raising prices to producers. These could take one or more of three principal forms: (1) provisions for causing consumers to pay higher prices through some type of monopoly control, (2) efforts to reduce output or (3) a narrowing of the spreads taken by distributors. The first method was likely to reduce consumption. The second was very difficult to carry out, and the third would run into strong opposition from the distributors.

As a temporary measure, the Secretary of Agriculture authorized, reluctantly, a storage-holding operation for butter very similar to that carried out with Farm Board funds in 1930. He also announced hearings on a processing tax and production control program, but this did not materialize. The producers, distributors and manufacturers pushed ahead with plans for a series of marketing agreements which would govern prices, define and allocate classes of milk, and regulate margins and milkshed areas. This was the procedure eventually adopted in many of the fluid milk areas.

The dairy programs were extremely controversial and passed through a number of stages. Chief reliance in the early period was on marketing agreements, reinforced by licenses issued by the Secretary of Agriculture. As a result of changes in the legislation, the later federal and federal-state programs relied on Secretary's orders instead of licenses as the means of enforcing procedures agreed on within the industry or prescribed by the Secretary.

The plan to impose a processing tax was abandoned, but programs were developed for reducing the number of dairy cows by stepping up the slaughter of tuberculous and other diseased animals. Some dairy products were purchased with Emergency Relief Administration funds and distributed to families on relief. The dairy producers themselves were not in general agreement as to what steps should be taken. The complex array of activities undertaken in behalf of the dairy farmers is discussed in greater detail in Chapters 6 and 11 of the companion volume on commodity programs.

The Rice Program

It was thought at first that the problems of the rice growers could be solved through marketing agreements entered into by the producers and handlers. The industry was small and the producing areas very compact. Production had been declining and was not then much in excess of domestic requirements. Separate agreements were established for the California area and the southern area. These specified prices to be paid to growers and charges to be made for milling, and provided for acreage allotments to growers based on their past production of rice.

In the California agreement a unique feature was added. The millers and growers agreed to establish a trust fund by withholding 40 per cent of the price due the grower. This was later to be distributed to those growers who complied with the acreage restrictions specified. In the South, a few of the millers who refused to enter into marketing agreements were brought under the plan by issuing licenses, which might be revoked if they failed to abide by the provisions of the agreement. The California arrangement worked moderately well but the southern agreement broke down.

There was considerable agitation for a processing tax and benefit payment plan to afford more general and effective control over acreage. This was authorized by the De Rouen amendment to the Agricultural

Adjustment Act (49 *Stat.* 45), enacted on March 18, 1935. The marketing agreement plan was then abandoned and a processing tax and benefit payment plan roughly similar to those for the other cereals was adopted.

Specialty Crop Programs

In addition to the major crops discussed previously there were a large number of specialty crops not listed as basic. These commodities were mainly fruits, nuts and vegetables. In most cases they were grown in rather limited areas, enabling growers to deal effectively with processors and handlers in developing marketing agreements. For these crops, the adjustment act contained no specific provision for production controls, processing taxes or other devices of that kind. Consequently, the marketing agreement technique was the only one available and also the one considered most workable and appropriate.

Marketing agreements relating to a number of these specialty crops were developed and were approved by the Secretary of Agriculture. In some cases the agreements specified the prices to be paid to growers, provided for retaining on the farms or destroying amounts produced in excess of those which would be delivered under the agreements, and placed limitations on the amounts that could be canned or handled by the processors and handlers. The procedure was an elaboration of one already being used to some extent in California, under the California prorate law, which had been passed as a means of regulating the flow of perishables to the market. These programs are more fully discussed in Chapter 9 of the volume on commodity programs.

Peanuts

After passage of the 1934 amendment which added peanuts to the list of basic crops, they were put under a program similar to those devised for cotton, wheat and tobacco. The 1934 arrangement made growers eligible to receive diversion payments on as much as 20 per cent of their output, provided they signed production adjustment contracts covering the 1935 crop. Vegetable oils and fats were high enough in price that considerable amounts of peanuts could be diverted to use as oil without heavy loss. Diversion payments for 1934 amounted to $750,000.

A processing tax of one cent per pound was applied to peanuts on October 1, 1934. For 1935 the contracts called for benefit payments of $8 a ton, with agreement on the part of the growers not to increase acreage of other basic crops. Substantial amounts of peanuts were to be diverted to oil production. Various modifications of this plan were considered but were dropped when the processing tax was invalidated early in 1936. Program expenses came to $3.7 million, which is identical with the amount shown for processing taxes collected.[28]

28. *Realized Cost of Agricultural and Related Programs.*

Surplus Relief Operations

In addition to the more direct production control and price-raising activities outlined above, the Secretary of Agriculture undertook to remove burdensome supplies from the market in various other ways, chiefly by purchase for free distribution to the needy. In the first period, these purchases were financed in part by funds derived from processing taxes and in part with funds assigned by the Emergency Relief Administrator at the request of the Secretary of Agriculture. In later years, such purchases were financed mainly with funds derived from customs duties, under the provisions of Section 32 of the act of 1935, and from emergency relief funds and special appropriations for school lunches.

In October 1933 the Federal Surplus Relief Corporation was incorporated under the laws of Delaware. It was the agency that actually handled the purchase and distribution of commodities taken out of the market under the surplus removal program. The Corporation combined powers granted by the Congress under the Emergency Appropriation Act, the Agricultural Adjustment Act and the public works phase of the National Industrial Recovery Act. The board of directors consisted of the Federal Emergency Relief Administrator, the Secretary of Agriculture, the Secretary of the Interior and the Governor of the Farm Credit Administration.

In 1935 the Corporation's name was changed to Federal Surplus Commodities Corporation and it was made more specifically an arm of the Department of Agriculture. It was at that time placed under a new board of directors consisting of the Secretary of Agriculture, the Administrator of the Agricultural Adjustment Administration and the Governor of the Farm Credit Administration. The Corporation was continued as an agency of the United States, under the Secretary of Agriculture, in the Agricultural Adjustment Act of 1938.

Under Reorganization Plan III (1940) the Surplus Commodities Corporation was combined with the Division of Marketing and Marketing Agreements to form the Surplus Marketing Administration. In the early stages of the war, concern shifted from surpluses to possible shortages and the need for surplus marketing activities declined. At that time the Surplus Marketing Administration was consolidated into the Agricultural Marketing Administration (by Executive Order 9069, February 23, 1942). The food subsidy and surplus relief operations are discussed more fully in Chapter 8.

The 1935 Amendments

The Agricultural Adjustment Act was extensively amended in 1935 (49 *Stat.* 750). Most of the changes were clarifications and more detailed specifications of procedure. However, the amendments included some important modifications of the basic legislation. For example, equality of purchasing power for farm products was redefined so as to include as part of the formula the changes in interest payments per acre on mortgage debt, and in tax payments per acre on farm real estate, which had occurred in the period since 1909–14. This meant that if interest payments and taxes had risen by a greater percentage than the prices of commodities bought by farmers, the computed "fair exchange value" for farm products would be higher than if based on commodity prices alone. Both interest payments and taxes had increased sharply from 1918 on, so the effect of this change was to raise the price goals established for farm products and thereby also to increase the amounts of processing taxes that could be collected.[29]

The technique authorized for controlling the operations of handlers and processors subject to marketing agreements was changed significantly. Under the Agricultural Adjustment Act of 1933 and under powers assigned to the Secretary of Agriculture under the National Industrial Recovery Act, such controls, if established, could be maintained by licensing the firms concerned. Failure to abide by the regulations promulgated by the Secretary could presumably result in loss of license, thus putting the offending operator out of business. There had been, from the first, considerable doubt as to whether such a far-reaching grant of power would be sustained by the courts. This provision was now changed to an authorization for the Secretary of Agriculture to issue "orders" regulating the activities of handlers engaged in the interstate movement of agricultural commodities if he found such action necessary to further the declared policy of the Congress.

The definition of what constituted interstate commerce was also modified in the hope that this would lessen the danger of adverse court rulings in regard to the appropriateness of the various regulations as controls over interstate commerce. Interstate handling was defined as that which "is in the current of interstate or foreign commerce or which directly burdens, obstructs, or affects, interstate, or foreign commerce." Broadly interpreted, this meant that a particular operator might be subject to federal regulation even though he did not himself actually move a commodity across state lines. If his activities "directly burdened" or "obstructed" or "affected" interstate commerce they were presumably subject to such federal regulation as might be prescribed.

Under the order procedure, handlers could be fined for specific violations but could not be put out of business as they could under the licensing provisions. Orders might be issued either in connection with or

29. The Secretary was also given authority to use for any commodity a base period other than 1909–14 "if the purchasing power during the specified base period . . . cannot be satisfactorily determined from available statistics of the Department of Agriculture." While ostensibly designed to meet the problem of inadequate data in the 1909–14 period, this provision opened the way for the selection of base periods for some commodities that would result in higher fair exchange values under the prescribed formula.

in the absence of marketing agreements. Where handlers refused to enter into marketing agreements, the Secretary could issue marketing orders if specified percentages of the growers affected voted in favor of such action.

The list of commodities with respect to which marketing orders could be issued was specifically limited in the 1935 amendment. Orders might be used in regulating the marketing of milk, tobacco, soybeans, naval stores, fruits (including pecans and walnuts, but not including apples or canning fruits other than olives) and vegetables (but not those purchased by canners, except asparagus).[30]

Section 32 Funds Authorized

One of the most flexible and diversely used authorizations given to the Secretary of Agriculture in the 1935 amendment was that contained in Section 32. This section provided that 30 per cent of the customs revenue received by the federal government was to be made available to the Secretary to enable him (1) to encourage exports of agricultural commodities by paying benefits or indemnities for losses in connection with such exportation or for payments to producers as additional returns on that part of their production required for domestic consumption; (2) to encourage domestic consumption of such commodities by diverting them from the normal channels of trade; and (3) to finance adjustments in the quantities planted or produced.

Since the funds thus provided could be used for products other than the ones designated as "basic commodities," on which processing taxes could be levied, this opened the way for a considerable array of expenditures designed to aid the producers of "nonbasic commodities."

Another provision of the act (Section 22) authorized the President to place quotas on imports of commodities if, after investigation by the Tariff Commission, he found that such importation would tend to render ineffective or operate to hamper the program for raising the prices of farm products. This provision was not important at that time as the Administration, in its broader program, was committed to a policy of lower tariffs and reduction of trade barriers rather than to increasing them. This section was revised and broadened in the late 1930s and 1940.

It was further revised in the Agricultural Act of 1948. By that time

---

30. Hops were added to this list by an act of April 13, 1938, but were eliminated from it in an act of May 26, 1939 (to be effective September 1, 1942). Later acts provided for deferring the effective date of termination.

The specific ban on the issuance of Secretary's orders for regulation of the canning industry was included because of opposition from the canners. Had these crops not been so excluded, the canners could have been forced into compliance whether or not they were willing to enter into a marketing agreement with the growers. The other handler and processor groups affected either were less well organized and influential or had less vigorous objection to being brought under the provisions of the act.

many of the support programs were being carried out under acts to which Section 22 did not apply; for example, those relating to flaxseed, soybeans, eggs and wool. The 1948 version of Section 22 directs the President to cause an immediate investigation to be made by the Tariff Commission if he has reason to believe that "any article or articles are being or are practically certain to be imported into the United States under such conditions and in such quantities as to render or tend to render ineffective, or materially interfere with any program or operation undertaken under this title," or under the Soil Conservation and Domestic Allotment Act or under Section 32 of the amendment of 1935 or any of the other loan or purchase programs and similar activities.

The Tariff Commission was directed to give precedence to such inquiries and, if its findings indicated the need for such action, the President was directed to impose fees not to exceed 50 per cent ad valorem on such imports or to impose quotas on the amounts imported. Imports for selected uses could be curtailed as well as those for all uses. Under the 1948 version, such action could not be taken if in conflict with treaties or international obligations. This restriction has since been eliminated and actions of this kind can now be taken regardless of the provisions of trade agreements or other international commitments.

This policy was further emphasized by the inclusion of Section 104 in the Defense Production Act of 1951 (65 *Stat.* 132). Section 104 applied particularly to certain fats and oils, butter, cheese, other dairy products, peanuts, and rice and rice products, but followed much the same lines as those earlier provided in Section 22. Under this section an embargo was placed on imports of butter in 1951 and quotas were later applied to several other dairy products and also to tung nuts and tung oil. There were many complaints from foreign countries about the restrictions applied under Section 104 and its provisions were allowed to expire on June 30, 1953. Until 1953, Section 22 was not used extensively. Only five investigations were carried out in the years 1935–1952, but in June 1952 the proclamations put into effect under Section 104 were continued under the powers granted in Section 22 and some others have been added since—those on filberts, almonds and oats.

The provisions of Sections 22 and 104 are in conflict with the over-all policy of fostering freer international trade which has been in effect since 1934. No satisfactory reconciliation has yet been worked out.

Control Programs for Potatoes and Rye Contemplated in 1935

The Potato Act of 1935 (49 *Stat.* 782), an amendment to the Agricultural Adjustment Act, authorized grower allotments and taxes on sales in excess of allotments. The procedure contemplated was similar to that authorized in the Bankhead and Kerr-Smith Acts for cotton and tobacco. Steps were taken looking to the use of such a program for the 1936 crop, but were abandoned when the Agricultural Adjustment Act was repealed on February 11, 1936.

Plans were likewise made for initiating a production control and benefit payment plan for rye, this to be financed through a processing tax along lines similar to those for wheat. The collection of processing taxes was started in September 1935 but this program also was abandoned before coming into operation.

Program Greatly Modified by Adverse Court Ruling

The adverse ruling of the United States Supreme Court in the Hoosac Mills case [31] (January 6, 1936), invalidated considerable parts of the Agricultural Adjustment Act of 1933. The constitutionality of the act was challenged through refusal of the receivers for the Hoosac Mills Corporation to pay certain processing and floor-stock taxes on cotton, which the government contended were due. The Court held that the processing taxes were an inseparable part of the plan as a whole and that the plan involved regulating agricultural production within the states, a power which was not granted in the Constitution of the United States. Since the taxes were levied for the purpose of carrying out an activity not within the constitutional powers of the federal government, the Court concluded, the tax was illegal.

This action ended the power of the Secretary of Agriculture to levy processing and compensating taxes, thereby depriving the Agricultural Adjustment Administration of its principal source of funds. It also meant that contracts and agreements with individual growers, of the kinds previously used, were thereafter illegal and unenforceable. As a result of the Court's decision on the Agricultural Adjustment Act, the Bankhead, Kerr-Smith and Potato Acts were repealed on February 10, 1936, since they were considered also to be within the purview of the Court's action. This meant that the Secretary no longer had power to regulate the production and marketing of cotton and tobacco by placing prohibitive taxes on amounts produced or sold in excess of those authorized. The taxes prescribed under the Bankhead and Kerr-Smith Acts did not yield significant amounts of revenue but those acts did provide a very effective method of controlling production and marketings.

More than $1.8 billion was spent on the agricultural adjustment program from May 12, 1933 to December 31, 1936. (See Table 21.) The $470 million appropriation for the first year of operation under the Soil Conservation and Domestic Allotment Act of 1936 is included, under amounts made available, but only a small portion of it had been used as of December 31, 1936. Since the later expenditures under the Soil Conservation and Domestic Allotment Act are closely interrelated with the over-all conservation program they are summarized in Chapter 9 as part of the cost of the soil conservation program.

31. *U.S.* v. *Butler et al., Receivers of Hoosac Mills Corporation,* 297 U.S. 1 (1936).

TABLE 21

Sources and Amounts of Funds Made Available to the Agricultural Adjustment Administration, Amounts Expended Therefrom, and Balances Remaining Available for Expenditure, from May 12, 1933 Through December 31, 1936

Sources of Funds	Amounts Made Available to Agricultural Adjustment Administration	Expenditures Through December 31, 1936	Balance of Funds Remaining January 1, 1937 [a]
Total	$2,400,496,459.10	$1,821,952,657.27	$578,543,801.83
Advances from the Treasury in anticipation of processing-tax collections [b]	1,234,434,659.68	1,234,434,659.68	
Advances from the Treasury in anticipation of tax collections under Tobacco Act [b]	756,324.20	756,324.20	
Warranted from processing taxes collected for purchase of beet sugar	476,487.51	476,487.51	
Transfer under National Industrial Recovery Act to supplement processing taxes	36,967,504.42	36,967,504.42	
Puerto Rico trust fund for making payments to producers in connection with sugar cane adjustment program in Puerto Rico	1,552,469.44	1,552,469.44	
Appropriation to liquidate obligations outstanding as of January 6, 1936, in connection with production adjustment programs in effect as of that date	265,731,900.00	238,870,381.68	26,861,518.32
Appropriation to put into effect Jones-Connally amendment to Agricultural Adjustment Act	117,270,250.00	114,315,598.38	2,954,651.62
Transfer under National Industrial Recovery Act for administrative expenses in connection with code histories	502,180.00	499,864.36	2,315.64
Allotment under Emergency Appropriation Act, fiscal year 1935, for drought relief	80,799,908.69	80,303,274.25	496,634.44

Transfer from Federal Emergency Relief Administration for administrative expenses in connection with submarginal land projects	$ 1,643,034.16	$ 1,592,709.82	$ 50,324.34
Appropriation for administrative and other expenses under Section 12(a) of the Agricultural Adjustment Act	99,700,000.00	16,468,921.83	83,231,078.17
Tobacco compacts and agreements among tobacco states	300,000.00	7.77	299,992.23
Appropriation to put into effect Section 32 of the act of August 24, 1935, in connection with exportation and domestic consumption of agricultural commodities	82,861,741.00	52,945,599.12	29,916,141.88
Allotment under Section 37 of the act of August 24, 1935 in connection with the elimination of diseased cattle and other purposes	7,500,000.00	145,404.27	7,354,595.73
Appropriation to put into effect agricultural conservation program authorized by the amendments to the Soil Conservation and Domestic Allotment Act, approved February 29, 1936	470,000,000.00	42,623,450.54	427,376,549.46

Source: U.S. Agricultural Adjustment Administration, *Agricultural Conservation, 1936,* A Report of the Activities of the Agricultural Adjustment Administration, 1937, p. 140.

a. Balances remaining do not constitute surpluses left over after accomplishment of the purpose for which the fund was made available. In practically all cases the balances were obligated for expenditure to complete the action for which appropriation or allocation was made.

b. Processing and other tax collections aggregated $969,282,450.58 through January 6, 1936.

Not all parts of the Agricultural Adjustment Act were voided by the court decision. The power to enter into marketing agreements with producers, processors and handlers remained in effect, though its standing in the event of serious challenge in the courts was somewhat open to question. The Jones-Costigan Sugar Act, as a separate piece of legislation, also remained on the books. However, since this act included some features very similar to those which had been invalidated by the Court, its constitutionality was dubious. Section 32, which provided funds derived from customs receipts, for diversion and price-raising activities, was not affected.[32]

THE SOIL CONSERVATION AND DOMESTIC ALLOTMENT ACT OF 1936

The Congress, the Administration and the farm groups were not prepared to abandon the attempt to bring production into better balance with demand and improve farm incomes. New legislation was immediately prepared and passed. Since the processing tax could no longer be used as a means of obtaining funds, direct appropriations were to be made annually for carrying out the program. In addition, funds were beginning to become available from customs receipts assigned to the Secretary of Agriculture, under the amendment of 1935, and from appropriations made in connection with other legislation. Money was also appropriated for payments to farmers on obligations which were incurred before the Hoosac Mills decision but now could not be financed out of the proceeds of processing taxes.

The new program was relatively simple in concept. It stressed the importance of conserving and improving soils, an objective that had been gaining prominence in the agricultural adjustment program but had not become a dominant part of it. Direct federal payments were to be made for taking land out of the production of "soil-depleting" crops and increasing the acreage of "soil-conserving" crops. This was a shift from the plan of making payments for not planting certain crops to making payments *for* planting types of crops that were considered desirable from the standpoint of soil conservation. Since the crops defined as soil-depleting were essentially those previously referred to as basic crops, this was in effect another way of paying for reducing the acreages of the principal cash crops.

A more general program applicable to all farms was set up in con-

32. The action taken by the Supreme Court in the Hoosac Mills case and other decisions relating to various features of the "New Deal" legislation led to the major struggle between the President and the Congress over the President's proposal to enlarge the Court. While this proposal for getting a Court that would be more willing to acquiesce in the radical changes in federal power sought by the Administration was defeated, the ideological balance within the Court was shifted shortly thereafter, partly through replacement of retiring justices with others more in accord with the policies of the Administration. As a consequence, later legislation embodying some of these same principles, but not the processing tax, has come into effect and has not been upset by the Court.

junction with the acreage reduction program. This provided for payments to farmers for carrying out specified soil-improving practices. Farmers growing soil-depleting crops could, if they chose, qualify for both types of payment. In addition, "benefit payments," that is, direct subsidies, were to be paid to producers of basic crops, on that portion of each farmer's production which constituted his prorated share of the domestically consumed portion of the crop.[33] The farmer was not to be eligible to receive payment for shifting acreage to soil-conserving crops or as benefit payments unless he kept his acreage of soil-depleting crops down to that specified by the Secretary of Agriculture.[34]

Thus the new program was a milder version of that which had preceded it. Payments still were made to induce downward adjustment in acreages of the principal cash crops, and income subsidies still were being provided for agriculture, but now through appropriations from the Treasury rather than through sales taxes passed directly to the consumers.

The Commodity Credit Corporation's loan program, on commodities designated by the President, was continued and the capital of the Corporation was increased to the $100 million originally authorized. Some of the marketing agreements remained in effect and some new ones were entered into. Diversionary purchases and other price-raising devices were continued, within the limits of the funds made available.

The droughts of 1933–1936 had caused the burdensome carry-overs of wheat and corn to be reduced, business conditions were improving somewhat, and the major part of the task of refinancing agriculture had been carried through. Consequently, the situation was not so desperate as in the years 1933–1936 and the need for financial aid to farmers was not so acute. The appropriation made for carrying out the new program, aside from miscellaneous funds of other types, was $470 million for the first year of operation.

The 1936 act contemplated an important change in the administration of the program. It provided for transfer of the soil conservation and benefit payment phase of it to the states, together with grants of funds to enable them to carry out the program under decentralized administration. This transfer was to be made by January 1, 1938, provided the states had passed appropriate legislation and set up administrative arrangements satisfactory to the Secretary of Agriculture. The effective date for making this change was later deferred to January 1, 1942 by

33. The benefit payments were at so much per eligible unit of product sold. The amount of such payment was to be determined by the Secretary of Agriculture but could not exceed the difference between the price received in the market and the parity price for the product. Funds that could be used for this purpose were limited to such amounts as the Congress might appropriate, plus such amounts as the Secretary of Agriculture might assign out of Section 32 funds. Appropriations for soil conservation and benefit payments were limited to $500 million per year.

34. Since 1943 no payments have been based on crop acreage allotments. This means, in effect, that this procedure is no longer used to restrict the acreage of soil-depleting crops planted.

an act passed by the Seventy-fifth Congress.[35] It has since been repeatedly deferred and so has not come into effect.

THE 1938 ACT—CHANGES IN EMPHASIS

The Agricultural Adjustment Act of 1938 [36] brought a second change in emphasis. The act of 1933 was primarily for the purpose of meeting an acute emergency. Quick action was regarded as more important than carefully devised plans for a workable long-term program. Regardless of whether this plan was or was not meritorious and effective, the Hoosac Mills decision made it necessary to devise a new approach. Furthermore, growing public opposition to the program as first set up, and the widespread concern over soil losses that resulted from the drought of 1934, made it expedient and appropriate to give more attention to longer-term objectives.

The 1936 act was in part a shift in the direction of such longer-term objectives, though it was also a stopgap measure to prevent breakdown of the program that had been initiated in 1933. The act reflected a shift in emphasis that had been taking shape for some time in the Agricultural Adjustment Administration, particularly in its program-planning division. Nevertheless, it was not regarded by legislators, the farm groups or the Administration as a satisfactory long-term plan for aiding farmers.

Almost immediately after the passage of the Soil Conservation and Domestic Allotment Act of 1936, steps were taken to develop an agricultural act that would be more permanent than that of 1933 and more comprehensive than that of 1936. This long-term program, which took shape in the Agricultural Adjustment Act of 1938, did not constitute abandonment of the program initiated in 1936 but rather added some features from the 1933 program and some new ones.[37] This program gave more emphasis to price maintenance than did the act of 1936 and less emphasis to acreage reduction than that of 1933.

The 1938 act left the main features of the Soil Conservation and Domestic Allotment Act of 1936 substantially unchanged but spelled out more fully the procedures to be used. It stressed particularly the use of price-support loans and purchases, and authorized the imposition of marketing quotas to regulate the flow of agricultural commodities

35. 50 *Stat.* 329.
36. 52 *Stat.* 31.
37. Some steps looking to more permanent and more carefully drawn legislation had already been taken in the Agricultural Marketing Agreement Act of 1937. The broad and loose provisions of the earlier authorization in respect to marketing agreements had long been regarded as vulnerable to court attack. This feeling was heightened by the unanimous and very critical adverse decision of the Supreme Court (*A.L.A. Schechter Poultry Corporation et al.* v. *United States,* 295 U.S. 495) that terminated the National Industrial Recovery Act, which included code provisions that were somewhat similar to those of the marketing agreements. Further doubts were raised by the Hoosac Mills decision. As a consequence, a new act was passed. This defined more clearly the powers of the Secretary of Agriculture in approving marketing agreements, and redefined "interstate commerce" in such a way as to make it more inclusive.

onto the market. The quota feature was, in effect, a reinstatement of the type of control provided for cotton and tobacco in the Bankhead and Kerr-Smith Acts, but it was now applicable to other basic crops as well.

The act made a few small changes in the way "parity" was defined. The new definition of parity prices was substantially the same as that previously used, except that freight rates as well as taxes and interest payments were to be included in the formula. However, this change was not put into effect since changes in freight rates are reflected in the prices of commodities. Hence, to include them in the parity formula would involve double counting. Parity of incomes was defined as "that per capita net income of individuals on farms from farming operations that bears to the per capita net income of individuals not on farms the same relation as prevailed during the period from August 1909 to July 1914." In the 1936 act, the relation specified was that between income per person on farms and income per person not on farms. Thus the new definition limited the farm income side of the equation to income "from farming operations." Specific provision also was made for parity payments, that is, payments from the Treasury which would equal the difference between the price received by the farmer and the parity price, provided funds for this purpose were made available by the Congress and provided conditions laid down by the Secretary of Agriculture as to acreage and quota limitations were complied with. Parity payments were made on some crops in some years but not in the full amount of the difference between the price received in the market and the parity price.

CCC Loans Made Mandatory under Certain Conditions

The provision for Commodity Credit Corporation loans to enable growers to hold crops off the market was broadened and made more specific. The granting of such loans was not left wholly to the discretion of the Secretary of Agriculture but instead was made mandatory under certain conditions which were spelled out in the act. The loan levels prescribed were related to prospective supplies, but there were minor variations in the provisions relating to specific crops. That is, if the prospective supply was large, the loan rate would be a smaller percentage of parity than if the supply outlook was normal or below normal.

For wheat and cotton, loans were to be made if the farm price on June 15 (August 1 for cotton) was below 52 per cent of parity, or if the July (August) crop estimate indicated a supply in excess of a year's normal domestic consumption and exports. Such loans were to be at not less than 52 per cent of the parity price and not more than 75 per cent of it. Similar provisions were to apply in respect to loans on rice. Corn loans were also to range between 52 and 75 per cent of parity, but they could be as low as 52 per cent only if the estimate of prospective supply was greater than 125 per cent of normal consumption and exports.

These provisions still implied protection against disastrously low levels of price rather than the maintenance of prices that would be satisfactory to farmers. Guarantees looking to the maintenance of lucrative prices were to come later. There still was a good deal of flexibility in the arrangement, and some opportunity for the exercise of discretion by the Secretary of Agriculture in managing the situation, though less than had existed under the act of 1933.

Quota System Established

Whenever the supply of tobacco, cotton, wheat, corn or rice was found to exceed amounts specified in the act, the Secretary of Agriculture was directed to announce the establishment of a marketing quota for the following year's crop. This meant that a grower could not sell, without paying a heavy tax, more than his allotted amount of the commodity.

Within a specified period after a quota was announced, a referendum was to be conducted among the growers of the commodity.[38] If more than a third of those voting in the referendum opposed the quota plan, the quota was not to go into effect. However, if the growers rejected a quota proclaimed by the Secretary, the nonrecourse loans described above were not to be made available earlier than the second marketing year thereafter. The provision of price-supporting loans was made contingent on acceptance by the growers of parallel provisions for keeping production within bounds. This was to prevent the government from becoming involved in heavy losses on loans and on purchases at prices likely to be in excess of market values.

In addition, the Secretary had power to allot acreages in accordance with the provisions of the Soil Conservation and Domestic Allotment Act and to make payments in connection therewith. Thus there were two methods of restricting supply. Acreage allotments might be used without marketing quotas or the two might be used together. The Secretary could refrain from using either of them if prospective supplies did not seem likely to be burdensome.

If allotments were made, conservation payments were to be available only to those farmers who complied with the allotments, and only those cooperating in the program were eligible to receive nonrecourse loans. If quotas as well as allotments were in effect, loans were to be made to noncooperators, but only at 60 per cent of the amount per unit for which cooperators were eligible and only on that part of the crop that would be subject to tax if marketed.

Parity payments (payments equal to all or part of the difference between the price received in the market and the parity price for the commodity) were to be made to the producers of corn, wheat, cotton,

38. The period specified varied somewhat for different crops. For several of them it was 20 days but for tobacco it was only 15 days.

rice and tobacco, to the extent that funds were made available for that purpose. Such payments were to be in addition to and not a substitute for any other payments authorized by law. The acts of 1936 and 1938 thus re-established in somewhat different form most of the types of activity authorized in the act of 1933.[39] Though the acreage allotment procedure still could be and was used, interest was shifting toward more reliance on direct support of prices through Commodity Credit Corporation loans and purchases.

Significance of Change in Nonrecourse Loan Procedure

The 1938 act, and later amendments to it, spelled out more specifically the procedures that were to be used in making nonrecourse loans for supporting agricultural prices, but they introduced modifications that constituted a serious threat to the long-run success of the program. Whereas, under the act of 1933, loan rates could be placed at such levels as the Secretary of Agriculture might determine, the new legislation provided that, for several of the major products, the loan rates must be at certain percentages of parity. In the 1938 act the range within which the Secretary might set the loan level was still rather wide, but later amendments were to push the minimum loan level to higher and higher percentages of parity. This progressively reduced the prospect that the price in the market would exceed the loan level and thus cause the growers to repay their loans, thereby relieving the government of the obligation to take over the stocks.[40]

The 1938 act, in the main, put into legislative form the policies that had already been established by the administrators of the loan program. The later modifications of the act reduced significantly the discretion allowed to the Secretary of Agriculture in determining loan rates. The procedure thus tended to become not an ever-normal granary but rather a device for accumulating huge stocks of farm commodities in much the

39. The act of 1938 included some provisions not directly related to acreage adjustment, prices and loans. Among them were the sections providing for a Federal Crop Insurance Corporation and for participation by the Secretary of Agriculture in efforts to reduce freight rates on farm products. (The crop insurance program is discussed in Chapter 10.)

The 1938 act, including the features carried over from the act of 1936, became the basic act in respect to agricultural price-supporting activity. Most of the later changes have been in the form of amendments to it.

40. While these legislative directives have reduced materially the flexibility of CCC operations and have increased the danger of its running into serious financial difficulty, it should be recognized that the Corporation officers and the Secretary of Agriculture still have a good deal of discretion in respect to some of the Corporation's activities, particularly those relating to the minor crops. However, the most rigid requirements in regard to high support loans apply to the major field crops, such as cotton, wheat and corn. These are the crops in which very large commitments of funds have to be made and hence constitute the most serious danger to the practical operation of a program of this kind.

same manner as that which had brought disaster to the Farm Board stabilization corporations.[41]

Scope of Commodity Credit Corporation Activities Expanded

The Commodity Credit Corporation's activities have been broadened greatly in later years. As the principal agency through which agricultural price-supporting activities of the federal government are carried out, it not only provides nonrecourse loans but buys up commodities in order to maintain their prices at specified levels. The Corporation also engages extensively in the purchase, leasing and financing of facilities for the care and storage of commodities owned by it.

While the functions of the CCC are similar to those of the cotton and wheat stabilization corporations of the Farm Board period, it has much greater flexibility and far larger financial resources. For the most part this agency has been operating in a period of rising prices and has been able to liquidate most of its loans and purchases without heavy loss. However, the losses in 1949, 1950 and 1951 ranged from $250 million to $350 million. In any one of these years the losses incurred, largely as a result of price adjustments, would have been large enough to have wrecked the organization had it had no greater resources available to it than the Farm Board had. In the early part of 1950 the holdings and loan commitments of the Corporation reached levels in excess of $4 billion and since then they have been much higher.[42]

This larger lending power constitutes the major difference between the Commodity Credit Corporation and the Farm Board's stabilization corporations. CCC has had available in recent years $100 million in capital stock and authority to borrow up to $10 billion, whereas the Farm Board had a fixed loan fund of $500 million.[43] The corporate form of organization, with authority to borrow, rather than a fixed loan fund, has apparently been an element of strength for the Commodity Credit Corporation, but even with this higher degree of flexibility its losses could become much larger than those of the Farm Board.

41. Until recently, the Corporation has not been subjected to the strains resulting from excessive accumulations in a prolonged period of heavy production and weak demand, except for a brief period just preceding the outbreak of World War II. A situation of that kind was developing in the period around 1940 and again in 1949 but unexpectedly large war demands provided the opportunity for easing down these top-heavy accumulations.

42. In the winter of 1953–54, CCC holdings and loans passed the $6 billion mark and by 1955 they had increased to more than $7 billion.

43. From 1933 to 1936 the Commodity Credit Corporation had a capital of only $3 million. This was subscribed by the Secretary of Agriculture and the Governor of the Farm Credit Administration. In 1936 the capital was increased to $100 million, through purchase of $97 million of its stock by the Reconstruction Finance Corporation. In 1938 the ownership of the Corporation was transferred to the United States and the President assigned authority over it to the Secretary of Agriculture (March 8, 1938). Its authorized borrowing power was initially placed at $500 million. This was raised to $2.65 billion in 1938, to $3 billion in 1943, to $4.75 billion in 1945, to $6.75 billion in 1950, to $8.5 billion in March 1954 and to $10 billion in August 1954.

The fact that the borrowings are mainly from the federal government emphasizes this danger. If borrowings were from private sources, the capital margin would undoubtedly have to be larger, loans and purchases would have to be on a more modest scale and the cost of funds would be higher. The government has, in effect, through its loans to the Corporation, carried a sizable risk cost, but most of it has not so far become an established loss. These lending and purchase operations are more fully discussed in Chapter 10.

Rising Prices and Higher Supports

The prices of farm products began to rise rapidly in 1941. Thereafter, more production was desired rather than less, and the principal controversy was over the levels at which *price ceilings* were to be established rather than over the levels of support to be provided. The price-support mechanism came to be used, however, as a means of encouraging production. The related procedures for holding down output were, for the most part, discontinued during the war and early postwar years.

The actions taken constituted, in effect, the assumption of most of the risk of price decline by the government, thus enabling farmers to proceed with full-scale production without fear of a severe drop in prices if output should become larger than needed. More important, for farmers, was the gradual writing into the law of postwar price guarantees to provide assurance against a disastrous break in prices just after the close of the war such as had caused much difficulty in the period just following World War I.

As a means of stimulating production this procedure was very effective. It is probable, however, that the very favorable prices prevailing in the market would have stimulated production in much the same way, except perhaps in the last years of the war, even if there had been no price guarantees. Farmers were soon in a financial position to introduce improved methods, use more fertilizer and buy more machinery. Weather conditions were favorable throughout the war, the patriotic urge was strong and almost any amount that could be produced was readily salable at good prices. Farm output rose from an index of 106 in 1939 (1935–39 = 100) to about 130 in 1944 and 1945.

During the war years, the major concern of the Administration was that the prices of farm products would go too high rather than that they would be too low. Rising food prices constituted a serious threat to the over-all price stabilization program the government was undertaking to carry out. Many congressmen from the agricultural states and many farm leaders were bitterly opposed to the establishment of price ceilings on farm products, or at least to holding them at anything less than 110 per cent of parity. Permitting them to go as high as 110 per cent of parity would have meant that some of them would go to more than double what they had been in the immediate prewar years. While their prewar prices may have been unduly low, the fact remained that such a rapid increase in food prices as was then occurring was bound to be disastrous to the effort to stabilize wages and nonfarm prices.

The price guarantees provided for farm products for the first two years following the close of hostilities were in part a compromise concession to the farm groups in return for agreement to permit price ceilings to be established at parity instead of 110 per cent of parity.[44] There were, however, more defensible reasons for assuring farmers that, if they went all-out in their efforts to expand production, they would not be faced by a price debacle of the 1920 type shortly after the close of the war. Not only was such a policy conducive to the attainment of the amount of farm production needed during the war years but also it provided some assurance that a severe agricultural depression would not develop in the early postwar years. As it turned out, such guarantees were not needed, but at the time they were made most people expected a severe recession when the war demand slacked off.

Some other price commitments were made during the war years as a means of stimulating production of particular products. These were in addition to the general guarantees in the major acts of this period and usually were in the form of special subsidy payments and incentive payments designed to make the production of these particular crops relatively more attractive in a situation where profit prospects were good in nearly all lines.[45]

The prices of farm products moved up from an index of 95 in 1939 to 123 in 1941 (1909–14=100). They reached 158 in 1942, 192 in 1943, and 196 in 1945.[46] Thus the prices paid to farmers had more than doubled by 1943. The first general price control legislation of the war period (the Emergency Price Control Act of 1942, 56 *Stat.* 23), passed in January 1942, prohibited the application of price ceilings on farm products at less than 110 per cent of parity.[47] This, whatever its merits in terms of justice, was clearly unstabilizing so far as the war effort was concerned. It meant more than doubling the prices of some important

44. For a fuller description of this controversy see M. R. Benedict, *Farm Policies of the United States, 1790–1950,* Twentieth Century Fund, New York, 1953, pp. 408–30.

45. Many of the farm representatives opposed subsidy and incentive payments vigorously, contending that the market prices of these products should be allowed to rise sufficiently to bring about the desired levels of production thus putting the burden on the users of the products rather than on the U.S. Treasury. This, for reasons already mentioned, was not acceptable to the Administration because of its unstabilizing effect on wages and the price levels generally.

46. U.S. Department of Agriculture, *Agricultural Statistics, 1952,* p. 682.

47. The provision in the act was actually more extreme than this statement implies. It stated that "no maximum price shall be established or maintained on any agricultural commodity below the highest of any of the following prices . . . (1) 110 per centum of the parity price of such commodity . . ., (2) the market price prevailing for such commodity on October 1, 1941, (3) the market price prevailing for such commodity on December 15, 1941, or (4) the average price for such commodity during the period July 1, 1919 to June 30, 1929" (56 *Stat.* 27).

foodstuffs as compared to their prices in 1939. Under strong pressure from the President, the Congress eventually receded from this position, but on the understanding that the prices of most farm products would be supported at 90 per cent of parity for two years following the close of the war.

The Steagall Amendment and Other Wartime Price-Support Legislation

In the act of July 1, 1941 (55 *Stat.* 498) extending the life of the Commodity Credit Corporation, a rider was added which is generally referred to as the Steagall Amendment. This amendment was the first of the special war acts designed to stimulate production and to protect growers against losses that might result from their efforts to comply with the government's request for increased production. The life of the Commodity Credit Corporation was extended from June 30, 1941 to June 30, 1943 and its lending capacity was raised from $1.4 billion to $2.65 billion. Under the Steagall rider, the Secretary of Agriculture was directed to use the powers of the Corporation, together with other funds available to him, to maintain through loans, purchases or other operations a price of not less than 85 per cent of parity for those nonbasic crops which growers had been asked to expand in order that defense needs might be met.

Even before this (May 1941), the Congress had, in effect, dropped the flexible price support provision pertaining to basic crops that had been used up to that time. Instead of permitting the Secretary of Agriculture to determine the level of support for these crops within a specified range, he was directed to support them at 85 per cent of parity, through Commodity Credit Corporation loans and purchases (55 *Stat.* 205). This may have been in part a step designed to encourage production, since demand was already increasing and the Lend-Lease Act had been passed in March. In the main, however, the Steagall Amendment reflected the stronger influence in the Congress of those who favored high price supports.

The Stabilization Act of October 1942 (56 *Stat.* 765) raised the level of support on these commodities to 90 per cent of parity and provided that this level would be continued for two years following the cessation of hostilities.[48] Though intended only as a measure for easing the transi-

48. This provision was included partly as a result of a suggestion made by the President in his effort to get the farm groups to agree to reduce the price ceilings on farm products from 110 per cent of parity to 100 per cent of parity. However, it is likely that some similar provision for the protection of postwar price levels would have been made, even if the controversy over price ceilings had not arisen.

The most important feature of the legislation was not the 90 per cent of parity support price for the immediate future, but rather the pledge to protect farmers against a sudden disastrous drop in farm prices after the close of the war, such as that which hit them so hard shortly after the close of World War I. The legislation was thus both a concession to secure passage of the amendments to the Price Control Act and a means of enabling and encouraging farmers to proceed with confidence in expanding production

tion from war to peace, these high wartime price supports have been continued in the years since 1948.

The Steagall Amendment was, in effect, a means of extending similar guarantees to the producers of many of the crops not classed as basic and hence not covered in the legislation pertaining to the basic crops. However, the amendment did not apply to all commodities not classed as basic. Guarantees were provided only for those products for which production increases had been specifically requested by the Secretary of Agriculture as a means of meeting war needs. Thus, it was more specifically related to war needs. The crops and products covered by this amendment have come to be referred to as the "Steagall commodities." The Stabilization Act of 1942 directed that the prices of the Steagall commodities, as well as those of the basic commodities, should be supported at 90 per cent of parity.[49]

Under the Steagall Amendment, the prices specified might be supported "through a commodity loan, purchase, or other operation." Commodity loans, purchases and combinations of the two have been used. Many of these commodities are perishables and hence do not lend themselves to the same types of price-supporting procedures as the storables.[50] Also, the legislative provisions relating to these supports were not so rigid as those pertaining to the basic crops. The Secretary of Agriculture was given more discretion in deciding about the level of price to be maintained. The Steagall commodities were to be supported at *not less than 90 per cent of parity,* whereas the Secretary of Agriculture was directed to support the prices of basic commodities *at* 90 per cent of parity. In 1945 the price supports on Steagall commodities ranged from 90 per cent of parity for eggs and potatoes to about 130 per cent of parity for milk and butterfat.

The amendment further declared that it was the policy of the Congress

---

to meet war needs. However, the inclusion of cotton, which was then in overabundant supply, reflects the political influence of the cotton-state representatives rather than war objectives. The significance of that influence is shown even more strikingly by the fact that the loan rate on cotton alone was further advanced to 92.5 per cent of parity on June 30, 1944, in the Stabilization Extension Act (58 *Stat.* 642, 643). The Surplus Property Act of October 3, 1944 (58 *Stat.* 765, 784) raised the rate to 95 per cent of parity for 1944 cotton.

49. For the Steagall commodities these support prices were minimum levels. Higher supports could be given if considered needed in order to bring forth sufficient quantities of the commodity. The 90 per cent support could be in relation to parity prices or, if these did not seem appropriate, the level of support might be on the basis of 90 per cent of "comparable" prices. The provision in regard to comparable prices was as follows: for those commodities of which the production or consumption "has so changed in extent or character since the base period as to result in a price out of line with parity prices for basic commodities," the price support shall be in relation to a price that is comparable, that is, as favorable as parity prices are for the basic commodities. Comparable prices were established for soybeans, peanuts for oil, dry peas and some others.

50. The Steagall commodities, that is the commodities for which expanded wartime production was requested, included hogs, eggs, chickens, turkeys, milk and butterfat, dry peas and dry beans (of certain varieties), soybeans for oil, flaxseed for oil, peanuts for oil, American-Egyptian cotton, potatoes and sweet potatoes.

that the Secretary of Agriculture should bring the prices and incomes to producers of other farm commodities (that is, commodities other than the basics and the Steagall commodities) up "to a fair parity relationship with other commodities." This support, however, was permissive rather than mandatory.[51]

The war made other changes in the price and income support program. For example, parity payments, that is, direct subsidies of the types used in the 1930s, were discontinued but subsidies and incentive payments were used to some extent as a means of encouraging specific types of production.[52] For most products, the guarantees provided were basically a forward pricing arrangement under which a certain minimum price was guaranteed by way of the market, through loans and purchases or by direct payments.

Demand Continues Strong in the Postwar Years

During the early postwar years, the immense need for foodstuffs in Europe, together with the very generous financial arrangements made by the United States and the high level of domestic demand, removed the likelihood of an immediate slump and continued the wartime level of food requirements. For some crops such as wheat, exports were even larger than in the war years. The removal of price controls and the high level of employment in the United States gave rise to a demand for livestock products that quickly carried their prices to levels well above those of the war years. Farm products, in fact, led off in the strong inflationary upsurge in prices that followed the war.

The fear of a later break continued, however, and the farm groups were powerful politically. There was much discussion in the Congress of the kind of long-term farm policy desired, but sharp differences of opinion as to what it should be.[53] Virtually all of the mechanisms described earlier were still usable under the basic legislation passed in the 1930s. Hence the problem was not so much one of devising new

51. Among the commodities of this latter group for which prices have been supported are wool, naval stores, American hemp, sugar beets, sugar cane, rye, black-eye peas and beans, certain fruits for processing, certain vegetables for processing, barley, grain sorghums, sea-island cotton, certain vegetable seeds, winter cover-crop seeds and hay and pasture seeds. See U.S. Department of Agriculture, Office of Information, release No. 2809–46, December 31, 1946. This is also the source of the list of Steagall commodities given above.

52. Incentive payments and production subsidies took various forms. As a means of increasing the production of milk, feed subsidies were provided. Wheat and corn were made available to livestock feeders (out of CCC stocks) at less than market price. Flaxseed growers were paid a bonus of $5 per acre, and supplementary payments were made to sugar beet growers. The very large so-called "consumer subsidies" on food were, in a sense, also subsidies to agriculture, in that they made possible higher prices for farm products than would have prevailed if food prices had been held down rigidly and no subsidy provided.

53. Various proposals which were not adopted are discussed in Benedict, *op. cit.*, Chapter 18.

methods for aiding agriculture as of deciding how those already available would be used and what the level of support would be. The turn might be in the direction of a freer market and less government intervention or toward more management and regulation by government.

Some groups wanted to return to approximately the policy outlined in the Agricultural Adjustment Act of 1938. Others wanted to retain, more or less indefinitely, the existing, high-level price guarantees and were willing to accept the almost inevitable rigorous controls on output that would be required to make them work. Some discounted the need for rigorous controls since chance developments had made possible the liquidation of heavy stocks in the middle 1930s and again in the period following 1940. The outcome of this struggle was a compromise known as the Agricultural Act of 1948 (62 *Stat.* 1247).

THE AGRICULTURAL ACT OF 1948

Title I of the 1948 act was brief and consisted essentially of a provision for continuing wartime levels of support for the basic crops until June 30, 1950.[54] For the Steagall commodities, this section of the act provided for some relaxation of wartime levels of support. Irish potatoes harvested before January 1, 1949 were to be supported at 90 per cent of parity. Similar support was to be given for milk and milk products, hogs, chickens and eggs until January 1, 1950. Wool was to be supported at the 1946 level (about 42 cents) until June 30, 1950. Other Steagall commodities were to be supported at not less than 60 per cent of parity. Among these were beans, dry peas, sweet potatoes, flaxseed, soybeans, turkeys, American-Egyptian cotton and potatoes harvested after January 1, 1949. Price supports for various other agricultural commodities were continued, under certain conditions and on a permissive basis, until January 1, 1950. This was merely an extension of the laws then in effect. These commodities were already on a "permissive" price-support basis.

Title II, which constituted the major and most widely discussed part of the act, was not to go into effect until 1950. The main features of Title II, so far as the basic crops were concerned, were in line with the general philosophy set forth in the act of 1938.[55] This title was commonly referred to as the "flexible" price-support program as contrasted with the fixed high-level supports contained in the postwar price guarantees and in Title I, which was originally the House measure. Price supports still were mandatory, but were to vary in accordance with the

---

54. The crops included in this provision were cotton, wheat, corn, tobacco, rice and peanuts, if marketed before June 30, 1950.

55. The allotment provisions and the soil conservation payment plan of the act of 1936 were retained, also the quota provisions of the act of 1938, together with authority to use Section 32 funds and marketing agreements and orders. Thus virtually all of the methods for aiding agriculture that had been provided in the legislation passed between 1936 and 1940 were retained.

amounts carried over and prospective supply in relation to expected demand.

The level of support provided for basic commodities was to be at a prescribed rate which could vary from 60 to 90 per cent of parity.[56] If the supply was only 70 per cent of "normal," as defined in the act, prices would be supported at 90 per cent of parity. If the supply outlook was as high as 130 per cent of normal, or more, support would be at 60 per cent of parity. Between these levels of supply, other specified rates of support would apply. If acreage allotments or quotas were in effect, "cooperators," that is, growers who complied with acreage and quota limitations, would have their prices supported at levels 20 per cent above those indicated, but not above 90 per cent of parity. If a quota had been announced and had been rejected by the growers, the level of support was to be 50 per cent of parity.

For nonbasics, except wool, the Secretary of Agriculture was authorized, after Title I had run its course, to support prices at no more than 90 per cent of parity.[57] Storable nonbasics could be supported with regular Commodity Credit Corporation funds. Nonstorable commodities, except Irish potatoes, could be supported only with Section 32 funds and with CCC reserves for the postwar price support of agriculture.

The plan thus contained what was, in essence, a provision for price floors designed to prevent price declines of disastrous proportions. It was not a guarantee of highly satisfactory prices. If the crop was short, say as low as 70 per cent of normal, the price in the market would in all probability be above the support price. Hence the level of support would be of little consequence. It was in times of large supply that such a plan would presumably have an important influence.

The principal intended effect of the act was to substitute a flexible price-support arrangement for the 90 per cent of parity supports provided in the wartime legislation but now about to lapse. It was a plan for a partial return to a freer market and a partial retreat from the government's commitment to support farm prices at high levels. If no action had been taken, the act of 1938, with its various amendments, would again have come into effect at the end of 1948 when the wartime guarantees expired. Thus the flexible support plan (Title II) provided higher levels of price support than the act of 1938 but lower ones than were specified in the wartime legislation. It would have reduced significantly the prospect of heavy government losses on nonrecourse loans and price-supporting purchases, as compared to what could be anticipated if the wartime legislation was extended indefinitely.

56. This did not apply to tobacco. The tobacco price was to be supported at 90 per cent if marketing quotas were in effect for the crop years to which support prices would apply.

57. Wool was to be supported at such a level between 60 and 90 per cent of parity as would encourage an annual production of 360 million pounds of shorn wool. The section relating to nonbasics was superseded by Section 201 of the Agricultural Act of 1949.

Revision of the Parity Formula

One of the much-discussed changes made by Title II was in the method of computing parity prices for the various products. Up to that time, parity was achieved for each commodity if its percentage increase over its average price in the base period (for most products the period 1909–1914) equaled the percentage by which the prices paid by farmers had increased above those of the base period.[58] This implied that the price of each product should have advanced by the same percentage, and that the relationships between the prices of the various farm products should have remained the same.

If parity prices, as measured by the old formula, were to be maintained, it was evident that the production of some commodities would be encouraged and others discouraged. Costs had not increased uniformly for the various agricultural products. Tractors and other mechanical improvements had reduced greatly the man-hour requirements in growing wheat and many other field crops. Livestock production, and some types of crop operation, had not experienced similar reductions in real cost. Consequently, if both groups had equal percentage gains in price the result would be to make the production of wheat and other highly mechanized crops very profitable, as compared to livestock and fruits and vegetables, which were the ones in which increases were most needed.

The new plan sought to overcome this difficulty by revising the base prices of the various commodities so they would bear the same relationship to each other as in recent years. This was to be done by taking the average price for each commodity during the most recent ten-year period and multiplying it by the ratio between the general level of prices received by farmers for agricultural products in the base period (1910 to 1914) and the general level of prices received by farmers in the most recent period. This would give the "adjusted base price." To obtain the new parity price, the adjusted base price would be multiplied by the ratio between the prices paid by farmers currently and the prices paid by them in the 1910–1914 period.

To illustrate, using hypothetical data, let us assume that the current price of wheat is $1.50 per bushel, as compared to $1.00 in the base period, and that of beef cattle $20 per cwt., as compared to $10 in the base period. Let us further assume that the prices of farm products as a whole are 75 per cent higher than in the base period. The adjusted base price for wheat would be 100/175 of $1.50, or $.857 instead of $1. The adjusted base price for cattle would be 100/175 of $20, or $11.43 instead of $10.

If the prices of things bought by farmers had increased 100 per cent over those of the base period, the new parity for wheat would be 2 x

58. There had been some changes in the prescribed formula as noted earlier, but the general principle was that stated above.

$.857 or $1.714 while that of beef cattle would be 2 x $11.43 or $22.86. Under the old formula, parity for wheat would be $2, and that for beef cattle $20. Thus under the new formula, support at a given percentage of parity would tend to encourage beef production and to discourage wheat production as compared to the relative incentives provided under the old formula.[59]

Title II Provisions Not Allowed to Come into Effect

Though carefully considered and well thought out, the price-support provisions of Title II were not allowed to come into effect. A bitter fight developed in the Congress between the proponents of this relatively moderate program and the group that insisted on the continuance of farm price supports at high percentages of parity. The struggle over the two versions, known respectively as the Aiken bill (Title II) and the Hope bill (Title I), continued into the last day before adjournment for the national political conventions. It was resolved only at the last minute, by combining the two bills and passing them as one.

By this action the wartime guarantees on the basic crops, which had been scheduled to lapse at the end of 1948, were extended by 18 months. For the Steagall commodities the wartime guarantees were relaxed to some extent though still retained for a year on milk and milk products, hogs, and chickens and eggs. The support level on Irish potatoes, which had proved very costly in 1948, was lowered from 90 per cent of parity to 60 per cent.[60] As a result of the extension of high supports on the basic crops, large accumulations of wheat and some of the other storables developed in 1949 and early 1950. The action taken was an election-year compromise which meant passing up one of the best opportunities of the postwar years for orderly and gradual return to freer and more flexible marketing arrangements.

AGRICULTURAL ACT OF 1949 CONTINUES HIGH SUPPORT LEVELS

The return of a Democratic majority in the Eighty-first Congress (1949) made it virtually inevitable that new legislation would be passed to supersede that of the Republican Eightieth Congress. Such action was taken, though not in the form proposed by the chief agricultural spokesman for the Administration, Secretary of Agriculture Brannan.[61] How-

59. The act provided for a "transitional parity" to be used during a period of adjustment from the old to the new formula. If computation by the new formula reduced the parity price for any commodity by more than 5 per cent from its parity price as computed by the old formula, the parity price used in support operations was to be reduced by 5 per cent per year until it reached the level provided in the new formula.

60. The cost of the potato program in 1948 was $206 million. It was smaller, though still sizable, in the years 1949 and 1950. Losses in 1949 amounted to $75 million and those of 1950 to $65 million. Support loans were abandoned in 1950, though purchases continued to be made in that year.

61. The plan proposed by Secretary Brannan would have provided mandatory high-level supports on a larger list of products which included eggs, chickens, milk, hogs,

ever, it may well be that the Brannan proposals had some effect on the levels of support provided in the act that was adopted.

The new act (the Agricultural Act of 1949, 63 *Stat.* 1051) extended the wartime levels of price support on the basic crops through the 1950 crop and marketing year but authorized, for those crops in surplus, a decrease to 80 per cent for the 1951 crop year. Though retaining the idea of a revised and modernized parity formula, it included features which tended to raise the parity goal itself by redefinition. The amounts paid to hired farm workers were now to be included in the formula, in the same manner as interest charges and taxes had been included under earlier legislation.

Significance of the Change in Parity Formula

At the time this change in the parity formula was made, the inclusion of wages paid to hired farm labor raised the over-all level of parity prices by about 5 points. That is, a level of farm prices which, without such inclusion, would have been 100 per cent of parity under the old formula would have been about 5 points (around 2 per cent) below parity under the new formula. The two series have since come closer together and were almost identical in 1953. In 1951, parity under the new formula was 8 points (about 3.3 per cent) higher than under the old and in 1952, 7 points higher (2.5 per cent). (See p. 546.)

The change discussed above relates to the over-all average level of farm prices as compared to the prices of things bought by farmers. The 1949 act also made another kind of change in the parity standard to be used in price-support activities. The method of computing parity prices provided in the 1948 act contemplated that parity prices would be raised on products for which demand had increased and costs had not been sharply reduced since the 1910–14 base period. Parity prices of the products for which real costs had been greatly reduced by mechanization and other factors (usually the field crops) would be lowered. Thus the two types of change would tend to offset each other, but would encourage the production of commodities such as meats and other livestock products for which demand was strong and would make the production of others, such as field crops, relatively less attractive, if both groups were supported at the same percentage of parity.

The 1949 act permitted the increase in parity prices provided in the 1948 act for the first group of commodities but deferred the time at which the lower parities contemplated for the second group of commodities would come into effect. The act required that, until 1954, the parity price for any basic commodity would be the parity price figured by the

---

beef cattle and lambs as well as the 1948 act "basics." It also proposed direct payments to farmers on perishable commodities rather than price support in the markets. For a fuller description of its provisions, see pp. 271–74 and Benedict, *op. cit.,* pp. 484–90.

new formula (that in the act of 1948) or the parity price computed by the old formula, whichever was higher.[62]

This meant that parity prices for livestock products and some others would be higher but the parity prices for wheat and several other commodities for which the relative costs of production had been reduced materially would not be lowered. The over-all effect was to raise the average level of farm prices that would be designated as parity for agriculture above what it would have been under either the formula provided in the 1948 act or that used before 1948.[63]

Support Levels under the 1949 Act

The idea of flexible price supports was retained in the 1949 act but the supply levels to which the formulas applied were raised significantly. The schedule in the 1948 act was probably too low. That in the 1949 act is almost certainly too high to contribute to stability and normal movement over any long period.

In the 1948 act, the prices of the basic commodities were to be supported at 90 per cent of parity if the "supply percentage" was not more than 70, and could go down to 60 per cent if the supply percentage was as high as 130.[64] For cooperating farmers, these support levels were to be 20 per cent higher if allotments or quotas were in effect, but could not exceed 90 per cent. That is, with allotments or quotas in effect, the range was to be from 72 per cent of parity to 90 per cent.

In the 1949 act, support on the 1950 crop was to be at 90 per cent of parity if the supply percentage was not more than 102 (for tobacco, corn, wheat and rice) or 108 (for cotton and peanuts) as compared to 70 in the 1948 act.[65] The minimum level of support was to be 75 per

62. On July 17, 1952 this feature of the price-support act was amended (66 *Stat.* 758) so as to provide that the old parity formula would continue to be used for basic commodities until January 1, 1956 if it resulted in prices higher than those computed under the new formula. The 1952 act also made mandatory the support of prices of the basic commodities in 1953 and 1954 at 90 per cent of parity (if marketing quotas were not voted down). In addition, long-staple cotton was made a basic commodity for price-support purposes.

63. These comments pertain only to parity prices for the basic commodities. Parity prices for all nonbasics are now computed in accordance with the "modernized" parity formula contained in the 1948 act. The crops on which the provision now in effect operates most significantly to keep parity prices higher than they would be if computed in accordance with the criterion set up in the 1948 act are wheat, corn and cotton. These are also the products which present the most serious problems of excessive CCC holdings.

64. The supply percentage as defined in the acts of 1948 and 1949 is the estimated percentage which the total supply (estimated production plus carry-over) is of the normal supply. Normal supplies are defined separately for each of the principal commodities.

65. For 1951 the support level, for basic crops, was to be not less than 80 per cent of parity (except on tobacco, for which support was to be continued at 90 per cent). Ninety per cent of parity support was extended through the 1951 and 1952 seasons by administrative decision based on the supply situation. As noted in footnote 62, this level of support was to be continued until 1955 by a provision in the act of July 17, 1952.

cent of parity if the supply percentage was 130 or more, as compared to 60 per cent in the act of 1948.[66]

Heavy accumulations developed in 1949 and early 1950, but the situation was relieved by the unexpected revival of demand that accompanied the outbreak of war in Korea. Still larger accumulations were acquired in 1953 and 1954 but restraints on production were put into effect in an effort to hold down further increases in government-held stocks. Acreage controls and quotas were applied to wheat and cotton, and acreage allotments on corn were in effect for the 1954 crop.

Price Supports for "Nonbasic" Commodities

The 1949 act made some changes in the price-support arrangements for certain of the "nonbasic" commodities. The provision in respect to shorn wool was the same as that in the 1948 act. Tung nuts, honey and Irish potatoes were to be supported at not less than 60 or more than 90 per cent of parity. (However, an act of March 31, 1950, 64 *Stat.* 40, 42, provided that no price support may be made available on Irish potatoes unless marketing quotas are in effect. There was no authority for establishing marketing quotas on potatoes. Consequently, potatoes were no longer eligible for support.[67]) Whole milk and butterfat and their products were to be supported at 75 to 90 per cent of parity as necessary to assure adequate supplies.

For other nonbasics (if storable), the Secretary was authorized to provide supports in accordance with a sliding scale ranging from 75 to 90 per cent of parity as related to the same supply percentages as for the basics. However, he might provide supports at less than the 75 per cent minima, or none at all, if in his judgment such action was warranted on the basis of such factors as supply in relation to demand, prices at which other competing commodities were being supported, availability of funds, perishability of the commodity, the possibility of disposing of the stocks acquired, the ability or willingness of producers to keep supplies in line with demand, the need for offsetting temporary losses of export markets, and the importance of the commodity to agriculture and

66. If marketing quotas are disapproved, for basic crops other than tobacco, the support level is to be reduced to 50 per cent of parity. For tobacco, there can be no support program if quotas are disapproved. This does not mean, of course, as is sometimes implied, that prices would drop to 50 per cent of parity if quotas were voted down. It does mean that the CCC would not step in unless and until prices dropped to 50 per cent of parity. Essentially, what such a vote on the part of the growers would mean would be that the free-market price would prevail, certainly a lower price on some products than that now maintained but almost equally certainly a price well above the 50 per cent level, so long as demand and buying power remain at or near their present levels.

67. The cotton acreage control bill, Public Law 290, passed on January 30, 1954, included a clause permitting the use of Section 32 funds for supporting the price of potatoes.

the national economy. That is, the support of such commodities was made discretionary so far as the Secretary of Agriculture is concerned.[68]

THE BRANNAN PROPOSALS

The proposals made by Secretary of Agriculture Brannan in the spring of 1949 were very widely discussed, but they are not part of the legislative background of the price-support programs described in succeeding chapters. They were not incorporated into law and, in fact, did not have strong congressional or farm organization support, except from the Farmers' Union. However, they no doubt had some effect on the provisions written into the act of 1949. Both the Brannan plan and the act of 1949 called for higher levels of price support than those contained in the act of 1948.

The most significant changes proposed under the Brannan plan were as follows:

1. The use of a very complicated "income standard" as a method of computing price-support levels for farm products. This took as its base the very profitable years 1938–1947 [69] and required that prices for an enlarged list of basic commodities be supported at levels that would yield farm incomes as favorable, relative to nonfarm incomes, as those of these base years. Under the conditions of 1949, this formula would have resulted in price-support levels generally somewhat higher than those prescribed in Title II of the act of 1948 and not markedly different from those provided in the act of 1949. This, however, was due to the large crops of 1949. Had production been sharply reduced, through droughts or other causes, the requirement that support prices be high enough to yield incomes comparable to those of the base years would have called for support prices at very high levels.

2. Supports for Group I commodities were to be mandatory at full "income parity" levels. Group I consisted mainly of the old basic commodities, plus eggs, chickens, milk, hogs, beef cattle and lambs.

This meant an even more rigid system than that established by the 1949 act and left almost no opportunity for the exercise of judgment in the management of supplies of Group I commodities. The inevitable difficulties that would otherwise arise from excessive government commitments in the form of accumulated stocks and nonrecourse loans were

68. The Secretary may increase the support price for any commodity above the 90 per cent level, if, after public hearing, he determines "that price support at such increased level is necessary in order to prevent or alleviate a shortage in the supply of any agricultural commodity essential to the national welfare or in order to increase or maintain the production of any agricultural commodity in the interest of national security." The act also requires the Secretary to announce the level of price support for field crops in advance of the planting season in order that growers may plan their operations accordingly.

69. Dropping each year the twelfth preceding year and adding the next preceding one. That is, for 1949 the base would be 1938–1947, for 1950 it would be 1939–1948, and so on.

to be met almost wholly through rigorous controls on production. That is, if workable, the Brannan plan would almost inevitably constitute a high-price, low-output type of program for the major commodities.

For the Group II products, the proposal was that they be supported at such levels as the Secretary determines will result in fair and equitable treatment of such producers, taking into account the availability of funds, supply and demand conditions, the perishability of the commodity, its importance in the national economy and the prospect for disposing of stocks acquired. Consideration was also to be given to the need for supporting farm commodities depressed because of temporary losses of export markets and to the ability and willingness of producers to keep supplies in line with demand.

3. The most striking feature of the Brannan plan, and the one most widely discussed, was a proposal that the incomes to growers of perishable commodities be supported through direct payment by the government of the difference between the price received in the market and the support price established. This would permit the commodity to move at its free-market price, presumably a low one.

Consumers would get more of the product and at a lower price, but would pay the cost of the subsidy through taxes rather than by higher prices in the market. It was contended that much waste would be avoided and, in most cases, it would be expected that the markets would be cleared without resort to destruction of crops, expensive processing and storage operations or extreme restrictions on output.[70] However, the cost to the Treasury would inevitably be large, if total returns to farmers were maintained at lucrative levels, unless production was kept down by acreage allotments and marketing quotas. The plan did provide for restrictions on output and marketings. However, if these were made rigorous enough to keep market prices high and thus hold government payments to modest levels, the result would not be low prices to consumers.

4. The other principal feature of the plan was a proposal that its benefits be limited to specified maximum amounts for any one farm.[71] This was widely discussed as a proposal for strengthening the family farm and discouraging large-scale agriculture. Actually, the limits sug-

70. Such a plan would probably necessitate some arrangement for quotas on sales since, without such restrictions, the bonus on amounts marketed would make it attractive for growers to put on the market even larger quantities than if no program were in effect. It is customary, in years of heavy supply, for some portion of many of the perishable crops to be left on the farm because market returns are not sufficient to cover costs of harvesting and shipping. If a substantial bonus were paid on all deliveries without restriction on amounts sold, such conditions could result in such glutted markets for some crops at some times that the return from the market would be less than the cost of handling. Yet the product might still be put on the market in order to qualify for government payments on it.

71. Larger amounts than those specified could be grown on large-scale farms but benefits could apply only for the amounts falling within the specified maxima.

gested were not such as to affect any large number of farms or farmers. A wheat farmer could produce more than 14,000 bushels of wheat or a cotton farmer more than 90,000 pounds of cotton without exceeding the limits proposed. These are not small-farm operations. At the then current prices, outputs of these magnitudes would represent gross incomes of $25,000 to $30,000 per year.

The implications of the Brannan proposals have been attacked and defended on the basis of rather widespread misconceptions of the issues. Most of the farm organizations, except the Farmers' Union, have opposed the plan vigorously on the ground that it would provide direct subsidies to agriculture and would make farmers dependent on the whim of Congress for the maintenance of their incomes. These farm groups contend that they want to derive their incomes from sales in the market, not from government handouts. This contention implies that there is no subsidy in the alternative methods of supporting farm prices and incomes, which, of course, is far from the truth. Nearly all of the price-support mechanisms involve subsidies of considerable size, though not so large as those that would probably be required under the Brannan plan.

Some consumer groups have likewise failed to grasp the full implication of the Brannan plan. It is looked upon as a low-price-of-foods program. For perishables, such a plan would result in lower prices in the market, as compared to the procedures used in 1949 for supporting the price of potatoes. The product would reach the market and would actually be used, unless the crop exceeded even the amounts desired by consumers. In this respect the plan is undoubtedly superior to those authorized under existing legislation.[72]

This does not mean, however, that the products would not be paid for at good prices. Part of the price would be paid in the market and part in the form of taxes. The incidence of this cost would, of course, be different from that which results from relying wholly on market prices for making payments to farmers. Consumers with extremely low incomes would get the product at lower cost since they would not pay in taxes any important part of the subsidy paid to farmers. However, the great bulk of the wage-worker group, with wages and taxes at present levels, would probably pay a good portion of the difference in taxes and would not have as effective control over the cost of their food supplies as they now have through their choices of foods in markets that reflect the total cost of the product.

Nevertheless, the plan in respect to perishables had merit from the

---

72. There are, however, very perplexing administrative problems that would have to be solved. Grading standards are notoriously hard to devise and enforce for fruits, vegetables and some other farm products. Such a plan, if loosely administered, could easily result in payments for low-grade products such that the incentive for supplying the market with high-quality products would be weakened or destroyed. Such abuses as the making of unwarranted payments could easily creep in and would be extremely hard to detect and control.

consumer standpoint. Crops would not be destroyed in order to hold prices up, as was done in the potato program and in some of the marketing agreement programs. Under the potato program, consumers paid high prices in the markets and also paid large amounts in the form of taxes, but still did not get satisfactory quantities and qualities of potatoes.

For the nonperishables, which constitute about half of the nation's agricultural production, the Brannan plan was by no means a low-price plan for the benefit of consumers. It retained and even increased the high-level price supports then in existence. Even with the large output of a year like 1949, the prices to be supported under the plan were about as high as those specified in the Agricultural Act of 1949.[73] Had the output been smaller, the formula proposed would have required much higher prices, since the price would have had to be enough higher to provide a given level of farm income in spite of the smaller quantities sold.

Developments from 1949 On

From 1949 through 1953, there was little change in farm legislation and price-support policy. The upsurge in demand that grew out of the Korean war relieved pressure on the markets and postponed some of the adjustment problems that were becoming apparent in 1949 and early 1950. Such action as was taken was mainly that of continuing support prices for the basic crops at 90 per cent of parity and deferring a shift to the modernized parity formula for those crops on which such a change would have resulted in a lower parity criterion.

The first major change in this policy came in the Agricultural Act of 1954 (Public Law 690, 83d Congress), which was passed in August 1954 after a bitter struggle between those who favored retention of high price supports and those who were seeking to make the program more

---

73. The minimum mandatory support levels under Title II of the act of 1948, under the act of 1949 and under the Brannan plan, if applied under 1949 conditions, would have been as follows for some of the more important crops.

Commodity	Title II of 1948 Act	1949 Act	Brannan Plan
Corn, per bu.	$1.11	$1.19	$1.39
Cotton, per lb.	.22	.26	.26
Wheat, per bu.	1.63	1.68	1.74
Tobacco, per lb. (flue-cured)	.43	.49	.46
Peanuts, per lb.	.11	.11	.09

(Data from George Mehren, "Comparative Costs of Agricultural Price Support in 1949," *American Economic Review*, May 1951, Proceedings Issue, p. 727.)

It should be noted that this comparison applies only to the year 1949, a year in which the volume of farm production stood at 140 (1935–39 = 100), the highest on record. Had the volume of production been smaller, this would not have affected the maximum supports under the acts of 1948 and 1949, since these were specifically limited to 90 per cent of parity. With a normal crop, for the commodities included under Group I, as defined in the Brannan plan, the levels of prices to be supported would be well above even the high levels provided in the acts of 1948 and 1949.

flexible and to move toward freer markets for farm products. The new act was a victory for those who favored a more flexible program but it did not change drastically the main features of the farm program. It was rather, for the most part, a reversion to the legislation passed in 1948 and 1949 by both Republican and Democratic congresses.

The new act permitted the fixing of price supports for the basic commodities within a range of 82½ to 90 per cent of parity for the 1955 crop and reversion thereafter to the 75 to 90 per cent range provided in the Agricultural Act of 1949 (provided producers have not disapproved marketing quotas). The production and marketing control features of the farm program were left virtually unchanged. The action taken also meant that, beginning in 1956, the gradual transition to the use of the modernized parity formula for all farm commodities would be resumed. The Agricultural Act of 1948 had provided for such a transition period, but its initiation had been deferred by the Agricultural Act of 1949 and subsequent legislation.

The other important change was the provision (in Title I) for a set-aside of very large quantities of the stocks held by the Commodity Credit Corporation. Up to $2.5 billion worth of these commodities was to be segregated for disposal through noncommercial channels with a view to getting them into use and relieving pressure on the Commodity Credit Corporation. These stocks are to be disposed of through donation or sale for relief purposes at home or abroad, barter for strategic materials, aid to school lunch programs and in various other ways, with a view to making effective use of them and bringing the commodity stock situation into better balance without putting undue pressure on the commercial commodity markets. This phase of the program, like the move in the direction of more flexible price supports, is an effort to reestablish a more normal marketing situation and to avoid the waste and heavy expense resulting from the maintenance of excessive stocks in the hands of the Commodity Credit Corporation.

The act of 1954 included also a number of minor provisions which were mostly clarifications or slight modifications of the previously existing body of farm legislation. They did not make important changes in objectives or methods except in the program for the support of wool prices. Here the Secretary of Agriculture was authorized to support the prices of wool and mohair by means of loans, purchases or *compensatory payments,* or in other ways. This is in some respects an experimental program limited to the years 1955 to 1959. The compensatory payment plan is designed to permit domestic wools to move freely in competition with foreign wools. The difference between the support price established by the Secretary of Agriculture and the price received in the market is made up by means of direct payments to growers from the government. The procedure is designed to lessen somewhat the inconsistencies arising out of an attempt to maintain domestic prices and at the same time to reduce barriers to international trade. It is also designed to prevent the accumulation of domestic wool in inactive stocks while foreign wools flow freely into the market. Payments are limited to 70 per cent of the amounts collected as tariffs on wool and wool products, and the level of support may not exceed 110 per cent of parity. The announced policy is to provide price incentives that will result in the domestic production of not less than 360 million pounds of shorn wool.

Chapter 8

Food Subsidies and the Disposal of Surpluses

THE FARM PROGRAMS described in the preceding chapter were based, in the main, on four kinds of action: (1) control of production; (2) control of amounts marketed; (3) direct transfers of income to farmers; and (4) marketing agreements. There has been, in addition, a less direct type of program which has absorbed large amounts of public funds and has had important effects on farm incomes, though not designed solely for that purpose. It includes expenditures for disposal of surpluses, making foods available to low-income groups, holding down prices paid by consumers (during the war years), aiding people abroad and finding new outlets for farm products.[1]

The purposes of these actions have nearly always been mixed, though the desire to strengthen or maintain the prices of farm products has been dominant in nearly all of them except the lend-lease and postwar foreign-aid programs. Often the immediate objective was to relieve the government itself of embarrassing accumulations of farm commodities, but these in turn had been acquired in the process of supporting the prices paid to farmers. A secondary objective was that of finding suitable outlets for commodities already produced and much needed by groups that were unable to buy them at full market prices.

Surplus Removal First Undertaken by the Farm Board

The idea of disposing of farm products by subsidizing exports was prominent in nearly all of the farm relief plans put forward in the 1920s. However, there was no legislation to provide for such action until the

1. The food subsidy program of the war years was ostensibly intended to hold down costs of living. However, it also had the effect of preventing a rollback of prices to farmers, if the policy implied in the Price Stabilization Act was to be carried out. Whether it should be regarded as a subsidy to agriculture or to consumers is debatable. If the same procedure had been followed here as in rents, the prices to farmers would have been pushed back to the levels they had reached at the time the price freeze was made applicable. The food subsidy program avoided that issue by making public funds available to permit the continuance of higher than base-level prices for farm products while holding prices to consumers relatively stable.

Those who interpret the payments as a subsidy to consumers contend that congressional policy was to allow farm prices to rise above the levels prevailing when other prices were frozen, partly as an incentive for larger production. The fact remains that farm prices were allowed to exceed the parity level, which was the criterion established by the Congress at the insistence of the President. It may be noted, however, that there was less down-grading of quality of farm products than for many of the nonfarm commodities for which prices were held nominally at ceiling levels.

277

Farm Board was established in 1929. The authority given the Board was broad enough to allow some use of such devices though they were not a part of its original plans and were used later only when it became apparent that accumulated stocks could not be disposed of through ordinary channels. Even then, the subsidization of exports constituted only a minor part of the Board's program. The Farm Board made some attempt to stimulate foreign purchases by extending credits directly to foreign governments (rather than to the trade). Some 47.5 million bushels of wheat were sold to Germany and China in 1932, paid for in government notes. At about the same time the Board entered into a barter deal with Brazil whereby it traded 25 million bushels of wheat for 2.5 million bags of raw coffee.

Since huge stocks of wheat and cotton were on hand and many people were desperately in need of food and textiles, the Congress in the spring and summer of 1932 donated to the Red Cross 85 million bushels of wheat and 844,000 bales of cotton out of Farm Board stocks. This action apparently was motivated in part by a desire to relieve the government of superabundant stocks and in part by a wish to give aid to the needy. Purely from a relief standpoint, it probably would have been simpler to give assistance in other ways. However, donating stocks to the Red Cross kept the operation in private channels, which was in accord with Administration policy at that time.

These early efforts to dispose of surpluses were not part of any considered plan. They were emergency operations undertaken to ease a desperate situation created by the virtual breakdown of normal trading arrangements. Similar steps taken in the first part of the succeeding administration were also emergency and stopgap operations.

DIVERSION AND RELIEF ACTIVITIES UNDER AAA

Diversion of supplies into abnormal channels and grants of foodstuffs for relief were not prominent features of the policy outlined in the Agricultural Adjustment Act of May 12, 1933.[2] Nevertheless, pressures and incentives for such action soon appeared and numerous experimental programs of this type were undertaken during the first years of the Roosevelt administration.

Sentiment for the use of export subsidies was still strong and it was almost inevitable that this procedure would be tried out experimentally. Secretary Wallace was not greatly impressed with the merit of the proposal but did approve some minor export subsidy programs which were put into effect. The Agricultural Adjustment Administration emphasized other ways of getting rid of unsalable stocks and relieving distress among domestic consumers.

Many of these activities were financed jointly by the Agricultural Ad-

2. The act stated that in addition to the principal purposes for which the proceeds from processing taxes were made available the Secretary might use such funds "for expansion of markets and removal of surplus agricultural products."

justment Administration and the Emergency Relief Administration, usually under a plan whereby the Adjustment Administration supplied the products and the Relief Administration financed processing and distribution. In some cases the Relief Administration made purchases with its own funds, but in accordance with the same general pattern.

From 1936 on, the removal of surpluses by resort to abnormal outlets came to have a more definite place in the program. The 1935 amendment to the Agricultural Adjustment Act contained a provision (Section 32) which assigned to the Secretary of Agriculture 30 per cent of the income from customs receipts, for use in supporting the prices of farm products. These funds could be used (1) to encourage the exportation of agricultural commodities and products, (2) to encourage domestic consumption of these products by diverting them from normal channels of trade and commerce, and (3) to re-establish farmers' purchasing power by making payments in connection with the normal production of any agricultural commodity for domestic consumption (that is, payments to increase return on the crops produced on allotted acres).[3] After money from this source began to be available, in 1936, most of the surplus removal and related activities were carried out under these authorizations.[4]

In the first year of the Agricultural Adjustment Administration, some attempt was made to stimulate exports by means of loans to foreign governments similar to those made to Germany and China by the Farm Board. The Reconstruction Finance Corporation made a loan commitment of $50 million to the Chinese government in July 1933. About $15 million of it was used ($7.1 million to buy wheat and flour, and $8.2 million to buy cotton). However, the Chinese cotton growers objected to the purchase of U.S. cotton under this plan and the project was abandoned. In a similar way, some 75,000 bales of cotton were exported to Russia. A plan for exporting pork to Russia fell through.

3. Purpose number 3 as stated in the original amendment was to finance adjustments in the quantity of agricultural commodities planted or produced for market. The section was amended in 1936 by substituting the purpose given above.

4. President Roosevelt objected to this method of appropriating funds, on the ground that continuing blanket appropriations of this kind were not in accord with sound budgeting practices. In his budget message of January 3, 1936, he recommended the repeal of Section 32. He contended that it denied the President opportunity to consider the need for such funds when reviewing budget estimates, and that it violated the principles of the Permanent Appropriation Repeal Act of 1934 and of the Budget and Accounting Act of June 10, 1921.

However, the Congress did not act on this recommendation and Section 32 has been continued on the books. The practice has been to require that planned expenditures be justified in the budget committee hearings. There is some tendency, however, for the congressional committees and the administrators to assume that the amounts thus set aside are to be available for these purposes and the restraints on such expenditures may be less rigorous than those relating to new appropriations of uncommitted funds. Perhaps a more significant criticism is that in prosperous times when the need is not pressing, customs receipts tend to be high, whereas in periods when the need is great the income from this source may be small. This is mitigated by the amendment passed in 1949 which permits carry-overs that will bring the fund up to $300 million before unused funds must be turned back to the Treasury.

The principal direct export subsidy was applied to wheat from the Pacific Northwest in 1933–34. This subsidy was handled through the North Pacific Emergency Export Association, set up under a marketing agreement between the Secretary of Agriculture and the millers, grain exporters and grain cooperatives of that area. About 28.4 million bushels of wheat were moved at an average loss of 23 cents a bushel and a total cost of $6.5 million.[5] After 1934, emphasis shifted to some extent toward efforts to increase domestic consumption and improve the diets of school children and people on relief. However, export subsidies were sizable in the period 1938 to 1942.

Creation of the Federal Surplus Relief Corporation

This shift in emphasis became apparent shortly after the Roosevelt administration took over. In October 1933 the Federal Emergency Relief Administrator, the Secretary of Agriculture and the Federal Public Works Administrator set up the Federal Surplus Relief Corporation, organized under the laws of Delaware. This, in the first period, was virtually a part of the Federal Emergency Relief Administration, though closely integrated with the Commodities Purchase Section of the Agricultural Adjustment Administration. In 1935 its name was changed to Federal Surplus Commodities Corporation and it became, in effect, a subsidiary of the Agricultural Adjustment Administration.[6]

The first activity of the Federal Surplus Relief Corporation was the distribution of surplus pork, butter and wheat acquired in price-support activities. The pork supplies consisted of about 100 million pounds of salt pork from the pig-sow slaughter campaign of 1933–34 and the products derived from an additional 2 million head of hogs bought by the FSRC itself. This operation, to the end of 1934, involved the movement of 293 million pounds of pork and 24 million pounds of lard at a cost of $33.4 million ($18.8 million came from AAA funds and $14.6 million from relief funds).[7]

5. These funds were supplied by the Agricultural Adjustment Administration out of receipts from the processing tax on wheat. For a fuller description of this operation, and others of the 1933–36 period, see Edwin G. Nourse, Joseph S. Davis and John D. Black, *Three Years of the Agricultural Adjustment Administration,* Brookings Institution, Washington, 1937, Chapter 7.

The largest use of Section 32 funds for export subsidies was in 1939–1940, when it amounted to $47.2 million. Since the war, export subsidies financed out of Section 32 funds have averaged about $24 million per year. This is in addition to the very large export subsidy on wheat under the International Wheat Agreement, which in the first four years of operation (that is, to June 30, 1953) amounted to $546.5 million. A loss of $56 million on exports was also incurred under the Foreign Aid Act of 1947, and there were other export subsidies in connection with the various foreign-aid programs that were of a more nebulous sort. More than half of the Section 32 funds used in financing export subsidies were for wheat and cotton.

6. At that time, the Federal Emergency Relief Administration was about to be abolished and the Secretary of Agriculture was being given more funds and authority to operate in this realm through passage of the amendment which included Section 32.

7. By the end of 1935, expenditures from the Federal Surplus Relief Corporation had amounted to $45.6 million.

Purchases to support the prices of butter, evaporated and condensed milk, and cheese were begun in the fall of 1933 and were continued until 1936. By the end of 1935, such purchases had amounted to 75.1 million pounds of butter, 18.1 million pounds of cheese and 46.7 million pounds of evaporated and condensed milk. In addition, 15.5 million pounds of dry skim milk were acquired. The total cost of this operation was about $24 million divided as follows: $11 million from the Treasury, advanced against processing taxes, which, however, were not levied as planned, $12 million from Jones-Connally Cattle Act appropriations and $1 million from relief funds.[8]

There was also a wheat and flour program, which grew out of purchases made in the fall of 1933 to support the price of wheat. These stocks came into existence in much the same way as the stocks accumulated by the Farm Board but not on so large a scale. In this case the purchases were made by the Farmers National Grain Corporation, in October 1933, to check a downturn in wheat prices which occurred at that time.

In all, some 16 million bushels of wheat were acquired. About half of this was distributed to farmers in the drought-stricken areas for use as feed, 4.5 million bushels were traded for corn, oats, barley and milo, also to be used as feed, and about 3.6 million bushels were distributed for use as food by families on relief. The cost, amounting to about $5 million, was paid out of relief funds. Later, during 1934 and 1935, some wheat was bought for distribution as seed in the drought areas and an additional 2.6 million bushels of Pacific Northwest wheat were acquired for distribution as feed in other parts of the country. In the spring of 1936 another 3 million bushels of Pacific Northwest and East Central states wheat were bought for relief distribution as human food. Here the payment for the wheat was made from Section 32 funds while the costs of milling and distribution came from relief funds.

The most significant volume of relief buying during this period was carried out in the drought relief purchases of cattle, calves, sheep and goats. About 8.3 million head of cattle and 1.4 million head of sheep were purchased. The money came mainly from the large special appropriation for drought relief which was made in 1934.[9]

8. The Supreme Court decision of January 6, 1936 outlawed the processing taxes, thus preventing the development of the plan contemplated at the time this advance was made. The Jones-Connally Act of April 7, 1934 designated cattle as a "basic agricultural commodity" and authorized an appropriation of $50 million "to enable the Secretary of Agriculture to make advances to the Federal Surplus Relief Corporation for the purchase of dairy and beef products for distribution for relief purposes, and to enable [him] . . . to eliminate diseased dairy and beef cattle, including dairy cattle suffering from tuberculosis or Bang's disease, and to make payments to owners with respect thereto." The relief funds were provided out of appropriations made available to the Federal Relief Administration.

9. Expenditures under the Jones-Connally and LaFollette Acts for buying dairy products and diseased cattle amounted to $93,772,003 in 1935 and $32,464,786 in 1936. U.S. House Committee on Appropriations, *Agricultural Department Appropriation Bill for 1937*, Hearings, p. 755.

Both the Federal Surplus Relief Corporation and its successor, the Federal Surplus Commodities Corporation, purchased from time to time considerable quantities of minor crops—rice, fresh apples, dried apples, citrus fruits, grapes, dried prunes, dried beans, cabbage, canned peas, white and sweet potatoes, eggs, processed milk, sugar, sirup, canned salmon and so on. These were diverted to relief channels. To some extent the expenditures thus made were a substitute for relief in other forms. However, the purchases were so timed and handled as to be principally for the relief of agricultural producers rather than consumers. Both purposes were served, but physical distribution of commodities through relief agencies is not an efficient way of getting food into the hands of needy families.

Diversion to Lower Uses

Another procedure was to pay bonuses for channeling surplus commodities into lower types of use. Payments were made for feeding peanuts to livestock instead of selling them, and for selling peanuts to crushers for the production of oil. Bonuses were also paid to the crushers. The pig-sow program involved some diversion to low-value products such as fertilizer, stock feeds and grease. The olive, raisin, prune and walnut marketing agreements also provided for converting part of the available supply into by-products of various kinds.[10]

Cotton Price Adjustment Payments on the 1934 Crop

In 1933 the Agricultural Adjustment Administration authorized loans on cotton at 10 cents per pound, which was above the prevailing market price. The loans of that year worked out relatively well. They strengthened prices without checking unduly the movement of cotton into trade channels. There was a good deal of pressure, however, for raising the loan level above 10 cents. The Agricultural Adjustment Administration yielded to this pressure and raised the rate to 12 cents for the 1934 crop. This applied not only to 1934 cotton but also to the remaining portions of the stocks acquired from the Farm Board. The result was that much of the 1934 cotton crop went under loan and failed to move freely.

To avoid further accumulations from the 1935 crop, the Agricultural Adjustment Administration offered, in August 1935, a cash payment on the 1935 crop.[11] This payment was to cover the difference between 12

10. There was also a small experimental diversion project for cotton. About $1.3 million was allotted, out of Section 32 funds, for the purchase of 10 million square yards of cotton fabric to be used in reinforcing concrete highways. During this same period small subsidies were provided out of Section 32 funds for aid in exporting pears and some types of tobacco. See U.S. House Committee on Appropriations, *Agricultural Department Appropriation Bill for 1938*, Hearings, p. 1192.

11. In the two succeeding years a substantial portion of the Section 32 funds received was used in financing the cotton price adjustment program. Some of the fund was also used in refunding to the Treasury advances made against processing taxes that were not

cents and the price prevailing in the market, but with an upper limit of 2 cents per pound. It permitted the market to function normally but maintained a 12 cent return to growers at the spot-cotton markets by providing a subsidy as a supplement to the price received in the market. The procedure was similar to that later proposed by Secretary Brannan for maintaining the returns to growers for perishables while allowing the markets to clear at free-market prices.

Both cotton exports and domestic consumption increased, but it is impossible to say how much of this increase was due to this subsidy and how much to other causes. The cost of this price adjustment was about $395 million, paid out of funds derived from processing taxes and customs receipts transferred to the Secretary of Agriculture under Section 32.

Export Subsidy and Diversion Programs, 1936–1941

The Hoosac Mills decision forced abandonment of processing taxes as a source of funds for export subsidies and other methods of disposing of surpluses through abnormal outlets. Thereafter, main reliance was on Section 32 funds for programs of this kind, though some funds became available under the Jones-Connally Cattle Act and the Jones-Costigan Sugar Act.

The Soil Conservation and Domestic Allotment Act of 1936 also authorized the Secretary to use some of the funds appropriated for expanding domestic and foreign markets for farm products, seeking new markets and removing surpluses. Through 1936 and 1937 such operations were on a modest scale; expenditures amounted to about $17 million in 1936 and $15.5 million in 1937. The quantities taken were too small, in most cases, to have any significant effect on prices, though the purchases did help in relieving temporary gluts in the markets for some of the minor crops. The products purchased and the amounts of money involved, for 1936, are given in Table 22.

Emphasis continued for a time to be placed on relief distribution and export subsidies. The experience with export subsidies was not sufficiently encouraging to lead to greater reliance on them. If used as a means of increasing exports of the major crops, they would have been very expensive and also a handicap to the efforts then being made to encourage normal international trade by reducing tariffs through agreements negotiated under the Trade Agreements Act of 1934. The widespread unemployment and poverty still prevalent in the United States made it logical to channel "surplus" foodstuffs to needy groups in this country rather than to try to dump them on foreign markets already glutted with products from other areas.

---

collected because of the invalidation of the Agricultural Adjustment Act. The agricultural conservation program was also financed in part from these funds during its early years.

TABLE 22

COMMODITIES PROCURED BY THE COMMODITY PURCHASE SECTION OF THE
AGRICULTURAL ADJUSTMENT ADMINISTRATION, CALENDAR YEAR 1936

Commodity		Quantity	Commodity Cost
Total			$13,382,835.53
Section 32 funds			11,752,206.40
Apples (fresh)	bushels	1,372,275	916,414.37
Beans (dried)	pounds	2,400,000	57,300.70
Cabbage	pounds	8,751,931	56,759.92
Carrots	pounds	2,637,900	24,663.80
Cauliflower	crates	78,760	45,677.00
Grapefruit	boxes	653,943	324,013.11
Onions	pounds	35,340,400	324,755.88
Peas (dried)	pounds	13,082,295	232,531.08
Oranges	boxes	198,312	194,489.50
Peaches (dried)	pounds	2,940,000	227,850.00
Pears (fresh Bartlett)	boxes	234,682	201,473.02
Prunes (dried)	pounds	54,192,425	2,436,815.81
Sirup (cane and sorghum)	gallons	263,068	92,132.96
Eggs (shell)	cases	31,472	194,604.48
Wheat for flour	bushels	3,041,824	2,471,143.76
Cattle and calves for dressed beef and veal	head	3,663	96,164.45
Cotton (raw baled)	bales	50,000	2,646,100.59
Cotton fabric	yards	2,906,896	351,594.66
Cotton road mats	pieces	89,535	355,266.95
Cotton ticking	yards	4,750,076	502,454.36
Jones-Connally funds			1,630,629.13
Butter	pounds	2,951,303	852,564.36
Cheese	pounds	932,038	143,083.26
Milk (dry skim)	pounds	3,595,663	299,629.51
Milk (evaporated)	cases (48 tall)	141,600	335,352.00

Source: U.S. Agricultural Adjustment Administration, *Agricultural Conservation, 1936,*
A Report of the Activities of the Agricultural Adjustment Administration, 1937, p. 80.

Direct distribution through the relief organizations was proving cumbersome and inequitable. Consequently the Agricultural Adjustment Administration soon undertook to devise methods for disposing of surpluses in more orderly ways. The principal results of this effort were the initiation of the School Lunch Program in 1936 and later the Food Stamp Plan. Export subsidies and diversion to new uses have been continued on a modest scale even through the war and postwar years.

The School Lunch Program

Under the school lunch plan, surplus commodities were given to the schools (both public and private) for use in serving lunches to pupils.

This was to make it possible to supply one good meal per day to school children, many of whom were not getting adequate or proper food at home.

Though it was desirable to improve the diets of school children in low-income areas and to channel surplus foods into constructive uses, this outlet by itself was not big enough to have much effect on the prices of the products distributed. For example, in 1938–39 only 30 million pounds of food were so distributed as compared with 1,970 million pounds made available to state welfare agencies.[12] Expenditures for the distribution of foods for the School Lunch Program were running at the rate of about $4 million per year in fiscal 1940.[13]

In the early years of the School Lunch Program, distribution was principally to schools in low-income areas. Meals were furnished without charge if they were made up in whole or in part from surplus commodities. This was made possible through the cooperation of the Works Progress Administration and of local educational, civic and welfare agencies. Funds for purchasing the surplus commodities were supplied from customs receipts assigned to the Secretary of Agriculture under Section 32. This informal arrangement was superseded in 1946 when a National School Lunch Act was passed.

As formalized in the act of 1946,[14] the plan provides for making funds available in accordance with a formula which takes account of the number of school children in the state and the relation of per capita income in the state to that in the United States as a whole. Maximum reimbursements for meals are 9 cents, 6 cents and 2 cents for types A, B, and C. Type A is a complete meal supplying from one third to one half of the daily nutritional requirement. Type B contains the same nutritional elements but in smaller quantities. Type C consists of one-half pint of milk only.

Each dollar of federal funds thus provided must be supplemented by $1.50 in funds supplied from within the state. Beginning in 1956 such supplementation must be at the rate of $3 for each dollar contributed by the federal government. In addition to the cash assistance thus provided, the Department of Agriculture supplies foods of suitable nutritional value and available in surplus amounts either from current production or in government-owned stocks. The Agricultural Act of 1954 (Public Law

12. U.S. Agricultural Adjustment Administration, *Report of the Associate Administrator of the Agricultural Adjustment Administration, in Charge of the Division of Marketing and Marketing Agreements, and the President of the Federal Surplus Commodities Corporation, 1939*, p. 53.

13. U.S. Department of Agriculture, *Agricultural Statistics, 1953*, p. 724. This was increased to $13 million in 1941 and to about $22 million in 1942. Thereafter it dropped off rapidly to less than $6 million in 1945 and 1946 and to only $2.3 million in 1947. The program was revived after the war and has involved Section 32 fund expenditures ranging from $16.5 million to $50 million in the period 1948–1952. These amounts have been supplemented by other funds since the passage of the National School Lunch Act of 1946.

14. 60 *Stat.* 230.

690, 83d Congress) made available an additional $50 million per year (from September 1, 1954 to June 30, 1956) for increasing the consumption of fluid milk by children in nonprofit schools of high school grade and under.

Until 1943 the distributions to state relief agencies and those made under the Food Stamp Plan absorbed much larger quantities of surplus commodities than in the years since then. After the discontinuance of the more general relief programs, the School Lunch Program provided the largest single outlet for surplus commodities purchased with Section 32 funds.

Sources and Amounts of School Lunch Funds

From its inception in 1935 until passage of the National School Lunch Act in 1946 the farm products supplied under the School Lunch Program were paid for with Section 32 funds, so far as federal contributions were concerned. Thereafter, direct appropriations were authorized for carrying on the program, but Section 32 funds continued to be used through 1948–49. In addition, commodities were donated out of price-support purchases made with Section 32 funds and under the authorization provided in Section 416 of the Agricultural Act of 1949.[15] Some farm products also were provided under authorizations contained in Section 6 of the National School Lunch Act. Section 6 authorized the Department of Agriculture to purchase commodities for distribution to the schools. In fiscal 1953, expenditures for these different authorizations amounted to $66,468,547 ($14,744,071 under Section 6 and $51,724,-476 under Section 32).

From 1936 through 1953 expenditures out of Section 32 funds for school lunch purposes amounted to $351.7 million. In addition, commodities worth $261.1 million were donated under Sections 32 and 416.[16] For the fiscal years 1950 through 1953, the amounts made available in cash under the National School Lunch Act were at about the rate of $65 million per year.[17] Donations of commodities in these years were approximately $55 million, $50 million, $32 million and $64 million respectively.[18] The school lunch operations thus involved federal expenditures of about $916.1 million for the period 1935 through June 1953. In fiscal 1953 the cost to the federal government was $131.6 million.

15. Section 416 authorized the Secretary of Agriculture and the Commodity Credit Corporation to make available to the Munitions Board or other government agencies products held by CCC that are in danger of deterioration or spoilage. Such commodities may be used in payment for commodities not produced in the United States (presumably strategic commodities). Amounts in excess of those so used may be made available for the School Lunch Program, the Bureau of Indian Affairs or to public or private welfare agencies.

16. *Agricultural Statistics, 1953,* p. 724.

17. For 1953, $67,185,000. *Ibid.*

18. *Ibid.*

Amounts and Value of Products Used

The 1953 contributions of foodstuffs for school lunches under the two acts authorizing such distribution [19] provided outlets for modest quantities of a number of minor crops but not enough to make important differences in the amounts received for them. The list included beans, cheese, cherries, peaches, peas, peanut butter, tomatoes, apples, dried milk and orange juice. In 1953 the largest items were turkeys ($21.7 million), pork products ($11.8 million), butter ($10.2 million), cheese ($6.1 million), eggs ($2.8 million) and milk ($2.3 million).[20]

Importance from the Standpoint of Diets

The provision of a subsidy for the purpose of making available better school lunches, or the same kind at lower cost, appears to have considerable support in the Congress, though on mixed grounds. It is based in part on the desire to improve the diets of school-age children. Undoubtedly, part of the backing for the program derives from its supposed usefulness in providing an outlet for surpluses, though it seems not to be very significant for this purpose. The amounts involved are, in most cases, so small a part of the total production that the effect on price is negligible.

It is not clear, in fact, that the School Lunch Program contributes as much to the adequacy of diets among school children as it is often assumed to do. The coverage is uneven and the quality of the lunches provided is by no means uniformly high. Participation in 1951, in terms of total school enrollment, ranged from a low of 14 per cent in South Dakota to a high of 68.1 per cent in Louisiana. In most states, participation was between 25 and 35 per cent of total enrollment. The average for the United States was 30.3 per cent.[21] Reimbursement from the federal government averaged only 4.4 cents per meal in 1952 and 4.9 cents in 1951.[22] It is doubtful that so small a subsidy would affect importantly the purchase of such lunches by school children generally.[23]

19. Section 32 of the act of 1935 and Section 6 of the National School Lunch Act.

20. See U.S. House Committee on Appropriations, *Department of Agriculture Appropriations for 1955*, Hearings, Part 3, p. 1038.

21. U.S. House Committee on Appropriations, *Department of Agriculture Appropriations for 1953*, Hearings, Part 2, p. 1405. The low figure in South Dakota was due to special circumstances affecting state appropriations for administering the program (see p. 1389). Only five other states, Connecticut, Nebraska, Nevada, Pennsylvania and Rhode Island, showed participation of less than 20 per cent. Of the total number of schools (approximately 200,000 including parochial schools), 54,000 were participating in 1951, or about 27 per cent (p. 1388).

The meaning of the term participation as used in the source quoted is not entirely clear. Apparently it is in terms of total enrollment in the schools that take part in these programs. This does not mean, of course, that all pupils in these schools actually benefit. Many of them carry their lunches, go home for lunch or buy lunch elsewhere than in the school cafeterias.

22. U.S. House Committee on Appropriations, *Department of Agriculture Appropriations for 1954*, Hearings, p. 1694.

23. In the 1953 hearings before the Senate Appropriations Committee, one supervisor (from California) was quoted as saying that if more than 20 cents is charged for school

By far the largest part of the expense is borne by the children themselves, by state and local governments, and by other local agencies. For
the fiscal year 1953 the estimated contribution by the pupils was $276
million, by state and local governments $57 million and by other local
agencies $46 million, or a total of $379 million as compared with $83
million in direct appropriations from the federal government and $52
million in donated commodities.[24]

The program undoubtedly served as a stimulus and an aid in spreading
the school lunch idea to areas where it was not previously in use, and
helped materially in improving the nutrition of school children during the
depression years. Under present conditions, the plan constitutes a very
thinly spread subsidy for school lunches generally and one that will become even thinner if participation increases, unless the appropriations for
it are increased substantially.

The Congress apparently contemplates shifting the cost of the program
more and more to the states and using the federal subsidy mainly as a
method of getting the work started. After 1955, the matching arrangement provided in the law currently in effect calls for contributions from
within the states (including parents' contributions) of $3 for each $1 of
federal expenditure. The present national rate of matching is almost 4 to
1 and is rising. There may be some states, however, in which the matching
ratio has not yet reached 3 to 1.

For the more prosperous states and communities, there appears to be
no significant gain from paying funds into the federal Treasury and having them redistributed from that source. Any thinly spread, general subsidy is bound to be very expensive and must eventually be paid by the
recipient states and communities, probably with much waste in the
process.

The effectiveness of federal expenditures in accomplishing the purpose
for which the program is designed could apparently be increased by providing a selective program aimed at bettering diets where the greatest
need exists. This might be combined with an educational program for
establishing and improving school lunch facilities in localities where the
general level of income is such that they could be supported locally. Distribution of surplus commodities for use in schools still could be carried on, by maintaining appropriate liaison between the Department
of Agriculture and the school authorities.

Under present arrangements, the amounts and kinds of commodities
turned over are more likely to be dictated by the need of the Commodity
Credit Corporation to unburden itself or by demands for aid to producer
groups than by the requirements for a well-planned, efficient system of

---

lunches only 50 per cent of the children will buy them, despite the charity provisions.
Thus the school lunches, unless they are heavily subsidized, may tend to benefit largely
the relatively well-to-do children rather than those most in need. See U.S. Senate Committee on Appropriations, *Agricultural Appropriations for 1954*, Hearings, pp. 993–94.

24. U.S. House Committee on Appropriations, *Department of Agriculture Appropriations for 1955*, Hearings, Part 3, p. 1037.

providing school lunches. If the school authorities themselves made the selections, appropriate foods that are available in surplus still could be used to the fullest extent possible, but in a program directed primarily to the improvement of diets. For commodities purchased with Section 32 funds, the composition of purchases and the effect on market supplies and prices, though slight, would probably not be much changed, especially if suitable cooperation were maintained between the school systems and the Department of Agriculture.

Food Stamp Plan Inaugurated in 1939

A second and more extensive plan for moving surplus foodstuffs into consumption was put into effect experimentally in 1939.[25] This was known as the Food Stamp Plan. Under it families on relief were allowed to purchase, for cash, orange-colored food stamps in amounts roughly equal to their normal expenditures for food. These stamps might be spent in food stores in the same way as money. The buyer of orange stamps received without charge blue stamps having a face value equal to 50 per cent of the value of the orange stamps. These could be used as money for the purchase of foods declared by the Secretary of Agriculture to be in surplus supply. The grocer accepting either type of stamp could exchange it for cash at face value, provided he had complied with the regulations as to types of commodities sold for blue stamps.

The orange stamps were self-financing. The blue stamps were redeemed out of funds supplied by the Secretary of Agriculture from the customs revenues allotted to him. Thus the net effect of the plan was to increase the food-buying power of eligible, low-income families, presumably by an amount comparable to the value of the blue stamps given out. It meant using Section 32 funds to enlarge the consumption of foodstuffs declared to be in surplus, but through purchase in the grocery stores after being handled in the regular channels of trade, rather than by direct distribution through welfare agencies.

The plan was a direct attack on a very real problem, though more cumbersome than the provision of relief in cash form. The producers of many farm products still were faced with weak and glutted markets while, at the same time, many people on relief were unable to buy adequate quantities of food.

A later version of the Food Stamp Plan, which was widely discussed in 1943 and 1944 but was not passed by Congress, would have established a similar arrangement for all low-income families. Under this plan it

25. The plan was first tried in Rochester, New York, in May 1939. It was extended to Dayton, Ohio, in June and to Seattle, Washington, Birmingham, Alabama, Des Moines, Iowa, and Pottawatomie County, Oklahoma, in July. Over the next three years it was extended to more and more areas. By June 1941 nearly 4 million people were participating. For a fuller description see U.S. Agricultural Adjustment Administration, *Report of the Associate Administrator . . . Federal Surplus Commodities Corporation, 1939*, pp. 54–56; also *Report of the Administrative Official in Charge of Surplus Removal and Marketing Agreement Programs, 1940*, pp. 10–13, and *Report of the Administrator of Surplus Marketing Administration, 1941*, pp. 15–19.

was proposed that the cost of an adequate minimum diet be ascertained and that any family be permitted to turn over a specified percentage of its income in return for food stamps sufficient to purchase the minimum requirement of food. If the specified percentage of income amounted to less than the value of food required for a minimum healthful diet, the family would find it profitable to exchange it for food stamps. High-income families would not find it to their advantage to exchange the required percentage of income for stamps since the income thus surrendered would amount to more than the value of the stamps.

This plan, which was proposed as part of the postwar agricultural legislation, was intended as a means of assuring adequate diets to all of the people and preventing destruction or curtailment of food supplies urgently needed by low-income families. Though it would have required large contributions from the Treasury, it would have avoided the very heavy cost of providing subsidies to keep the prices of foods down for all consumers whether in need of such aid or not. It was the extension of food subsidies to all consumers that caused the wartime food subsidy program to be so costly to the government and made it the target of such vigorous criticism by the farm groups. Though there was much discussion of this proposed plan in the Senate Committee on Agriculture and Forestry, the Congress did not act on it.

The more limited food stamp program, available only to people eligible for public assistance, grew rapidly in the early 1940s. By 1942, expenditures under it were amounting to more than $100 million per year.[26] The rapid upsurge of employment and incomes in 1941 and 1942 removed much of the need of consumers for such a program, and food surpluses were no longer a matter of concern. The plan was discontinued in 1943 and has not been revived.

Cost of the Food Stamp Program

The experimental food stamp program of 1939 was on a small scale and its cost was only about $100,000. Expenditures from 1939 through 1943 were as follows (in millions):[27]

1939	$ 0.1
1940	16.7
1941	104.0
1942	115.8
1943	49.2
Total	$285.8

26. There was a similar but relatively small-scale attempt to stimulate consumption of cotton by means of a cotton stamp program. This reached its largest volume at $3.5 million in 1942 and was not important either as a stimulus to cotton consumption or as an aid to low-income families.

27. U.S. Production and Marketing Administration, *Section 32 Handbook*, 1953, p. 29. During these years the funds made available under Section 32 were supplemented by

If the Food Stamp Plan were to be expanded as much as some have advocated, its cost would be very large. Gold, Hoffman and Waugh, in a study published in 1940, reached the following conclusion, based on the public assistance rolls and prices of the late 1930s:

> On the basis of the experience to date, about 75 per cent of the persons to whom the plan is made available may be expected to participate. If the plan were made available to all persons in the United States who receive public assistance, it would be necessary to provide blue stamps for approximately 15 million people. With blue stamp expenditures amounting to $25 to $30 per person per year, the cost of the program to the Federal Treasury would be from $375 million to $450 million per year.
>
> If the plan were also to include employed families with incomes of less than $1,000 per year in all towns and cities over 2,500 population, an additional expenditure of about $200 to $240 million would be required. A program for all relief people and all employed low-income families in both rural and urban areas could cost about a billion dollars per year.[28]

Effect on Consumption and on Farm Incomes

The same writers undertook to estimate the probable effect on incomes to farmers from a food stamp program requiring federal expenditures of $125 million per year and of a larger one involving expenditures of $400 million. The estimates are in terms of 1940 prices and conditions. At that time some 18 to 20 million people were eligible for or receiving public assistance. A number of assumptions had to be made in drawing the conclusions arrived at. For example, it was assumed that those who do not participate in such a program will, if food prices are reduced, buy no more than enough to keep their food expenditure the same as before. It was also assumed that about 75 per cent of the blue stamp expenditure would be a net increase in demand and 25 per cent a substitution of blue stamps for regular expenditures.[29]

It was estimated that, on the basis of probable size of the program then contemplated (not more than $125 million), total farm income would be increased by 1 to 2 per cent. (See Table 23.) However, the benefit to producers of the specific commodities included in the program would be greater than this.[30] On the basis of studies made in six cities in

---

direct appropriations. These, however, were provided for the same purposes as the receipts from customs, principally as a means of financing the food stamp program, which in itself, during 1941 and 1942, involved expenditures that were larger than the amounts transferred from customs receipts.

28. *Economic Analysis of the Food-Stamp Plan*, A Special Report by the Bureau of Agricultural Economics and the Surplus Marketing Administration of the Department of Agriculture, by Norman Leon Gold, A. C. Hoffman and Frederick V. Waugh, 1940, p. 86.

29. For a fuller statement of the various assumptions made, see *ibid.*, pp. 86–87.

30. It should be noted that the wholesale prices of foodstuffs are now more than 2.5 times what they were in 1940. This change in the price level would reduce materially the percentage change in farm incomes resulting from a food stamp program of any given size in terms of dollars.

TABLE 23

POSSIBLE INCREASES IN CONSUMER EXPENDITURE AND FARM INCOME AS
A RESULT OF THE FOOD STAMP PLAN UNDER SPECIFIED ASSUMPTIONS

	Increase, Assuming a $400 Million Program			Increase, Assuming a $125 Million Program		
Assumed Elasticity of Nonpar- ticipants' Demand	Consumer Food Expenditure	Total Farm Income	Total Farm Income from Food Crops	Consumer Food Expenditure	Total Farm Income	Total Farm Income from Food Crops
	Millions		*Per Cent*	*Millions*		*Per Cent*
1	$300	$240	4.0	$ 90	$ 72	1.2
$\frac{2}{3}$	435	348	5.8	135	108	1.8
$\frac{1}{2}$	555	444	7.4	180	144	2.4

Source: Economic Analysis of the Food-Stamp Plan, A Special Report by the Bureau of Agricultural Economics and Surplus Marketing Administration of the Department of Agriculture, by Norman Leon Gold, A. C. Hoffman and Frederick V. Waugh, 1940, p. 87. It is assumed that about 40 per cent of the amount paid by consumers normally goes to farmers.

TABLE 24

ROUGH ESTIMATE OF PERCENTAGE OF DOMESTIC SUPPLIES "NORMALLY"
PURCHASED BY 15 MILLION LOW-INCOME PERSONS, AND PERCENT-
AGE THAT NATIONAL FOOD STAMP PLAN WOULD PROVIDE [a]

(Based on surplus lists—July 16 through December 15)

Commodity	"Normal" Percentage of Market	Blue Stamp Percentage of Market
Butter	5	13
Eggs	6	13
Rice	14	17
Dry beans	12	23
Dried prunes	4	30
Raisins	5	28
Apples	2	11
Peaches	4	16
Pears	8	5
Cabbage	9	14
Peas	6	16
Tomatoes	3	17
Onions	7	16
Lard	10	23

Source: Economic Analysis of the Food-Stamp Plan, A Special Report by the Bureau of Agricultural Economics and Surplus Marketing Administration of the Department of Agriculture, by Norman Leon Gold, A. C. Hoffman and Frederick V. Waugh, 1940, p. 89.

a. The normal purchases were roughly estimated by calculating the share of the market that 15 million people would provide if their purchase habits were like those of 1935–1936 nonfarm, nonrelief families having incomes of less than $500. The figures have been rounded to the closest whole per cent.

1939, the increases in consumption of specific commodities, under a $125 million program, were estimated to range from 5 per cent for pears to 30 per cent for dried prunes.[31] (See Table 24.)

The effect of the Food Stamp Plan as carried on was apparently to transfer buying power to people on relief by an amount roughly comparable to the contribution by the government and to increase returns to farmers by about a similar amount. Since more direct and presumably more efficient channels for giving aid to the needy are now available, there does not appear to be a strong case for using this device in times of high employment when most products are moving into consumption in a normal way.[32] If a situation should again arise in which great numbers of families are unable to buy much-needed foods, while foodstuffs are being destroyed or not grown because of inability to find markets for them, such a plan might well be given serious consideration. The food

31. A later and more extensive study by Joseph D. Coppock (published in 1947) resulted in conclusions that were similar to those presented above though the approach used by Coppock, a psychologist, relates more to the primary effects on consumers than to the secondary and more strictly economic effects. Coppock's conclusions (the study itself is too extensive and technical to summarize here) were as follows:

"Many people have looked upon the Food Stamp Plan as one of the devices by which some of the inadequacies and imperfections of the economic system could be overcome. There can be no doubt as to its usefulness within a limited sphere. The operating experience of the Food Stamp Plan from 1939 to 1943 stands as the test of this technique. If the Stamp Plan had turned out to be no better than a straight cash subsidy in achieving particular aims, the Special Purpose Money technique would have been in ill repute for many years to come.

"Unquestionably the Food Stamp Plan brought more food to poor people than a straight cash subsidy would have done. It also brought larger revenues to sellers of food, at the expense, of course, of other people, primarily as taxpayers but also to a slight extent as buyers of food. But there is sound basis for believing that the Plan, if revised, can be made even more effective. It is possible to administer the Food Stamp Plan so that at least 80 per cent of the total subsidy will go into increased food expenditures by participants instead of the 60 or so per cent apparently obtained in 1941. Hence the technique it represents may be employed on future occasions with reasonable assurance that good results will be obtained.

"A final note of warning should be sounded. An economic system which stands only with the support of stamp plans and other such props is not a permanently satisfactory system. Employable persons in the United States generally want to receive their income in return for worth-while services rendered. The dependent young, the dependent old, the physically and mentally handicapped, and the temporarily unemployed deserve to have their livings provided them by means which do not brand them as social outcasts. Properly-managed stamp plans can give us time to devise and institute needed changes in our economic structure. We need these changes in order to utilize better our manpower, technology, and resources in satisfying more fully the wants of ourselves and our fellows. Stamp plans must not blind us to these greater tasks."

(Joseph D. Coppock, "The Food Stamp Plan, Moving Surplus Commodities with Special Purpose Money," *Transactions of the American Philosophical Society*, Philadelphia, May 1947, pp. 132–99. Conclusions quoted are from p. 186.)

For a study of the legal aspects of the plan, see Samuel Herman, "The Food Stamp Plan: A Study in Law and Economics," *Journal of Business of the University of Chicago*, Chicago, October 1940, pp. 331–59, and January 1941, pp. 11–35.

32. The above statement probably gives too little weight to one of the major purposes of the program, namely, making available to families on relief more of the body-building and protective foods which they are unlikely to buy in sufficient quantity out of their small cash incomes. Undoubtedly the food stamp procedure is much superior to direct physical distribution of surplus commodities. The latter procedure involves high expense, much waste and uneven distribution. If surplus commodities are to be made available free or at less than full market price, there is unquestionably a marked advantage in having them handled through the regular channels of trade.

stamp plan is a depression mechanism rather than one well suited to ordinary conditions.[33]

WARTIME FOOD SUBSIDIES AND INCENTIVE PAYMENTS

The outbreak of war brought a quick change in the kinds of problems faced by administrators of the government farm programs and by those in charge of war programs affected by the policies relating to farm products. Stocks of the major storable products were extremely large, but these now could be looked upon as important war assets rather than as a threat to the agricultural price structure. The prices of farm products were rising rapidly and it soon was apparent that these accumulations could be put to use without much loss to the Commodity Credit Corporation and with distinct advantage to the public.

Nevertheless a very serious problem was emerging for those charged with administering the war program as a whole. All-out war necessitates a government demand for many products that is not much affected by price increases. The amounts bought are about the same regardless of price. Under these conditions prices may rise sharply without bringing forth quickly any substantial increase in the quantity produced. Since government buying power may be increased almost without limit through borrowing, such a situation can result in enormously inflated costs for carrying on the war and much disturbance to the whole economy.

For many commodities the government becomes the major buyer and civilian supplies must be severely curtailed. With civilian incomes increasing rapidly, through fuller employment and rising wage rates, such a situation tends to result in a continuing upward inflationary spiral of prices and costs that is likely to set the stage for a disastrous recession when the wartime demand comes to an end. In the meantime, the owners of many production resources will have made huge windfall gains without making any corresponding contribution to the war effort. Because of this, virtually all nations now find it necessary to establish rigorous controls over prices and supplies when engaged in war.

In such times, resources must be shifted quickly to the production of war materials. This means that the production of goods consumers want and can afford to buy must be held down, if manpower and other resources are to be available for the war program. Labor must be induced or required to transfer from lines supplying consumers into activities that will contribute to the war effort. Unless this is to be accomplished by wholesale regimentation of labor, it must be brought about by holding down wages in nonessential lines and allowing them to increase

33. The successful operation of a food stamp plan requires the wholehearted cooperation of grocers and other retail dealers. In times of depression this can usually be obtained. It is far less likely to be obtainable in times when sales are brisk and store personnel fully employed.

enough in the war industries to draw workers away from their customary jobs.

Efforts to Stabilize Prices and Wages

The United States, like all the other belligerents, undertook to stabilize prices and wages. It applied price controls at first only on a selective basis and to strategic commodities. The Administration pressed for stronger price control legislation during the fall of 1941 but was unable to get through an act satisfactory to the President. The sudden attack on Pearl Harbor and involvement in a major war on two fronts brought realization that far more rigorous controls would be required, if prices were to be held anywhere near stable and if resources were to be shifted quickly to the production of essential war materials.

An Emergency Price Control Act was passed on January 30, 1942 which gave the Office of Price Administration broad powers to fix ceilings on commodity prices. However, its power to fix ceilings on farm products was restricted in important respects. (See pp. 259–60.) These ceilings left room for increases so large that they would inevitably cause a sharp rise in the cost of living. For example, the price of wheat rose 83 per cent between August 1939 and April 1942, but could rise an additional 74 per cent under the formula written into the law. Corn was up 74 per cent over 1939 and could rise another 34 per cent. Butterfat had gained 65 per cent and could go another 19 per cent. The corresponding figures for chickens were 42 per cent and 15 per cent; for eggs, 46 per cent and 33 per cent and for apples 114 per cent and 13 per cent.[34]

Farm prices were low in 1939 and increases were in order, both in justice to the farmer and to provide incentives for increased production to meet war needs. However, the increases permitted under the legal formula almost certainly were larger than would be required to meet either of these criteria. Prices as high as the ceilings thus prescribed were bound to make unworkable the effort to stabilize wage rates in the non-war industries. Labor would inevitably refuse to accept wage stabilization if living costs were allowed to move up rapidly.

Wage Control Problems

Labor was in a situation different from that of the farmer. For the most part, the farmer was in the position where he could be most useful. No important change in methods, equipment or place of work was needed. He was asked to do the thing he had been wanting to do all along: produce to the limit of his capacity for a market in which he could

34. Walter W. Wilcox, *The Farmer in the Second World War*, Iowa State College Press, Ames, 1947, p. 123.

sell all he could produce at good prices. But many nonfarm workers had to be induced to give up customary kinds of work, move to new locations, accept poor and crowded housing conditions and learn new trades. To bring about the needed reshuffling of workers it was considered necessary to permit markedly higher wage rates in the war industries than those being paid in most of the civilian industries.

The Administration sought to stabilize wages in a flexible way through regulations and guidance provided by the War Labor Board. Nevertheless, the earnings of nonfarm workers did rise, partly through having many more people employed, partly through longer hours and overtime rates and partly through transfers to the high-paying war industries. The farm groups contended that the earnings of labor had increased enough so they could pay higher prices for food without hardship, and that farm prices had so long been below parity that farmers should be allowed to make up for these lean years by parity-plus prices during this period of strong demand. Some legislators from the farm states insisted that there be no ceiling on farm prices, or if one was applied that it be no less than 125 per cent of parity.[35]

Although the total earnings of labor were increasing rapidly, much of this gain was due to the shift of millions of workers from unemployed to employed status rather than to increased wage rates, except in the war industries and in agriculture. Millions of workers who had not changed jobs were being held to wage levels envisaged under the "Little Steel" formula, which permitted increases of not more than 15 per cent over the 1940 levels.[36]

Dilemma Faced by the Administration

The Administration was faced with a difficult choice. Both farmers and labor wanted more money. Demand was sufficiently active to enable them to get it if the market was left free of controls. Farmers regarded the Administration as prolabor and contended that labor would be allowed to gain at the expense of agriculture unless wage rates were frozen. Labor was restive and certainly would not agree to continuing under the Little Steel formula if costs of living mounted rapidly. If the

35. Many millions of workers who had been unemployed during the depression years could equally well have argued that wage rates should not be held down now that labor shortages had appeared and employers were willing to pay more. It was clear, however, that both wage rates and food costs could not be allowed to move up freely unless a full-scale war inflation like that of World War I, with its probable aftermath of severe recession, was to occur. Furthermore, the President pointed out repeatedly that such a policy would mean continuing too much of the labor force in its customary peacetime activities and would jeopardize the war effort.

36. This criterion applied only to wage disputes brought before the War Labor Board. Employers could increase wage rates voluntarily by larger amounts. Under the labor and profit conditions then existing, many employers were bidding well above the 15 per cent level in order to keep their employees or add new ones. As a result of pressure from the farm groups, an act of September 15, 1942 made it mandatory that all wage adjustments be brought under the supervision of the War Labor Board.

Little Steel formula was abandoned, there was little prospect that any similar line could be established and held even at a higher level.

As a partial solution to the problem, the Office of Price Administration issued its General Maximum Price Regulation of April 1942. This froze retail prices, and the cost of services at retail, at the levels prevailing in March 1942.[37] Rentals on residential properties were also frozen. However, under the legislation then in effect, the prices of farm products could not be put under ceilings until they reached substantially higher levels.[38] Consequently, they continued to rise and were creating a serious threat to the whole stabilization program.

As a result of vigorous presidential pressure, the Congress was induced to pass, in October 1942, an amendment (56 *Stat.* 765) which permitted the establishment of ceilings on the prices of farm products at parity or the highest price paid between January 1, 1942 and September 15, 1942, whichever was higher. At the same time all adjustments in wage rates, whether by settlement of disputes referred to the War Labor Board or by voluntary agreement, were placed under the Board's supervision. Guarantees of support for farm prices, mostly at 90 per cent of parity, for two years after the close of the war were also included.

In addition, the government offered incentive payments or subsidies on some farm products with a view to stimulating production of those regarded as most essential and shortest in supply.[39] Some of the farm groups opposed the incentive payment plan vigorously, contending that prices should be allowed to rise enough to bring forth the quantities needed.[40]

37. Direct controls over prices and wages are seldom if ever fully effective. The best that can be expected is a slowing down and delaying action which can be regarded as successful if it keeps price and wage advances small. Rationing of scarce consumer goods is an essential part of the process. Rentals were held most nearly stable, but even here there was some gradual upward movement. For many consumer goods, prices were nominally stabilized but quality declined or other products were substituted under the same names.

38. The President, in his message of April 27, 1942, stated that the lowest average level at which ceiling prices on farm products could be placed was 116 per cent of parity.

39. Since the law prohibited the placing of ceilings on farm products at less than parity or some higher figure, the price stimulus on products in very short supply and much needed was held to the same level as that of products that were less essential and more abundant. To overcome this difficulty, the various subsidies provided were intended as an added inducement to shift to these products. Fats and oils were scarce because of the loss of vegetable oils from the Pacific area. Sugar was scarce because of shipping difficulties and labor shortages. Milk production was failing to keep pace with the greatly increased demand.

40. The opposition eventually became so strong that the Congress refused to appropriate money for programs of that type and wrote into the bill appropriating money for the Office of Price Administration specific prohibitions against the use of any of the money provided in that bill (57 *Stat.* 417) for making incentive payments. However, the Administration sidestepped this prohibition and did assign $30 million of Section 32 funds for making incentive payments on potatoes and truck crops. Payments that were, in effect, incentive payments were later made, some with rather reluctant approval from the Congress and some by indirect means.

The Rollback of April 1943

To check the advance of living costs and save the stabilization program, the President issued his famous "hold-the-line" order of April 8, 1943. In this he took a strong stand, demanding that no further price increases be permitted that would add to the cost of living and directing that some of the prices of "cost of living" items be rolled back.[41]

In the meantime some processors and handlers of foodstuffs had been caught in a squeeze. The prices they might charge for finished products were being held down, under the General Maximum Price Regulation, but the prices of raw materials, mainly farm products, had been allowed to creep up. In order to ease this pressure without forcing farm prices down, and also to permit some reduction in prices to consumers, a food subsidy program was initiated in connection with the hold-the-line order of April 1943.

The food subsidy program was much criticized by spokesmen for some of the farm groups. The price reductions and subsidies were relatively small per unit, but since they applied to the whole domestic consumption of several major products the total expenditure required was very large. The payments were made partly through the Commodity Credit Corporation and partly by the Reconstruction Finance Corporation. Total costs borne by the Commodity Credit Corporation, through June 30, 1949, amounted to $2,101,956,519 divided as follows: [42]

Milk and dairy products	$1,312,885,784
Grain and grain products	272,918,137
Fruits and vegetables	181,335,725
Oilseeds and products	131,861,067
Sugar	115,444,708
Livestock production and meat	80,102,287
Beverages	7,319,467
Miscellaneous	89,344
Total	$2,101,956,519

Subsidies paid by the Reconstruction Finance Corporation, largely as a means of holding prices to consumers stable, were slightly larger in

41. At about this same time, the President vetoed the Bankhead bill, which had passed both houses by large majorities and would have permitted further inflationary increases in the prices of farm products. In doing so he pointed out that the prices received by farmers had increased 107 per cent between August 1939 and January 1943 while the prices of things bought by them had increased only 26 per cent, and that farm prices, which were 30 per cent below parity in August 1939, had risen to 15 per cent above parity by January 1943.

42. Commodity Credit Corporation, *Report of Financial Condition and Operations as of June 30, 1949*, p. 31.

total amount.[43] The products subsidized and the direct recipients of the payments were as follows: [44]

Type	Subsidy Paid to	Amount
Livestock slaughter	Slaughterers	$1,547,138,094
Flour production	Millers	348,431,265
Butter production	Creameries	181,617,850
Coffee importation	Distributors	40,699,968
Sugar transportation [a]	Transportation agencies	25,011,274
Total		$2,142,908,451

a. Program assumed by CCC in December 1942.

The only CCC expenditures officially classified as subsidies were those made for the purpose of keeping retail prices within the maxima established by the Office of Price Administration.[45] These were presumably for the benefit of consumers though they also had the effect of permitting farmers to continue to receive higher prices than they would have received if farm prices had been forced back to the levels necessary to hold food costs at the levels implied by the President's hold-the-line order.

In the Stabilization Extension Act of 1944 (58 *Stat.* 642) the Congress took steps looking to the discontinuance of food subsidies. The act prohibited subsidy operations by any government corporation after June 30, 1945, unless funds were specifically appropriated for that purpose. However, this prohibition was removed for the year 1946 by an act of April 12, 1945 (59 *Stat.* 50) and subsidy operations for fiscal 1946 were to be limited to $913 million. Under this authorization some $843 million in subsidies was provided, more than $500 million of it as subsidies to dairy producers.[46]

The other major items were beef production ($33 million), fruits for processing ($32 million), soybeans ($33 million), sugar ($70 million) and vegetables for processing ($63 million). Three new programs were initiated for 1946—sheep and lambs, flaxseed, and barley for feed. A joint maximum of $869 million for food subsidies applying to the combined outlays of CCC and RFC was established for the fiscal year ending

43. The RFC purchases were made through a subsidiary, the Defense Supplies Corporation, which was organized on August 29, 1940 to acquire and carry reserves of strategic materials and supplies needed in the national defense program. Very small amounts of U.S. dried fruits and tobacco were also purchased by the U.S. Commercial Company, which was organized during the war to engage in preclusive buying. It dealt mainly in nonagricultural products.

44. Comptroller General of the United States, *Report on Audit of Commodity Credit Corporation and Its Affiliate, War Hemp Industries, Inc., Fiscal Years 1946 and 1947,* House Doc. 615, 81st Cong., 2d sess., 1950, p. 41.

45. The procedures used in providing food subsidies are described in some detail in Comptroller General of the United States, *Report on Audit of Reconstruction Finance Corporation and Affiliated Corporations, Defense Supplies Corporation,* House Doc. 439, 80th Cong., 1st sess., 1948, Vol. 5, especially pp. 24–31.

46. *Ibid.,* p. 42.

June 30, 1947, but this became inoperative as a result of the abandonment of price controls on all commodities except sugar in the fall of 1946.

No hard and fast conclusion can be drawn as to who was being subsidized. Attitudes on the matter depend on the assumptions made as to the level at which farm prices should have been stabilized. The livestock, flour and butter subsidies may be classified as subsidies to consumers or to farmers depending on whether one does or does not assume that farm prices should have been rolled back as many other prices were. Subsidizing made it possible to continue to pay prices to farmers that were higher than they would have been if farm prices had been stabilized in accordance with the over-all plan. The coffee payments, though not large in amount, were clearly consumer subsidies. The sugar transportation subsidies likewise can be classed either as war measures or aids to consumers. The fluid milk, oilseed, potato, vegetable and sugar subsidies were in a different class and can be regarded primarily as war expenditures. Here the purpose was to stimulate production as a means of contributing to the war effort.[47]

Effect on Consumer Expenditures

The savings to individual consumers were nominal. The increased costs for food could have been passed on to them without significant hardship [48] had it not been for the psychological effects and the threat to the wage stabilization program.

The cost of the program was in excess of $4 billion. Its merit is dubious because it required additional borrowing at a time when inflationary pressures were great and farm incomes high, and when most consumers were in a position to pay higher prices. However, the significance of food

47. The Production and Marketing Administration describes the subsidies on potatoes and vegetables as follows:

"In order to encourage increased production, special 'incentive' payments were offered in 1943 to potato and truck crop producers. The potato payment, announced after the potato goal had been increased 100,000 acres, was based on acreage planted to potatoes in excess of 90 per cent of the farm goal, not to exceed the larger of 1 acre or 20 per cent of the goal. The rate of payment per acre was 50 cents per bushel times the normal yield.

"The payment on truck crops for fresh market was made on the same basis, and the payment rate was $50 per acre. Vegetables included were carrots, snap beans, lima beans, beets, tomatoes, cabbage, onions, and green peas grown for fresh consumption, and the acreage of other vegetables double-cropped exclusive of watermelons, cantaloups, and cucumbers.

"These incentive payments were financed by an allotment of 30 million dollars from the Section 32 appropriation."

(U.S. Production and Marketing Administration, Information Service, *Agricultural Conservation and Related Programs, A Compilation of Information on Such Programs up to and including March 15, 1948*, p. 22.)

48. The Bureau of Agricultural Economics "market basket" of annual food cost for a family of three average consumers was put at $317 for 1940, $347 for 1941 and $407 for 1942. The abrupt rise in early 1943, which resulted in the President's hold-the-line order, carried it up from $440 in January to $484 in May. U.S. Bureau of Agricultural Economics, *Agricultural Outlook Charts, 1945*, p. 16.

subsidies in inducing acquiescence in the stabilization program cannot be ignored.

Probably half or more of this outlay could have been avoided without much hardship to anyone, by holding farm prices to lower levels or by letting consumers pay more.[49] Most of the remainder, consisting largely of payments made or expenses incurred for maintaining or increasing production, probably could not have been avoided without upsetting the price stabilization program. Allowing prices to rise to bring about added production would have implied a partial return to free-market prices, a development that would have been inconsistent with the general philosophy of the price control program.

ABNORMAL EXPORTS

From about 1941 on, there was no pressing need for surplus removal operations of the kinds undertaken in the 1930s, except possibly for some of the minor crops such as raisins and prunes, which were heavily dependent on export markets that had been cut off by the outbreak of war. Though the need for widespread relief was disappearing, the School Lunch Program and the diversion of supplies to institutions were continued. Most of the people who wanted to work and were able to do so found it easy to obtain employment, especially from 1942 on. During the war years, consumer buying power was high and domestic per capita consumption was higher than in any earlier period for which records are available. In addition, both in the war years and after, the United States government was financing a series of programs that affected farm prices almost in the same way as a gigantic surplus removal operation would have done. Huge quantities of food were shipped to Britain and Russia under lend-lease. Wheat was made available to livestock producers at less than market prices and appreciable quantities of wheat and corn were used in the production of alcohol for the synthetic rubber and munitions programs.

After the war, and to some extent even before the war ended, great quantities of food and some cotton were supplied to other nations under the United Nations Relief and Rehabilitation program and through the Economic Cooperation Administration and the Mutual Security Agency. There were large shipments for civilian feeding in the liberated areas, especially in Japan and Germany, and considerable amounts were purchased by Britain with the proceeds of the $3.6 billion British loan of 1946.

These operations were far larger in scale and much more powerful as price-raising influences than any surplus removal operation that would conceivably be undertaken purely for that purpose. Combined, as they

49. That is, from a strictly economic standpoint, which of course ignores the political aspect of the problem. The strong position of the farm and labor groups made such a solution politically impractical.

were, with an abnormally strong domestic demand, they created a situation in the food markets which was markedly inflationary instead of the deflationary one that was so generally expected to develop after the war ended.

During the war years, the objectives of the foreign-aid programs were almost wholly military and political. American agriculture benefited, but only by chance not by design. After the war, the government-financed foreign-aid programs had a similar strengthening effect on U.S. farm prices but the objectives were not wholly military and humanitarian. Aid in reconstruction and the feeding of needy peoples still were the primary purposes of the steps taken, but some purchases were made as a means of aiding U.S. producer groups threatened by glutted markets and low prices. Some of the shipments also helped in reducing holdings acquired by the Commodity Credit Corporation in its price-supporting operations.[50]

Had it not been for these abnormal types of export, government expenditures for the support of farm prices in the postwar years would undoubtedly have had to be considerably larger than they were, because of guarantees that had been made during the war. However, production would probably have been cut back, both by more cautious planning on the part of farmers and by government restrictions, which no doubt would have been initiated if postwar stocks had become very large.

Costs Not Properly Chargeable to the Farm Program

The cost involved in these operations was so predominantly in furtherance of national objectives rather than for the purpose of maintaining the prices of farm products that these outlays cannot properly be regarded as part of the farm program. Nevertheless, they did have an important effect on farm prices and incomes during the period 1942 to 1952. The principal reason for including them in this analysis is to give some indication of the size of operation that would be required to produce important price effects through surplus removal programs.

Some small portion of the expenditure was made to support farm prices, but even here there were mixed incentives for the actions taken. Foreign aid in other forms would probably have been substituted if the particular crops bought on a price-support basis had not been available.

50. These holdings were also reduced as a result of sales of wheat at less than market prices for use as livestock feed. An act of August 6, 1942 authorized sale of 125 million bushels at 85 per cent of parity. Additional sales amounting to 225 million bushels were authorized in 1943, these to be at the parity price for corn. During the years 1942 through 1945 nearly a billion and a half bushels of wheat were used for livestock feeding and about 160 million bushels for industrial purposes, chiefly in the production of alcohol. These amounts compare with a normal use for such purposes of 100 to 125 million bushels per year. The Commodity Credit Corporation did not lose on these transactions, because of the large increase in prices that occurred after the wheat was acquired. Very heavy losses on the huge stocks held by CCC, and under loan from it, would have been inevitable had it not been for the abnormal demands that grew out of the war.

It should be recognized too that the price effects observed were due partly to the fact that this abnormal demand was superimposed on a domestic demand that was very large and very insistent. The disposal of similar quantities, through artificially created outlets, in a time when domestic demand was more normal would very possibly have different and probably less pronounced price effects.

Also, in times of severe depression, if heavy stocks are held, the price effect of a surplus removal operation of a given size, even one of rather large proportions, might be relatively small. If it did not curtail significantly the amounts available in the domestic market the effect might be mainly on the size of the immobile stocks. An example is that of cotton stocks in the early 1930s. Despite the action of the Farm Board and co-operating agencies in taking some 3.5 million bales out of the market, the quantities available still were more than adequate to take care of the small mill requirements of that period.[51]

As a result of the large abnormal exports financed by the government, and the strong domestic demand for foodstuffs, the wartime farm price guarantees were nearly costless so far as Commodity Credit Corporation and the Department of Agriculture were concerned. They were also of little significance in maintaining prices during the early postwar years. They did, however, set a pattern which may prove much more expensive in the years ahead. The major losses under the price-support program have resulted from the continuance of high levels of support in the 1948 and 1949 acts and in later legislation rather than from the wartime legislation itself.[52]

Farm Products Shipped under Foreign-Aid Programs

The amounts of farm products taken off the U.S. market under the various foreign-aid programs from 1941 through June 1952 ranged from $4,779 million for wheat down to $7.8 million for fertilizer and insecticides. The total for the eleven years was $15,105 million. (See Table 25.) These amounts presumably do not include purchases financed by means of the British loan of 1946, though the loan did undoubtedly lead to

51. This, of course, was not a genuine surplus removal operation, except for some small quantities diverted to inferior uses and some portion of that turned over to the Red Cross. The stocks held by the Board and those financed by the banks still were available. However, the operation, large as it was, did not result in any significant shortage of free-market stocks except in one or two short periods. The situation in wheat during that period was similar.

52. The postwar price situation was quite the reverse of what was expected in view of the severe recession that occurred shortly after the close of World War I. However, the differences between the two periods are by no means attributable wholly to the foreign-aid program or to postwar price guarantees. American participation in World War II was much longer and vastly more intensive. Shortages were more acute, savings were much larger, and both farmers and urban groups were in a far better financial position than in 1920. The disastrous land-price inflation of 1919 and 1920 was not repeated. Banking structure and financial policy were more fully developed and were geared to inflation rather than deflation.

TABLE 25

COMMODITY CREDIT CORPORATION: DELIVERIES FOR EXPORT BY
COMMODITY GROUPS, FISCAL YEARS 1941 TO 1952 [a]

(*Millions*)

Commodity Group	Deliveries for Export
Total	$15,105.3
Dairy products	1,363.0
Poultry products	1,243.1
Fats and oils	1,154.6
Soap and related products	37.0
Dried fruits	184.7
Fruits (except dried)	163.1
Potatoes	104.0
Vegetables (except potatoes)	116.3
Soups	42.0
Whole grains	4,778.9
Flour	744.2
Grain products (other)	90.2
Pulses	229.2
Meats	2,073.7
Fish	335.9
Beverage materials	26.4
Sugar and related products	424.3
Miscellaneous food commodities	166.8
Fiber products	958.6
Naval stores	21.0
Seeds	109.8
Livestock	23.4
Tobacco	693.2
Fertilizer, insecticides	7.8
Miscellaneous nonfood commodities	13.9

Source: U.S. Department of Agriculture, *Agricultural Statistics, 1953,* p. 592. There
are minor discrepancies as a result of rounding figures.

a. For most of the commodities, especially livestock products, the bulk of the shipments was made in the years 1942 through 1947. From 1947 on, by far the largest part
of the shipments consisted of wheat, flour, fats and oils and sugar, though cotton shipments were still sizable in 1948 and dried fruit shipments were relatively high in 1948
and 1949. Dairy and poultry product shipments still amounted to $95 million in 1948
and to $47 million in 1949 but dropped off sharply from then on. For breakdown by
years, see Appendix B.

some supplementing of the amounts that would have been taken under
normal trading arrangements.[53]

53. Shipments financed by the British loan cannot be segregated, since these funds
went into the British Treasury and thus were added to the over-all dollar balances available to the British government. They helped bridge the gap between the termination of
lend-lease shipments in 1946 and the beginning of the ECA program in 1947. Purchases
made with these funds are included, in part, in the $7.5 billion worth of agricultural
commodities exported through private channels in the years 1941 to 1949.

Some of the foreign governments bought part of their farm products directly from the
U.S. Department of Agriculture rather than through private trade channels. Such amounts
as were purchased in that way, with funds provided by means of the British loan, are

Furthermore, it should be recognized that the wartime gift and loan shipments were not net additions to a "normal" level of exports. There is no way of determining precisely what the volume of exports would have been during the 1940s had there been no war and no foreign-aid program. However, if we assume a level somewhat comparable to that of the late 1920s, the volume of agricultural exports during the 1940s can be roughly related to it.[54]

Agricultural exports, in dollar value, from 1926 through 1930 amounted to $8.1 billion or an average of about $1.6 billion per year. For the period 1946 through 1950 the comparable total was $17.3 billion and the average per year about $3.5 billion.[55] However, the difference in dollar value was due very largely to the higher prices that prevailed in the late 1940s. The physical volume of agricultural exports was only about 3 per cent higher in the late 1940s than in the late 1920s.[56]

This comparison with exports in the late 1920s is somewhat unrealistic in that agricultural exports during that period were among the highest in the nation's history and they included almost twice as much cotton. If allowance is made for the very large decrease in the amount of cotton exported, the physical volume of exports in the late 1940s was in the order of 25 per cent greater than in the late 1920s.

There is much reason to question whether, in the absence of war, agricultural exports would have been as high in the late 1940s as in the late 1920s. The physical volume of agricultural exports had been declining in the first decade of the 1900s and was again showing a downward trend in the late 1920s. Even with the foreign-aid programs, cotton exports were at a low level, as compared to the 1920s. Cured pork exports were down to a fraction of their pre-World War I levels and even lard was being exported only in about the quantities shipped in the early 1900s.[57] The big offsetting factor was the great increase in exports of

presumably included in the figure given as "foreign-aid shipments." The amount probably was not large, as Britain had war stocks to draw on and much of the British loan was used in meeting part of her obligation to dominion, colonial and other sterling area governments, which had become very heavy as a result of wartime credits granted by them. Lend-lease shipments were terminated on V-J Day (August 21, 1945) except for goods already in the pipelines. The final closing date for lend-lease was December 31, 1946. The British loan was entered into in July 1946 and the Marshall Plan was launched in 1947.

54. This comparison must be qualified because of the great difference in cotton exports in the two periods. During the late 1920s cotton exports were mostly at a rate of 8 million to 8.5 million bales per year. In 1926 they were 11.3 million bales. During the late 1940s, cotton exports ranged mostly between 3.5 million and 5 million bales, with a high of 6 million bales in 1949. If cotton exports had been as large in the late 1940s as in the late 1920s, exports would have been some $600 million to $700 million greater than they were, assuming that prices were similar to those actually received. Thus the increase in exports of foodstuffs was enough to more than offset this large decrease in cotton exports.

55. Data derived from U.S. Office of Foreign Agricultural Relations, *Foreign Agricultural Outlook Charts, 1952*, p. 6.

56. Based on indexes of physical volume of agricultural exports as given in *Agricultural Statistics, 1952*, p. 556.

57. *Ibid.*, p. 556.

wheat and other grains. Wheat exports were at a rate two to three times that of the late 1920s and exports of other grains were well above the 1920 levels.

Another way of looking at it, and possibly a more realistic one, is to take as a starting point the volume of exports in the late 1930s and assume that there would probably have been a moderate recovery from the low levels of the depression decade. During 1937, 1938 and 1939, the physical volume of agricultural exports was about 60 to 65 per cent of what it had been in the period 1924–29. With gradual recovery from the deep depression of the 1930s it might have reached 75 to 80 per cent. This would imply that the abnormally financed exports of the post-war period and the abnormal demands growing out of the war may have caused U.S. agricultural exports to be 25 to 30 per cent higher than they would have been under peacetime conditions.

Effect on Postwar Markets for Farm Products

Whatever the basis used in making comparisons, it is apparent that the special foreign-aid programs of the war and postwar years materially strengthened the demand for some of the farm products. Wheat is the most notable one, but pork and lard exports were stepped up markedly in the war years and fruits in 1947 and 1948. Grains other than wheat also benefited and some support was given to the tobacco and cotton markets.

In dollar terms, the foreign-aid shipments of farm products for the fiscal years 1941 through 1952 amounted to more than $15 billion, nearly all of which had much the same effect on farm prices as though it had been a huge surplus removal project.[58] This effect was damped down to some extent during the war years by rationing and price con-

---

58. The values of these shipments by years were as follows (in millions):

1941	$ 29.3
1942	792.0
1943	1,137.8
1944	1,988.3
1945	2,618.1
1946	2,011.6
1947	1,710.0
1948	1,559.0
1949	1,554.6
1950	753.6
1951	548.6
1952	402.3
Total	$15,105.3

(Data supplied by U.S. Production and Marketing Administration. Figures rounded.)
There was also a sizable amount of export through private channels during this period. For the years 1941 through June 1949, such exports amounted to about $7.5 billion. Part of this was trade with countries other than those included in the lend-lease, ECA and MSA programs and part was to countries in the above categories but financed either with free dollars earned or owned by them or obtained through dollar loans such as the British loan of 1946.

trols. When these were abandoned, in 1946, the huge domestic and foreign demand caused farm products to lead off in the postwar inflation of prices. The general index of prices received by farmers rose from 206 (1910–14 = 100) in 1945 to 234 in 1946, 275 in 1947 and 285 in 1948.

For most farm products, foreign-aid shipments fell off sharply after the close of the lend-lease period.[59] Though the heaviest purchases in the postwar period were those of grain and grain products, it does not follow that these were the ones for which prices were most effectively supported. The price-supporting effect of foreign-aid purchases was very significant for some of the minor crops for which normal export markets had been greatly curtailed.

Dried fruits, chiefly prunes and raisins, reached their highest volume in 1947 and remained somewhat above the levels of the war years through 1948 and 1949. Fruit juice exports, from 1946 through 1949, were nearly three times those of the war years.[60] Animal fat exports also continued high in the postwar years.

Strong Market Due Principally to High U.S. Demand

While the government-financed export programs undoubtedly had a very important influence on the prices of these few products, it should be recognized that the major support for farm prices generally came from the domestic market. The value of farm products exported, 1946–1950 inclusive, amounted to about 12 per cent of U.S. cash farm income in those years. That amount of export undoubtedly was sufficient to strengthen farm prices very significantly (for some commodities) compared to what they would have been without it. However, as already noted, it was in part a replacement of normal commercial exports. If commercial exports had been as large in the late 1940s as in the late 1920s, the dollar values would have been similar to what they were under the foreign-aid programs.

For some commodities such as meats, for which prices reached very high levels, the volume of postwar exports, either private or governmental, was almost negligible. The big factor in the heavy postwar consumption of foods was an increase in civilian population (from 133 mil-

59. During the war the emphasis was on highly concentrated protein foods. Shipping space was desperately short and every effort was made to produce in Britain the cheaper, more bulky foodstuffs that could not well be brought in from abroad. Both Canada and the United States entered the war with heavy stocks of wheat and it was agreed that shipments of wheat to Britain, and such small amounts as went to Russia, would be mainly from Canadian supplies. Consequently, U.S. shipments centered heavily on pork products, dried eggs, processed milk, dried fruits and fruit juices. After the war, especially during 1946 and 1947, the food situation in Europe was so desperate that heavy reliance was placed on wheat as a mainstay for enabling people to weather through until European food production could be built up.

60. Fifteen to 21 million gallons as against 5 to 6 million in the years 1941–1944.

lion in 1941 to 153 million in 1952)[61] and a much higher level of per capita income than in the 1930s.[62]

Even if there had been no foreign-aid programs, many parts of agriculture would have been prosperous in these early postwar years, but the wheat situation would have deteriorated. The underlying problem would have been similar to that of the early 1920s, but it would have taken a different form. With postwar price guarantees in effect, heavy government-owned stocks would have accumulated quickly. Acreage control programs would undoubtedly have had to be instituted long before 1954. The dried fruit and citrus industries would also have been severely affected and rice production would very likely have been cut back.

For most of the other farm products, it seems apparent that the high level of domestic earnings, the accumulated spending power and the rapidly growing population would have provided a market that would have kept farm prices and incomes relatively high.[63] Even the huge amounts spent on foreign aid would not have been sufficient to insure farm prosperity if industrial activity and national income had declined sharply.

This conclusion, if tenable, has an important bearing on the practical possibility of alleviating agricultural distress by means of diversionary programs. It is scarcely conceivable that, in periods of depression not associated with war, the Congress would seriously consider providing abnormal outlets for the major farm products on such a scale as to make the difference between agricultural depression and moderate prosperity.

Diversionary programs can assist materially in providing outlets for some of the minor crops and may at times, if large enough, be useful in disposing of burdensome accumulations of the more widely grown crops. However, to serve this purpose they must usually be on a scale that implies major intergovernmental arrangements, such as are usually entered into only in case of war or a devastating national catastrophe.

Results similar to those derived from heavy foreign-aid shipments can at times be achieved by channeling grains, particularly wheat, into lower-grade uses such as feed for livestock. That procedure, however, is likely to create more problems than it solves, except in periods of abnormally high wartime demand. In the early 1940s, wheat was provided to livestock producers at less than market prices and some was used in making alcohol. However, the shift of wheat to the feed market in periods of weak demand would undoubtedly be strongly opposed by the growers of corn and other feed grains, and its use in alcohol production would ordi-

61. Data from *Agricultural Statistics, 1952*, p. 810.
62. Civilian per capita consumption moved up from an index of about 100 (1935–39 = 100) to 119 in 1946. It dropped back to 111 for the years 1947 through 1951. See *Agricultural Statistics, 1953*, p. 812. Much of the great increase in population during these years still consisted of very young children.
63. The analysis here presented and other analyses seem to indicate that the importance of the foreign-aid programs as a factor in the postwar agricultural situation may have been overemphasized in many of the public discussions of recent years, except in regard to wheat and a few of the tree fruit crops.

narily be uneconomical when other materials are in plentiful supply and demand is at a lower level.

For some of the minor crops, diversionary purchases can be more important, though even here their greatest usefulness is in relieving temporary acute situations rather than in continuous support of price structures. For the major crops, disposal through channels of this kind is likely to be impractical except as a way of getting rid of burdensome accumulations and clearing channels of trade.

Postwar Uses of Section 32 Funds

During the prewar years, the bulk of the Section 32 fund expenditures consisted of outlays for commodities that were later contributed to the relief, school lunch and food stamp programs, plus some minor diversions to lower uses. The principal exceptions were the export subsidies provided as a means of disposing of cotton and wheat. Cotton export subsidies (chiefly in 1939–40 and 1946–47) amounted to $98.6 million. Similar subsidies on wheat and flour exports, mostly in the period 1939–1942, totaled $46.7 million.[64]

From 1939 to 1943, expenditures in connection with the Food Stamp Plan were large (more than $285 million). Thereafter, until 1947, sizable contributions were made to the School Lunch Program and export subsidies were in the order of $20 million to $30 million per year from 1945 through 1951. For the 17-year period (1935–1952), about 70 per cent of the $1.45 billion spent on these programs went for the purchase and donation, food stamp, school lunch and milk programs (aside from funds transferred to other programs). About 18 per cent went into the export programs and 7 per cent into diversion programs.[65]

The National School Lunch Act of 1946 (60 *Stat.* 230) provided legislative authorization for a continuing school lunch program and also authorized regular appropriations for financing it. However, the program was financed out of Section 32 funds for the years 1946–47 through 1948–49. The schools participating in the program now buy most of their foods locally with funds derived from sales to pupils and in other ways, plus the amounts received from the federal government out of appropriations made specifically for the School Lunch Program.

As the abnormal demands of the war and early postwar years eased off there was increasing demand for larger use of Section 32 funds in removing surpluses and supporting prices, particularly for the perishables and minor crops. This led to a gradual change both in the legislation itself and in administrative decisions relating to it.[66]

64. See U.S. Production and Marketing Administration, *Section 32 Handbook*, 1953, p. 31.
65. *Ibid.*, p. 29.
66. The law has been changed from time to time. In an act of February 11, 1936 (49 *Stat.* 1117) authority was given temporarily to donate Section 32 commodities for relief purposes. This was made permanent in an act of June 28, 1937 (50 *Stat.* 323). In February 1938 a 25 per cent limitation was placed on the amount of Section 32 funds

Relation of Section 32 Funds to the ECA Program

During the early years of the European aid program, some of the commodities purchased with Section 32 funds were supplied to ECA at less than market prices in order to relieve pressure on the domestic markets for these products. In the 1952 appropriations hearings, the House subcommittee began to scrutinize more carefully the practices followed in this connection. Chairman Whitten stated his position as follows:

I would like to seek ways and means of stopping the use of section 32 funds as an increment for the foreign-aid program and to use the section 32 funds for the purpose for which they were set up in law, for the removal of surplus commodities . . .

I think the best way to approach it would be to provide in the foreign-aid bill that the amounts paid for American commodities should be at the prevailing price. If you do that, then those in charge of Mutual Security could not insist on getting agricultural commodities at reduced prices and have the Department of Agriculture, through section 32 funds, make up the difference between what they paid for it and what the actual value was, so far as the prevailing market is concerned.[67]

The merit of this position is debatable. It can be argued that, since the Department of Agriculture was acquiring surplus commodities as a means of supporting prices, it would have to find abnormal outlets for them at less than prevailing prices. Hence if ECA bought them at full price its appropriations would, in effect, be used to supplement Section 32 funds. If the commodities were the ones ECA would purchase at full price, as a means of furthering its own objectives, a strong case can be made for full payment. If, on the other hand, ECA would buy them only

---

that could be spent on any one commodity. This replaced the earlier prohibition on expenditure of these funds for unmanufactured cotton (52 *Stat.* 38).

Expenditure of Section 32 funds to increase the use of surplus agricultural commodities by persons in low-income groups was authorized on June 30, 1939 (53 *Stat.* 975). Their use for price-support purposes was authorized temporarily on July 1, 1941 (55 *Stat.* 498) and permanently on January 1, 1950 (63 *Stat.* 1054).

In April 1948 a change was made that was important for some of the specialty crops (Section 112 of the Foreign Assistance Act of 1948, 62 *Stat.* 137). Under this provision, payments of up to 50 per cent of the sales price could be made to encourage the sale of surplus agricultural commodities for foreign-relief assistance, if paid for with U.S. government funds. However, during the fiscal year 1952–53 the use of Section 32 funds was prohibited on exports financed from funds made available under Title III of the Mutual Security Appropriations Act of 1953 (66 *Stat.* 655).

Title II of the Agricultural Act of 1949 (63 *Stat.* 1054, effective January 1, 1950) required that Section 32 funds be used principally for perishable "nonbasic" agricultural commodities (other than those designated in Title II of the Agricultural Act of 1949). A carry-over of up to $300 million in funds unexpended from previous fiscal years was authorized, effective January 1, 1950. This replaced a previous requirement that funds be used within the appropriate fiscal year (62 *Stat.* 1257). For fuller summary, see *Section 32 Handbook*, pp. 3–6.

The more recent changes described above reflect the growing pressure from the producers of perishable crops to force increased use of Section 32 funds for aid to them and to prevent dissipation of the funds through programs that could be carried out in other ways.

67. For fuller explanation see U.S. House Committee on Appropriations, *Department of Agriculture Appropriations for 1953*, Hearings, Part 2, p. 1411.

because they were available at less than market prices, and as an aid to the Department of Agriculture in disposing of unwanted stocks, the practice followed seems defensible.

Actually, the situation was not one that could be easily dealt with in terms of these simple generalizations. The two agencies did work in close cooperation and with a dual objective, namely, supplying foodstuffs to Europe and supporting farm prices in the United States. The merit or demerit of Department of Agriculture sales at less than prevailing market prices can be judged only by taking account of the specific conditions relating to each purchase.

Some of the products undoubtedly would have been bought for shipment abroad, even if it had been necessary for ECA to pay full market price for them. Others would not have been included in that program except as they were available at bargain prices. The products most significantly affected by arrangements of that kind were dried fruits and citrus concentrates. For these products, the foreign-aid program was particularly beneficial and served in considerable measure to replace, temporarily, the export markets lost as a result of the war.

Minor Crop Programs

Since most of the nonperishables were being absorbed at good prices, and also were being given support under special legislation, the Section 32 funds came to be used largely as a means of providing aid in disposing of the minor crops, especially the perishables. Income from the earmarked 30 per cent of customs revenue was in the order of $100 to $150 million per year.[68] These funds, though large, were not sufficient to meet in any important way the cost of supporting prices for the major products such as cotton, wheat and dairy products.[69] These came to be handled through purchase and loan programs financed by the Commodity Credit Corporation and with funds provided for aid to other countries.[70]

68. In recent years, expenditures of Section 32 funds have not been large in comparison with the amounts available. Only once since the end of World War II have they approached $100 million ($90.9 million in fiscal 1946). There is some indication that the fund may be larger than is needed for the purposes specified and that this could lead to careless spending on marginal projects if not carefully managed by means of internal checks.

In 1949 a small new program was launched with a view to promoting the consumption of plentiful foods. This also included the offer of supervisory assistance to state and local groups in promoting the preservation of foods for year-round use.

69. There was, however, some use of Section 32 funds in the dairy, eggs and poultry, cotton, grain and livestock programs. (See Table 27.) In 1946 and 1947, cotton purchases amounted to $52 million. More than $15 million was spent on dairy products in 1950, and egg and poultry purchases from 1948 to 1950 inclusive accounted for nearly $50 million. For the period as a whole (1946 through 1952) the largest expenditures were for fruits ($105 million) and vegetables ($72 million).

70. There has been some use of Section 32 funds to relieve CCC of burdensome surpluses. As a consequence CCC's books have shown smaller losses than they would have done otherwise. Such use has been extensive in the cotton, potato, wheat and egg programs (to June 1952, $186 million on cotton, $141 million on eggs, $133 million on wheat and $106 million on potatoes).

As stocks of these commodities became top-heavy, in 1949 and after, special surplus removal programs relating to them were authorized by the Congress. Among them were the export subsidies provided under the International Wheat Agreement and the special grants of aid to India and Pakistan. The increases in Commodity Credit Corporation holdings were also surplus removal operations of a kind, though they did not in themselves remove supplies from the market permanently.

The minor crops, especially those which cannot be stored, are more subject to temporary and local gluts and shortages than are the storables. Hence they lend themselves to smaller-scale and shorter-term programs. For many of them (except the tree crops), production can usually be adjusted rather quickly if prices become unduly low. Furthermore, aid can be given in respect to individual minor crops without making commitments that exceed the amounts that can be made available under Section 32 fund authorizations.

Expenditures for Section 32 Programs

The principal types of action taken have been purchases for direct distribution, encouragement of exportation, diversion to by-product and new uses and the setting up of marketing agreements and orders. During the fiscal year 1953, expenditures under these headings amounted to about $74.8 million divided as follows: for direct purchase $58.7 million, for export subsidies $11.7 million, for diversion to by-product and new uses $1.2 million, for surplus removal operating expenses $1.9 million, for marketing agreements and orders $1.2 million, and for foreign market promotion and import controls $0.1 million. For the period 1935–36 to 1952–53, the over-all cost of Section 32 programs is shown by type in Table 26.

The commodities acquired through direct purchase were mostly transferred to the school lunch and charitable institution programs. In 1953 the contribution thus made amounted to $58.7 million. The largest items were dry beans ($27.2 million), butter ($17.0 million), milk ($4.4 million), fresh pears ($1.9 million), honey ($1.4 million) and beef ($1.4 million).

Subsidies on exports (including those under the Foreign Assistance Act) were about $25 million in each of the fiscal years 1950 and 1951. In 1953 they amounted to $11.7 million. The largest items were oranges ($4.4 million), prunes ($4.6 million) and honey ($1.5 million).

The aid given to other producer groups through use of Section 32 funds was of minor significance. Marketing agreements and orders were in effect for milk, tree nuts, tree fruits, potatoes and other vegetables. National food drives were also conducted to expand consumption of products listed as available in abundant supply. During the fiscal year 1952, expenditures by commodity groups totaled $51.2 million, divided as follows: fruits, $23.8 million; livestock products, $12.3 million; dairy

TABLE 26

Section 32 Expenditures Annually, by Type of Program,
1935–36 through 1952–53

(*Millions*)

Fiscal Year	Total Expenditures [a]	School Lunch Cash Payments [b]	Administrative Expense	Commodity Programs				
				Total	Purchase and Donation	Export	Diversion	Stamp Plan
Per Cent	*100.0*	*8.9*	*4.0*	*87.1*	*43.7*	*17.8*	*6.9*	*18.7*
Total [c]	$1,530.0	$136.7	$60.4	$1,332.9	$669.3	$271.8	$105.8	$286.0
1935–36	17.0	—	0.1	16.9	13.0	0.9	3.0	—
1936–37	15.4	—	—	15.4	11.6	0.9	2.9	—
1937–38	55.6	—	1.3	54.3	46.1	0.9	7.3	—
1938–39	81.4	—	1.6	79.8	67.3	9.8	2.6	0.1
1939–40	189.8	—	4.6	185.2	118.2	47.2	3.1	16.7
1940–41	219.2	—	7.0	212.2	84.4	10.6	13.2	104.0
1941–42	189.2	—	6.5	182.7	49.0	10.6	7.3	115.8
1942–43	93.6	1.0	6.5	86.1	15.0	6.7	15.2	49.2
1943–44	60.5	33.7	3.8	23.0	15.0	1.3	6.7	—
1944–45	62.8	45.4	3.6	13.8	9.1	4.2	0.5	—
1945–46	90.9	56.6	4.0	30.3	6.2	20.3	3.8	—
1946–47	75.2	—	3.5	71.7	16.2	33.7	21.8	—
1947–48	75.1	—	1.8	73.3	45.4	19.9	8.0	—
1948–49	55.6	—	2.3	53.3	25.8	27.0	0.5	—
1949–50	77.5	—	3.9	73.6	41.7	24.6	7.3	—
1950–51	42.1	—	3.7	38.4	13.5	24.9	[d]	—
1951–52	54.3	—	3.0	51.3	33.2	16.8	1.3	—
1952–53	74.8	—	3.2	71.6	58.7	11.7	1.2	—

Source: U.S. Production and Marketing Administration, *Section 32 Handbook*, 1953, p. 29. Figures for 1953 are added.

a. Excludes transfers to other uses by legislative action and allotments and transfers to cooperating agencies. From 1935–1936 through 1951–1952 these transfers amounted to $561 million and $41 million respectively.

b. Excludes transfers of $215 million from 1946–1947 through 1948–1949 by legislative action to finance operations under the National School Lunch Act.

c. Totals of unrounded figures.

d. $2,000.

and eggs and poultry, $6.7 million; tree nuts, $3.8 million; and vegetables and miscellaneous products, $4.6 million. (See Table 27.)

Efforts to Reduce CCC Stocks

During recent years, the Congress has acted several times, on an ad hoc basis, to help CCC unburden itself of accumulated products. In the Surplus Property Act of 1944 (58 *Stat.* 765) it authorized CCC to export at competitive world prices any farm commodity not in short supply. The Foreign Aid Act of 1947 provided that certain commodities could

TABLE 27

Removal of Surplus Agricultural Commodities (Section 32):

Fiscal Year	Total	Cotton	Dairy	Eggs and Poultry	Fruits	Grain
Total	$1,261,320,808	$185,667,016	$142,888,744	$146,904,480	$247,383,143	$176,521,436
1936	16,896,182	4,059,978	—	198,604	2,439,281	5,764,307
1937	15,451,587	6,836	368,386	2,136,766	6,290,222	653,290
1938	54,251,221	133,829	5,876,612	1,726,868	17,330,045	13,812,962
1939	79,845,708	1,894,431	38,995,906	570,549	11,851,799	18,236,037
1940	185,208,471	49,472,402	17,884,220	15,489,520	25,557,097	44,302,278
1941	212,333,028	54,008,941	14,855,720	14,753,283	33,000,818	22,479,059
1942	182,739,272	12,238,044	29,379,618	25,977,967	29,967,124	29,155,316
1943	86,119,266	6,475,499	10,382,973	11,895,850	11,839,079	19,137,498
1944	23,090,142	1,319,636	3,610,624	5,883,402	1,242,780	1,314,938
1945	13,732,600	273,764	—	3,072,033	3,069,212	4,154,712
1946	30,286,835	18,586,865	—	—	—	3,751,462
1947	71,706,645	34,458,392	—	10,697,769	34,062	—
1948	73,341,643	2,482,582	—	19,713,194	19,543,631	—
1949	53,225,610	235,371	1,823,100	13,857,261	10,138,591	4,191,686
1950	73,542,543	20,157	15,546,069	13,267,266	27,798,052	2,473,527
1951	38,330,844	289	—	5,108,041	23,457,117	7,094,364
1952	51,219,211	—	4,165,516	2,556,107	23,824,233	—

be sold by CCC at a price equal to the domestic price for a quantity of wheat having the same caloric content as that of the commodity sold. Under this act losses amounting to $56.2 million were incurred, chiefly on eggs ($24.2 million), dried fruits ($15.6 million) and Irish potatoes ($13.8 million).[71]

The Foreign Assistance Act of 1948 (63 *Stat.* 137) provided that CCC might sell surplus commodities for foreign relief at cost or at the domestic price, whichever was lower. The Secretary of Agriculture was authorized to pay, out of Section 32 funds, up to 50 per cent of the loss incurred through sales of that kind. During 1948 and 1949, government agencies reimbursed CCC to the extent of $62.3 million on abnormal sales of various kinds in addition to the $23 million paid from Section 32 funds. Section 416 of the Agricultural Act of 1949 authorized CCC to barter certain types of stocks held by it for strategic materials available in foreign countries.

In the Mutual Security Act of 1953 (Section 550) the President was authorized to use between $100 million and $250 million for the purchase of surplus agricultural commodities which were to be sold abroad for local (foreign) currencies. The funds thus obtained in foreign currencies are to be credited to a revolving fund for the purchase of military equipment. However, the act contained a provision which required that such sales should not displace usual marketings from the United States or friendly countries. From July 1953 through January 15, 1954 the

71. See Comptroller General of the United States, *Report on Audit of Commodity Credit Corporation,* House Doc. 674, 81st Cong., 2d sess., 1950, pp. 56–57.

TABLE 27

Expenditures by Commodity Groups, Fiscal Years 1936–1952

Livestock Products	Peanuts and Products	Tobacco	Tree Nuts	Vegetables	Misc.	Fiscal Year
$83,945,892	$28,548,057	$18,083,921	$19,101,881	$183,886,194	$28,390,044	Total
—	306,550	1,090,213	1,289,188	1,707,599	40,462	1936
107,229	—	1,720,637	1,544,360	1,365,684	1,258,177	1937
—	2,301,818	1,555,838	1,611,723	7,942,674	1,958,852	1938
—	—	400,897	1,232,127	5,466,358	1,197,604	1939
25,826,388	699,353	—	1,408,633	3,685,463	883,177	1940
30,719,343	8,125,877	—	669,197	24,724,596	8,996,194	1941
14,221,175	462,200	367,361	1,830,902	35,394,445	3,745,120	1942
440,000	1,049,970	1,694,000	679,881	21,898,063	626,453	1943
367,194	—	2,708,475	—	6,403,824	239,269	1944
—	—	—	—	3,143,083	19,796	1945
—	—	—	—	7,948,508	—	1946
—	—	—	—	26,516,422	—	1947
—	—	8,546,500	1,133,820	21,099,758	822,158	1948
—	10,167,023	—	—	11,096,628	1,715,950	1949
—	4,559,192	—	3,928,890	5,254,775	694,615	1950
—	876,074	—	—	226,616	1,568,343	1951
12,264,563	—	—	3,773,160	11,698	4,623,934	1952

Source: U.S. Production and Marketing Administration, *Section 32 Handbook,* 1953, p. 30.

Foreign Operations Administration had approved disposal of surplus commodities under this authorization in the amount of about $63 million. Included in these authorizations were tobacco ($20 million), beef ($17 million), cottonseed oil ($11 million), lard ($8 million), prunes ($5 million) and soybeans ($2 million).

The Secretary of Agriculture stated in the 1954 appropriation hearings that, although there is considerable political support for increasing the scale of this program, it is not likely that it can be increased to the extent desired by those who favor action along these lines. The provision that such sales must not displace usual marketings from the United States or friendly countries places severe limitations on the amounts that can be moved in this way. The Secretary pointed out, however, that without such provision we would be in difficulty with our allies on the ground that we were "dumping" our surplus commodities in their markets. If, as recently proposed by the President, considerable amounts of the stocks now in hand are set aside and barred from sale in the domestic market, there will presumably be a greatly increased effort to expand abnormal outlets of this kind or to find other ways of transferring surplus commodities to undersupplied countries.

The Potato Program a Special Case

The surplus removal and foreign-aid programs described above were, in the main, carried out in pursuance of general objectives that were of wider public interest than those of the producer groups affected. The potato program of the late 1940s was on a different basis and for a different purpose. It was, in part, a poorly timed carry-over of legislation designed to stimulate potato production in the war years. In the early part of the war, concern over the adequacy of food supplies caused the Secretary of Agriculture to request an expansion of potato production (in November 1942). This automatically put potatoes on the list of Steagall commodities for which price supports at 90 per cent of parity were later guaranteed for a two-year period following the war.

The general legislation pertaining to most of the major crops and to many of the minor ones precluded a reduction in the levels of price support until the end of 1948. Support at 90 per cent of parity proved unduly stimulating to the industry. Yields were very high, partly as a result of improvements in methods of production, increased use of fertilizer and favorable weather. Acreage was subsequently reduced but yields continued to be so large as to result in quantities much in excess of the amounts that could be sold at the prices prescribed by the law.

The 1946 and 1948 crops were much above the amounts needed to meet normal requirements, even if there had not been (as there was) a decline in per capita consumption. Since potatoes cannot be stored and carried over from one year to another and since there are few alternative uses for them, the government found itself faced with commitments to take over huge quantities for which there was no market at guaranteed prices.[72] Huge quantities were destroyed or sold for livestock feed at giveaway prices.

The Agricultural Acts of 1948 and 1949 permitted a reduction in support price, to 60 per cent of parity, but yields continued high. Heavy losses were incurred on the 1950 and 1951 crops. In 1951 the Congress acted to end price supports on potatoes, unless marketing quotas were in effect. Since there was no legislation which provided machinery for setting marketing quotas on potatoes, their prices were not supported in the years 1950, 1951 and 1952. Some support is being provided currently with Section 32 funds under new legislation passed in 1954.

The diversionary activities relating to potatoes were the most criticized and the most costly of those undertaken by the federal government. Their cost was more than $600 million and there was little in the way of collateral benefits. Prices to consumers were kept high while huge quantities of potatoes were destroyed. Thus, consumers paid for them both in the market and through taxes, and still did not receive an abundant supply of high-quality potatoes. The program and its results are more fully described in Chapter 10 of the companion volume on commodity programs.

---

72. The quantities produced were so large that it is unlikely that all of the crop could have been sold even at much lower prices.

The International Wheat Agreement

The International Wheat Agreement is also partly a surplus removal program. The primary purpose of the Wheat Agreement is presumably the stabilization of the international market for this key product. Not only is the price of wheat a very important consideration for many thousands of farmers in the United States and Canada; wheat is also one of the most important farm products in world trade. The large expansions and contractions of U.S. output sought during and after World Wars I and II have given wheat prime importance in the adjustment and price-support programs nearly all through the first half of the present century.

Some parts of the agreement were entered into tentatively in 1941 and were carried out informally during the war years. It was revived in 1948 and was ratified by the Congress in June 1949. Its principal provisions were that the importing countries would be assured of a minimum delivery of wheat by the exporting countries at not more than agreed maximum prices and the exporting countries would be assured of a minimum outlet for their surpluses at not less than agreed minimum prices. If wheat was in plentiful supply, prices paid for wheat bought by the importing countries would presumably be at the minimum price in the range ($1.20 per bushel under the 1949 agreement). If wheat was scarce and priced in the free market at more than the maximum ($1.80), the exporting countries would be obligated to supply the minimum agreed quantities at that price.

With the strong wheat market that prevailed from 1946 on, the importing countries were interested in assuring themselves of being able to buy enough wheat to cover their minimum needs even if world supplies should be short. The exporting countries were willing to accept a relatively low maximum price (as judged by prices in the preceding postwar years) in order to insure themselves to some extent against a serious break in prices and a demoralized world market if wheat supplies should become too heavy.

Since the United States was supporting wheat prices at levels above those which could be obtained under the Wheat Agreement, it was under obligation to supply wheat at the lower price and to make up the difference through contributions from the Treasury. Thus, the arrangement constituted to some extent a surplus removal operation carried out by means of export subsidies.

Some part of the wheat would no doubt have been exported even under free-market conditions. Hence, the operation cannot be regarded as wholly a surplus removal program, though this has been its principal characteristic to date.[73]

73. Under the price guarantees established in the United States, wheat not needed for domestic consumption is acquired automatically by the Commodity Credit Corporation if not exported. If, under the agreement now in effect, CCC chooses to dump wheat abroad, the 209.5 million bushels the importing countries have agreed to take will not have to be sold at less than the $1.55 per bushel provided as a minimum under the

Contributions made by the U.S. government in carrying out the agreement by fiscal years have been as follows (in millions):

1950	$ 75.6
1951	180.4
1952	171.3
1953	130.8
Total	$558.1

These payments constitute part of the cost of the wheat price-support program as a whole. The subsidized wheat export under the Wheat Agreement provides mainly a way of keeping realistic touch with prices in the export market at a time when wheat prices are supported in the United States at higher than world market prices. The government outlays under the agreement are in effect a price-support subsidy (or export subsidy) for the benefit of U.S. wheat growers. They do not constitute the whole of such subsidy since any losses that may be incurred on government stocks accumulated in the United States will be an additional cost of supporting the price of wheat. For fuller explanation of the operation and its effects, see Chapter 3 of the companion volume on commodity programs.

Significance and Place of Surplus Removal Programs

Few broad generalizations about the surplus removal programs are warranted. They have taken many forms and have been financed in various ways. Generally speaking, they appear to be better suited to depression periods than to times when employment and incomes are high. Few will question the desirability of trying to get commodities that are overabundant into the hands of people who need them and cannot afford to buy them. This was attempted in the relief programs of the 1930s and in the school lunch and food stamp plans that came later. However, the mechanics, scope, timing and locations of such programs need further study and the various alternatives need further exploration.

The general trend in relief activities appears to have been in the direction of cash payments to needy families with purchases made through normal market channels. This is undoubtedly more practical, efficient and equitable than the early efforts to distribute food directly to needy families. If unemployment and the need for relief should again become widespread, a revival of the food stamp idea would merit serious consideration. It constitutes a form of class pricing for consumers but not for producers, if the government provides funds for redeeming the stamps at par.

---

agreement. However, in 1954 the United States did not require the importing countries to absorb the maximum amounts they were obligated to take and did not lower the price to the minimum prescribed.

It should be recognized that a food stamp plan is not likely to be easily or economically administered in times when eligible purchasers are few and scattered. Neither is it likely in such times to be well received by local retailers, since it involves bother, extra work and more bookkeeping on their part. If such a plan is to be reasonably equitable, it would seem that some means should be found for relating the cost of stamps roughly to the incomes of the beneficiaries (as under the Aiken Plan, see pp. 289–90). Such a plan would avoid the granting of aid of this kind to one beneficiary and denying it to another who has only a slightly larger monthly income or who is in a different category in respect to relief aid.

The administrative difficulties of handling such a program would be formidable. The income of each family applying would have to be determined, and the possibilities of concealing income, misusing food stamps and otherwise defeating the purposes of the program would have to be considered. If large numbers of families were to be included, the costs would be large, very possibly larger than the Congress would be willing to meet except possibly in a general and severe depression.

The School Lunch Program also presents problems. As now handled, it is spread very thinly and does not provide food in the amounts needed in the areas most in need of assistance. For prosperous communities, there seems little advantage in paying into the federal Treasury the amounts involved and then receiving them back as grants from the federal government. The need is apparently for a more selective use of the funds and commodities provided and for channeling them to the schools and groups most in need of such aid. Neither the school lunch nor the food stamp plan can be very effective in raising nutritional levels if the primary consideration is the disposal of surplus products rather than the upgrading of diets.

Export subsidies have not shown much promise as a solution to the farm problem, except in special situations as a means of relieving congestion at terminals or tiding over minor industries that have experienced sudden and disastrous contractions of their export markets. The largest export subsidy has been that applied to wheat under the International Wheat Agreement. It does not seem to provide a satisfactory long-term solution to the wheat problem, though it is undoubtedly superior to straight export dumping without an agreement with the importing countries or with competing export countries. The minor export subsidy programs undertaken by the Farm Board and the AAA did not prove sufficiently encouraging to lead to their continuance.

The attempt to use Section 32 funds as a means of developing new uses for farm products has not thus far shown much promise. Some diversion to lower-grade uses may be feasible in some situations, mainly as a way of reducing stocks, for example, the sale of wheat at reduced prices for use as feed or in the production of alcohol. It is scarcely conceivable that such a procedure would be acceptable as a continuing program, partly because of objections from the growers of competing products.

Large-scale foreign aid, where feasible, and if the people of the United States are willing to bear the cost, can provide outlets for very sizable amounts of farm products. Lend-lease and the postwar foreign-aid programs did provide such an outlet and undoubtedly strengthened farm prices, but at very high cost and under very special conditions. However, even the billions of dollars so spent apparently would not have been sufficient to bring prosperity to agriculture if domestic demand had been weak. In a period of serious depression, other countries as well as the United States are likely to be in depression and unwilling to receive large-scale shipments, even if we are willing to provide them. Nevertheless, sizable foreign-aid shipments, if used in a discriminating and mutually satisfactory way, can at times be a means of easing down burdensome stocks.

On the whole, there appears to be merit in having available a modest fund, such as that provided under Section 32, which can be used in very diverse ways as a means of aiding in acute and especially in localized situations, particularly with respect to minor crops. In order that unwarranted demands for the use of such funds for these purposes may be minimized, there may be need for a more careful spelling out of criteria to govern the expenditure of them. Probably more of the emphasis should be on providing aid in making readjustments, where the trouble seems likely to be chronic or to recur at frequent intervals. Question may be raised also as to whether the fund needs to be as large as it currently is.

All in all, surplus removal does not seem to offer as much promise, as a way of strengthening demand, as many believe. It is the over-all demand, based on the levels of employment and earnings, that is the major factor in farm prosperity or depression. However, there is much to be said for programs designed to enlarge the use of commodities that are in excess supply provided too much is not expected of them. That is particularly true in times of severe recession, when the economy is faced with the anomaly of large stocks of food for which there is no suitable market while large numbers of potential consumers are in need.

Even in more normal times there is warrant for special efforts to channel surplus foods to people who for one reason or another are not able to buy adequate amounts and kinds of food to meet reasonable minimum standards of diet. While in most cases such transfers are not likely to be large enough to affect importantly the returns to farmers, they may be of great importance to the consumer groups concerned. Also, vigorous action to stimulate movement and consumption of highly perishable commodities that are temporarily in excess supply may well benefit both producers and consumers. The demand side of the farm problem should be kept continuously under study and, so far as practical, efforts should be made to increase demand in preference to reducing supply.

Chapter 9

Conservation and Soil Building

THE CONSERVATION of soils has become an accepted part of American farm policy. The interest in soil conservation is an outgrowth of the more general conservation movement that began to take shape in the late 1800s and early 1900s. The policy of conserving the remaining timber, water-power and mineral resources became well established during the administration of Theodore Roosevelt, but the conservation of soils was not strongly emphasized at that time. Soil resources had been deteriorating, but as long as vast areas of new and fertile lands were available for exploitation the public did not become much concerned about soil losses and soil deterioration. However, as early as 1910, the Commission on Country Life took note of the loss of soil fertility that was then becoming evident though it did not give this problem a prominent place in its recommendations.[1] The Department of Agriculture and the state experiment stations were by then carrying on a considerable amount of research and education looking to the maintenance and improvement of soils, but the problem was looked upon as one for the individual farmer, not a matter that required national action in the general public interest.

Woodrow Wilson, following the general tradition of the Theodore Roosevelt era, stressed the importance of soil conservation in some of his early messages to Congress and apparently intended to make it a part of his agricultural program. However, the onset of war and his preoccupation with other reforms caused it to be dropped into the background shortly after he took office.

During the 1920s, the farm journals and agricultural leaders continued to emphasize the need for safeguarding and building up soils and began to give more attention to the physical loss of soils, as well as to losses in soil fertility. As a result of this growing interest, the Congress, in 1929, provided an appropriation of $160,000 for investigation of soil losses from erosion. Regional soil erosion experiment stations were set up under the Bureau of Chemistry and Soils in the Department of Agriculture.[2]

The studies thus initiated soon led to a growing recognition of the seriousness of the losses from wind and water erosion. The problem of sheet erosion in particular had been little recognized until brought under specific study. Sheet erosion is the process in which surface soil is gradu-

---

1. *Report of the Commission on Country Life,* University of North Carolina Press, Chapel Hill, May 1944, pp. 83–90.
2. In cooperation with the Bureau of Agricultural Engineering and the Forest Service.

ally carried off by wind or water without making noticeable changes in the appearance of the land. Losses of this kind were found to be very large and of increasing significance. Gullying and actual destruction of the land surface were also evident in many of the older and poorer areas.

Appropriations for soil erosion investigations were increased in 1931, to $330,000 a year. The results of these studies were widely and aggressively publicized by the soil erosion specialists of the Department of Agriculture. As a result, both the public and the Congress began to take a renewed interest in the conservation of natural resources and especially in the conservation of soils.

When Franklin Roosevelt became President, the country was in deep depression. He was much interested in finding ways to stimulate employment in lines that would not add quickly to the supply of goods available for sale. This situation, coupled with Roosevelt's keen interest in conservation, led to a large expansion in activities relating to this problem during his administration. The movement also received great impetus from the devastating and widespread drought of 1934 which caused crops to be lost on hundreds of thousands of acres. The dust storms of that year carried off millions of tons of fertile top soil, ruining many farms and making some areas almost worthless.

A survey made in 1934 indicated that erosion had badly damaged more than 280 million acres of crop and grazing land and that considerable areas of crop land had been virtually destroyed by water and wind erosion. Some erosion damage was apparent on another 775 million acres of crop, grazing and forest lands.[3] It had become evident that national action of some kind would be required if such losses were to be checked and eventually brought under control. One of the nation's primary resources was being destroyed at a rate that constituted a serious threat to its future welfare.

PUBLIC CONCERN OVER FOOD-PRODUCING CAPACITY

The adequacy and dependability of food supplies has long been a matter of vital concern to all the world. From earliest times, many groups have lived under the threat of hunger, or mass starvation. That threat

3. As reported in *Our American Land, The Story of Its Abuse and Its Conservation,* Soil Conservation Service, U.S. Department of Agriculture, Miscellaneous Publication No. 596, 1950, p. 4.

Even now, the Soil Conservation Service estimates that about one fourth of the crop land on farms is being damaged at a critically severe rate and another fourth is eroding at a less rapid but serious rate. It is stated that, unless corrected or offset, these tendencies could lead in 10 or 15 years to substantially smaller yields on about a quarter of the nation's crop lands, and to serious deterioration on another 25 per cent in 20 to 30 years. If accepted at face value, these estimates indicate that the soil erosion problem is a very important one from the standpoint of the national welfare as well as that of the operators of the farms affected.

During the early 1930s the principal emphasis was on the control of erosion. Later, especially in the 1940s, interest shifted more to the possibility of increasing farm output through more use of commercial fertilizers and improved farm practices.

existed, even in the western world, up to about 1800. It was highlighted by the widely discussed views put forward by Thomas Malthus and others in the early part of the nineteenth century.

For the countries of western Europe, concern about this problem was quickly and unexpectedly pushed into the background by the industrial revolution and the great improvements in transportation that accompanied and followed it. The rapid introduction of railroads, steam-powered ships, and, later, the growth of highways and automotive transport, made practically available a vastly greater land area than Malthus and his contemporaries could visualize. Much of it was virgin territory in the Western Hemisphere, including vast areas of the richest farm lands of the world.

Under the impetus of this revolutionary change in methods of transportation, associated with almost equally revolutionary changes in production methods, the upsurge in output was so rapid that the countries of the Western Hemisphere soon came to be more concerned about surpluses and low prices than about shortages and high prices. In fact, the whole western world, including western Europe, came to be better fed than at any time in its history. It was able to eat moderately well, and to be relatively free from anxiety about the adequacy and dependability of its food supply.

Because of its rapid industrialization and consequent population growth, Europe fell farther and farther below self-sufficiency in food production, but was able to maintain a comparatively high standard of living through sale of its industrial products. Most of Asia, and many other parts of the world, continued, as they had for centuries, to be poorly fed and in constant danger of famine.

Renewed Concern over Food Supplies in the 1940s

World War II brought a quick change in the demand for agricultural raw materials throughout the world. While much of the shortage of the 1940s was due to the disruptions and destruction brought about by war, there were indications that the balance between population and food supplies was undergoing more profound and lasting changes. Population was growing rapidly and the surplus-producing nations were finding a ready outlet for all they could produce. New international agencies were created in an effort to step up food production throughout the world. Though this sharply increased demand was partly artificial, it was more and more apparent that, for much of the world's population, the adequacy of food supplies had again become a primary concern.[4]

4. Even before the upsurge in population growth that marked the decade 1940–1950, world population was increasing at a rate that foreshadowed food problems of first magnitude. The number of people to be fed is now more than four times what it was in 1650. It has doubled since 1800. Notestein comments that if this rate of increase had prevailed from the beginning of the Christian Era the world's population would now

In the United States, food production has continued to be abundant and the population well fed. However, output and requirements appear to be coming more nearly into balance than in the past, even in this country which has long been the world's largest supplier of export farm products. During the nineteenth century the United States had one of the fastest rates of population growth ever experienced by any important nation and its rate of growth has been high even in the twentieth century, except in the depression of the 1930s. The number of people to be fed here at home has doubled since 1900 and is still growing at a rate of more than 2 million a year. The increase since 1940 has been more than 25 million, which is about the same as adding to our domestic food requirement an amount that would feed the entire populations of all of the Scandinavian countries and the Netherlands. Another ten years will apparently add a domestic food requirement of similar size.

It seems apparent that the terms of trade, which for more than a century were unfavorable to agricultural producers, are shifting in the direction of a balance which will eventually place agricultural producers in a stronger position relative to other groups and will increase the national and international concern over the need for maintaining and increasing the productivity of the land. It seems unlikely that the food situation of the western world will be as easy over the foreseeable future as it has been during the century just past. For the great overpopulated areas of Asia and parts of the Orient, food problems are bound to be prominent in the making of national policies.

Higher Costs Probable in the Years Ahead

For the United States, the century just past was unique in respect to the ease of supplying food requirements. During this period, much of the increase in food production was actually achieved at lower real costs, as a result of gaining access to more productive lands and the introduction of far more efficient means of production. This fact lay at the heart of the difficult problem of balancing farm output with demand in such a way as to make returns to farmers seem equitable and fair. So long as costs could be reduced by producing more, output was kept high even when prices tended to be reduced more rapidly than costs.

This period is probably nearing its end. Much more food can be pro-

be more than fifty times as large as it is. (See Frank W. Notestein, "Population—The Long View," in *Food for the World,* edited by T. W. Schultz, University of Chicago Press, Chicago, 1945, pp. 36–57.)

Great progress has been made in reducing the death rate but the birth rate has not declined correspondingly. The result is an accelerating rate of population growth. Reducing the death rate, particularly among infants, is popular and effective. Reducing the birth rate is unpopular and extremely difficult. Technological advances will undoubtedly increase food supplies much beyond their present levels, but almost certainly not at such a rate as to banish hunger and famine as a major concern for large parts of the world's population.

duced in the United States than is now being turned out, but both the real and cash costs of achieving this larger production may be higher per unit of output in the future than in the past. The best and most accessible lands are now in use. The change-over to tractor power, which freed some 70 million acres for nonfeed uses, was largely completed between 1920 and 1950. A similar gain in lands available for producing human food cannot be expected from this source. Technological gains will continue, but possibly not at so fast a pace as in the past three decades. More use of fertilizer, improved care of the land, better strains and more effective protection against pests will increase output, but in many cases at higher cost.

All of these factors point to the need for encouraging and facilitating the protection and improvement of soil resources. The extremely wasteful and destructive practices of the past two centuries cannot be tolerated or afforded. At the time the United States became an independent nation, or shortly thereafter, its small population of only four or five million people was endowed with a heritage of natural resources unparalleled in the world's history. It could afford to use it wastefully, and did so. But there is no comparable heritage in prospect for the future, and the benefits to be derived from the assets remaining must now be divided among some forty times as many people.

NEED FOR CONSERVATION ACCEPTED—CONTROVERSY OVER METHODS

There is general, perhaps almost universal, agreement that soils should be protected and improved. The policy issues relating to conservation are nevertheless complex and far-reaching. Among them are the following: To what extent is the preservation of soils a public responsibility, and to what extent a function that should be performed by the farmer, in his own interest as well as that of the public? How define the values that accrue to the public as against those that accrue to the individual, in order that an equitable sharing of expense may be arrived at? As a corollary, what kinds of projects should be paid for by the public and what kinds should be paid for privately? How much expenditure for conservation, especially of public funds, is warranted in any given period?

There is no specific, identifiable level of conservation activity that is "right." Ordinarily, more investment of money and labor will save or improve more land, but beyond a certain level of expenditure, additional inputs will not yield equally large returns and may not add enough to cover their cost. Furthermore, the return itself often can be ascertained only vaguely. The gains will appear in later years and their values are not known. For some of the larger undertakings, and in fact for some of the small ones, the real costs may be far less if they are deferred to a time when labor and other resources are idle and thus almost costless from a social point of view. This consideration is especially important in plans relating to large-scale flood control, irrigation and erosion control projects.

In addition, there are very perplexing problems of organization and method for bringing about soil-conserving actions and practices. In part the problem is one of educating farmers in the constructive use of their lands. In many cases, technical and engineering aid are required or, under present programs, special financial incentives. Institutionally, these activities have come into being through different agencies. Interagency rivalries and antagonisms have become acute and serious in some areas. The manpower used in the conservation program as a whole may be greater than is needed for carrying on efficiently the present level of soil-conserving activities. The public interest is therefore a large one, both in assuring reasonably adequate protection of a great and essential national resource and in determining the intensity and method to be used in saving and improving the soil.

Conservation and the Farmer

The farmer has both a private financial interest in soil conservation and, as a member of society, the general interest described above. Under most conditions, soil-conserving types of farming are more profitable in the long run than soil-depleting practices.[5] Nevertheless, there are many exceptions to this general rule. The recovery of values invested in soil conservation requires time. A tenant or an owner, well along in years or heavily in debt, may find it profitable to extract as much as possible from the soil in a short period. This is especially true on tenant-operated farms, if there is no provision for recapture of the tenant's investments that have not yet been used up at the time he leaves the farm. Over most of the United States, there is no provision for such payments.

If the farmer knows the optimum input of conservation expenditure, from a profit standpoint, it may be assumed that he will spend privately about the amounts required to keep up his plant, unless faced by institutional barriers beyond his control. The most common inhibiting factors are lack of knowledge, short-run outlooks on the part of many farmers, insufficient capital, the absence of suitable organization for group action, limited tenure and inadequate technical assistance.[6]

To overcome the lack of knowledge education is of first importance. Generally speaking, society seems willing to supply educational help at

5. From a strictly private point of view, much of the destructive handling of both soils and forests may have been profitable in the pioneer period. So long as additional virgin soils or forests were to be had at almost no cost it probably would not have been profitable to make the expenditures needed for conserving the soils and forest areas already in use. Much of the destruction of values arose, however, from lack of knowledge about how to prevent such losses.

6. There is also, in many cases, a lack of sufficient desire for increased income to induce the farmer to put into use the best practices known to him. Inertia and the lack of pressure for more income often are very significant factors in keeping farms at a low level of efficiency.

public expense. The principal question is how and by whom. Should it be provided through the agricultural extension services or through a specialized agency like the Soil Conservation Service which can provide some technical assistance along with the educational work? The lack of capital can be overcome by making credit available in suitable forms. Much progress has been made on this through the facilities of the production credit system, the Farmers Home Administration and some of the private banks. However, reluctance to borrow is an inhibiting factor in many cases, even where credit is available. Organization for group action, mainly on a privately financed basis, has now become fairly general through an extensive system of soil conservation districts, set up under state laws but aided and encouraged by the Soil Conservation Service.

Conservation Payments Most Controversial Feature

The most controversial and also the most expensive phase of the overall program, so far as individual farms are concerned, is the provision for conservation payments which was initiated through passage of the Soil Conservation and Domestic Allotment Act of 1936. Under this plan, the government paid farmers for shifting land from "soil-depleting" to "soil-conserving" crops and for instituting improved practices in the handling of their soils.[7]

The payments for shifting from soil-depleting crops were made on the basis of crop quotas for such crops as corn, wheat, cotton, rice, tobacco, peanuts and potatoes which were classed as "soil-depleting." For these crops national goals were established and each farmer (in the principal producing areas) was given an allotment which specified the acreage of such crops he might grow and still be eligible to receive payments. If a farmer exceeded the acreage allotted him, deductions were made from his conservation payments. Thus this phase of the program was largely a method of reducing the acreages of basic crops. It was discontinued at the close of the 1943 season and has not been used since that time, but payments have been continued for carrying out specific soil and water conservation measures. To some extent these have also involved shifts

7. This program has been handled through the state and county committee system of the Production and Marketing Administration, not through the Soil Conservation Service. The Soil Conservation Service provides educational and technical aid through a system of voluntarily established soil conservation districts. It does not make cash payments to farmers. The agricultural extension services also carry on educational work in methods of conserving soils. Early in 1953 the agricultural conservation payment program was taken out of the Production and Marketing Administration (under Secretary's Memorandum No. 1320) and was assigned to the Research, Extension and Land-Use Group under the title Agricultural Conservation Program Service. The nature of the program was not changed materially. This is presumably a temporary arrangement since further reorganization including the possibility of transfer of some of these functions to the states has been discussed and considered from time to time.

from soil-depleting to soil-conserving crops, though not on the basis of allotments.

Critics of the payment of subsidies to induce farmers to adopt soil-conserving practices, or to reduce acreage of soil-depleting crops, have contended that this means paying farmers for doing what they should do in their own interest. Proponents contended that this was the best and quickest way of getting results and arousing farmer interest in the problem. There can be no doubt that the conservation payment plan has had a marked influence in speeding the adoption of soil-conserving practices. Also, however, particularly in the period 1936 to 1943, it was a way of continuing acreage controls and income-supplementing payments to farmers when this could not be done under the Agricultural Adjustment Act of 1933, which had been invalidated.

Granting that payments for introducing improved practices have stimulated interest in conservation and have been effective as an educational device, there still is reason to question the need for continuing such payments indefinitely. A more serious question is whether these payments, as now handled, constitute an efficient way of promoting conservation activities. Good practices are already in use on many farms, and some areas are far less subject to soil deterioration than others. It would seem logical that if a given amount of public money is to be spent for conserving soils it should be spent where the returns per dollar will be largest. This would mean selective use of funds rather than general distribution regardless of need.[8]

As a general guiding principle, it seems reasonable to assume that the farmer should pay privately for such part of the cost of conserving soils as will be profitable to him. Such further action as society chooses to take should be at public expense. The public interest in having the farmer conserve his soil seems clearly to be important enough to warrant providing educational help that will make clear to him the kinds and amounts of conservation activity that will be profitable for him, as well as useful to society.

However, even though the farmer may be convinced that it would pay him to conserve his soil, he may not know how to go about it. Usually he needs technical assistance in working out a conservation program for his farm and plans for such engineering structures as may be needed. Such activities are more in the nature of special service than of education, but there has been strong sentiment in the Congress for supplying this type of assistance as well as more strictly educational aid.

8. The tendency is to make conservation payments in all parts of the United States regardless of need or effectiveness. It is recognized that the Soil Conservation Service, in its desire to cover all areas, may also distribute inputs in such a way that they do not achieve the largest possible result per dollar expended. However, since active participation in the soil conservation district programs is largely financed by the farmers themselves, there is less likelihood that programs carried on through them will be continued where they are not needed. Both types of program need to be examined carefully and frequently to see where savings can be made.

It is also necessary to weigh carefully the rate of improvement that is reasonably feasible and the amount of detailed assistance the public agencies should give. Reversing a trend that has persisted for a century or more is bound to be a slow process. It can be speeded up if enough funds and manpower are applied, or it can proceed at a less rapid pace with more modest annual inputs. A full-scale and effective conservation program requires the working out of individual farm plans, and some continuing supervision. At best it can be carried out only over a period of many years and with a sizable input of manpower and funds.

In general, the aim should be to intensify such efforts in times of recession and possibly to de-emphasize them somewhat in other periods. In time of war, it is recognized that some depletion of accumulated soil fertility may be logical and in the public interest. Certainly deferrable demands on manpower and other resources should be minimized in such periods. Public expenditure on large-scale conservation projects likewise may well be held down in periods when there are other heavy demands on the budget and when manpower and materials are in short supply.

DEVELOPMENT OF SOIL CONSERVATION IN THE 1930s

Though the primary emphasis in this section is on the conservation of soils it should be recognized that soil conservation is only part of the more general conservation program of the federal government. It was not, in fact, the most prominent part of it in the first years of the Franklin Roosevelt administration. The effort to conserve and improve forest resources, which began near the end of the last century, has been continued vigorously. The development of unused water power has likewise bulked large in the thinking of conservationists, and the efforts to conserve and use demoralized human resources had a bearing on the nature and extent of the program in the 1930s. Lesser aspects of the over-all program had to do with the protection of watersheds and the preservation of wildlife.

The success and popularity of the emergency conservation program, which was initiated in 1933 to provide healthful and useful work in the national forests for unemployed young men, led to active interest in the possibilities of conservation work as a means of providing employment.[9] The effort to provide work for the unemployed on conservation projects was at first limited to the improvement and protection of forest lands. Soon, however, it was expanded to include erosion control activities on other types of land as well.

9. This program involved the creation of a Civilian Conservation Corps in which young unmarried men might enlist for work on conservation projects. They lived in camps, and were provided with food, lodging and a small monthly wage. Some educational facilities were also provided. The extensive program of reclamation, water-power development and public building construction, launched under the Public Works Administration, was likewise undertaken principally as a means of providing employment.

Only a few months after the Civilian Conservation Corps was created, the President established the Soil Erosion Service in the Department of the Interior. Its work included both direct measures on public lands and demonstration projects partly or wholly on private lands.[10] Parts of the Civilian Conservation Corps were assigned to this agency and were used in sloping and terracing eroding lands, planting trees and grass and building check dams.

The agency soon was under pressure to expand its demonstration program as a means of keeping its labor force busy. This, together with the growing interest in conservation activities, led to agitation for a more comprehensive attack on the soil conservation problem as a whole, including a much more vigorous effort to check the deterioration that was occurring on farm lands.

Establishment of the Soil Conservation Service

The need for a more comprehensive program covering both private and public lands was recognized by the Congress in the Soil Conservation Act of 1935 (49 *Stat.* 163). This provided legislative authorization for the work, and implied a broader conception of the task by changing the name of the agency from Soil Erosion Service to Soil Conservation Service.[11] During the summer of 1935, 150 Civilian Conservation Corps camps were transferred from the Forest Service and more than 300 additional ones were assigned to the Soil Conservation Service, for an expanded program of demonstration projects.[12]

The program of the Soil Conservation Service was modified to some extent by later legislation, but the major changes were in its own emphases and methods.[13] In the earlier period it depended heavily on

10. The Soil Erosion Service was established in October 1933 to carry out provisions of the National Industrial Recovery Act in respect to the prevention of soil erosion. In March 1935 it was transferred to the Department of Agriculture, by order of the Administrator of Public Works with the President's approval. The Secretary of Agriculture consolidated all of the soil erosion agencies under it at that time.

11. The general acceptance of the need for an active and comprehensive program for conserving soils is indicated by the fact that the bill passed both houses of Congress without a single dissenting vote.

12. The responsibility for carrying out conservation work on Department of Interior lands was turned back to that Department in 1940.

13. The Omnibus Flood Control Act of 1936 (49 *Stat.* 1570) directed the Department of Agriculture to institute investigations "of watersheds, measures for run-off and water-flow regulation and measures for the prevention of soil erosion on watersheds." The act provided that the upstream, on-the-land phase of the flood control program was to be handled by the Department of Agriculture while the downstream engineering structures for the control of flood damage were to be provided through the Army Corps of Engineers.

In the same year a Great Plains Committee was established, by executive order, for joint consideration of ways of controlling erosion in the Plains area. This was followed in 1937 by the Pope-Jones Water Facilities Act (50 *Stat.* 869) to provide facilities for water storage and utilization in the arid and semiarid areas. That act authorized the Secretary of Agriculture to undertake action programs in this field. Further authorizations for water conservation and flood control activities were provided in the Wheeler-Case Act of 1939 and the Flood Control Act of 1944.

demonstration projects to encourage the use of soil-conserving techniques on farm lands. From about 1937 on it shifted emphasis to the formation of soil conservation districts under state laws. Copies of a model state law designed for this purpose were circulated to the various state governors, together with a letter from the President requesting that the states enact legislation authorizing the formation of soil conservation districts. The first state to pass such a law was Arkansas, which took action on March 3, 1937. The first district actually formed was the Brown Creek District in Anson County, North Carolina, organized on August 4, 1937.

The movement spread rapidly, and by 1952 all 48 states and Alaska, Hawaii, Puerto Rico and the Virgin Islands had passed laws under which such districts could be formed. Under these laws, some 2,467 soil conservation districts had been formed. They included nearly 5 million farms and 1.4 billion acres of land.[14] The bulk of the nation's land resource had thus been organized for cooperative effort in conserving and improving soils.

The soil conservation districts are local organizations, set up and presumably run by farmers who wish to cooperate in protecting their lands. In practice, much of the leadership and guidance has been supplied by Soil Conservation Service technicians. The districts have authority to ask and receive technical aid from the state and federal governments and at times have been given help by being granted the use of heavy machinery. They are primarily self-help organizations. Only in California and Colorado do the soil conservation districts have power to levy taxes, and there only on a very limited scale. In no state do they have the power of eminent domain.

The states do, however, contribute about $3.5 million a year toward their support and the districts receive a good deal of technical assistance from the field staff of the Soil Conservation Service in the form of farm plans designed to check erosion, and advice and counsel in regard to soil-conserving practices. This close working relationship with the district officers and members has resulted in a considerable amount of popular support for the type of program carried on by the Soil Conservation Service and has important political significance.

Conservation Activities under the Act of 1936

The conservation payment program, which was initiated under the Soil Conservation and Domestic Allotment Act of 1936 (49 *Stat.* 1148), paralleled and to some extent competed with that of the Soil Conservation Service.[15] The act of 1936, though technically an amendment to the Soil Conservation Act of 1935, had broader and somewhat different

14. U.S. Soil Conservation Service, *Report of the Chief, 1952*, p. 13.
15. While competition and overlapping have been much emphasized, there are many respects in which the two programs have been complementary and mutually helpful.

objectives. Its principal purpose was to continue acreage controls and income payments to farmers without running afoul of the restrictions set up by the Supreme Court in its adverse decision on the Agricultural Adjustment Act of 1933. The program initiated under it thus had a dual purpose: the continuance, in modified form, of the adjustment program and the launching of a more vigorous effort to conserve soils. Soil improvement had been a secondary objective even in the earlier programs of the Agricultural Adjustment Administration. It was now given greater emphasis and, nominally at least, was put forward as the primary purpose of the new act.

Under the new act, which in amended form is still in effect, funds are provided through direct appropriations from the Treasury. Farmers are paid for carrying out changes presumed to be effective in checking erosion and building up soils. Until 1944, the subsidies provided were in two forms: payments for shifting acreage from soil-depleting to soil-conserving crops, and payments for adopting soil-conserving practices. Since then only the second form of payment has been used.[16]

The Agricultural Adjustment Administration thus came to have a function similar to that of the Soil Conservation Service but carried out by a different method and through a separate set of county and state committees. It had no direct contact with or relation to the soil conservation districts. Furthermore, since it could provide direct subsidies to farmers for the dual purpose of controlling acreage and encouraging soil conservation, it was in a strong position to build up support for this alternative or supplementary approach. Its principal support in the rural areas came by way of the county and state committees set up to administer soil conservation payments and other activities of the Agricultural Adjustment Administration.

Problems of Coordination

Efforts were made during the late 1930s to bring these activities, and others having similar objectives, into harmony through county land-use planning committees. This effort was abortive, partly because of the shift to war emphasis from 1941 on.[17]

16. Legislative authority still exists, however, for making both types of payments. The cash crops were, in the main, the ones that tended to reduce soil fertility. They were classed officially as "soil-depleting." Thus a financial incentive was provided for curtailing the acreages used in producing them. Grasses, legumes and cover crops were not ordinarily sold as cash crops, and many of them did tend to improve soils and prevent erosion. They were therefore classed as "soil-building" crops. The practices for which payments were made included terracing, contour plowing, more use of fertilizer and so on.

17. The county defense boards (later county war boards) had come to have a similar coordinating function. Also, the American Farm Bureau Federation was opposing continuance of the county land-use planning committees, which it regarded as potential competitors of the county farm bureaus. Funds for the land-use planning activities were discontinued and this approach to the problem of coordination has not been revived.

In 1942, the Agricultural Adjustment Administration was consolidated into the Agricultural Conservation and Adjustment Administration as the Agricultural Adjustment

The agricultural conservation payment and Soil Conservation Service programs were not necessarily in conflict, though extremely close cooperation would have been required if they were to be brought entirely into harmony. The crop control objective in the conservation payment program did not necessarily result in the kinds of shifts in acreage that would be recommended by the Soil Conservation Service with its single-purpose objective. Practices for which payments were made, partly as a means of transferring income to farmers, were not always those that would be recommended by professional conservationists, and were not necessarily in accord with any adequate over-all conservation plan for the farm. Thus there were abundant opportunities for friction and lack of coordination. The situation also was one in which rivalries could easily arise in the quest for farmer support and cooperation and in the drives for congressional appropriations.

This duplicating and competitive form of organization gave rise to a number of serious questions which were discussed repeatedly in the Congress. Numerous efforts were made to iron out the difficulties through administrative conferences and directives, but these were not entirely successful. The basic inconsistency between conservation expenditures specifically for the achievement of conservation objectives and those designed in part for other purposes still remains and has not been entirely resolved by the reorganizations thus far put into effect.

Another but less serious problem is coordination of these activities with those of the agricultural extension services. One important aspect of the conservation program is educating farmers in what practices to use and how to use them. In each county there is a county agricultural extension agent whose principal function is educational. Should he attempt to teach conservation, or should this be left to the soil conservationist?

The farm adviser and the representative of the local committee are presumably not specialists in conservation techniques, though each may have both opportunity and ability to do educational work in that field. As a further complication, the objective of the farm adviser may not harmonize with that of the soil conservationist. The farm adviser, in helping to develop a farm plan, will emphasize the maximization of farm profit while fostering conservation to the extent that is consistent with that aim. The conservationist will place major emphasis on conservation, and may either ignore the income and profit aspects or be unequipped to give sound advice in regard to them.

Agency (under Executive Order 9069). In the following year it was transferred to the War Food Administration under the President's war powers (Executive Order 9322). In 1945, when the War Food Administration was terminated, its functions were transferred to the Secretary of Agriculture. He in turn created (on August 18, 1945) the Production and Marketing Administration, assigning to it the functions formerly administered by the Agricultural Adjustment Agency. From then until 1953, when the Department was reorganized, the county and state committees through which the conservation payment program was administered were known as PMA committees.

ACTIVITIES AND EXPENDITURES OF SCS

The principal continuing activity of the Soil Conservation Service is that of providing assistance to soil conservation districts and other cooperators. In 1953 that phase of its program accounted for $57.5 million of the $62.3 million obligated.[18] All research activities were transferred out of the Soil Conservation Service in the reorganization of 1953 and the lands acquired earlier under the submarginal land purchase program were turned over to the Forest Service. The other activities relate to emergency restoration of stream channels damaged by floods and to land treatments designed to produce direct flood prevention benefits. Expenditures on these projects amounted to less than $5 million in 1953. The scale of expenditure for the Soil Conservation Service field program has become somewhat comparable to that of the agricultural extension service.[19] Both maintain large field staffs and work directly with individual farmers and farm groups.

In 1952 the Soil Conservation Service had 11,675 full-time employees, mostly field men located in the agricultural areas. The agricultural extension service had a field staff of about 12,600. When account is taken of the fact that a considerable part of the time of the field staff of the Production and Marketing Administration, which was nearly as large (10,455), was being used for making and supervising soil conservation payments to farmers, and that some of the time of the field agents of the Farmers Home Administration (see Chapter 6) was used in a similar way, it becomes apparent that extremely heavy emphasis is being placed on soil conservation.[20]

These figures are not cited as criticism of the activities carried on, but rather to bring out the size and diversity of the effort to improve conditions in agriculture, and especially the scale of the program now under way for checking the deterioration of soils. Some of the problems resulting from this development of new agencies are discussed in a later section.

Accomplishments Impressive

The accomplishments of the past twenty years in soil conservation have unquestionably been phenomenal. The Chief of the Soil Conserva-

18. This $62.3 million does not include some $4.1 million for flood prevention, administered by the Soil Conservation Service but financed through a separate appropriation.

19. Federal expenditure for the extension services, including the state and national staffs, amounted in 1952 to about $33 million. This was supplemented by some $46 million of state and county funds. The total input of public funds was thus about $79 million. Expenditures by the Soil Conservation Service, for demonstration work and technical aid, amounted to approximately $58 million. State contributions to soil conservation districts were in the order of $3.5 million, making a total input of public funds of about $61.5 million.

20. The field staff working with farmers has more than quadrupled in the past two decades. In addition to these full-time employees, the PMA had 94,734 part-time county and community committeemen who gave some time to conservation matters.

tion Service was able to state, in 1951, that "more than a fifth of the basic conservation job needed for full protection of farm and ranch land has been completed." [21] Even allowing for some overoptimism in the reports on accomplishments, the achievement constitutes one of the most significant planned changes ever brought about in American agriculture.[22]

Some of the kinds of change brought about can be more readily visualized through a listing of specific activities carried on under the soil conservation programs. Cumulative data, to June 30, 1952, are given below.[23] These data are for first-time application only and do not include duplication of acreage for reapplication or maintenance of these same practices year after year.

Activity	Unit	Amount
Contour farming	acres	28,601,869
Cover cropping	acres	19,171,931
Stubble mulching	acres	47,957,022
Strip cropping	acres	7,370,853
Seeding pasture and range	acres	12,213,204
Woodland management	acres	18,882,506
Tree planting	acres	931,799
Farm and ranch ponds	number	277,122
Terraces	miles	858,967
Diversion channels	miles	36,568
Farm drainage	acres	7,545,646
Irrigation land preparation	acres	1,836,923
Improved water application	acres	3,770,108
Field windbreaks	miles	11,371
Range and pasture improvement	acres	77,869,406

Increasing Support from Congress

The favorable attitude of the Congress toward the work is reflected in the gradual but steady growth of funds allotted to the Soil Conservation Service.[24] Its expenditures (on soil conservation programs only) from 1932 through June 1952 are shown in Table 28.

21. U.S. Soil Conservation Service, *Report of the Chief, 1951*, p. 2. As of June 30, 1952, Soil Conservation Service technicians were working with 1.12 million active farmer cooperators (chiefly in the development of detailed farm conservation plans).

22. It should be noted, however, that many of these practices, while included in Soil Conservation Service plans, were also of such a nature that PMA payments could be claimed for them. Hence, they are not solely the result of the work of the Soil Conservation Service. The adoption of improved practices undoubtedly would have been much slower and less general had there been no conservation payments of the type provided through PMA.

23. From U.S. House Committee on Appropriations, *Department of Agriculture Appropriations for 1954*, Hearings, p. 1421.

24. Expenditures for research on soil conservation have been continued on a modest scale since 1937, but part of the research program was transferred to the Bureau of Plant Industry, Soils and Agricultural Engineering in October 1952. In November 1953 the remaining research in SCS was transferred to the Agricultural Research Service. As

TABLE 28

EXPENDITURES OF THE SOIL CONSERVATION SERVICE, 1932–1952

(*Millions*)

Year	Amount	Year	Amount
Total	$575.5	1942	$ 24.3
		1943	24.3
1932	0.3	1944	26.0
1933	0.3		
1934	0.2	1945	29.2
		1946	35.4
1935	0.3	1947	44.6
1936	3.7	1948	42.4
1937	21.6	1949	49.3
1938	24.9		
1939	26.5	1950	54.1
		1951	53.9
1940	31.8	1952	58.6
1941	23.8		

Source: Data from U.S. Department of Agriculture. Amounts given are for soil conservation programs only. The Soil Conservation Service also engaged in other types of activity. Over-all costs for the agency are given on p. 340.

Flood Prevention Activities of SCS and Forest Service

The Flood Control Act of 1936, and subsequent legislation, authorized the Department of Agriculture and the Department of the Army to cooperate in reducing flood damage. In most cases the Army's Corps of Engineers takes responsibility for the major engineering structures on the lower parts of the watersheds while the Department of Agriculture carries out flood control operations in the upstream areas.[25] The purpose of these upstream operations is to improve cover, increase absorption and stabilize run-off as a means of protecting the lands upstream and aiding in the control of run-off that causes damage on the lower reaches of the rivers.

The work proceeds in three stages—preliminary investigations, survey reports (if authorized on the basis of the preliminary investigations) and the construction of installations where these are authorized by the Congress on the basis of surveys. As of 1952, the Congress had authorized

of 1952 the amounts obligated to the Bureau for soil and water research, management practices and other aspects of soil conservation amounted to about $2.5 million. In the meantime research expenditures by the Soil Conservation Service itself had been reduced to about $575,000. Its total research expenditure through June 1952 had amounted to about $23 million. This does not include the comparatively small expenditures made prior to 1934. The figure given does not include expenditures for soil conservation research carried on through agencies other than those mentioned.

25. The Soil Conservation Service has over-all responsibility for establishing policies, principles, procedures and standards for the work carried on under the Flood Control Act, but under Secretary's memorandum No. 1325 (April 1, 1953) the Forest Service was given responsibility for carrying out the program in watersheds administered by the Forest Service and on range lands adjacent to national forests if they are used in conjunction with the forests.

more than 1,000 preliminary investigations, and reports had been prepared on 178 watersheds. Of these, 148 recommended surveys. Remedial work was authorized by the Congress on 11 of the projects but no new projects of this kind have been authorized since 1944.[26]

The flood prevention funds of the Department of Agriculture are assigned to the Soil Conservation Service and the Forest Service by the Secretary of Agriculture. Funds assigned to the Soil Conservation Service for this purpose have, in recent years, ranged from about $2 to $6.6 million. Total annual expenditures, including those administered by the Forest Service, have been about $7 to $8 million per year.[27] Since 1937, expenditures by the Department of Agriculture as a whole on flood control and flood prevention have amounted to about $50.2 million (through June 1953).

Water Conservation and Utilization

The work of the Soil Conservation Service includes also a minor program of water conservation and utilization which is carried on under the Wheeler-Case Act (53 *Stat.* 1418), passed in 1939 to provide assistance in developing relatively small irrigation projects for settlement of families displaced by droughts. This activity is a holdover from the drought and depression period. It was costing about $400,000 per year in 1953. Total expenditures through June 1953 had amounted to about $7.3 million. Of this, $2.5 million was reimbursable.[28]

The Land Retirement Program

The Soil Conservation Service also has had responsibility for administering the remnants of the submarginal lands program which was initiated by other agencies in the early 1930s but was later transferred to SCS. This program was, in the main, a depression measure rather than a continuing part of the long-term plan for the conservation of soils and human resources. However, it has some continuing significance and still has a bearing on some of the administrative problems relating to the

26. For more detailed explanation of the flood prevention work see U.S. Soil Conservation Service, *Report of the Chief, 1951*, pp. 18–22 and *Department of Agriculture Appropriations for 1954*, Hearings, Part 4, pp. 1852–1923.

27. This program has not been carried out in accordance with the time schedule originally contemplated. Work has now been under way on 11 watersheds for a number of years. Their original cost (adjusted to 1952 prices) was estimated at $175 million. Of this only $34 million had been obligated through appropriations as of June 1953. Thus while 68 per cent of the work was scheduled for completion only 19.5 per cent of the funds had been authorized. See *Department of Agriculture Appropriations for 1954*, Hearings, pp. 1460–61.

28. The Wheeler-Case program was essentially a relief measure. Apparently the Bureau of Reclamation, to which it was originally assigned, was reluctant to continue this program, since it could not be justified under ordinary standards of feasibility. However, the Congress has continued to make appropriations for new projects. The activity is now unimportant and very local. It apparently should be discontinued when current projects are completed.

general problem of land management. Its purpose was to buy up and take out of crop production lands considered too poor or too hazardous for successful operation as farms. The adoption of this plan constituted to some extent a reversal of earlier land policy.

From the time the nation was first formed, there had been emphasis on methods of transferring public domain lands to private ownership. Presumably, any land not wanted by the government for its own use would be made available for private use if anyone chose to acquire and operate it. The principal exceptions to this policy were the provisions for retaining considerable areas as national forests and parks and the re-acquisition of some lands in rounding out forest and park units.[29] Much of the publicly owned land in the range areas had remained open for homesteading long after the lands suitable for crop farming had passed into private ownership. As a result, homesteaders had taken up large amounts of land that would not, in most years, provide a suitable living for the operator if cropped in the usual way.

Lands of this kind were now to be reacquired by the government, reorganized for extensive types of use, and retained in government ownership, so that small farmers would not try to farm them. It was hoped in this way to eliminate some of the problem areas that were perennial candidates for drought loans, relief and other kinds of assistance. Some cutover and deteriorated areas in other parts of the country were also included in the plan.

This general idea had been strongly supported by several of the farm organizations for a number of years, but on different grounds. Since it was felt that production was overabundant, the view was widely held that a logical solution would be to take out of production enough of the poor land to bring supply and demand into better balance, rather than to hold good land out of production as was being done under the procedures used by the Agricultural Adjustment Administration.

Fuller study developed the fact that vast areas, including most of the farm land in some states, would have to be taken out of production to accomplish such a result. By far the largest part of the commercial output of agriculture comes from the good land areas, not from the "marginal" areas. The idea of controlling production in this way soon dropped into the background. The principal objective of the land retirement program came to be to get out of crop production those lands that were so poor that farmers could not be expected to make a living on them,[30] and to

29. The Weeks and Clark-McNary Acts, both passed in 1924, did, however, provide for the acquisition of entirely new units of forest land. All of the national forests in the eastern part of the United States have been acquired by purchase rather than by reservation.

30. Some of the lands acquired were farms that had come into the hands of the states as a result of tax delinquency. In most states these were not under management. Often they were used without charge by ranchers whose sole interest was to get as much off them as possible without regard to further deterioration of soils or vegetation.

purchase lands needed to round out or develop publicly managed units organized for more extensive types of use, such as grazing, forestry and parks.

Origin of the Program

The land purchase program was initiated in 1933 and 1934 by the Federal Emergency Relief Administration, the Program section of the Agricultural Adjustment Administration and other agencies. The Relief Administration organized its land program section in June 1934. It had available some $78 million of relief funds for this activity. Fifty million dollars of this was impounded, in January 1935, so the funds actually available amounted to $28 million. During this early period, 245 projects in 469 counties were approved, 18.9 million acres were scheduled for purchase, 14.3 million were appraised and 6.2 million were optioned. Final approval was given to 82 projects involving 5.4 million acres and expenditures of $25.5 million.

The land acquisition program was later carried on by the Farm Security Administration and the Bureau of Agricultural Economics. It was transferred to the Soil Conservation Service in 1938. The bulk of the land acquired was purchased in 1936 and 1937, though expenditures in 1939 and 1940 amounted to $4.6 million and $10.0 million respectively. In recent years the amounts purchased have been negligible. The principal activity has been supervision of the lands previously acquired and not yet transferred to other agencies. The taking of options was discontinued in 1942.

It was not intended that lands so acquired would be retained by the agency making the purchase. They were to be transferred to operating agencies such as the Grazing Service or the Forest Service. Under the recent reorganization of the Department of Agriculture those still held by the Soil Conservation Service were transferred to the Forest Service.[31]

Income from these lands, chiefly for forest products and grazing use, was running at a rate of about $1.5 million per year in 1953. From the beginning of the operation to June 30, 1953, expenditures on the program amounted to about $102 million, not including $2.5 million paid

31. Total purchases under the National Industrial Recovery Act, the Emergency Relief Act of 1935 and Title III of the Bankhead-Jones Farm Tenant Act of 1937 amounted to approximately 11.3 million acres, to June 1947. (Bureau of Agricultural Economics, *Federal Rural Lands,* June 1947, pp. 43–44.) There have been no significant purchases since that time. As of then, about 4.4 million acres had been transferred to the Forest Service, Bureau of Land Management, Fish and Wildlife Service and other agencies. Approximately 7 million acres were still under the jurisdiction of the Soil Conservation Service. Of this, about 90 per cent consisted of land used for grazing and 7 per cent for forestry, the remainder being assigned to wildlife protection, recreation and crop production. (U.S. Commission on Organization of the Executive Branch of the Government, *Task Force Report on Natural Resources,* 1949, Appendix L, p. 45.) The recent transfer of these lands may still leave them somewhat out of place so far as management is concerned, though the Forest Service is undoubtedly better equipped to manage them than SCS. Most of the land transferred was grazing land.

to counties.[32] Income from the land has been approximately $10 million. Thus the over-all net outlay by the federal government has been about $95 million.

While the lands so acquired have some value as a source of continuing income to the government, such income is not large and is not likely to be in the future, except for possible income from oil and mineral deposits. The principal gain from the program has been the removal from crop use of lands that are not suitable for farming, thereby preventing the exploitation of settlers or the maintenance of inappropriate types of farming in areas where they are not likely to succeed. It can be considered at best a belated effort to correct some of the maladjustments that grew out of the lack of appropriate land classifications and policies when these public lands were transferred to private ownership.

It does not seem likely that this activity will be an important phase of the conservation program in the future. There will undoubtedly be some further transfer from private to public ownership, and vice versa, as the lands are blocked up into suitable units for effective use. Except in extreme situations where there are small bypassed populations or serious erosion problems, there seems little warrant for further federal acquisition of private lands, unless it is related to plans for putting them under orderly management by one of the agencies established for that purpose, that is, the Forest Service, the Division of Range Management,[33] the National Park Service, the Fish and Wildlife Service or some appropriate state agency.

Over-All Cost of the Soil Conservation Service Program

The Soil Conservation Service program as a whole, from its inception to June 30, 1953, has involved costs of approximately $771 million. These, by types of activity, were as follows (in millions):

Demonstration work and technical assistance	$569
Investigations [a]	23
Submarginal land retirement and management [b]	95
Water conservation and utilization [c]	5
Emergency funds used by SCS	65
Other [d]	14
Total	$771

a. Includes Everglades experiment station. Does not include conservation research carried on in other agencies.
b. Includes payments to counties, but income received from lands (approximately $7 million) is deducted. Includes outlays by predecessor agencies except those of FERA.
c. Wheeler-Case program.
d. Does not include flood prevention, since these costs are shown elsewhere. Figures are based on obligations authorized rather than actual expenditures.

32. Twenty-five per cent of the income goes to the counties in which the land is located, as a payment in lieu of taxes. The other 75 per cent goes into the Treasury.
33. Successor to the Grazing Service.

SOIL CONSERVATION PAYMENTS BY AAA AND PMA

The conservation payment plan, previously described, provided direct financial inducements for making adjustments in farming and for adopting soil-conserving practices. The acreage adjustment and income subsidy aspects are discussed in the companion volume which describes the various crop adjustment programs. However, since the conservation payments cannot be broken down into costs relating to the various purposes for which they were made, the total expenditures for this phase of the conservation and crop control program are included in the data given below.

The use of "conservation" and "parity" payments to induce compliance with acreage allotments helped materially in bringing about changes that were desirable as conservation measures. Not only did it result in a shift to more acreage in grasses and legumes, which help to build up soils, but also it provided an incentive for using more fertilizer on the acreages permitted under the allotments. This larger use of fertilizer tended, of course, to offset to some extent the efforts to reduce output but it also contributed to soil improvement.

The procedure used was to allot to each grower an authorized acreage of a given crop which was a percentage of the acreage of that crop grown by him in a specified base period. If in compliance with the regulations, the farmer received a payment for keeping within his allotted acreage. If the price of the commodity was below parity he could also be paid a certain amount per pound, or other unit, of the normal amount produced on the allotted acreage. This payment could not exceed the amount by which the price received in the market fell short of the parity price. If the acreage grown by him exceeded his allotment, the grower was ineligible for either type of payment. Parity payments were discontinued from 1943 on but soil conservation payments are still made though on a somewhat different basis.

The procedure used from 1936 to 1943 was virtually the same as that used from 1933 to 1936, under the original Agricultural Adjustment Act, except that the method of financing was different. Under the original act, rentals for the acres taken out of production were derived from processing taxes levied against the specified products at time of processing. These were, in effect, sales taxes.[34] Under the acts of 1936 and after, payments were made out of funds appropriated by the Congress, and therefore derived from taxation or borrowing. The processing tax was paid in proportion to the amount of the product used, whereas funds provided through regular appropriations arise in large part from graduated income taxes which do not bear heavily on those who receive low incomes, many of whom are farmers.

Professional technical assistance and educational activity were not sup-

34. Not all of the income from processing taxes was used for acreage and production control. Part went for other activities to raise prices and incomes. See Chapter 7.

plied along with the conservation payments, except as provided through cooperative arrangements with the Soil Conservation Service and the extension services. To the extent that these payments were for acreage adjustments and price supplements, they were allocated geographically in accordance with the locations of the lands producing the crops for which acreage allotments and price supplements had been authorized, not in accordance with the need for conservation. The fact that they were called conservation payments did, however, help to emphasize the conservation objective in the minds of farmers and undoubtedly contributed significantly to a wider appreciation of the need for conserving and improving soils. From 1942 on, the emphasis was changed, as a result of price improvement and the need for increased production. Less effort was made to reduce acreage and more attention was given to the improvement of soils and expansion of production.

The price of cotton reached parity in 1941. Thereafter, payment was made only for the land held out of cotton, not on the normal production of the allotted acreages. This kind of change accounts for the drop in payments for some of the other crops as well. Acreage allotments were discontinued in 1943. Thereafter, the payments were exclusively for soil-conserving practices, except the special incentive payments on flax and sugar crops and the payments made under the naval stores program, which is still being carried on. The amounts paid out in the form of conservation and adjustment payments are shown by years in Table 29.

Payments for Improved Practices

The other part of the conservation payment program was that for carrying out conservation practices without reference to acreage allotments. These payments were not limited to the farms growing specific crops, but could be made to any farmer who adopted the practices for which payments were approved. After acreage allotments were discontinued, this became the only form of conservation subsidy.

Among the practices for which such payments are made are the following: [35]

> applications of commercial fertilizer
> use of green manure and cover crops
> mechanical erosion controls (terracing,
>   contour farming, strip-cropping, sod
>   waterways, crop residue management
>   and so on)
> drainage
> construction of irrigation facilities

35. For a full summary of the amounts and kinds of conservation activity for which such payments were made up to 1951 see U.S. Production and Marketing Administration, *Conservation Practice Summary, 1947 to 1951,* January 1953.

artificial seeding of pastures
construction of stock watering facilities
fire protection
weed control
tree planting
maintaining windbreaks

The total amount paid to farmers for improved conservation practices and for acreage adjustment, from 1933 through 1952, has been $6.4 billion. This does not include such part of the cost of maintaining the state and county PMA committees as is chargeable to the soil conservation subsidy program, nor does it include costs of administration at the national level.

It is evident from the nature of the activities listed that most of them are practices that intelligent and competent farmers are likely to follow in their own interest, once they are familiar with them. Even in the early years of the program, farmers in some areas were paid for using practices that were already well established on the better managed farms of their localities. Thus the procedure used has in many cases been more in the nature of an income subsidy than a means of increasing conservation activity.

However, the provision of direct financial incentives for putting into effect specified practices brought the conservation idea sharply into the thinking of farmers and helped to give the necessary push to get them to change long-established ways of handling their soils. Backed by the intensive campaign of the Soil Conservation Service and emphasized by the disastrous droughts of the 1930s, the program has profoundly influenced American agriculture.[36]

The pertinent question today is whether these special incentives still are needed. It can scarcely be argued now, as it could in 1936, that this amount of income subsidy to farmers is of great importance to the farmers receiving it. The subsidy provided makes a difference of less than one per cent in the gross income of American agriculture. As now distributed, it probably does not achieve maximum conservation results per dollar invested.

Payments Needed in Some Areas

There are undoubtedly some exceptions to this generalization. In areas that have become badly eroded or seriously deteriorated through long neglect, the farm operators may need guidance, encouragement and some financial aid over a considerable period of years, if the soils are to be brought back or built up to a satisfactory level of productivity. This,

36. The adoption of improved farming practices was also greatly stimulated by the active demand and high prices of the 1940s. These provided strong incentives for quick adoption of the best practices known and funds with which to put them into effect.

TABLE 29

ADJUSTMENT OR CONSERVATION PAYMENTS BY CROPS AND PROGRAM YEARS, 1933–1952

(Thousands)

Year	Total	Cotton	Wheat [a]	Corn [a, b]	Rice	Tobacco	Peanuts	Commercial Potatoes	All Others	Naval Stores	General Conservation
Total	$6,407,433	$1,187,926	$705,802	$440,945	$21,329	$147,043	$9,894	$51,638	$130,543	$12,844	$3,699,469
1933	276,890	181,025[c]	93,806	—	—	2,059	—	—	—	—	—
1934	324,671	115,226[c]	105,554	—	—	43,930	—	—	59,961[d]	—	—
1935	290,102	120,451[c]	114,988	—	9,642	16,020	3,713	—	25,288[d]	—	—
1936	420,088	86,884[e]	43,389	—	2,593	15,380	1,251	—	7,517[f]	466	262,608[g]
1937	308,193	68,742[e]	—	—	2,763	11,471	871	—	3,629[d]	360	220,357[g]
1938	444,645	142,595	50,126	61,048	1,966	10,622	1,217	6,095	—	997	169,979[g]
1939	497,311	118,817	83,941	89,791	1,539	7,476	652	5,632	1,910[h]	1,639	185,941[g]
1940	442,711	102,564	47,754	85,956	916	12,573	464	5,491	2,584[h]	1,178	183,231[g]
1941	456,454	97,251	49,127	86,271	806	11,687	1,084	4,697	2,317[h]	1,740	201,474[g]
1942	386,335	80,167	57,442	66,703	495	8,365	669	4,130	—	1,247	167,117[i]
1943	438,841	74,204[j]	59,675	51,176	609	7,460	—	25,593[k]	4,882[k]	1,110	214,132[i]
1944[l]	293,867	—	—	—	—	—	—	—	—	850	293,017[i]
1945	253,523	—	—	—	—	—	—	—	22,455[m]	674	230,394[i]
1946	267,555	—	—	—	—	—	—	—	—	469	267,086[i]
1947	244,747	—	—	—	—	—	—	—	—	695	244,052[i]
1948	124,503	—	—	—	—	—	—	—	—	246	124,257[i]
1949	223,855	—	—	—	—	—	—	—	—	282	223,573[i]
1950	252,006	—	—	—	—	—	—	—	—	414	251,592[i]
1951	245,740	—	—	—	—	—	—	—	—	477	245,263[i]
1952[n]	215,396	—	—	—	—	—	—	—	—	—	215,396[o]

344

Source: U.S. Department of Agriculture, *Agricultural Statistics, 1946*, p. 655 and later issues.

a. Wheat and corn included in general soil-depleting acreage under 1936 and 1937 agricultural conservation programs.

b. Commercial corn area only.

c. Payments were rental and benefit payments and were made under the provisions of the Agricultural Adjustment Act of 1933.

d. Sugar.

e. Made under the Soil Conservation and Domestic Allotment Act of 1936 from a special appropriation to "enable the Secretary of Agriculture to meet all obligations and commitments . . . heretofore incurred under the provisions of the Agricultural Adjustment Act . . ." (Public Law 440, 74th Congress).

f. Rye, $208; sugar, $5,257; flax, $2,039.

g. Includes depletion, soil-building and range payments.

h. Commercial vegetables.

i. Includes soil and range building.

j. Allotments and quotas were discontinued for cotton, consequently payments for compliance and quotas were discontinued after this season.

k. Payments made with funds from Public Law 320, Section 32, 74th Congress.

l. From 1944 on, conservation payments for specific commodities were discontinued when acreage allotments were discontinued.

m. Flax payments authorized by Public Law 551, Section 5, 78th Congress.

n. Preliminary data.

o. Includes assistance under naval stores program.

345

however, implies selective application of conservation funds, not the provision of a thinly spread subsidy on all lands in use. Critics of the program argue that only the special problem areas should receive such aid, and that they should receive it only on the basis of clear evidence that its use can bring about a real improvement and that such improvement will not come about unless financial aid is given.[37]

This conception of the place of conservation payments implies that the criteria as to where soil conservation payments are warranted and needed should be established by the Soil Conservation Service, the agency best qualified to make such determinations. Even here, there would be need for an effective check on the misuse of funds in such ways as building up agency support or granting favors to particular groups of farmers. Sound public policy would seem to require that if such payments are to be made, they should be in furtherance of well-considered national plans in which the problem areas are identified, appropriate criteria are established and suitable interagency or congressional review is provided.

Organizational Problems

The conservation activities of the Department of Agriculture are now in process of reorganization but the new program has not yet been fully worked out. There appears to be a possibility of providing better service to farmers, reducing overhead and making significant savings in the public outlays required.[38] Whether the changes contemplated, when more fully developed and perhaps modified by the Congress, will have these results cannot be stated at this time. The improvements in service to the farmer, if made, would presumably result from the fact that he would need to deal with only one soil conservation agency at the local level instead of two as at present. As yet, this simplication of procedures and administration has not been accomplished. If feasible, such a plan should make possible a reduction in administrative costs since technical assistance, follow-up, recommendations for aid and checking on compliance would all be carried out by one group of field men.

The Production and Marketing Administration maintained a very large field staff for administering a program in which about 2.8 million farmers participated during 1952. Its staff had, of course, other duties than administration of the conservation payment program. However, that activity constituted a substantial part of its work. The annual cost for

37. A similar procedure has been suggested for initiating and encouraging more effective use of farm woodlands and other small forest holdings (see, for example, John D. Black, "Conservation and the Good Society," a speech presented at Dartmouth College, Hanover, November 14–15, 1949, pp. 19–27). Mr. Black also takes the position that the subsidy arrangement should be discontinued once the improved practices have become well established and accepted.

38. If payments of this kind were eliminated entirely, the saving would be in the order of $200 to $250 million a year. It is probably more realistic to assume that an amount approximating $100 million a year, or more, could be saved without cutting down seriously on the use of conservation practices by farmers.

the county committees, in 1952, was about \$21.2 million, and that for state and national administrators about \$5 million. Thus the annual administrative cost in the conservation subsidy program and the activities associated with it was running at more than 30 per cent of the cost of the entire program of the agricultural extension service and about half that of the Soil Conservation Service demonstration and technical aid program. The total personnel of all the agencies, at the county level, seems clearly to have become excessive for supplying the types of service now provided.[39]

SOIL CONSERVATION WORK OF THE TENNESSEE VALLEY AUTHORITY

In addition to the two major soil conservation programs described above, a third but much more limited one is carried on by the Tennessee Valley Authority. It is handled in a different way and is confined mainly to the seven-state area covered by TVA. The TVA soil conservation program was initiated before the programs of the Soil Conservation Service and PMA came into existence. Consequently, it is a carry-over of a plan of operation that was developed without much reference to programs later undertaken by the other two agencies.

The emphasis in the TVA program is on research in the manufacture of fertilizers and on educational work carried on largely by means of demonstration farms. When the soil conservation district plan was put forward, TVA chose to continue with the plan it had put into operation earlier. For a time the Soil Conservation Service was, in fact, specifically excluded from operating in the TVA area.[40]

The TVA plan is less formal than that of the Soil Conservation Service. TVA makes contracts with the land-grant colleges and works chiefly through the county farm adviser system. The program is not a general one applying to all farms. Principal emphasis is on test-demonstration farms, on the assumption that improved methods demonstrated in this way will be adopted voluntarily on neighboring farms.

The procedure used is essentially as follows: Fertilizers produced in the TVA plants are first given laboratory tests in the agricultural experiment stations. The county farm adviser then calls the farmers of a com-

39. The county committee system has been continued, under the recent departmental reorganization, on about the same basis as under PMA. However, further changes may be made as later steps in the reorganization are taken.

40. The problem of relationship between the various federal and state agencies concerned with soil conservation in this area has proved a perplexing one. Soon after it was established, TVA adopted a policy of working through the agricultural extension services in close cooperation with the Farm Bureau. The Department of Agriculture accepted, in 1935, a policy proposed by TVA which virtually excluded the Soil Conservation Service from undertaking work in the Valley. Later, conflicts arose over the relationship between this program and those of the Farm Security Administration and other agencies. The decision to rely mainly on one agency for handling soil conservation work had merit, but many have questioned whether the particular plan of operation chosen is now the one best suited to the problem.

munity together and explains the program. The group thus set up in any given community selects a farm to be used for demonstration. The demonstration farm is mapped and inventoried, and the necessary changes are made under supervision of the farm adviser, the college and a local committee. TVA supplies the fertilizer free, except for the cost of transportation. Theoretically the demonstration farm thus becomes a community enterprise. The extent to which it actually does so varies, of course, from community to community.

In recent years the system of test-demonstrations has been extended to cooperating colleges of agriculture outside the seven-state area administered by TVA.[41] However, the work is centered in the TVA area.

As of the end of June 1950, some 67,000 test-demonstration farms had been established, though many of them were not active participants in the program at that time. About 50,000 of them were in the TVA area, 7,000 in other parts of the seven Valley states and 10,000 in 25 other states. In the fiscal year 1952, fertilizer materials were supplied to 1,539 farms in the Valley, to 366 other farms in the Valley states and to 546 farms in 14 other states. From the beginning of operations to June 30, 1950, the Authority had supplied for these purposes 271,000 tons of concentrated superphosphate, 81,000 tons of calcium metaphosphate, 100,000 tons of fused tricalcium phosphate and 28,000 tons of ammonium nitrate.[42]

Soil Conservation Not a Major Function of TVA

TVA is a special type of organization unlike any of the other government agencies that work on conservation problems. It is a government-owned corporation which was given very broad powers and a good deal of autonomy, as a means of developing and improving the Tennessee Valley area. It came into existence in part as a means of administering the Muscle Shoals power and nitrogen-fixation facilities that were constructed during World War I.[43] Its conservation program includes the development and sale of hydroelectric power and considerable emphasis on flood control and navigation, as well as activities specifically related to the conservation and improvement of soils. Since many of the expenditures are for multipurpose structures and activities, the costs attributable to the soil improvement program cannot be entirely separated from those incurred by the corporation in its other activities. The cost of the

41. The TVA area includes parts of Mississippi, Alabama, Tennessee, Kentucky, Virginia, North Carolina and Georgia. It consists of the region drained by the Tennessee River.

42. *Annual Report of the Tennessee Valley Authority,* 1950, p. 45, and *ibid.,* 1952, p. 57.

43. For a fuller explanation of the background and nature of the organization, see M. R. Benedict, *Farm Policies of the United States, 1790–1950,* Twentieth Century Fund, New York, 1953, pp. 321–24.

test-demonstration farm program is running currently at about $1 million per year.[44]

Controversy over TVA Type of Conservation Program

There has been much controversy in the Congress over the merits of the TVA procedure in fostering soil conservation, especially as compared with the soil conservation district approach. The districts have more vitality and power of self-direction than do the more informal TVA groups, which are almost wholly dependent upon leadership from the extension services. Either procedure involves less expense and more exclusive concern with conservation than does the PMA type of program with its extensive array of committees and high overhead, together with its large outlay of public funds for direct payments to farmers.

When the TVA plan was adopted it was considered to be an appropriate and effective way of accomplishing the end sought. In this pioneer period there was undoubted merit in trying out various methods of encouraging soil improvement. There does not seem to be reason now for continuing a special regional program which duplicates to some extent the more general national program. If the TVA procedure is superior to that of the Soil Conservation Service it would seem logical for the Soil Conservation Service to adopt it. If it is not superior, the SCS program apparently could well be extended to the areas not now covered, as fast as the farmers are ready for it.

This, of course, should not preclude arrangements for testing new fertilizers under varying conditions. However, that could be done by the state experiment stations and extension services and does not seem to require continuance of a situation in which the Soil Conservation Service, the extension service and TVA all are engaged in carrying on soil conservation activities in the same area. Emphasis should now be on ways of simplifying the organizational arrangements and introducing economics.

If the major part of the field work in soil conservation were to be assigned to SCS and the extension services, the implication would be that TVA activities in this realm would consist mainly of fertilizer production, and experiments in producing new and more efficient types of fertilizer. TVA would then logically turn to straight commercial production of fertilizer, except for a modest amount of expenditure on research in the production, marketing and use of fertilizers and pilot operations. This

44. *U.S. Budget, 1955,* p. 209. In 1952 the corporation as a whole had an investment of approximately $1.4 billion and an annual income of more than $115 million. Though it is much more heavily concerned with the production and distribution of electric power, and with flood control and similar activities, than with the conservation of soils, the fertilizer and munitions program accounted for about $20 million of its $115 million income in 1952. Expenses were about $95 million. The munitions phase (nitrogen fixation), is, in the main, a military use of a resource that otherwise could be used for the production of fertilizer.

does not imply any very marked change from the policy TVA now has. It now assigns much of its field work to the agricultural extension services.

MANAGEMENT OF PUBLIC DOMAIN LANDS

The programs discussed in the preceding pages relate principally to privately owned lands, especially those in the humid areas. In addition, there are vast areas of land still owned by the federal government which have not, until recently, been organized for effective management. Much of this is land still held in the classification known as "public domain." The public domain lands do not include those specifically set aside for national purposes such as forest reserves, public parks and monuments, wildlife refuges and so on. Until the middle 1930s, these lands were left open for homesteading or private purchase in accordance with the general laws governing alienation of public domain lands.[45]

The operations relating to federally owned lands touch very intimately the economic life of the western states because of the large acreages involved. They constitute nearly half the total area of the 11 western states and give rise to many problems, both for the federal government and for the states and communities in which they are located. Much of the land has low economic value per acre, except where there are mineral resources. A good part of it is mountainous or semiarid and useful mainly as recreational and scenic areas or for grazing. Large areas consist of range and mountain country left in public ownership because it was not sufficiently productive to warrant acquisition by private operators.

During the 1930s and 1940s, most of these lands that were not already assigned to specialized federal agencies for management and supervision were organized into grazing districts or assigned to the Bureau of Land Management, as described in succeeding pages. As of 1950, the amounts of land assigned to the various federal agencies (in eleven western states) were roughly as shown in Table 30.

Farmers and ranchers are concerned mainly with policies relating to the ownership and supervision of the publicly owned lands used and usable primarily as grazing land. On the federally owned lands now in grazing districts some 2.25 million head of cattle and large numbers of sheep are grazed. The total number of animal unit months, that is, animals grazed times the number of months per animal, in the grazing

45. The organization for handling public domain lands has been changed materially in recent years. The General Land Office, which was established as a Bureau of the Treasury Department in 1812, was transferred to the Department of the Interior at the time that Department was created in 1849. It was charged with the duty of selling or otherwise disposing of public domain lands, but had no land management functions. In 1946 the remnants of the General Land Office were combined with the Federal Grazing Service to form the Bureau of Land Management (under the President's reorganization plan No. 3). For a more detailed account of the changes and the reasons for them, see Charles McKinley, *Uncle Sam in the Pacific Northwest,* University of California Press, Berkeley and Los Angeles, 1952, pp. 236–43.

TABLE 30

RURAL LAND HOLDINGS IN FEDERAL OWNERSHIP, 1950,
ELEVEN WESTERN STATES, BY AGENCY

Department and Bureau	Number of Acres
Total	403,181,140
Interior	
National Park Service	11,632,980
Bureau of Indian Affairs	45,854,154
Bureau of Land Management	178,290,551
Bureau of Reclamation	9,837,772
Fish and Wildlife Service	1,564,859
Defense	14,323,105
Agriculture	
Forest Service	136,875,912
Soil Conservation Service	4,132,606
Other agencies	669,201

Source: Compiled from data in U.S. Department of Agriculture Circular 909, May 1952, pp. 72–77.

districts and the national forests, has been estimated at approximately 25 million.[46] Though poor in quality, these lands are a very important basic resource in the agriculture of the West. At the same time, the fact that the range areas are very sparsely settled and that the government-owned lands are not on the local tax rolls makes the financing of local government activities difficult. The tax base for supporting local institutions is often inadequate. Large mileages of highway per unit of population are required and administrative costs are high. On the other hand, many parts of these areas consist of tourist attractions which are important to the local communities but are maintained and supervised by the government. Highways also are supplied largely by the federal government.

Grazing District Plan Established in 1934

The progressive deterioration of the publicly owned range lands had long been recognized and various proposals had been made for bringing them under management. However, no action was taken until the 1930s. By 1934, the growing interest in conservation led to the passage of new legislation (the Taylor Grazing Act, 48 *Stat.* 1269) which reflected a marked change in policy with respect to lands of this type.

Until that time, most of the public domain grazing lands were used by ranchers who had little claim to them except that of being so located that they could get their livestock onto them and use them before some-

46. Data from report of House Committee on Public Lands, House Report 2456, 80th Cong., 2d sess., 1948.

one else could. Under these conditions there was little incentive for constructive handling of this large resource since no given rancher could be sure of reaping the benefits of improved practices if he put them into effect. Most of the land was overgrazed and the quality of the vegetation was deteriorating. The livestock enterprises based on it tended to be unstable because of the lack of clearly defined rights to continuing use of the resource. This in turn made it impractical for ranchers to provide and maintain suitable watering facilities or to develop long-term plans for efficient use of such lands.

The Taylor Grazing Act, together with the amendments to it, provided for bringing the bulk of the federally owned grazing land of the West under management, with continuing federal ownership but private operation. The procedure used was to organize grazing districts in which local livestock growers would have rights to graze specified numbers of animals at a small fee per head. Local advisory boards elected by the livestock growers using grazing district lands were established informally when the districts were set up. They were given legal recognition and permanent status by an amendment to the act in 1939.[47] A National Advisory Board Council was established in 1940. Shortly thereafter, state advisory boards were formed in several of the states. Both the state and federal advisory boards were made official in 1949, through an amendment to the Federal Range Code for Grazing Districts.[48]

Since the change consisted largely of bringing under management a resource already owned by the government, no large public expenditure was involved. There is, however, no important return to the government from the grazing rights granted on this vast area of land, except indirectly through income taxes paid by the operators. A considerable portion of the fees paid is retained locally, through payments made in lieu of taxes, and expenditures for management of the districts and improvement of the range. The arrangement does, however, give prospect of a gradually improving basic resource for the livestock industry in the range areas and of more widely distributed benefits from the government-owned lands than would be likely if they were under private ownership. With private ownership, or government ownership without management, there has been in the past a tendency for such lands to be acquired or operated by a few very large operators.[49]

47. The background and development of the grazing district legislation are described more fully in J. Russell Penny and Marion Clawson, "Administration of Grazing Districts," *Land Economics,* February 1953, pp. 23–34.

48. For a more detailed description of the form of organization and methods of operation of grazing districts see U.S. Bureau of Land Management, *The Federal Range Code for Grazing Districts, Revised to October 1, 1949* (and later revisions), October 1949.

49. This difficulty has not been entirely overcome. There is still criticism in some quarters that the lands are not made available to a sufficiently large group of livestock growers. This stems in part, however, from the fact that the publicly owned lands must usually be associated with privately owned water resources and headquarters facilities.

At the time the Grazing Service was set up, the remaining vacant public lands amounted to about 166 million acres, mostly in the western states.[50] The original act limited to 80 million acres the area that might be organized into grazing districts. In 1936 this limit was raised to 142 million acres and in 1954 it was removed entirely.[51] The program thus established made it possible to bring under some type of management, either private or public, most of the national land resource that was not already under supervision of one kind or another. The national forests, which then consisted of about 160 million acres, had been brought under management earlier. However, the level of management is relatively low on much of the publicly owned forest lands and very low or negligible on considerable areas of private forest lands, especially those held speculatively and in small units.

Bureau of Land Management Established in 1946

Under a reorganization plan adopted in 1946, the Grazing Service was incorporated in the newly established Bureau of Land Management (Department of the Interior), which has responsibility for administering not only the lands in federal grazing districts but also other publicly owned lands which have not been assigned to specific federal agencies for management. A principal component of the Bureau of Land Management is the Division of Range Management, which has essentially the same functions as those assigned to the Federal Grazing Service under the act of 1934.

Controversy over Policies

Policies relating to the range areas have long been a matter of vigorous controversy. Though not privately owned, much of this land has been controlled by private operators in one way or another. A major problem is how far to recognize and perpetuate these shadowy claims to the product of such lands and how far to proceed in handling them as a national resource belonging to all the people. Even more serious is the fact that the resource itself has deteriorated badly through unregulated exploitation which has been destroying its value as a public and private asset.

More than half a century ago the decision was reached that some types of forest land could best be handled by being kept in government ownership. The policy adopted implies acceptance of the view that large parts of the forest resource will thus be best protected and the national interest

50. The federal government also administers, in trust, some 57 million acres of Indian lands and has set aside about 15 million acres of lands for national parks. There are also large acreages in military reservations, wildlife refuges, Bureau of Reclamation holdings and so on.
51. Public Law 375, 83d Cong., May 28, 1954.

best served. Presumably the product of such lands is to be sold at or near its competitive value.

In the case of publicly owned grazing lands, powerful economic and political groups have insisted on a policy that results in granting to the users of the land most of the net economic rent that may arise from it. Until recent years the amount of such net rent was not large, but with the higher prices for livestock which have prevailed during most of the time since 1942 the subsidy provided to the industry may be considerable. The issues and problems presented are too complex and far-reaching for adequate discussion here.[52] Certain conclusions do appear to be warranted, however.

The experience of the past indicates that these lands will not be properly managed and conserved without some more orderly system of control than prevailed prior to 1934. Also, there are many who doubt that they could and would be brought under private ownership and management in an orderly and equitable way. The issues involved have not as yet been clearly defined. Among the policies advocated are the following: (1) retention of federal ownership and control, presumably with reasonable flexibility so that land can be transferred into or out of private ownership in specific situations where that is found to be in the public interest; (2) transfer of such lands to the states for state management, or sale to private operators; (3) direct sale by the federal government to private operators; and (4) retention of ownership by the federal government but with more specific rights granted to livestock producers and possibly the privilege of treating grazing rights as negotiable assets which can be bought or sold. This privilege already exists in effect, since producers can, under Bureau of Land Management regulations, buy and sell water rights or the adjacent land, whichever is controlling.

Range Improvement Needed

Nearly all of the interests affected agree that improvement work on the lands should be continued and expanded. Reseeding of grasses, the development of water facilities and controlled grazing can materially increase the productivity of the range areas and will benefit both the public and the ranchers concerned. Presumably, the funds needed for such improvement, and for administering the lands, should come mainly from earnings, as in any other soundly operated business. The lands are not valueless and their earnings are not negligible.

There also is rather general agreement that the management policies should be in harmony with the best interests of the communities, in-

52. An excellent discussion of this problem is given in McKinley, *op. cit.*, Chapter 6. While this writer is not wholly in agreement with the conclusions implied, particularly in regard to the undesirability of using local advisory groups in administering grazing districts, the treatment given provides an excellent factual statement and a very useful summary of the issues involved.

cluding the need for stabilizing the livestock industry. This means that if the lands are continued in public ownership, either federal or state, procedures and organization are needed which will provide for consultation with local groups and governments in the establishment of policies and administrative arrangements.

Under existing organization and policies there appears to be insufficient recognition of the interests of the general public. The resource is made available to the users on a basis that provides almost no net return to the federal government.[53] Presumably a reasonable and equitable portion of the real net return on the land, comparable to that derived from private property, should go to the support of local institutions and government. Growers using the land should be charged a fee that is commensurate with the returns they derive from its use, with opportunities for profit comparable to those on privately owned lands. This implies a sliding scale fee related both to the quality of the range and to the prices of animal products, but with due consideration given to changes in operating costs.

Official Reports Do Not Reflect True Situation

The actual outlay of federal funds for administering the federally owned grazing lands has not been large. A minimum level of management has been provided for a national resource that had been virtually without any management whatever. However, the official reports do not reflect clearly the situation with respect to these lands. For example, the Bureau of Land Management, in reporting the results for the fiscal year 1951, makes the following comment:

Operating on the belief that a Federal program like a large business enterprise should show a net gain, the Bureau of Land Management balanced its books at the end of the fiscal year 1951 and is able to show the following figures: $8,786,543 in appropriations for management of land and resources contrasted with an estimated $49,082,331 in receipts payable to state and federal treasuries.

The record thus reveals approximately $6 for every dollar of appropriation. This does not account for returns in the form of homes for veterans, and more minerals and timber and forage supplies for defense.[54]

This, of course, is not a logical concept of profits. No mention is made of the fact that these figures relate to a vast national asset consisting of some 180 million acres, nearly 10 per cent of the total land area of the United States. The $49 million reported as income is not income in the ordinary sense. More than 70 per cent of it came from the disposal of

53. There is, of course, a tendency for the values associated with such grazing rights to be capitalized into the values attributed to the water rights and lands owned by the operators who have permits to graze livestock on the grazing district lands.
54. U.S. Department of the Interior, *Annual Report, 1952*, p. 247.

minerals, chiefly oil and gas. Some was from the sale of lands.[55] Only about \$2.5 to \$3 million of it can be regarded as ordinary operating income, that is, income from grazing and other fees, nonmineral leases and so on. Of this, some 25 per cent must be deducted for payments to counties in lieu of taxes, an operating expense that would have to be paid in a different form if the lands were privately owned.

The costs of operating the livestock industries that use the grazing resources of this vast area are borne privately and the profits from these operations accrue to private individuals and corporations. Some small part of the return from the use of the lands is collected by the Division of Range Management and is used to cover part of the cost of maintaining general administration over the resource.[56]

55. The sources of the income received by the Bureau of Land Management for the fiscal year ending June 30, 1953 were as follows:

Mineral leases and permits	\$49,176,703
Oregon and California and Coos Bay grant lands	12,990,849
Sales of public lands	1,024,829
Grazing fees	2,111,921
Fees and commissions	438,819
Rights-of-way	75,214
Sales of Indian lands	2,182
Timber sales	831,217
Miscellaneous receipts	194,029
Total	\$66,845,763

(From U.S. Bureau of Land Management, *Report of the Director, 1953,* Statistical Appendix, p. 108.)

The costs for management of the land resources assigned to the Bureau were:

Lease and disposal of mineral resources	\$ 604,625
Land use and land disposal	1,341,738
Management of grazing lands	1,550,518
Forestry	2,369,195
Cadastral survey (for identification and classification of public domain lands)	1,126,003
Soil and moisture conservation	1,436,377
Squaw Butte experiment station	37,765
Fire suppression	319,080
Weed control	1,312,122
General administration	1,203,592
Construction	1,107,199
Maintenance of physical facilities	24,327
Total	\$12,432,541

(As broken down in the hearings on the 1955 Budget. Includes sums reimbursable from other accounts. Does not include \$445,956 for range improvement which was supplied by users.)

Payments were made to states and counties from Bureau receipts in the following amounts:

Oregon and California and Coos Bay lands	\$ 6,447,026.63
Sales of public lands and timber	66,655.47
Mineral leases and permits	17,255,526.91
Taylor grazing leases	161,955.60
Taylor grazing districts	184,209.90
Total	\$24,115,374.51

56. Some of the federal agencies, particularly the newer ones, are seriously remiss in failing to present clear, concise and logical reports on their financial operations. The tendency to use the annual reports as an argument for and defense of the agency program is understandable and probably unavoidable. There is, however, a clear responsi-

Where private profits arise from the use of a national asset, it is generally assumed that a charge will be made that will be in keeping with the commercial value of the asset. To make available to private operators the use of valuable range lands at the mere cost of administering them appears to be no more warranted than to turn over to a lumber company the stand of trees on government forest lands at no cost except that of negotiating the contract and supervising the cutting. The commercial value of the product is very different in the two cases but the principle is the same.

The problem is complex and not wholly within the control of the officials in charge of the Bureau of Land Management. Some of the difficulty arises from restrictions written into the laws by the Congress itself. Also, it seems clear that funds should be provided for establishing a more adequate accounting system. In part, the difficulty stems from lack of agreement within the agency and unconcern as to the kinds of information that should result from the accounting procedures used. Such problems are not uncommon in newly established agencies whether private or public. Further study is needed of both the accounting and reporting procedures required to provide the Congress and the public with the kinds and amounts of information necessary to develop policies relating to this large and important resource.

Investment May Be Required

It may be that for some years to come government expenditure on the lands administered by the Bureau of Land Management might well be larger than the returns derived from them. Granted that much of this land is poor or even worthless for private ownership and operation, the real problem, which has not yet been faced realistically, is to determine what level of management and investment is warranted on the basis of future private and public returns, and to seek to justify that input as a logical investment of public funds, even though it may not all be returned to the Treasury currently. Few of the nation's privately owned lands were economically productive until substantial amounts of investment and organization had been provided by their owners.

The remaining public domain lands are not highly productive and they do not warrant heavy investment of either public or private funds.

---

bility on the part of both the various agencies and the General Accounting Office to see that adequate, orderly and logical accounting is made of the handling of these vast funds and properties. The need for better reports has grown enormously in recent years as the size and complexity of government activity have increased.

The task of the Congress and the public in evaluating the vast array of government activities has become increasingly difficult. The Congress itself could lighten its load and increase its efficiency by insisting on competent and adequate accounting of government funds and resources, instead of being forced to drag the information out through hearings and investigations. Question may well be raised as to whether the agencies themselves would not in the long run create a better attitude and gain better support by more objective and businesslike reporting.

Nevertheless, moderate inputs for classification, organization and improvement are warranted. These are properly government expenses of an investment nature, necessary but not likely to produce immediate income.

Reseeding of grasses, water development and controlled grazing are activities which the land owner, in this case the federal government, is normally expected to provide. Most of this expense presumably should be covered out of current income, though some of it may be needed as an investment to bring the land to a condition where there is any margin of return over costs of operation. An approach along these lines, appropriately analyzed and documented, would seem to merit public and congressional support within modest limits. It does not imply major changes in the current program but does suggest more adequate and analytical reporting.

Political Problems Involved

Some livestock interests do not want the ranges managed in ways that are considered necessary for conserving and increasing their productivity. Demand is strong in some quarters for making them available for private purchase. There are, however, large groups of livestock men who prefer government ownership and management but resist any effort to have the use of the lands put on a commercial basis with charges related to their real rental values.

Whether these lands are to be retained by the public or gradually transferred to private ownership is a matter for the Congress to decide. If they are to be made available for private purchase, new provisions are needed and prices should presumably be based on the commercial values of the various types and qualities of land. Such a solution would undoubtedly favor the large operators and companies, but in the course of time it would probably result in better management of the ranges than if they were held as public domain without management. Improvement almost certainly would not be so vigorous or effective, however, as under a good program of government management.

Past experience does not lend encouragement to the view that these lands would quickly pass into private ownership and come under good management, even under the most liberal and realistic arrangements for purchase. They need to be organized into units large enough for efficient operation and realistically related to water and feed resources. However, long-established public policy in respect to the alienation of public domain lands would imply that, so far as practical, opportunity should be provided for considerable numbers of ranchers to operate on a moderate scale rather than for a few large ones to build up very large holdings. This would make possible the development of a stable livestock industry and a social organization suited to the conditions in these areas.

Duplication of Functions in Land Management Agencies

The problems arising in connection with the public domain lands that are not now organized into grazing districts are much like those pertaining to the lands acquired under the submarginal-land purchase program and not yet assigned to appropriate management agencies. For these lands, the Bureau of Land Management is essentially a caretaker agency. Presumably they are to be inventoried and classified and, wherever feasible, turned over to the agencies specifically organized for the management of the various types of publicly owned land. Some undoubtedly should be transferred to state or county agencies for incorporation in state or county forests and recreation areas. Some of them, though too isolated for organization as grazing districts, are now handled in much the same way as though they were a part of the grazing district system.

A striking example of the problems that arise from failure to reassign lands that should be brought under specialized management is the situation in respect to the O and C lands of Oregon. These lands, amounting to some 2.5 million acres, are scattered in checkerboard fashion in the Douglas fir region of the Willamette Valley of Oregon. They were originally granted to the Oregon and California Railroad and Coos Bay Wagon Road to aid in the construction of these lines of communication. They reverted to the federal government in 1916, because of failure of the companies to carry out the provisions under which the lands were granted.

The Bureau of Land Management maintains a sizable staff of professional foresters to administer them, though the same area is served by a well-staffed regional office maintained by the Forest Service. This division of responsibility is not only wasteful of funds and manpower but actually a barrier to orderly and effective management of the federally owned forest lands of that area, because of the checkerboard pattern in which the land is held.[57]

Management responsibilities cannot be separated sharply between such agencies as the Forest Service and the Bureau of Land Management. The Forest Service must inevitably take responsibility for management of some of the grazing land areas where they are intermingled with timber lands in the national forests. However, some of the 70 million acres of grazing land now managed by the Forest Service undoubtedly should be transferred to the Division of Range Management and sizable acreages now controlled by the Bureau of Land Management should be trans-

57. The background of this situation is much more complicated than is implied by this brief statement. Involved in it is the fact that the county governments are given 75 per cent of the income from O and C lands whereas they would get only 25 per cent if they were administered by the Forest Service and only 5 per cent if the lands were part of the public domain. For a detailed discussion of the problem see Wesley C. Ballaine, "The Revested Oregon and California Railroad Grant Lands," *Land Economics*, August 1953, pp. 219–32.

ferred to the Forest Service, especially such tracts as the O and C lands of Oregon.[58]

There does not appear to be any logical reason for the wide variations in fees charged for the use of public lands administered by different public agencies or for the differences in the contributions made to local governments. There is need for a consistent and logical over-all policy with respect to these charges and contributions. At present the policy varies markedly between the agencies administering publicly owned lands.[59]

Cost of the Range Management Program to 1952

The income from grazing fees has thus far been less than the cost to the government for administering the lands, including expenditures for soil and moisture conservation. Receipts and expenditures for the years 1935 to 1952 are shown in Table 31.

OTHER CONSERVATION PROGRAMS OF THE FEDERAL GOVERNMENT

The conservation programs described above, except those relating to publicly owned lands, constitute, in the main, an individual farm approach.[60] There are, in addition, three older and more general conservation programs which are not primarily for the benefit of agriculture though all of them affect agricultural activities to some extent. These are the programs of the Bureau of Reclamation, the Forest Service and the Army Corps of Engineers.

58. The acreage of grazing land reported as in the national forests varies considerably in different sources. The Commission on Organization of the Executive Branch of the Government puts it at 65 million (*Task Force Report on Natural Resources,* Appendix L, p. 41). The same source uses a figure of 90 million on p. 190. The acreage administered by the Forest Service, which includes large amounts of land scattered through the timbered area, is the one most subject to variations in classification.

59. For example, the fees charged for grazing in the national forests are on a sliding scale related to a base charge which prevailed (for cattle) in the period 1921 to 1931. (The base period for sheep is 1920–1932.) The fees vary in accordance with the prices received for livestock. For cattle, the Forest Service fees have ranged from 7.51 cents per animal month in 1934 to 64 cents in 1952. They are based on "a comparison of the value of national forest ranges with what stockmen pay for private and other publicly owned ranges, but with liberal discounts which bring the national forest fees well below those paid for other comparable ranges." (See U.S. House Committee on Public Lands, *Forest Service Policy,* Hearings, 80th Cong., 1st sess., 1947, p. 10.)

In contrast, the charges made by the Division of Range Management have remained at very nominal levels. In 1947 they were put at 6 cents per animal month plus 2 cents for range improvement. They now stand at 10 cents plus 2 cents for range improvement. It does not follow that the Forest Service and the Bureau of Land Management fees should be the same. Some of the Forest Service range land has a special value because of its location and the seasonal nature of the demand. However, there seems not to be warrant for a difference of several hundred per cent between the two rates of charge.

For a fuller discussion of the problem of administrative coordination as it relates to these agencies see *Task Force Report on Natural Resources,* Appendix L, pp. 40–49.

60. Some of the soil conservation districts have undertaken group projects but none involving large investments. For the most part, their emphasis is on what the farmer himself can do, with some technical aid and some relatively small-scale collaboration with his neighbors.

TABLE 31

RECEIPTS AND EXPENDITURES OF FEDERAL GRAZING SERVICE
AND DIVISION OF RANGE MANAGEMENT, 1935–1952

Fiscal Year	Receipts	Expenditures			
		Total	Management of Grazing Land [a]	Payments to States	Range Improvement [b]
Total	$16,987,186	$33,106,018	$13,424,178	$6,803,758	$12,878,082
1935	—	75,335	75,335	—	—
1936	—	281,781	281,781	—	—
1937	—	626,887	387,857	218,967	20,063
1938	—	1,040,683	535,886	421,459	83,338
1939	—	1,326,581	594,445	512,267	219,869
1940	—	1,495,559	684,708	373,315	437,536 [c]
1941	—	2,213,646	709,328	556,508	947,810
1942	4,165,522 [d]	2,766,929	744,507	1,105,542	916,880
1943	980,314	1,898,170	806,436	490,333	601,401
1944	1,015,818	2,260,081	1,133,949	494,701	631,431
1945	996,330	2,262,489	1,159,094	500,326	603,069
1946	960,395	1,968,733	795,197 [e]	418,896	754,640 [f]
1947	1,040,736	1,837,263	472,741	454,877	909,645
1948	1,408,333	1,810,006	507,426	334,824	967,756
1949	1,230,844	2,508,915	957,276	226,403	1,325,236
1950	1,525,991	2,189,442	984,698	13,459	1,191,285
1951	1,683,392	2,986,286	1,085,111	380,400	1,520,775
1952	1,979,511	3,557,232	1,508,403	301,481	1,747,348

Source: U.S. Budget, seriatim, and U.S. Bureau of Land Management.

a. Administrative costs only.
b. Includes soil and moisture conservation work.
c. The soil and moisture conservation work in the range areas was carried on by the Soil Conservation Service until 1940.
d. Cumulative through 1942.
e. From 1946, under the Bureau of Land Management, administrative expenditures for the grazing activities have been handled in a slightly different way than in the earlier years. Hence the data for the two periods are not entirely comparable.
f. The soil and moisture conservation data from 1946 on include all such work on lands administered by the Bureau of Land Management, not merely those organized into grazing districts. However, most of the expenditure was on the grazing district lands.

Bureau of Reclamation

Of these three agencies, the one most closely related to agriculture is the Bureau of Reclamation in the Department of the Interior. Its program is one of the largest and most expensive conservation activities of the federal government. However, full exploration of it, and of the policies relating to it, would require a major study including matters which lie outside the immediate interests of agriculture.

The Bureau of Reclamation, formerly the Reclamation Service, was established under the Reclamation Act of 1902. It was set up for the purpose of undertaking large-scale water storage and distribution installations as a means of developing arid lands unsuited for crop production except under irrigation. Much of the land to be benefited, especially in the earlier years, was unoccupied or was operated as grazing land in large units on which the return per acre was very small. Thus most of its developed value was attributable to the water made available through the dams and canals built by the federal government, except for land improvements and structures provided by the settlers after they acquired the land.

The projects had purposes other than irrigation, the principal one being the production of electric power. Some flood control, navigation and recreational values result from several of the projects, and in many of them significant community values are created through more stable and diversified production, increased population and larger tonnages for the railroads and other carriers. As a result, there has been a continuing controversy, which is by no means resolved, in regard to the appropriate division of costs among the various types of beneficiary.

So far as agricultural lands are concerned, there are two principal types of subsidy—one, the provision of funds on a no-interest basis (for building dams and other structures) and, two, amounts expended for agricultural purposes which have not been or will not be recovered. The no-interest feature originated through the use of income derived from the sale of public lands in the West, and other revenues derived from western lands.[61]

When the original act was passed, it was contended that these funds came from the sale of land resources of the West and should therefore be used for the development of other lands in that region. This source of revenue has long since become inadequate for carrying on reclamation activities on the scale authorized by the Congress. Most of the money now being spent is provided through special appropriations. Hence the contention that such funds are costless, if it ever had validity, is no longer pertinent.[62]

61. As originally authorized, the program was limited to funds derived from the sale of lands and repayments by settlers. Since the income from land sales had declined and only small payments were being made by the settlers, only one new project was constructed between 1907 and 1920. To overcome this difficulty the Congress passed in 1920 the Mineral Oil Leasing Act, which provided that 52.5 per cent of oil royalties derived from public land leases would go into the reclamation fund. The Hayden-O'Mahoney Amendment of 1939 added to this a provision that 52.5 per cent of all receipts, including penalties, received from the naval oil reserves between 1920 and 1938, and all monies received from power sold from the reclamation projects, were to be covered into the reclamation fund.

As now set up, the program involves a continuing drain on the Treasury with no provision for a return flow. For a fuller explanation of the arrangements described above, see *A Water Policy for the American People,* Report of the President's Water Resources Policy Commission, 1950, Volume 1, p. 151.

62. These expenditures could be considered relatively costless, from a social standpoint, if they were made only in times of depression, as a means of employing labor and resources that would otherwise be largely unemployed. However, there has been little

Farmers Not Principal Advocates

The pressure for reclamation does not and never has come primarily from farmers. Hence these costs cannot properly be regarded as a direct subsidy to existing farm operators. The pressure has arisen partly from the desire of landless people to acquire land but much more importantly from business interests in the areas affected, from owners of land who may gain through increases in values and from congressional representatives interested in having large federal expenditures made in their states. Users of electric power also have frequently been strong proponents of the power projects.

In recent years the situation has been complicated by the fact that some of the developments, particularly those in the Central Valley of California, are designed to provide additional water for areas already intensively cultivated but threatened by increasing drains on the water supplies they have used in the past. In the main, however, the agricultural expenditure for reclamation has been for adding new irrigated acreage to benefit prospective settlers, not a contribution to farmers already in business. As such, its economic implications have seldom been analyzed adequately either by proponents or by the Congress.

If more land in cultivation is needed, it can be brought in either through reclamation or by extending the margin of cultivation at many points in already occupied territory. Actually, much of the farm program of recent years has involved an attempt to shrink the margins and take land out of cultivation. Large expenditures have been made to bring that about. Therefore, if heavy expenditures for land reclamation are warranted they must be justified on other grounds.

In some areas a good case can be made for such outlays, at least on a modest scale. The arid regions tend to be dependent on a few enterprises, especially livestock production, and also to be particularly vulnerable in times of drought. They are, in most cases, too sparsely settled to maintain a well-rounded economy. In such situations, the introduction of irrigated agriculture, in conjunction with range agriculture, can help to stabilize feed supplies and can bring in enough additional people to make feasible more adequate schools, better roads and a more developed community life.

The values thus created accrue partly to the farmers on the lands irrigated and partly to the public, both local and national. To the extent that they are capturable by the private operator, the costs, within reasonable limits, should presumably be borne by him. The remainder is a public expense, but one that needs to be more carefully appraised than it has been to determine whether it is justified.

---

attempt to apply this principle. Pressure for heavy expenditure on reclamation projects continues in good times as well as bad, and significant social costs are involved.

Relation of Public to Private Irrigation Development

Until recent years, most of the investment in irrigation structures consisted of private funds derived from the sale of bonds issued by irrigation districts. The districts are semigovernmental units set up under state law. They have powers somewhat similar to those of school districts and various types of special improvement districts. Assessments are made against the lands in the district for operating and maintaining the district and for paying interest and principal on the bonds. In most cases, the assessments vary in accordance with the quality of land served. That is, the charge is not in proportion to service rendered (amount of water supplied). Instead, it is roughly in accord with the values created by supplying the water.

The great bulk of irrigated agriculture (in terms of value of product) still is in the private projects. The federally financed projects, for the most part, are those which were not attractive as private ventures. Either the required structures were too large for financing by privately formed district organizations or the land was not sufficiently good or well located to induce private development of irrigation structures. Thus the government ventures occupy an intermediate zone between the lands clearly suitable for private development and those clearly unsuited for either private or public development, with some overlapping into each of the two types.

A broader public interest is also involved. Underdeveloped water power constitutes a continuing waste which is being offset by drains on nonrenewable resources such as coal, oil and gas. The values involved are public values and relate to the future rather than the present. No precise measurement is possible. In general, it would seem sound policy to press forward with structures for conserving power resources whenever such expenditures can be made without adding to an already overburdened and inflationary budget, and wherever the value of the power produced will come reasonably near to eventual repayment for the outlay.

The federal projects thus constitute multiple-purpose undertakings in which both general and agricultural values are created, but in which both types of value are difficult to define and measure. Except as the projects supplement existing water supplies in areas already under irrigation, or round out and stabilize feed supplies, they are, in the main, an investment for the benefit of prospective farmers and nonfarm groups rather than an aid to established agriculture. Heavy subsidies are involved, since in most of the projects the costs will not be fully recovered by the Treasury.

Acreages Irrigated and Numbers of Farms Created

It is not proposed here to attempt any comprehensive cataloguing of the achievements of the Bureau of Reclamation or to make an appraisal of the activities carried on by it. Rather, the purpose is to indicate in a general way the size of the program, particularly its agricultural aspects, and its relation to the conservation program as a whole.

As originally conceived, the hydroelectric power aspects of the reclamation program were considered to be of secondary importance, but in recent years the production of electric power has become a dominant objective in many of the projects and the major source of income from them.

This change in emphasis is of great importance and raises a number of very controversial policy problems. Their principal significance for agriculture lies in the very complex issue of the assessment of costs against the lands irrigated as compared with the costs assigned to power production. Another controversial feature is the question of the charges to be made and the policies to be applied in supplying supplemental irrigation water in areas where the land has already been developed and irrigated through private investment.[63]

From the standpoint of number of farms affected, acreages involved and contributions to over-all agricultural production, the reclamation program is far less comprehensive than the soil conservation program and much more local in its significance. As of June 1952, approximately 125,000 farms were receiving water from federal reclamation projects. Some 6.7 million acres had been brought under irrigation and developed for intensive crop production. The Bureau of Reclamation has estimated the current annual value of crops produced on these lands at approximately $822 million.[64]

This, of course, should not be interpreted as income from the investment in irrigation structures. It is a return for the labor and other inputs of the families operating the farms plus whatever return there was on the government's investment. It constituted a gross value of crops per farm of about $6,500. Solely as farming ventures, the majority of the reclamation projects have not been notably successful. However, there are collateral values of great significance. The community values created and the contributions to stability of feed supplies, as well as the direct additions to food- and fiber-producing resources, are significant but virtually unmeasurable.

The current rates of expenditure in the reclamation program are similar to those for soil conservation, but the values created (in the form of dams and related structures) are presumably more lasting. They consist mainly of capital outlays for permanent structures and can be expected

63. Particularly in the Central Valley Project of California, where there has been bitter controversy over the Bureau of Reclamation efforts to force subdivision of the larger farms as a condition of receiving supplemental water.

64. U.S. Department of the Interior, *Annual Report, 1952*, pp. 24–26. There was, of course, some small return from these lands before they were brought under irrigation. However, in most of the areas served by the federal projects the land was used mainly for grazing and the return per acre was very small.

to last longer without further inputs of funds than the gains in soil fertility achieved by means of the soil conservation program.[65]

Bureau of Reclamation Expenditures

The income from the sale of public lands has now become a minor item in the Reclamation budget. It amounted to less than $1.7 million in 1952.[66] The largest single source of revenue now, aside from direct appropriations by the Congress, is the power income from reclamation projects ($43.5 million in 1952). Next largest is the income received from other agencies [67] ($23 million) chiefly proceeds under the oil-leasing act. These amounted to $20.1 million for the fiscal year 1952. The third major item was that resulting from collections, chiefly payments from farmers on the reclamation projects, which amounted to $11.3 million. The total accretions and collections of the reclamation fund for 1952 thus amounted to $77.7 million. Annual appropriations and total expenditures from 1902 through fiscal 1952 are given in Table 32.

The Bureau's total investment in plant and property is now roughly $2 billion, distributed as follows: [68]

Completed works	
Multipurpose	$742,276,788
Irrigation	492,079,694
Electric	407,847,676
Municipal water plant	14,047,905
Flood control	11,137,488
Construction in progress	483,358,354
Other physical property	17,534,988
Total	**$2,168,282,893**

65. Some would contend, however, that soil conservation plans and know-how, if they become generally established and institutionalized, are in the nature of permanent assets and may be continued even without extensive continuing inputs of federal funds.

66. The total amount collected from the beginning of the program to June 30, 1952 was $118.1 million. (See U.S. Department of the Interior, *Annual Report, 1952*, p. 102.)

67. *Ibid.*, p. 102. The amounts received from other agencies for the fiscal year 1952 and totals to June 30, 1952 were as follows:

	Fiscal Year	Total to June 30
Sale of public lands	$ 1,665,706	$118,143,670
Proceeds from oil-leasing act	20,088,780	168,018,830
Proceeds from federal water-power licenses	116,817	1,282,715
Proceeds from potassium royalties and rentals	1,027,542	5,585,762
Receipts from naval petroleum reserves acts of May 1920 and May 1938	none	29,778,300
Proceeds from rights of way over withdrawn lands to 1952	428	10,978
Lease of lands	19,918	51,898
Town lot sales	1,100	724,646
Timber sales and other miscellaneous	32,529	191,223
Total	$22,952,820	$323,788,022

68. *Ibid.*, p. 105. Figures given are for June 30, 1952.

TABLE 52

Appropriations for Bureau of Reclamation, Fiscal Years 1902–1952

Fiscal Year	Total	Reclamation Fund — Regular [a]	Reclamation Fund — Power Revenue	General Fund — Regular	General Fund — Colorado River FW and LS	General Fund — Colorado River Dam Fund	Emergency Relief Funds [b]	Permanent Appropriations
Total	$646,889,090	$38,658,118	$1,752,053,358	$24,219,780	$903,395	$192,478,530	$73,879,780	$2,730,082,051
1902	c	165,000 c						
1903	c	5,950,000 c						
1904	2,000,000 c	18,440,000 c						
1905	c	8,758,000 c						
1906	15,363,800 c	27,494,961 c						
1907	c	43,569,161 c,d						
1908	18,051,161	18,176,161 c						
1909	9,562,038	9,562,038						
1909	9,180,700	9,180,700						
1910	9,183,300	9,183,300						
1911	26,896,790	26,896,790						
1912	8,262,367	8,262,367						
1913	8,300,508	8,300,508						
1914	15,931,922	15,931,922						
1915	1,261,411	1,261,411						
1916	13,530,000	13,530,000						
1917	8,902,557	8,887,557		15,000				
1918	8,537,213	8,227,000		310,213				
1919	9,840,277	9,397,081		443,196				
1920	7,848,927	7,300,000		548,927				
1921	9,124,177	8,463,000		661,177				
1922	20,601,871	20,266,000		335,871				
1923	15,359,530	14,800,000		559,530				
1924	14,114,067	13,800,000		314,067				
1925	11,890,809	11,890,809						
1926	12,613,240	12,563,240			50,000			
1927	7,511,320	7,436,320		40,000	35,000			

367

TABLE 32 (continued)

Fiscal Year	Total	Reclamation Fund		General Fund		Colorado River Dam Fund	Emergency Relief Funds [b]	Permanent Appropriations
		Regular [a]	Power Revenue	Regular	Colorado River FW and LS			
1928	$12,198,800	$12,148,800		$15,000	$35,000			
1929	14,443,400	14,138,400	$190,000	15,000	100,000			
1930	19,403,000	8,253,000	390,000	10,660,000	100,000			
1931	9,582,000	9,087,000	395,000		100,000			
1932	32,371,000	6,971,000	300,000	25,000,000	100,000			
1933	15,867,288	2,442,288	375,000	13,050,000				
1934	114,991,000	3,003,000	405,000	8,000,000	48,000		$103,535,000	
1935	35,252,750	860,750	316,000	15,900,000			34,076,000	
1936	42,776,100	1,022,100	366,000		50,000		25,438,000	
1937	42,671,600	12,028,600	316,000	34,850,000		$350,000	4,873,000 [d]	$1,100,000
1938	81,640,100	11,991,600	331,000	30,655,000	15,000	500,000	37,047,500	4,600,000
1939	46,533,112	10,574,600	366,000	32,980,000	15,000	500,000	2,502,488 [d]	
1940	84,393,947	13,269,600	606,000	64,200,000	15,000	575,000	28,347	5,700,000
1941	81,009,300	9,429,600	571,000	63,750,000	15,000	768,000	124,300 [d]	6,600,000
1942	105,986,070	7,446,600	664,400	94,245,031	50,000	1,000,000	19,961 [d]	2,600,000
1943	94,262,539	2,651,060	956,900	86,628,565	47,895	1,379,250	1,131 [d]	2,600,000
1944	47,207,334	2,422,500	2,091,975	35,578,000	75,000	1,443,100	72,709 [d]	5,669,468
1945	33,184,169	5,321,000	2,328,800	17,734,200	340,000	2,200,000	22,332 [d]	5,282,501
1946	127,130,108	34,089,290	2,528,600	82,858,000	612,500	2,550,000		4,491,718
1947	122,222,831	36,315,968	3,284,245	75,931,805	100,000	1,814,330	30,396 [d]	4,806,879
1948	148,730,438	20,127,250	5,549,500	115,420,288		2,088,000		5,545,400
1949	270,897,242	29,952,663	6,999,601	226,801,503		2,450,000		4,693,475
1950	366,366,902	35,447,705	9,327,097	311,434,175		2,123,100		8,034,825
1951	277,329,514	46,917,365		222,453,635		2,308,000		5,650,514
1952	240,763,522	51,422,347		180,665,175		2,171,000		6,505,000

Source: U.S. Department of the Interior, *Annual Report, 1952,* p. 101.

a. Prior to fiscal year 1916, funds were made available from the Reclamation fund by allotment authorized by the Secretary of the Interior.

b. Emergency relief funds include allocations from NIRA, PWA, and ERA funds.

c. Allotments made prior to the Fallon, Nevada, conference on July 27, 1907 were canceled and summary allotments issued. Original amounts excluded from total column.

Conservation Activities of the Forest Service

The Forest Service has long played a leading role in the drive for conservation of natural resources. Though the agency was set up primarily for the protection and development of large areas of forest land, its conservation interests relate to water conservation, erosion control and range management as well. It has a well-developed framework of policy and widespread support from the public.

The principal direct contact with agriculture is in the management of the grazing lands in the national forests. Here the relationship is mainly with one particular segment of agriculture, the livestock producers. Grazing rights in the national forests are granted for a fee, usually on a seasonal basis. While these privileges and the charges for them are of great significance to the particular farmers and ranchers served, the number affected is not large. The activities of the agency are, in the main, a matter of concern to the public generally rather than to farmers. They are discussed here only in general terms and mainly for the purpose of indicating their scale and significance in the over-all conservation program.

Forest lands, together with related watershed lands, comprise about one third of the total land area of continental United States. The Forest Service has direct control over about 160 million acres of this area.[69] Its activities are of six principal types:

1. Management, protection and development of the national forests.

2. Cooperation with the states and with private owners of forest land to bring about better fire protection, induce the use of improved forest practices, and stimulate development and constructive management of state, county and community forests.

3. Forest and range research including research on upstream problems of flood control.

4. Control of forest pests.

5. Flood prevention and watershed protection.

6. Management of 80 land utilization projects relating to submarginal lands acquired during the depression.[70]

More than half of the total area in national forests is located above

69. The total acreage in national forests, including those in Alaska and Puerto Rico, was about 180 million in 1952. This figure is for land actually owned by the federal government, not for all land included in national forest boundaries. The amount of publicly owned forest land is being gradually increased through exchange of stumpage on the national forests for cutover lands owned by private forest operators. When stumpage rights are granted the land base is retained. Restrictions are placed on the amounts and kinds of cutting that can be done in harvesting the stumpages so disposed of. The cutover lands acquired by means of the exchange are incorporated in the national forests and brought under management. Some forest lands have also been acquired through purchase, as a means of rounding out and consolidating the national forest holdings and by additions of unreserved public lands.

70. For a fuller statement of these activities, see U.S. Forest Service, *Report of the Chief, 1953.*

timber line or is covered with brush, as in southern California. The brush areas are of great importance in controlling floods and reducing erosion, but yield no direct return to the Treasury. Yet, because of the very large public interests involved, they must be protected from fire. The cost of protecting and managing this noncommercial forest area, consisting of some 108 million acres, is estimated to be about $27 million per year. The Forest Service also carries on a sizable program of work relating to land outside the national forests such as research, educational work, cooperation in fire protection and similar activities.

The commercial forest area within the national forests amounts to about 73 million acres. Only within the last ten years has there been any extensive cutting on these lands. During the 1930s, with the demand for lumber at a low level, it was considered desirable both by the Forest Service and the lumber industry to allow the privately owned forests to supply most of the lumber required. This policy was changed in 1940. Thereafter, plans were made for cutting nearly up to the sustained yield of the national forests, an amount which is estimated to be about 6 billion board feet per year. The timber cut from the national forests was about 2 billion board feet in 1941 and has since been increased to about 4.7 billion feet. Income from stumpage has been raised from $7 million to about $70 million, partly as a result of higher prices.

Forest Service estimates place current income (from timber only) at about $77 million per year and expenses (in connection with the 73 million acres of commercial forest land) at $60 million, not including the 25 per cent of the income which is paid to the counties. The net return is roughly $17 million, but this is about offset by the $17 million paid to counties in lieu of taxes. Since the cut, even now, is less than the annual rate of growth, there is in addition an increment in value which is not currently being converted into cash income.[71] The 1953 estimate of receipts and expenditures for the Forest Service as a whole is shown in Table 33.

The national forests are still in process of development and will be for many years to come. The actual forest operations appear to be approaching a self-supporting status, or one that may show a growing net cash income in most years. Because of the multiple-use policy followed, the income from the forests includes large intangible items that do not appear in the above tabulations. Most important of these are watershed protection and recreation. Such intangible values constitute a much larger portion of the social income derived from the forest lands than from grazing lands.

71. The value of this inventory increase is extremely difficult to estimate. Cutover lands and those from which timber is being harvested show gains from growth. Virgin timber stands normally do not produce net increments until brought into operation. The loss from dying out and decay about equals new growth. However, the provision of fire protection tends to increase the available supply even in the virgin stands.

TABLE 33

National Forest Gross Costs and Income, Estimates as of April 1, 1953, and National Forest Budget Estimates for Fiscal Year 1953 versus National Forest Receipts, Fiscal Year 1953

Item	Appropriations	Receipts
Protection and management	$29,550,000	$76,900,000
Fighting forest fires, emergency	6,000,000	
Cooperative range improvement	310,000	
Forest roads and trails	11,000,000	
Research	900,000	
Acquisition, 3 items	366,680	
Blister rust control	1,750,000	
Forest pest (insect) control	2,029,400	
Roads and trails for states, 10 per cent fund	6,950,000	
Flood prevention surveys and works of improvement	744,173	
Totals (net cash)	$59,600,253	$76,900,000
Net profit (exclusive of contribution to states)		17,299,747
Gain in capital values (growth and price) estimate		$300,000,000
Funds not included above because they are not national forest work funds:		
Research for outside national forests	$4,500,000	
State and private forest cooperation— fire, etc.	10,685,164	
School funds, Arizona and New Mexico	131,587	
Payments to Minnesota	45,000	
Payments to states, 25 per cent fund	17,375,000	
Flood control surveys and works of improvement, outside national forests	696,742	
Cooperative work paid for by others	9,350,000	
Total		$42,783,494

Source: U.S. Senate Committee on Appropriations, *Agricultural Appropriations for 1954*, p. 357.

The brief factual summary here presented, and such amount of analytical treatment of it as has been included in this study, do not warrant any attempt to draw conclusions as to the adequacy and appropriateness of the funds assigned to this activity. For this a much more detailed study would be required. However, the forest lands have enormous capacity to absorb investment and are especially well suited for effective use of countercyclical expenditures, particularly for providing useful and wholesome employment in times of depression.

Work of the Army Corps of Engineers

A still older phase of conservation effort is that carried on by the Army Corps of Engineers. This consists mainly of engineering structures for the control of floods and improvement of navigation, including the improvement of rivers and harbors. It has some agricultural implications, however, in that flood control structures protect considerable acreages of farm land. Also, some of the flood control storage dams contribute to stabilizing water supplies used for irrigation.

The marked difference between the work of the Corps of Engineers and that of the Bureau of Reclamation lies in the fact that the projects carried out by the Corps of Engineers do not contemplate repayment by the beneficiaries. Local groups seeking benefits through these types of expenditures tend therefore to favor construction by the Corps of Engineers, if a given project can be interpreted as being primarily for flood control or navigation.[72]

There has long been an active jurisdictional conflict between the Bureau of Reclamation and the Corps of Engineers over the division of labor between the two.[73] This has become particularly apparent in undertakings like those relating to the Missouri River Valley. Here there is need for comprehensive planning for many types of benefit, including flood control, power development, navigation, irrigation, recreation and various others. Often the plans for flood control and navigation are inconsistent with those for power development and irrigation. This difficulty was encountered in the Tennessee Valley and has come up repeatedly in the Missouri Valley plans. There it has resulted in a compromise known as the Pick-Sloan plan, which has been widely criticized as extravagant and unsuitable.

Repeated efforts have been made to bring about a reorganization of these activities, but the problem is heavily charged with political implications and bureaucratic rivalries.[74] No attempt is made here to analyze

72. The attitudes of farm communities are also affected by the fact that the Corps of Engineers does not impose limits on the size of land unit that can be benefited, whereas the Bureau of Reclamation is directed to limit the acreage to be supplied with water to 160 acres per individual. Most lands brought under irrigation, if farmed at all, were previously handled in large units under extensive types of agriculture. Thus the owners are, in many cases, holders of large acreages and the number of small farmers is limited.

73. In areas subject to flood damage the responsibility for protection by means of dikes has long been assigned to the Corps of Engineers. Hence, the Bureau of Reclamation has not been in a position to participate in these activities and the questions of reimbursement for benefits and control of the pattern of land ownership have not arisen. In recent years, activities of the Corps of Engineers have been extended more and more into the upper reaches of the watersheds. This has led to more frequent and bitter jurisdictional conflicts.

74. The Commission on Organization of the Executive Branch of the Government recommended drastic reorganization of the Department of the Interior and the transfer to it of the rivers and harbors and flood control functions of the Corps of Engineers. In addition, it has proposed that a Board of Impartial Analysis and Engineering be

the problem or to separate out its agricultural phases. The major part of the program of the Corps of Engineers is only peripherally related to agriculture and it is not possible on the basis of data currently available to separate the portion of this outlay which is assignable to the protection and improvement of agricultural lands. Unquestionably this aspect of the program is a minor one as compared to the other activities of the agency. Nevertheless the operations of the Corps of Engineers do constitute a large and costly phase of the conservation program as a whole. The Hoover Commission placed the total expenditures by this agency at more than $5 billion for the period since 1902. As of 1953, its annual expenditures for flood control were running at a rate of about $350 million.

Since the projects constructed by the Corps of Engineers are presumably for generalized benefits of such a nature that they cannot be charged to specific individuals or groups, there is no direct income to offset the expenditures, even where privately owned lands are benefited. In projects which involve extending activities into the upper portions of the watersheds, as in the Missouri Valley, the direct benefits provided in the way of irrigation water and flood control become more prominent. Under these conditions the provision of individual and group benefits at no cost to the beneficiaries sets up powerful incentives for political pressures and contributes to the continuing controversy over which agency, the Corps of Engineers or the Bureau of Reclamation, should carry out specific projects which fall in the twilight zone where the two jurisdictions overlap.

THE CONSERVATION PROGRAM AS A WHOLE

The conservation movement consists of two principal segments, the older one relating to forests, water power, minerals and navigation and the more recent one primarily concerned with the conservation of soils. This later emphasis has come into prominence only in the last twenty years. The following discussion relates mainly to the soil conservation phase of the problem since this is the one most closely related to agriculture.

Important progress has been made. A downward trend in productivity that had persisted since colonial times has been recognized and to some extent checked, and a good start has been made in building up the fertility of the land. However, the program, up to now, has been a pioneering effort and somewhat experimental. It has also been very expensive. The conservation movement now appears to be at a stage where it should be carefully reviewed to see whether it can be made more economical and efficient without losing gains already achieved.

created to review proposed projects. For a fuller discussion of the problem, see U.S. Commission on Organization of the Executive Branch of the Government, *Department of the Interior*, March 1949, especially pp. 2–6 and 24–36.

As of 1953, the program included seven major segments:

1. The activities of the Soil Conservation Service, which were costing in 1953 about $60 million per year.[75]

2. The conservation payment program, costing about $270 million a year.

3. The work of the Bureau of Land Management, in which the principal emphasis is on the conservation of grazing resources. Its net expenditures on current operations, other than sale of resources and the cadastral survey,[76] amount to about $10 million per year.

4. The Bureau of Reclamation program, largely of investment character and now heavily oriented to the conservation of water power. Its cost to the Treasury is now about $225 million per year.

5. The work of the Army Corps of Engineers (for flood control), costing about $350 million annually.

6. The Forest Service activities, which currently are more than offset by increases in the inventory values of the forest holdings.

7. Flood prevention activities, costing about $6 million.

In addition, the agricultural experiment stations, the agricultural extension services and the Tennessee Valley Authority are using parts of their resources in furtherance of the movement. The over-all annual national outlay on the principal types of conservation activity is thus currently in the order of $1 billion. Of this, about $300 million to $350 million can be regarded as primarily in the interest of conserving soils on farms.

Problems and Controversies

The conservation movement as a whole presents a number of unsolved problems. Among them are the matters of method, of interagency relations, of the need for direct financial aid and of criteria as to where, when and how much conservation effort to apply. The principal methodological approaches are those of the Soil Conservation Service, with its emphasis on soil conservation districts and technical aid, the subsidy program of the Agricultural Conservation Program Service, and the educational approach stressed by the extension services and TVA.

There appears to be need for a closer tie between the Soil Conservation Service approach and that of the extension services and the Agricultural Stabilization and Conservation committees (if the conservation payment program is to be continued). The importance of a continuing broad educational program is obvious. For this the extension services and the Soil Conservation Service appear to be best fitted. There is need also for the kind of technical guidance the Soil Conservation Service special-

75. Not including expenditures for flood prevention which are carried on in cooperation with the Forest Service.

76. A cadastral survey is essentially a large-scale inventory of the extent, value and ownership of land.

ists can provide and for the kind of local cooperation and stimulus that can be brought into focus through the soil conservation districts.

Aside from the development of closer and more cordial working relationships on the part of the various agencies engaged in conservation activities, the principal need is for a coordinated joint approach to the making of whole-farm plans. A first step in the work of the soil conservation specialist is to develop a plan for the farm that will check erosion and build up the soil. This may be an excellent plan from a conservation standpoint but may not be a profitable one, or at least not as profitable as it could be. The farm also needs to be analyzed in terms of its profit-making possibilities and the two plans should then be reconciled in light of these two objectives.

Such a plan, when developed, may show a need for a different combination of products, possibly for additional acreage, better livestock or more equipment as well as for contour plowing, terracing, drainage and so on. Credit needs would thus be brought into focus, probably in a form which could be used in obtaining credit if it is needed. The result should be a reorganization plan that would meet reasonably well the requirements for both better conservation of resources and improved income.[77]

The methods used by the Agricultural Conservation Program Service in its subsidy program do not fit into such a logical and comprehensive plan of procedure, though presumably they could be made to do so if coordination could be carried far enough. At best, however, this would result in a cumbersome three-headed effort to deal with the problem, with the Agricultural Stabilization and Conservation committees contributing comparatively little in the way of special skills. Their function is almost solely to prescribe conditions for payments, check results and make payments. With all three agencies operating in many of the areas, the amount of overhead in the way of personnel, travel costs and demand on farmer time has reached a level where there is need for serious effort to simplify and streamline the arrangements.

Most counties now have an agricultural extension staff, a soil conservation staff, an ASC staff, an FHA representative, and, in some cases, a county agricultural commissioner with a number of assistants. In addition, there are local representatives of the Rural Electrification Administration, the farm credit agencies, the Reclamation Service, the Bureau of Land Management, the Forest Service and the Employment Service.

77. This does not mean that each farm should be so planned each year. Such plans would be long-term readjustments worked out in close cooperation with the farmer and at his request. They would be carried on at such a rate as available manpower and farmer demand make feasible. This procedure has recently been tried out in Massachusetts under the guidance of Professor John D. Black of Harvard University and appears to give promise of more effective results than the less intensive methods commonly used. Since it would provide a basis for more effective use of credit and larger profits, it should minimize or possibly eliminate the need for cash subsidies.

Most of these are performing useful and needed services, but the overhead organization of agriculture has become almost intolerably complex, cumbersome and expensive. This great expansion of service and advisory staffs is almost wholly a development of the past twenty years. In part, it is a result of the effort to bring about changes quickly. It is time now, however, to re-examine it to see if the forced-draft rate of change could be eased down without disadvantage to the farmer and the public and with considerable savings in expense and manpower.[78]

Are Direct Subsidies Still Needed?

If, as seems probable, the time has come when farmers are sufficiently interested in conservation and know enough about it so that many of them would continue to follow soil-conserving practices without subsidy, question may be raised whether the subsidy program could be reduced and a substantial saving made without much damage to the program or serious hardship to farmers. If so, operations at the county level could be reduced and simplified, and local costs for the program as a whole could be less than they are now.

If the Congress should determine that subsidies are needed and warranted for certain areas or types of farms or farmers, such funds as might be provided could be administered by the local representatives of the Soil Conservation Service, with checking by soil conservation district officers or other appropriate personnel. This procedure would replace the expensive and cumbersome dual responsibility that now exists.

The credit arrangements now available to agriculture are sufficiently liberal and comprehensive that it would seem that most farmers could make needed and economically feasible improvements without direct subsidy. Where needed changes are so costly that credit cannot be obtained for them, conservation subsidies in the amounts now provided probably are not large enough to finance them. If this view is warranted, the principal function of the payments now made is to stimulate interest in conservation activities. For this purpose, it is a costly and relatively inefficient tool which could perhaps now be dispensed with, at least in many areas.

How Much Should Be Spent on Conservation?

An ever present problem is that of how much to spend on conservation and when. The values arising from conservation efforts often lie in the future and are difficult or impossible to measure. For soils, it seems

78. In some counties, rivalries, particularly between SCS, PMA and extension service personnel, have led to considerable friction and loss of efficiency running even beyond the wastes resulting from duplication of effort. See, for example, *Department of Agriculture Appropriations for 1952*, Hearings, Part 2, pp. 687–99.

probable that the large-scale, intensive effort applied during the past twenty years was necessary and worth while, as a means of giving impetus to a major corrective movement. Now that momentum in the new direction has been achieved, a more settled long-range program is appropriate and would probably be effective. For this purpose the Soil Conservation Service, the extension services and the soil conservation districts appear to be the most suitable mechanisms.

In the public land programs, the most urgent needs are for completion of suitable land classifications to determine the best uses, reblocking in appropriate management units and the development of more adequate and uniform policies in regard to compensation for the use of land. The two principal competent agencies for exercising professional management are the Forest Service and the Division of Range Management.[79] Their jurisdictions touch each other at many points.

Readjustments and coordinated policies would be more easily obtained if both were in the same department. In any case, steps are needed to bring about promptly, where appropriate, the transfer of Forest Service grazing lands, outside the forests, to the Division of Range Management and the transfer to the Forest Service of forest lands now held by the Bureau of Land Management. The current duplication of management services and the confusion of policies are wasteful and useless. A single presidential order or a mere body of recommendations is not likely to bring about an effective solution of this complex problem. There will be need for continuing and detailed study, in cooperation with the departments and agencies concerned, and probably for a series of executive orders and congressional directives rather than some one specific action.

Problems of Timing and Criteria

The rate of improvement on both the forest and the grazing lands could with benefit be scheduled, so far as practical, on a countercyclical basis. That is, work should be intensified in times of recession and slowed down in times of high employment and business activity. It would appear that the resources committed to land improvement are now so large that they should support most of the needed work, except as the Congress may choose to provide funds for stepped-up activity in times of depression.

Policy for reclamation activities is much more difficult to assess than for the Forest Service and the Bureau of Land Management. A first need is for more adequate reporting of the costs, incomes and financial situations for the various projects, especially those in which the development of farm lands plays an important part. The adequacy of the criteria used

79. As of now, the Division of Range Management is the pertinent operating agency. It may eventually become a staff agency if contemplated arrangements for multipurpose field offices are put into effect by the Bureau of Land Management.

in determining economic feasibility needs thorough and competent review by a qualified group not made up of persons drawn from the Bureau of Reclamation itself.

The policy of providing construction funds on a no-interest basis needs to be carefully re-examined, and a competent outside board of review should pass upon the justifiability of projects put forward not only by the Bureau of Reclamation but by the Army Corps of Engineers as well. The competition between these agencies has long been notorious, and the lack of objectivity in presenting the arguments for specific construction programs is also well known. The conflicts in jurisdiction and the contrasts in policy contribute to a waste of funds which seems likely to become more serious as the number of remaining projects suitable for development becomes more restricted.[80]

Here, even more than in the other agencies, attention could be given to the timing of expenditures. Vast amounts of needed public construction can be carried out at relatively small real social cost provided they are so timed as to use resources that would otherwise be idle. The tendency is, however, for both political and bureaucratic pressure for large projects to continue strong, or even to increase, in periods when the best interests of society would be served by limiting construction activity. Realistic adjustments to such a general policy as that indicated above must, of course, be made. It is recognized that many major projects, once they are started, must be carried through. Nevertheless, there needs to be a soundly conceived over-all policy.

The Bureau of Reclamation now has some $2 billion invested in vast power and irrigation projects. These, it would seem, should provide sufficient income to maintain a continuous building program of sizable

80. The Natural Resources Committee of the Commission on Organization of the Executive Branch of the Government comments:

"The committee has no illusion concerning the difficulties of effecting a real unification of functions. It is fully aware of the fact that it is much easier to unify on paper than in actuality, and that many intangible values of experience, tradition, and morale are lost in any great reorganization. Nonetheless, the committee can in all honesty see no solid reason for continuing the separate existence of two great river development agencies whose responsibilities now so largely overlap. Painful as the operation may be, the case for a unification of functions of the Corps of Engineers and the Bureau of Reclamation is so overwhelming that it ought to be effected without further delay." (*Task Force Report on Natural Resources,* Appendix L, p. 29.)

The Committee also presents, in broad outline, a suggested general policy for guidance in setting up more specific policies. This, so far as financial arrangements are concerned, is summarized as follows:

"Although the committee is not prepared to make specific recommendations, it believes that the most pressing need for statutory revision has to do with financial policy. As a general principle costs should be repaid as far as practicable by the beneficiaries, much more so than at present. Federal contributions should be limited to amounts proportionate to the estimated national benefits involved. State and local contributions should be required where practicable as a regular policy on all projects where localized benefits demonstrably exist. Where localized benefits to both public and private beneficiaries are vendible, charges should be made with due regard for the volume of the benefits. Where such benefits are nonvendible, suitable techniques should be devised for assessment. Existing discriminations with respect to repayment by beneficiaries should be removed insofar as possible. Attention should be given to the development of standards of project feasibility, benefit-cost evaluation, and cost allocation." (*Ibid.,* p. 28.)

proportions without large appropriations from the Treasury. Actually, the level of appropriations in 1953, about $200 million, was some four times what it was in the depression years, whereas a policy oriented to economic stabilization would call for an opposite relationship in the amounts expended in the two periods.

Conservation Program as a Whole Has Accomplished Much

The many-sided program for conservation of natural resources has achieved, on the whole, very significant results. The public apathy toward the problem has been overcome. A large start has been made in checking soil erosion and improving the productivity of the nation's farms. More than 150 million acres of neglected and fast deteriorating public domain have been brought under some degree of management and started on the way to recovery.[81] The national forests are being gradually but steadily improved, and great progress has been made in harnessing the nation's water-power resources.

The investment in this undertaking runs to an impressive figure, more than $10 billion in the past two decades. More than half of this sum went for subsidies to farmers, to induce soil-conserving changes in their operations and to add to their incomes. This expenditure has resulted in a significant but unmeasurable increase in the inventory value of the nation's soils. A considerable portion of the other types of expenditure has taken shape in investments of a more tangible character, such as dams, canals and power plants.

To put it another way, these outlays were in part an investment in permanent or semipermanent assets and in part a current expense. Probably the major part of the $200 million to $300 million in annual payments to farmers should be regarded as a current expense. There is reason to think that this heavy outlay could now be reduced substantially without losing the gains already made or foregoing the prospect of continuing steady, though less sensational, progress in the future. Conservation as a national and individual policy has become well established and the need for direct income subsidies to farmers is much less pressing than it was in the 1930s.

This does not mean that it would be wise or profitable to eliminate suddenly all financial aid for making needed changes in conservation practices. Some farmers and some areas probably are still in need both of financial aid and money incentives if the conservation program is to carry on without a setback. A recent study by the Bureau of Agricultural Economics of the reasons why farmers in western Iowa do not do more to stop erosion indicates that the principal barriers, in the minds of the farmers at least, are (1) the changes required in farm enterprises,

81. Only about 134 million acres are in grazing districts, but conservation work is also carried on in some areas that are not organized as grazing districts.

(2) rental agreements, (3) mortgage indebtedness, and (4) short expectancy of tenure.[82] Some question may be raised, however, as to whether conservation payments have or will overcome these obstacles. In part, the problem is one for continuing research and education. Nevertheless, there are undoubtedly some situations in which financial aid will be needed if the gains of recent years are to be retained and carried further.

82. U.S. Bureau of Agricultural Economics, *The Agricultural Situation,* June 1952, pp. 9–10.

Chapter 10

Price Support Through Loans and Purchases
The Role of the Commodity Credit Corporation

THE LOAN AND PURCHASE program, which has been carried on by the Commodity Credit Corporation since 1933, is essentially a modification and improvement of the procedure used by the Federal Farm Board in its efforts to maintain prices in the period 1929 to 1932. The conditions under which it has been carried out have been markedly different and, up to this time, the results have been more satisfactory.

The Farm Board was attempting to prevent a disastrous decline in the prices of wheat, cotton and wool. The program carried out by the Commodity Credit Corporation in the 1930s was, for the most part, an effort to raise prices from a low level. In recent years, the problem has again become that of trying to hold prices up to a pre-existing level. With the easing off of war and postwar demands, the Corporation is now faced with a situation somewhat similar to that which the Farm Board stabilization corporations sought to deal with in 1931 and 1932, but much less acute because of a strong domestic demand which eases the problem greatly as compared to that of the early 1930s. The Commodity Credit Corporation's financial resources are much greater than those of the stabilization corporations, and the congressional attitude toward its price-supporting activities is much more favorable.

The Commodity Credit Corporation is not itself a policy-making body like the Farm Board. It is a mechanism for carrying out policies established by the Congress and by the Secretary of Agriculture. Thus, its role is similar to that of the Farm Board stabilization corporations rather than to that of the Farm Board itself. In the analysis here presented, decisions and policies attributed to the Commodity Credit Corporation should be understood as those of the Secretary of Agriculture and of the Congress rather than of the Corporation as such.

In recent years, the Congress has tended to prescribe legislatively and in considerable detail the policies to be followed in making loans and purchases and in managing stocks held. The opportunity for discretionary action by either the Secretary of Agriculture or the governing board of the Corporation has been progressively reduced from 1938 on. Hence, the policies discussed or implied should be regarded as those of the Congress rather than of the implementing agency or of administrative officials. However, since by far the largest part of the price-supporting activity of the government is concentrated in the Commodity Credit Corporation, a review of its operations provides the most direct and concise summary of the major price-support policies now in effect and of the problems to which they give rise.

The activities of the Corporation are, of course, intimately related to those of other agricultural agencies such as the Production and Marketing Administration and, more recently, the Commodity Stabilization Service. They are part of a broader program which includes production and marketing controls, Section 32 fund operations, the International Wheat Agreement and various others. Most if not all of these tend to facilitate and strengthen Commodity Credit Corporation activities, but the major financial operations and the principal influences on the market are by way of the Corporation itself. It is therefore important that its background, operations and significance be considered in shaping plans for the future.

ORIGINS OF NONRECOURSE LOAN PROGRAM

Farm Board Experience

Since the efforts of the Farm Board to support the prices of wheat and cotton have been described in Chapter 4, they are touched on only briefly here. The Board gained some experience and cushioned the severity and suddenness of the decline to some extent. Yet, the over-all outcome was not such as to make resort to this type of program attractive to the new administration which came into power in 1933. Nevertheless, under the pressure of circumstances, it did very shortly adopt some features of the earlier program and came gradually to rely more heavily on them.

The Farm Board program as originally conceived did not emphasize price support or price raising, except as these were implied in the authority given it to aid in stabilizing prices as between years of large and small production, or in periods of sharply decreased demand. Its principal function was expected to be that of increasing and stabilizing returns by improving market organization and by assisting farmers to establish cooperative selling agencies under their own control.

The chaotic marketing situation that developed in the fall of 1929 and in 1930 led the Board to undertake price-sustaining activities mainly in wheat, cotton and wool. The support consisted of both purchases (by the wheat and cotton stabilization corporations) and loans at higher rates than those that could be obtained through private lending agencies. These loans, except those to the stabilization corporations, were not officially nonrecourse loans. That is, the borrowing cooperatives were obligated to repay the loans, if they could, even though the commodity was sold at a loss.

Actually, the financial resources of the cooperatives and of the stabilization corporations were insufficient to meet any sizable losses. It was

evident that large losses would have to be absorbed by the Board's revolving fund. Thus, the loans were, in effect, of the nonrecouse type.
If prices increased the cooperatives or their members would profit from
the increase, but if losses were incurred the Board would have to take
them.

Where commodities are not moving freely, such an operation soon
ties up very large amounts of money and puts a heavy burden on available storage facilities. The Farm Board had been granted a specific fund
($500 million), not a loan authorization. This fund was not adequate
for carrying out such a program on a large and continuing scale. Once
the funds were committed, either as frozen loans to cooperatives or
through ownership of stocks held by the stabilization corporations, the
Board had no other resources to draw on and could not do other than it
did, that is, stop making loans and discontinue price-supporting purchases. Thus when it became necessary to withdraw support, prices
dropped precipitately and the government was left holding heavy stocks
of wheat and cotton that tended to weaken prices in the succeeding
period.[1]

Shift to Emphasis on Production Control

The Board soon recognized that it could not continue to support
prices by means of high-level loans and purchases if production continued greatly in excess of the amounts that could be sold at the prices it
sought to maintain. It therefore urged farmers to cut back production
so as to supply only what the market could be expected to take at customary prices. Lacking any authority or mechanism for reducing production, it could only make recommendations, which, in the conditions then
existing, were almost wholly futile.

Free-market prices in the period following withdrawal of support were
probably lower than they would have been if the Farm Board had not
intervened. However, this does not necessarily mean that returns for the
period as a whole were less than they would otherwise have been. In the
first part of the period, the Board's action kept prices higher than they
would have been in a free market. Whether the over-all effect was a lower
average price for the period as a whole cannot be stated with assurance
since the commodities affected are world-trade products and many factors enter into the price as of any given period. It is probable that heavy
stocks would have accumulated, either on farms or elsewhere, even if
there had been no intervention by the Farm Board.

The lessons of the Farm Board experience were not lost on the legislators and officials who drafted plans and legislation for the program that
took shape in 1933. They placed immediate and vigorous emphasis on
readjustment of production. Along with this, they provided emergency

1. See Chapter 4; see also the companion volume, *The Agricultural Commodity Programs,* Chapters 1, 3 and 8.

supplementation of prices received in the market, by direct transfers in the form of benefit payments, rentals for land not used, and in various other ways.[2]

AAA under Pressure to Raise Prices Quickly

The efforts to adjust production could not be expected to raise prices quickly. Heavy stocks of the major storable commodities were already in existence and would keep the markets abundantly supplied for a time, even if production was cut back sharply. But farmers and many of the congressional representatives were pressing strongly for some faster-acting program designed to strengthen farm prices and put more money into the farm areas where it was desperately needed. Farmer unrest in the cotton and corn regions became so evident by the fall of 1933 that the Administration felt obliged to undertake more direct action than that contemplated in the crop adjustment program.

The loan plan adopted was partly a means of heading off much more radical proposals which were gaining momentum. In the South, farmers were holding meetings and advocating vigorous and radical action. A delegation from the cotton states came to Washington with demands that the President inflate the currency, that he fix a minimum price for cotton at 15 to 20 cents, and that the 1934 crop be limited to 9 million bales. In the Corn Belt, some of the groups were urging even more radical solutions. The Farmers' Holiday Association had initiated a series of farmer strikes. Some judges were threatened with lynching if they authorized foreclosure of farm mortgages. A conference of governors from ten of the Corn Belt states demanded that the Administration peg the prices of farm products at parity and fix quotas on sales.[3]

Thus, the Agricultural Adjustment Administration was under both political and economic pressure to take steps that would speed up and supplement the price-raising efforts already under way. Furthermore, there still was a widespread belief that the channeling of funds into the farm areas would help to speed recovery in the economy as a whole. Though the action taken at that time had much to commend it, there is reason to doubt that this method of supporting farm prices was viewed with much favor when the new farm programs were being planned and launched. The Farm Board was regarded as a failure, both as to effectiveness and in terms of cost to the government. Furthermore, a new administration just taking office naturally was not anxious to adopt as

2. Since the discussion in this chapter relates primarily to the programs carried on by the Commodity Credit Corporation, most of the related activities are omitted from consideration. They are described in earlier chapters and in *The Agricultural Commodity Programs*.

3. See Edwin G. Nourse, Joseph S. Davis and John D. Black, *Three Years of the Agricultural Adjustment Administration*, Brookings Institution, Washington, 1937, pp. 151–57.

an important phase of its program a procedure which had so recently been a principal and presumably unsuccessful feature of the one used by its predecessor.

The Agricultural Adjustment Act of 1933 contained only a minor reference to the making of advance loans. Section 8(1) authorized advance payments against commodities stored under seal on farms, but these were to be only in the form of advances of benefit payments. When the loan program was inaugurated, the agency set up for handling it was organized under more general legislation rather than under authority granted in the Agricultural Adjustment Act itself.[4] This agency, the Commodity Credit Corporation, did not in fact achieve specific legislative sanction until 1935. Even after that time, its charter continued to be on a somewhat precarious basis until the passage of the permanent Charter Act in 1948.

The CCC during the Depression

The Commodity Credit Corporation differed from the stabilization corporations of the Farm Board in that it could lend on any commodity for which such action was authorized, whereas each of the Farm Board stabilization corporations was designed for making loans on one particular commodity. Furthermore, it was specifically a government corporation, not an agency nominally created by the farmers' cooperative marketing associations.[5] Its $3 million capital did not come from the Agricultural Adjustment Administration but from special funds assigned by the President.[6] It was to be operated under an eight-man governing board consisting of the Secretary of Agriculture, the Administrator of the Agricultural Adjustment Administration, the Governor of the Farm Credit Administration, the Assistant to the Director of the Reconstruction Finance Corporation and four other government officials drawn from these organizations.[7]

4. The CCC loan program was not a direct offshoot of the loan and purchase operations of the Farm Board. It was a new start financed in a different way. The remaining assets of the Farm Board stabilization fund were channeled off so as to provide, in a different way, services similar to those for which the Board was originally intended, that is, the strengthening and financing of farmer-owned cooperative marketing associations. This was to be accomplished by means of loans and educational assistance provided through the banks for cooperatives.

5. For an explanation of the origin of CCC and the source of its funds, see pp. 235–37. Since there was no specific legislation authorizing its establishment, the President acted under authority granted in Section 2(a) of the National Industrial Recovery Act (48 *Stat.* 195). The procedure was similar to that used in setting up the Federal Surplus Relief Corporation, the Soil Erosion Service and the Resettlement Administration, all of which were later given specific legislative authorization, though under other names.

6. Out of funds provided through an appropriation authorized by Section 220 of the National Industrial Recovery Act and the Fourth Deficiency Act, fiscal 1933 (48 *Stat.* 274).

7. The other four directors were Oscar Johnson, Director of Finance in the AAA; Herman Oliphant, General Counsel of FCA; E. B. Schwulst, Special Assistant to the Board of Directors of RFC, and Stanley Reed, General Counsel of RFC.

In this first period, CCC was operated virtually as a subsidiary of RFC. RFC field agencies acted as examiners and as distributors of the money loaned on commodities.[8] Because of its small capitalization and large volume of loans, CCC could not go into the private money market and obtain funds at low rates of interest. Consequently, it continued for some years to rely on RFC for funds. However, RFC acted on the advice of the Secretary of Agriculture in determining policies relating to CCC. In this period, the Commodity Credit Corporation had only banking functions. Other powers and duties were to be assigned to it in later years.

The Corn and Cotton Loans of 1933–34

CCC began operation in the fall and winter of 1933–34 by offering loans to growers of corn and cotton on their 1933 production, provided the stocks were stored under conditions acceptable to CCC. For cotton, the loans were based on negotiable warehouse receipts issued by approved cotton warehouses and with a requirement that the warehouses meet inspection standards of the U.S. Department of Agriculture. For corn, the procedure was to seal the collateral in storage facilities on the farm. The borrowers had to agree to sign the cotton or corn-hog production control contracts that were then in use or in preparation.

These were "nonrecourse" loans. That is, the borrower could either pay off the loan and repossess the collateral, or surrender his collateral at the termination of the loan period and thereby cancel all obligation to make further payment. If the price rose above the loan rate and the farmer chose to pay off his loan, he could profit from the price increase. But if the price remained below the loan rate, he could surrender the commodity, and the loss, if any, would be borne by the Commodity Credit Corporation (but indirectly by the government).

The cotton loans were put at 10 cents a pound, about the value then current in the principal spot markets. Thus, they were approximately 100 per cent of value loans as compared to the 65 to 75 per cent loans that were customary in commercial operations. For corn, the loan rate of 45 cents per bushel was one third or more higher than current values. As of November 1933, farm values of corn ranged from about 31 cents to 37 cents over much of the Corn Belt.[9]

8. RFC loaned money to CCC at 3 per cent and CCC loaned it to farmers at 4 per cent.

9. Nourse, Black and Davis, *op. cit.*, p. 157. The loans were at fixed rates regardless of location. There were, however, some variations by type in the case of cotton. This flat rate caused considerable unevenness in the portion of the crop put under loan in different localities (in this first year of operation). It was, of course, more favorable to outlying areas than to those lying close to central markets. See Geoffrey Shepherd, "Stabilization Operations of the Commodity Credit Corporation," *Journal of Farm Economics,* August 1942, pp. 589–610. This apparent defect in procedure may actually have been desirable at that time since it was, in general, the outlying areas that were hardest hit. The drop

Results of the First Loan Program

Since this first loan program was so important in establishing CCC lending as a continuing and increasingly important feature of the price-support mechanism, the experience with it is summarized here.[10]

The corn loans worked out better than could reasonably have been expected at the time they were made. Corn prices rose during the year and nearly all of the loans were repaid. The Commodity Credit Corporation made a profit of nearly half a million dollars. The administrative arrangements were handled well, and the operation as a whole was looked upon with a good deal of favor by the farmers who benefited from it and by government administrators and legislators.

In principle, the procedure was very similar to that followed by the Farm Board. However, the first year in which the program was in operation was marked by one of the worst droughts in the country's history. Corn production dropped from 2.4 billion bushels in 1933 to about 1.5 billion in 1934, though the acreage planted had been reduced only about 8 per cent. The season average price to farmers rose from 52 cents in 1933 to 81.5 cents in 1934.[11]

The over-all effect of the corn loans was salutary from the standpoint of both the growers and the public. Feeding was reduced in the fall of 1933 and corn was held over for feeding in 1934–35, when its usefulness was much greater. Also, money was channeled into the farm areas at a time when it was desperately needed. Corn prices were kept somewhat higher in the fall of 1933 than they would have been had the loans not been available.[12] Since carry-overs were increased, prices were no doubt lower in the fall and winter of 1934–35 than they would otherwise have been. However, since both the higher and lower prices pertained to a commodity used principally by farmers themselves, the price variations were not of first importance. Much more significant was the fact that part of the excess supply of corn available in 1933 was retained for use in 1934 without a corresponding delay in obtaining cash with which to meet 1933 requirements. Had 1934 proved to be a good corn year, the results might, of course, have been quite different, though the loans might still have been advantageous to the farmers concerned.

---

in central market prices, without a corresponding reduction in freight rates, had caused a greater percentage decline of prices in the areas remote from central markets than in those that were close in. Since the central markets were well supplied, there was little merit in causing outlying stocks to flow into them.

10. For a more detailed analysis, see *The Agricultural Commodity Programs,* Chapters 1 and 5. See also the discussion in Nourse, Davis and Black, *op. cit.,* and the preceding studies of the same series from which it is drawn.

11. U.S. Department of Agriculture, *Agricultural Statistics, 1952,* p. 36.

12. As the drought damage of 1934 became apparent, market prices rose above the loan rates and the loans ceased to have a supporting effect on prices. A loan rate of 55 cents was offered in the fall of 1934. It was intentionally kept below market prices. However, former borrowers were permitted to convert old loans to new if they chose to do so. For a more detailed analysis, see Nourse, Davis and Black, *op. cit.,* pp. 157–63.

Though the amount of corn actually stored under CCC loans was only 268 million bushels, the higher prices maintained by means of the loan program apparently caused some liquidation of livestock, and feeding to lighter weights, in the winter of 1933–34. Corn prices, to farmers, were 40.6 cents per bushel in November 1933 as compared to 19.4 cents in November 1932.[13] The total October carry-over in 1933 was about 116 million bushels above that of 1932 and more than double the amounts carried over in the period 1929–1931.[14]

Cotton Loan Less Significant as a Price Influence

The cotton loan, though relatively successful, was less significant either as a price influence or as a stabilizer of supplies. The loans undoubtedly strengthened prices somewhat in the fall of 1933, but since they were approximately at market level, the loans did not raise prices materially. Production was down about 3.5 million bales in 1934, but carry-overs were still so large that no shortage developed, nor would one have developed had there been no CCC cotton loan. Not much over half of the cotton loans had been repaid by July 31, 1934, and the government was still financing about 3 million bales, nearly as much as the highest amount financed by the Farm Board. For a more extended analysis of this operation, see *The Agricultural Commodity Programs,* Chapter 1.

Since the purpose here is mainly to trace the development and significance of the Commodity Credit Corporation as a policy-implementing device, principal emphasis is on the organization as such rather than on the impact of its operations on commodity prices. These are more fully described and analyzed in the companion volume on *The Agricultural Commodity Programs.* The following pages deal mainly, therefore, with the changes in legislation pertaining to the Corporation and with its financial history. Commodity programs are touched upon only as needed in explaining changes in the Corporation's financial situation and holdings and its place in the farm price-support program.

Growing Recognition of CCC by the Congress

An increasing interest in the Commodity Credit Corporation as an instrument of policy is reflected in the fact that it was given legal recognition by the Congress in January 1935 (49 *Stat.* 1). Thus, it no longer had to rely on the National Industrial Recovery Act for authorization to exist and operate.[15] Thereafter, its charter was extended through peri-

---

13. *Agricultural Statistics, 1937,* p. 47. This increase in price obviously was not all due to the corn loan. There was a general speculative upsurge in farm prices in the summer of 1933 which carried the price of grains up from an index of 34 (1910–14 = 100) to 94, in July. However, the index had dropped back to 69 by October and stood at 73 in December (*ibid.,* p. 400).

14. *Agricultural Statistics, 1952,* p. 43.

15. However, there was much controversy over the extension of its charter at various times thereafter.

odic legislative acts until 1948, at which time it was given a permanent federal charter.

In March 1938 the President designated the Secretary of the Treasury as the agent of the government to receive from the Secretary of Agriculture and the Governor of the Farm Credit Administration the capital stock of the Corporation (Executive Order No. 7848). Shortly thereafter its capital was increased to $100 million.

More Reliance on CCC, 1938–1942

From 1938 on, CCC began to require much greater financial resources and was given a larger and more specific role in the farm program. In the Agricultural Adjustment Act of 1938, the Congress directed that the loan program was to be integrated with the acreage adjustment program and that CCC was to make nonrecourse loans to producers of wheat, cotton and corn at specified percentages of parity (unless quotas were disapproved). For cotton and wheat the loans were to be at such rates as the Secretary of Agriculture might specify within a range of 52 to 75 per cent of parity. For corn, the range was to be between 52 and 75 per cent of parity but the rate to be applied within this range was spelled out in the law instead of being left to the Secretary of Agriculture. The loan rate was to be in accordance with a sliding scale based on the quantities available and likely to be produced. Loans on certain other commodities, such as dairy products, were also authorized, but these were to be at rates to be determined by the Secretary of Agriculture.[16]

To enable CCC to meet these heavier financial requirements, it was authorized to issue debentures and notes in the amount of $500 million. The amounts it is permitted to borrow have been gradually increased, from $900 million on March 4, 1939 to $1.4 billion on August 9, 1940 to $2.65 billion on July 1, 1941 and in further successive steps, until it now has authority to borrow up to $10 billion.[17]

The act of 1938 (52 *Stat.* 107) also directed the Secretary of the Treasury to make an appraisal each year of the assets of CCC and provided that, if its capital had been impaired, he was to make payments which would restore it to $100 million. However, if there was a surplus above $100 million, CCC was directed to transfer this surplus to the United States Treasury.[18] It should be noted, however, that such impair-

16. The 52 to 75 per cent loans specified in this act for cotton, wheat and corn were the first in which the loan rates were determined directly by congressional action.

17. The borrowing power of the Corporation was increased from $6.75 billion to $8.5 billion on March 20, 1954 and to $10 billion on August 31, 1954. The March 1954 act (Public Law 312) made a further change by providing that capital impairments can be made up only by appropriation of funds, not by a cancellation of Treasury notes, which was the procedure specified by the Congress for some of the earlier capital restorations.

18. The appraisal was to be made at the market prices prevailing on March 31 for commodities owned or held as security for loans. Beginning with 1942, and for each of the years since, until 1954, the basis of appraisal was "cost, including not more than one

ments and surpluses are not realized gains or losses. They consist of realized gains and losses plus changes in the valuations assigned to the Corporation's holdings in accordance with the valuation procedures specified by the Congress. (See footnote 18.) Changes in book value may not become realized gains or losses for several years and, of course, are likely to be smaller or larger than the amounts shown for any given year. Public Law 312 (1954), in effect, shifts the procedure from an appraisal of values to an actual audit of costs and losses. Future restorations will cover only realized gains and losses.

Banking Operations of CCC

Other functions were assigned to CCC from time to time as part of the over-all farm program. In July 1940 an amendment to the Agricultural Adjustment Act of 1938 added Section 391(c).[19] This required the Corporation to loan to the Secretary of Agriculture amounts up to $50 million per year for making crop insurance premium advances, for advance payments under the Soil Conservation and Domestic Allotment Act and to pay administrative expenses of county agricultural conservation associations. Such loans were to be repaid with interest, the rate to be set by the Secretary of Agriculture but not at less than the cost of the money to CCC.

Since then, CCC has been used for a number of banking operations of similar type. For example, part of the cost of the program for combating foot and mouth disease was financed with loans of this kind. The International Wheat Agreement, for which annual costs cannot be forecast accurately, has also been financed by CCC. Expenditures and losses from these operations have then been repaid out of appropriations made in succeeding years.[20]

Because of this more intimate relationship with the various activities of the Department of Agriculture, the President transferred the Corporation to that Department in 1939 (by Reorganization Plan No. 1 of 1939 —53 *Stat.* 1423) and vested in the Secretary of Agriculture exclusive voting rights of its capital stock (Executive Order 8219, August 7, 1939). Up to that time, loans had to be made on recommendation of the Secretary of Agriculture but with the approval of the President, a cumbersome and meaningless procedure in operations of that kind.

---

year of carrying charges . . . or the average market prices of such assets for a period of twelve months ending with March 31 of each year, whichever is less." In 1945 the date of appraisal was shifted to June 30, and the basis for computing the value of holdings was changed to the average market price during the last month of the fiscal year. The March 1954 act (Public Law 312) provided that appraisal was thereafter to be made on the basis of cost to CCC.

19. 54 *Stat.* 727, 728.

20. Advances were also made to facilitate diversion programs such as those carried out by some of the associations of fruit growers. Loans of this kind provided ready cash until the diversion could be completed.

Problems of the Late 1930s

Until 1938, CCC was able, for the most part, to make loans at its own discretion and to keep them at relatively modest levels, in terms of percentages of parity prices. The principal exception was the cotton loan of 1934. Under heavy pressure from members of Congress, the loan rate was raised to 12 cents a pound, a rate which proved to be too high to permit normal movement. About half of the small 1934 crop went under loan and CCC became involved to the extent of nearly $283 million on that crop alone.[21] It still was financing about 3 million bales of the 1933 crop. The total United States carry-over at the beginning of the 1935 season was more than 7 million bales.[22] This was some 2 million to 3 million bales above what might be regarded as a normal carry-over. Only small amounts were loaned in 1935 and no loans were made in 1936.

With demand improving and subsidies provided to bring the effective sales price of cotton more nearly into line with the true market price, the carry-over declined in 1935 and 1936. The sharp curtailment in output resulting from the AAA program also helped materially to bring about a better balance in the cotton market. But the big 1937 crop, nearly double those of the three preceding years, recreated the problem of excess stocks. More than 5.5 million bales went under loan to CCC and loans amounting to some $243 million were made.

From then on, the carry-over of cotton was heavy until the close of World War II. It reached an all-time high of 13.3 million bales in 1939. The situation was made more difficult by legislation enacted in 1939 which limited sales of CCC-owned cotton to 300,000 bales per month and 1.5 million bales per year. It also specified that sales should not be made at less than an amount that would recoup all costs, including storage and interest. These restrictions were not suspended until April 12, 1945. They account in part for the very heavy stocks carried from 1938 on.

Corn and Wheat Carry-Overs Large from 1939 On

The droughts of 1934 and 1936 eliminated the excess carry-overs of wheat and corn. Consequently, these commodities did not pose serious problems until late in the decade. However, the mandatory price-support loans provided in the act of 1938 began to cause trouble soon thereafter. During the years 1939, 1940 and 1941, more than 800 million bushels of wheat were pledged to CCC and the Corporation made loans thereon of nearly $680 million. As of July 1, 1942, the United States carry-over was 630 million bushels, nearly twice the 377 million bushels reached in 1933 when the stocks acquired by the Farm Board were an important element causing uncertainty in the wheat market.

21. *Agricultural Statistics, 1952,* p. 758.
22. *Ibid.,* p. 81.

Large amounts of corn were also put under loan in the late 1930s. Loans were made on some 635 million bushels in the years 1938, 1939 and 1940. Advances made in these three years amounted to more than $360 million. The October 1 carry-over of corn (in all ownerships) reached a record level of 687 million bushels in 1940.[23]

These were much larger accumulations than those which were causing so much trouble at the close of the Farm Board period. However, a price break of similar type did not occur. There were two principal reasons for this different outcome in a situation that had many similarities to that of 1932. Increased funds were provided to CCC to enable it to continue making price-support loans, and the outbreak of World War II created a markedly different outlook in respect to the need for reserve stocks. By August 1940, the borrowing power of CCC had been raised to $1.4 billion, a far larger amount than the Farm Board had had to work with. Furthermore, the CCC loans had not been based on prices so far above those that would have prevailed in a free market, and the economy as a whole was making some recovery instead of dropping farther and farther into the depths of depression, as it did in 1932.

It is apparent, nevertheless, that this second attempt to support prices by means of high-level, nonrecourse loans would soon have resulted in serious difficulties had it not been for the sudden upsurge in demand and prices that resulted from the outbreak of war. If war had not broken out and if CCC had had to discontinue loan operations, the demoralization of the market might have been very difficult to deal with as the quantities held were much larger than in 1932.

In the meantime, legislation providing for acreage allotments and marketing quotas had been passed. Consequently, remedial measures could no doubt have been applied more quickly and more effectively than in the earlier period. Nevertheless, the developments of this period point to a significant limitation on the use of the nonrecourse loan procedure by itself as a means of maintaining prices at levels well above those of the free market. This weakness has become more apparent in the years since 1949.

Direct Purchases and Trading Operations

By 1937, CCC began to be involved in trading as well as loan operations since it became necessary to transport, store and dispose of commodities acquired in the settlement of loans. In the fall of 1939 it moved still further in that direction when it began making direct purchases in the market as a means of supporting prices. Thus, it followed even more closely the procedures used by the Farm Board stabilization corporations.

Activities of this kind were extended much more widely during the

23. For amounts carried over up to that date. Larger amounts have been carried over in 1949 and the years since then.

war years as a means of carrying out various programs relating to the conduct of the war. These are touched on briefly in a succeeding section, though they are not, in the main, closely related to the price-support program of the 1930s or that of the late 1940s and early 1950s. Some of the programs did, however, enable CCC to unburden itself of stocks that had earlier been a matter of much concern. On some of them, the Corporation was able to make substantial profits to offset losses incurred in the price-support operations themselves.

CCC IN THE WAR YEARS

The wartime activities of the Commodity Credit Corporation are not important as a means of throwing light on its current and future place in the farm program though some of its largest financial transactions were carried out during those years. More important from the long-run standpoint were the legislative commitments made in that period and continued thereafter. The principal activities relating specifically to the prosecution of the war itself were the procurement of supplies for lend-lease and other export programs and the administration of part of the food subsidy program. Procurement at first was handled by the Surplus Marketing Administration, with a revolving fund set up by CCC. Later, it was handled directly by CCC. The Corporation purchased large amounts of sugar, wool, fats and oils, and rubber, and also served as the procurement agency for handling huge quantities of foodstuffs in connection with lend-lease, military and price control activities. Trading operations conducted by CCC, to June 30, 1945, included more than 300 separate programs and a volume of commodities having a disposal value of more than $11 billion. These operations reached a peak of $2,618 million in 1945 when the volume of purchases averaged more than $7 million a day. The Corporation made a profit of about $200 million on them.[24]

This type of activity has been continued in the postwar years but on a much smaller scale. The principal duties in recent years have been: (1) procurement for other government agencies such as the Foreign Operations Administration, (2) procurement for foreign governments, and (3) procurement for international relief organizations. An act of July 16, 1943 (57 *Stat.* 566) required that, in operations of this kind,

24. Comptroller General of the United States, *Audit Report on the Examination of Commodity Credit Corporation,* House Doc. 148, 81st Cong., 1st sess., 1949, pp. 12–13. Most of this profit and some of the offsetting losses are, in considerable measure, purely of a bookkeeping nature. Some $122 million of gain was attributed to cotton and $152 million to the General Commodities Purchase Program. Losses of $25.5 million were incurred on wool. The gains from the General Commodities Purchase operation resulted mainly from sales to other agencies of government, principally the Lend-Lease Administration. A small part of the gain on cotton, which resulted from the price advance during the war years, was distributed to the growers as additional payments. Losses, such as those on wheat and wool, were absorbed by the Corporation. For a more detailed analysis, see *ibid.,* pp. 13–15.

the agency for which the work was done must reimburse CCC for the services performed, losses sustained and operating costs. Though the costs of the foreign-aid and other export programs have been borne by other agencies, they have at times served a dual purpose, furnishing supplies to allied nations and at the same time disposing of surpluses held by CCC. In the period from June 30, 1941 to July 1, 1953, the gain to CCC through operating the supply program was about $305 million.

In addition, CCC operated a foreign-purchase program which was initiated for the purpose of protecting Latin American countries from economic disaster and obtaining strategic commodities needed in the United States. The principal activities were: (1) the acquisition and sale of foreign agricultural commodities that had been frozen in the United States by the War Production Board shortly after our entry into the war, (2) purchase of commodities from friendly nations to help offset their losses of export markets and the procurement of materials in short supply in the United States, (3) entering into agreements with individuals in other countries for procurement of commodities needed for war purposes, and (4) the importation of strategic commodities under delegation from the Board of Economic Warfare, that is, preclusive buying to keep them from falling into enemy hands.[25]

On October 6, 1943, the President transferred the work of procuring and developing food, food machinery and food facilities in foreign countries to the Foreign Economic Administration (by Executive Order No. 9385).[26] CCC continued to handle procurement of food in Canada and sugar in the Caribbean area because of the close relationship of these activities to the domestic food programs.[27]

Food Subsidy Program Shared with RFC

A food subsidy program was put into effect in fiscal 1943. The Secretary of Agriculture had announced production goals and price supports to encourage production of certain scarce agricultural commodities. Since few of these were subject to effective price ceilings under the laws then in effect, the President authorized the use of CCC funds to buy agricultural commodities for resale at a possible loss. This subsidy program consisted mainly of three types of action: (1) payments to processors to enable them to increase or maintain the prices paid to producers, (2) direct payments to farmers to help offset increased production costs, and (3)

25. U.S. Department of Agriculture, Commodity Credit Corporation, *Annual Report, 1942*, p. 7.

26. These responsibilities were returned to CCC in September 1945 (Executive Order No. 9630).

27. Procurement in Canada consisted partly of the purchase of wheat for use in feeding livestock in the United States. The sugar purchases, mainly from Cuba, were closely interrelated with the domestic sugar program. (See *The Agricultural Commodity Programs,* Chapter 7.)

sale of feed and fodder purchased or supplied from CCC-owned stocks at reduced prices.[28]

The most extensive subsidy carried out by means of CCC funds and facilities was that designed to maintain the production of fluid milk without increasing OPA ceiling prices. This involved expenditures of more than a billion dollars. Payments were made to producers on the basis of milk and butterfat produced. In addition, CCC lost nearly a quarter of a billion dollars on the sale of wheat at corn prices (by direction of the Congress). This action was taken to increase livestock and poultry production.[29]

Other activities included: the making of loans to cotton growers; price supports and equalization payments to maintain the production of vegetable oils, and of high-protein meal and cake for livestock feeding; purchase and sale of the 1943 and 1944 wool clips to maintain production and income in the wool industry; purchase of the Caribbean sugar crop to prevent a rise in prices to consumers; price support and equalization payments to stimulate production and processing of canning crops; and the purchase of flue-cured tobacco for lend-lease and sales abroad to maintain markets for American leaf.[30]

Increase of Price-Support Levels

The efforts to stimulate production in the war years plus the strong bargaining position of agriculture set the stage for the postwar problems that have grown out of the high levels of support established in that period. In May 1941 the Congress passed an act (55 *Stat.* 203) directing CCC to make loans to cooperators in the 1941 programs for rice, tobacco, cotton, corn and wheat at 85 per cent of parity.[31] This was partly a result of the lend-lease commitment that had been assumed in the preceding March, partly a recognition of the strengthening demand for farm products, and partly a means of aiding growers of export crops whose foreign outlets had been sharply curtailed.

At that time, shortages were not in prospect. Stocks of wheat, cotton and corn were so large as to be considered an embarrassment rather than an asset. CCC had purchased or had loan commitments on two thirds of

28. For a more general description of the wartime food-subsidy and price-support programs, see M. R. Benedict, *Farm Policies of the United States, 1790–1950,* Twentieth Century Fund, New York, 1953, Chapter 16, and refer to *The Agricultural Commodity Programs.* See also U.S. Production and Marketing Administration, *Subsidy Programs,* 1947.

29. It also served to reduce significantly the heavy stocks of wheat owned by CCC at the time the United States entered the war. During 1942, 1943, 1944 and 1945, about 1.4 billion bushels of wheat went to feed use as compared to a customary use for such purposes of a little more than 100 million bushels per year. In the preceding four years, about 465 million bushels had been so used (*Agricultural Statistics, 1952,* p. 15). About 265 million bushels also went into industrial uses in the period 1942 to 1945, mainly for the production of alcohol.

30. Commodity Credit Corporation, *Annual Report, 1944,* p. 3.

31. Peanuts were later added to the list (55 *Stat.* 860).

the 1940 raisin crop, half of the prunes, a third of the flue-cured tobacco, a quarter of the cotton and a third of the wheat crop.

The significance of war demand in furthering the tendency to raise support levels became more apparent during the summer of 1941. The country was by then in the "defense period." The United States was not yet a belligerent but the danger of involvement in the war was apparent and war preparations were gaining headway, as a means both of strengthening the United States and of supplying aid to Britain, France and Russia. The Secretary of Agriculture was beginning to urge expansion of production in some lines and farm prices were rising.

The bill extending the life of the Commodity Credit Corporation which included the rider known as the Steagall Amendment required the Secretary of Agriculture to support at 85 per cent of parity the prices of all nonbasic commodities for which he had requested increases in production. (See pp. 261–63.)

The Steagall Amendment, with its later modifications, came to constitute the main governmental price-support commitment for many of the perishable and minor products not covered in the Price Support Act of May 1941, which applied only to the "basic" crops. Those for which support was provided under the Steagall Amendment came to be commonly referred to as the "Steagall commodities." So far as wartime guarantees are concerned, they were treated in much the same way as the major storable crops. In the postwar years, important differences in the treatment of the two groups have been made, partly because of the perishability of some of the Steagall crops, and partly because of differences in the marketing problem encountered, or in the relative political strengths of the grower groups concerned.

Further Increases in 1942

As a result of the struggle over price controls on farm products which developed in 1942, a compromise act known as the Stabilization Act of October 1942 was passed. The Emergency Price Control Act of January 1942 had forbidden the placing of price ceilings on farm products at less than 110 per cent of parity (or alternative levels that might be higher). Because of the threat posed to the over-all price stabilization program, the President insisted that the Office of Price Administration be permitted to establish price ceilings at parity. The Congress refused to yield and it was only after agreement was reached on raising the support levels and extending them for two years after the close of hostilities that the new Stabilization Act was passed. This authorized the imposition of price ceilings on farm products at parity and at the same time raised the support levels for both the basic and the Steagall commodities to 90 per cent of parity.[32]

32. In 1944, the support level on cotton was raised to 92.5 per cent of parity (for cotton harvested after December 31, 1943—58 *Stat.* 632, 643, June 30, 1944). It was

These guarantees were to continue for two years after the war as a means of preventing a disastrous break in farm prices such as that which followed World War I and also as an encouragement for all-out production during the war years. It was this provision, renewed from time to time in the postwar years, which established the high-level support program now in effect.[33]

CCC at War's End

By the end of the war, CCC was in relatively good shape. The carry-overs of wheat and corn had been reduced to levels that were, if anything, lower than desirable, in view of the heavy requirements that were shaping up. The United States wheat carry-over as of July 1, 1945 was only 279 million bushels. It was to decline to dangerously low levels in the two succeeding years (1946, 100 million bushels; 1947, 84 million), in spite of crops that were running well above a billion bushels per year.

The corn carry-over was down to 172 million bushels by October 1, 1946. The supply was soon to become seriously deficient as a result of the short crop of 1947. Only in cotton was there any continuing problem. Stocks were still almost at peak levels but were soon to be reduced by heavy shipments to western Europe. Although the unusually generous arrangements to be provided in 1947 under the Marshall Plan could not then be foreseen, it was evident that exports would increase as soon as the war-devastated nations could obtain funds with which to make purchases.

The working capital of the Corporation had been restored by heavy transfers to cover expenditures under the war programs and it was still serving as a procurement agency at substantial profit to itself. In the sugar operations, CCC could acquire title to sugar in Cuba and thus could bring it in without payment of duty. Though Cuban prices were strengthening, this added operating margin made possible a relatively stable price to United States consumers.[34]

---

later raised to 95 per cent (for cotton harvested after December 31, 1943 and planted before January 1, 1945—58 *Stat.* 765, 784).

33. For a fuller account of this controversy between the President and the Congress and the steps that led to the compromise, see Benedict, *op. cit.*, pp. 408–17. For some commodities, the establishment of ceiling prices at parity still permitted price increases of more than 100 per cent over those of 1939.

During this and the immediately following period, CCC became to some extent a political football in the struggle between the President and the Congress. Both the food subsidy and the incentive payment programs were unpopular in the Congress. Since CCC was one of the agencies used in implementing them, the renewal of its charter was at times in doubt as a result of either the failure of Congress to act or the possibility of a presidential veto. See *ibid.*, pp. 418–30.

34. This was, in effect, an additional Treasury subsidy not shown in the over-all figures on food subsidies. The Treasury was foregoing the customs receipts on sugar so purchased and thus was making a contribution which does not appear as a fund transfer. This does not imply that the procedure followed was undesirable. U.S. consumers profited from the bulk-buying operations. See *The Agricultural Commodity Programs*, Chapter 7. The Comptroller General estimated the savings thus made, to June 1945, at $150.4 mil-

In the years 1940 and 1942, CCC had made repayments to the Treasury amounting to about $71.6 million. The payments were made possible by the sharp increase in prices, which enabled CCC to recover more than it had invested in some of the stocks sold. A small capital restoration payment was made from the Treasury in 1941 ($1.6 million). From 1943 to 1946, heavy Treasury payments were made to the Corporation to offset losses incurred on the food subsidy and other war programs. These, for the four years, amounted to about $1.8 billion. Capital restorations of more than $200 million had been made in 1938 and 1939 in connection with price-support operations in the prewar years. See Table 34 for capital restorations and payments to the Treasury in the years 1938 through 1946.

TABLE 34

RESTORATIONS OF CAPITAL OF CCC AND REPAYMENTS TO
THE TREASURY, 1938–1946

Date of Appraisal	Restorations of Capital	Repayments to Treasury
Total	$2,035,576,290.97	$71,572,244.69
March 31, 1938	94,285,404.73	—
March 31, 1939	119,599,918.05	—
March 31, 1940	—	43,756,731.01
March 31, 1941	1,637,445.51	—
March 31, 1942	—	27,815,513.68
March 31, 1943	39,436,884.93	—
March 31, 1944	217,327,996.11	—
June 30, 1945	921,456,561.00	—
June 30, 1946	641,832,080.64	—

Source: U.S. Commodity Credit Corporation, Report of Financial Condition, February 28, 1954, p. 9.

The financial record shown in Table 34 for the period 1938–46 does not, of course, give any clear view of the results of CCC operations as a price-support mechanism. Prospective losses on the heavy stocks carried into the war period did not have to be taken, because of the war-induced increase in prices. Some commodities were transferred to lend-lease and other agencies at prices above those that would otherwise have been obtained. Profits were made on some of the trading and service operations. Though such profits may have been larger than necessary, it does not follow that so huge and complex an operation could well have been handled exactly at cost. Such gains as were made were in effect, however, largely transfers of additional capital to CCC from other government agencies.

---

lion, stating that they "either increased program gains or reduced program losses correspondingly, and likewise decreased the Corporation's borrowing requirements from the Treasury." Audit Report on the Examination of Commodity Credit Corporation, p. 20.

The operations from 1949 on give a better indication of the problems that arise under nonwar conditions but even here account must be taken of factors that are not likely to be present in more normal and longer-term operations. Among them are the huge governmentally financed foreign-aid programs and the opportunities afforded CCC to dispose of some of its holdings through abnormal channels.

PROBLEMS OF THE POSTWAR YEARS

In the years following the war, CCC did not encounter major difficulties until near the end of the decade. Most prices were above support levels and stocks of most commodities were below desired levels rather than above, partly as a result of the foreign-aid programs, but more importantly because of the high level of domestic buying power and employment.

Fortunately, the good yields of the war years continued and United States agriculture was able to meet the heavy demands made on it for relief shipments and domestic consumption. If crops had been short during the war years, as they had been in World War I, it would have been found that reserves of wheat and feed grains had been reduced too rapidly and a serious pinch would have developed. Wheat production continued at well above the billion bushel level until 1951, and even in that year was nearly up to the billion bushel mark.[35] Corn production, also, continued high, except for the year 1947, when it was more than 800 million bushels below the high level of 1946. Demand for grains was so strong, however, that prices moved up rapidly in spite of these large increments of supply. The domestic demand for meat animals was even more insistent. Farm products as a group led off in the inflationary upsurge of prices that followed the war. Most of the major products were at levels that provided little reason for resort to price-support loans and hence created no serious problem for the Commodity Credit Corporation.[36]

Principal Problems in Cotton and Wool

The principal problems were in cotton and wool, where heavy carry-overs, largely financed by CCC, were still in existence. However, the postwar foreign demand, partly financed by the United States, and the high level of domestic consumption led to unexpectedly rapid liquidation

35. Until 1944, there had not been an outturn of that size since 1915 when the first billion bushel crop was harvested.

36. By 1947, food grains were at 270 per cent of the 1910–14 level, oil-bearing crops at 363 per cent and meat animals at 329 per cent, whereas the all-commodities index of wholesale prices stood only at 222 (*Agricultural Statistics, 1952*, pp. 682–83). Fruits were low at 174 but all other groups except feed grains and hay were well above the level of prices generally. The general parity ratio between the prices of farm products and those of things bought by farmers stood at 109 in 1945, 113 in 1946, 115 in 1947 and 110 in 1948.

of these carry-overs and to sales of CCC-owned cotton at prices that netted a profit. The heavy world stocks of wool were also worked down at a surprisingly rapid rate.

Total United States carry-overs of cotton had remained above 10.5 million bales from 1938 to 1945 and stood at 11.2 million bales at the beginning of the 1945 season. This was from two to three times the amounts customarily held over in the 1920s, when there was no direct government intervention in the marketing process. Of this, CCC owned about 3.8 million bales as of June 30, 1945, and was financing 1.2 million bales, making a total of nearly 5 million bales, or close to half of the total amount carried over. By the end of June 1946, CCC holdings had been reduced to 1.36 million bales and the problem was largely solved for the time being.[37]

At the end of June 1947, the United States carry-over was only 2.5 million bales and the CCC operation as a whole showed a substantial profit. This was due almost wholly to the fact that much of the CCC-held cotton had been acquired as early as 1938 and had benefited from the wartime rise in prices. The price of cotton rose from an index of 74 in 1939 (1910–14 = 100) to 237 in 1946 and to 272 in 1947.[38]

For some few commodities there were difficult problems of adjustment. Dried fruits and some other specialty crops had not been able to recover their prewar markets abroad. The dried egg and dried milk industries had been overexpanded during the war period, in terms of peacetime needs. The citrus industry was in difficulty because of shrinking foreign outlets and overproduction. However, the over-all level of farm prices ranged from 110 to 115 per cent of parity and did not decline to 100 until 1949. Consequently, even a 90 per cent of parity level of support was largely inoperative. Most prices would have been about what they were regardless of whether there was any provision for supporting the market.[39]

Supply Operations Taper Off

The other activities of CCC in this period were mainly of a more general character and not classed as price-support operations. The food subsidies were largely wound up by the end of 1946. The operations in sugar and wool, which were still dominated by war influences, are described in Chapters 7 and 8 of *The Agricultural Commodity Programs* and hence are not discussed here. Procurement for lend-lease was ter-

37. Comptroller General of the United States, *Report on the Audit of Commodity Credit Corporation and Its Affiliate, War Hemp Industries, Inc.*, House Doc. No. 632, 81st Cong., 2d sess., 1950, exhibits on pp. 31–32.
38. *Agricultural Statistics, 1952*, p. 682.
39. The all-commodities index stood at 241 in 1948 (1910–14 = 100), a figure that still was inflated as a result of shortages of some commodities such as consumer durables. All farm commodity groups except fruits, truck crops and poultry and eggs were above this level. Livestock and livestock products were up to 314. The all-commodities index dropped to 226 in 1949. *Agricultural Statistics, 1952*, pp. 682–83.

minated but to some extent was replaced for a time by similar purchases made for the United Nations Relief and Rehabilitation Agency (UNRRA). Exports, for the most part, shifted back to regular commercial channels. Though CCC activities continued at a high level in 1947, the major portion of the business transacted was in the procurement of commodities for the foreign-aid programs, for other governments and for the various United States agencies.

Some minor crop price-support programs were carried out in 1947 and 1948, most of them at losses not large enough to cause any serious difficulty so far as CCC was concerned. The realized net loss on price-support operations in fiscal 1947, as reported by the Corporation, was $71.9 million and for 1948, $125.4 million. The principal losses in 1948 were on eggs ($25.8 million), potatoes ($47.4 million), prunes and raisins ($15.5 million), sugar ($11.9 million) and wool ($19.5 million).[40]

CCC Given Permanent Charter in 1948

Throughout the period from 1933 to 1948, the Commodity Credit Corporation had the status of a temporary, emergency-type agency. The charter granted in 1935 was renewed from time to time but only for short periods. At times, the opposition to such renewals was vigorous. The Government Corporation Control Act (59 Stat. 597), passed at the close of the war, brought all government corporations under closer control and required that wholly owned government corporations must be chartered by the Congress. They were not to be permitted to operate under state charters after June 30, 1948. The act also required that such corporations submit an annual budget and that a commercial-type audit of their books be made by the Government Accounting Office. (This latter provision was already in effect for CCC.)

As a consequence, the Congress was under the necessity of rechartering CCC if it was to continue as an agency of the United States. The new charter act (62 Stat. 1070), passed on June 29, 1948, authorized the Corporation to:

(1) support the prices of agricultural commodities through loans, purchases, payments, and other operations;
(2) make available materials and facilities required in connection with the production and marketing of agricultural commodities;
(3) procure agricultural commodities for sale to other government agencies, foreign governments, and domestic, foreign, or international relief or rehabilitation agencies, and to meet domestic requirements;
(4) remove and dispose of or aid in the removal or disposition of surplus agricultural commodities;
(5) increase the domestic consumption of agricultural commodities by expanding or aiding in the expansion of domestic markets or by develop-

40. Data supplied by the Commodity Credit Corporation.

ing or aiding in the development of new and additional markets, marketing facilities, and uses for such commodities;

(6) export or cause to be exported, or aid in the development of foreign markets for, agricultural commodities;

(7) carry out such other operations as the Congress may specifically authorize or provide for.

The charter also required that the Corporation use to the fullest extent practicable the usual and customary channels, facilities and arrangements of trade in its purchasing, selling, transporting, handling and warehousing operations. It was not to acquire any real property except office space and that already leased when the act was passed.

CCC's capitalization remained at $100 million and it was to pay interest on the capital, and on obligations purchased by the Treasury, at a rate to be set by the Secretary of the Treasury. At that time, its borrowing power was limited to $4,750 million; the limit has since been raised from time to time, reaching a level of $10 billion in August 1954. Management was put in the hands of a five-man board, one member to be the Secretary of Agriculture or his nominee. The other four were to be appointed by the President but only three could be employees of the federal government.

Further Changes Made in 1949

Several of the provisions included in the Charter Act of 1948 were changed shortly after the shift in party control that occurred in 1949 (through the act of June 7, 1949—63 *Stat.* 154). Instead of being managed by an independent board as contemplated in the original act, the Corporation was to be under the immediate supervision of the Secretary of Agriculture. The board of directors, which was increased to seven members, was to be subject to his general supervision and direction. Instead of being an ex-officio member of the board, the Secretary was now to be its chairman. Also, the power to appoint officers and personnel was shifted from the board to the Secretary.

A new Advisory Board, to perform some of the functions of the old board, was created. This consists of five members and is to reflect "broad agricultural and business experience in its membership." The board is appointed by the President and not more than three of its members may be of the same party. Meetings are on call of the Secretary of Agriculture but must be held not less often than once every 90 days.

The restrictions on ownership of storage facilities were also relaxed. In the fall of 1948, large crops caused a severe shortage of storage facilities. As a consequence, the prohibition against acquisition of real property was eliminated and CCC was authorized to acquire such property, or an interest in it, as a means of providing storage for carrying out its own programs. However, before doing so, it must determine that privately owned storage in the area concerned is not adequate. Refrigerated storage cannot be constructed except with funds specifically provided by Congress. In addition to its own purchase and lease program, the Corporation was directed to make loans to grain growers in need of storage facilities.[41] The other principal change was the inclusion of a section authorizing CCC to barter agricultural commodities for critical and strategic materials produced abroad.

Other Acts Relating to CCC Operations

Some other provisions made both before and after passage of the permanent charter act affected CCC operations in one way or another. In 1946, the First Supplemental Rescission Act (60 *Stat.* 6, 8—passed on February 18) provided a $500 million reserve for postwar price-support operations. Losses incurred in 1947, 1948 and 1949 were charged against this reserve.[42] By 1950, it had been entirely used up.

The Foreign Aid Act of 1947 (61 *Stat.* 934) authorized disposal of CCC-owned stocks for assistance and relief to foreign countries at prices that would be equivalent to the domestic market price of a quantity of wheat having the same caloric value. This permitted the Corporation to subsidize sales of some of the more expensive commodities, such as dried eggs and dried fruits, without coming into conflict with the general pro-

---

41. As a result of this change, CCC has developed an extensive storage facilities program. It purchases and maintains granaries and equipment for care and storage of grain it owns or controls; makes loans to producers, or guarantees loans for construction, expansion or equipment of farm storage facilities; guarantees the occupancy of new commercial storage in order to encourage construction or expansion of commercial storage facilities; and undertakes such other operations as may be necessary to provide storage adequate for carrying out effectively the CCC programs undertaken. See Commodity Credit Corporation, *Annual Report, 1950*, p. 9. Loans on farm storage structures could be as high as 85 per cent of the cost and could run for five years. This loan limit was reduced to 80 per cent in 1951. The interest rate was put at 4 per cent. Equipment loans were limited to 75 per cent of cost, the other terms being similar to those above.

Section 417 of the Agricultural Act of 1949 permitted the banks for cooperatives to loan up to 80 per cent of the cost of new facilities built, provided the borrowing cooperatives had received guarantees that CCC would lease them. The guarantees, as specified by the statute, assured rentals on 75 per cent of the capacity of new facilities for three years and on additions to old facilities for two years. As of June 30, 1953, CCC owned storage facilities having a capacity of 543 million bushels and had $42 million in loans and commitments on farm storage, which had a capacity of 147 million bushels. Guarantee and occupancy agreements covered an additional 26 million bushels of capacity. Administrative expenses for the storage program were running at a rate of about $1 million per year as compared to $14 million for the price-support programs. Total storage cost was much higher. Storage cost as a whole was reported in February 1954 to be in the order of $500,000 per day. See testimony of Department of Agriculture officials before the House Committee on Banking and Currency, *Increase Borrowing Power of Commodity Credit Corporation*, Hearings on H.R. 7339, 83d Cong., 2d sess., February 25–26, 1954, p. 51.

42. This was essentially an additional restoration of capital. The losses thus charged off were: for 1947, $59,950,695.59; for 1948, $10,294,307.81; and for 1949, $429,754,996.60.

visions requiring that commodities be sold at prices that would cover fully the amounts invested in them.[43]

A section of the Foreign Assistance Act of 1948 (62 *Stat.* 137, 148) also provided an outlet for some of the commodities held by CCC. Under this legislation, CCC could sell surplus commodities for foreign relief at cost or at the domestic price, whichever was lower. The Secretary of Agriculture was authorized to pay up to 50 per cent of the cost of such operations, out of Section 32 funds. For sales made pursuant to the provisions of this act, CCC received in the fiscal years 1948 and 1949, $62,309,000 from other government agencies and $23,006,000 from Section 32 funds.[44]

The opportunities for diversion of excess stocks were also increased somewhat by the provisions of Section 416 of the Agricultural Act of 1949, which authorized donations to other federal agencies of commodities in danger of loss through spoilage or deterioration.[45] Some liquidation of stocks was also accomplished by sales made under the International Wheat Agreement. Exporters of wheat and flour covered by the Agreement receive export payments amounting to the difference between the current domestic price and the price received under the Wheat Agreement. Congress reimburses CCC at the end of the year, not only for these payments but for losses sustained on any contributions from its own stocks to shipments made under the Agreement.

Reluctance to Abandon Wartime Levels of Support

The unexpectedly favorable price situation of the postwar years, and the fact that the price-support program had not as yet run into any major difficulties, led to an increasing tendency to favor the retention of wartime support levels as a guarantee of continuing prosperity in agriculture. The wartime legislation was presumably based on the expectation of a return to relatively free market conditions once the danger of a severe postwar break in prices was past. If no new legislation had been passed, the provisions of the Agricultural Adjustment Act of 1938, as amended in 1948, would have come into effect from June 30, 1950 on. The support levels originally provided in the 1938 act, though high enough to cause some excessive accumulation of stocks in the late 1930s, almost certainly would not have caused much difficulty in the highly receptive market of the late 1940s.

In fact, a transition to a relatively free market for farm products could have been made in 1948 with almost no jolt whatever. Farmers were

43. Losses under this authorization were limited to $57 million and were actually $56,239,000, divided as follows: on eggs, $24,245,000; on Irish potatoes, $13,806,000; on dried fruits, $15,581,000; on grapefruit juice, $1,732,000; and on honey, $875,000.

44. The use of Section 32 funds to aid in financing foreign-aid programs was prohibited in the Mutual Security Appropriations Act of 1953.

45. For details see Chapter 8.

operating in what was, for the most part, a wholly free market and prices were well above the levels of support provided even in the wartime legislation. At the same time, the safeguards set up in the 1938 act would have cushioned any severe decline and the quota and allotment provisions available would have made possible some measure of planned readjustment if prices dropped seriously.

However, the Congress and many farm leaders still were apprehensive about the possibility of a return to the depressed conditions of the 1930s. Many nonfarm groups were also expecting serious dislocation and much unemployment in the early postwar years. Anti-depression farm legislation based on the troubles of the 1930s was under consideration almost continuously from 1944 on. The outcome was the passage of the Agricultural Act of 1948, an act based largely on that of 1938, which was the most carefully drawn body of agricultural legislation passed up to that time. The main body of the 1948 act provided flexible supports, presumably on a continuing basis. That is, the prices supported would be relatively high if supplies were normal or below normal, and lower if surpluses were developing. However, they could not be less than 60 per cent of parity unless farmers rejected control measures. Actually, they were unlikely to be as low as 60 per cent since the minimum support level was to be 72 per cent of parity if quotas or acreage restrictions were in effect. With prospective supplies large enough to result in a minimum level of support, marketing and/or acreage restrictions would almost certainly be put into effect unless voted down by the growers.

Wartime Support Levels Retained

This carefully worked out approach to the problem was largely nullified as a result of differences between the House and Senate groups working on the legislation. The effective date of Title II, which contained the flexible support provision, was deferred until June 30, 1950, and the wartime levels of support for basic commodities, that is, 90 per cent of parity, were continued through 1949 and early 1950. The 1949 act, passed by the succeeding Congress, changed the definition and application of the parity formula in such a way as to raise to some extent the level of prices that would be defined as 90 per cent of parity.[46]

From 1949 on, the Congress acted from time to time to continue in effect the 90 per cent support of prices of the basic commodities, thereby contributing to the storage-stock problem which has developed in the years since. For the perishable commodities and many of the specialty crops, modifications have been introduced which have eased the problems of CCC and the Department of Agriculture to some extent.

46. The 1949 act also contained a flexible provision but in a form which called for higher levels of support than those provided in Title II of the act of 1948. For details see Chapter 7; also Benedict, *op. cit.*, Chapter 18.

Trouble Spots Show Up in 1948, 1949 and 1950

The relatively easy situation in respect to price supports that had marked the first postwar years began to taper off in 1948. The first major difficulty arose in respect to potatoes, a highly perishable Steagall commodity which was under mandatory 90 per cent of parity support until December 31, 1948. During the war years, the principal concern had been to assure adequate supplies. Greatly increased yields from a reduced acreage led to a heavy excess of production in 1946, and CCC took over about 10 per cent of the crop with a net loss of about $63 million. Acreage and production were reduced in 1947, but CCC again found it necessary to purchase about 8 per cent of the crop at a cost of $47 million. The 1948 crop was again large and the loss incurred by CCC amounted to more than $200 million.

The Agricultural Acts of 1948 and 1949 permitted a reduction in support levels to 60 per cent of parity. However, yields continued high and losses were incurred on the 1949 and 1950 crops. By 1951, public opposition to the program had become so strong that the Congress took action to discontinue price supports on potatoes unless marketing quotas were in effect. Since there was no legislation authorizing marketing quotas for potatoes, this ended the effort to support potato prices directly at a specified percentage of parity. Conservation payments and diversionary and relief payments financed with Section 32 funds still could be made, but these were on a relatively small scale.

The potato programs, through fiscal 1953, had cost more than $600 million, including CCC losses of $478 million, expenditures of $132 million from Section 32 funds and conservation payments of $26 million. Public indignation was widespread and there was little support in Congress for continuance of the program. It had been fully demonstrated that for a crop of this kind, which could not be stored or exported and for which domestic demand was very inelastic, prices could not be supported practically in this way. Production had proved very responsive to high support prices and had surged up at a wholly unexpected rate. Large quantities were destroyed or used as livestock feed, and prices to consumers remained high while quality deteriorated.

Similar problems were beginning to arise in respect to some of the storables, but here the facing of the issue could be deferred through accumulation of stocks, and time could be afforded for devising ways to meet it. Storable and transportable commodities might perhaps be exported and more effective production adjustment programs could be put into effect. Nevertheless, accumulations of large size cannot be readily disposed of without serious danger to the price structure or huge expenditures for give-away programs of one kind or another.

CCC Commitments High in 1949–50

CCC commitments began to increase sharply in 1948. In the first quarter of 1949, loans outstanding, mainly on cotton, wheat and corn, approximated $1,750 million. Much of this collateral was acquired by CCC as the loans fell due and were not repaid. By the first quarter of 1950, CCC held, or had loan and purchase commitments on, more than $4 billion worth of farm commodities.[47] The problem of burdensome accumulations which had plagued the Farm Board in 1932 and CCC in the late 1930s was now shaping up in such a way as to constitute a serious threat to the price-support program as a whole.

Similar commitments and acquisitions in the Farm Board period had never exceeded $500 million. Yet the size of these commitments and the discontinuance of the program gave impetus to the severe price decline that occurred in 1932 when the Farm Board withdrew from the market. The loan and purchase commitments of 1950 were more than eight times as large and seemed likely to go even higher. This difference was partly due to the higher levels of prices prevailing in the late 1940s. Since the prices of farm products were more than twice those prevailing when the Farm Board commitments were being made, the comparative level of obligation can be more reasonably put (in 1932 dollars) at some four times that of the 1930–32 period.[48]

Farm prices were sagging in 1949 and the delayed postwar adjustment appeared to be getting under way, though there still was some abnormal support for the export markets as a result of the foreign-aid programs and the International Wheat Agreement which came into effect in August 1949. However, wheat exports, plus military procurement, had dropped off from 510 million bushels in 1948 to 303 million in 1949.[49] Cotton exports were higher in 1948 and 1949 than in any year since 1939 but the carry-over was increasing. The cotton carry-over had been reduced from 11.2 million bales at the beginning of the 1945 season (nearly up to the all-time high of 13 million bales held in 1939) to 2.5 million bales in 1947. It was back up to 6.8 million bales as of the beginning of the 1950 season.[50]

There was clear indication that sales must be increased and production cut back or CCC would be faced with an impossibly cumbersome volume of stored commodities and sooner or later might have to discontinue loans and purchases much as the Farm Board had been forced to do in 1932. The Congress postponed this dilemma for the time being by

47 U.S. Department of Agriculture, *Commodity Credit Corporation Charts,* November 1953, Tables 4 and 7.
48. As of November 30, 1941, the Corporation's commitments in the form of loans, commodities owned, and loan and purchase guarantees had been $1.4 billion, this likewise being in relation to a much lower level of prices than that prevailing in 1949.
49. *Agricultural Statistics, 1952,* p. 15.
50. *Ibid.,* p. 81.

increasing CCC's borrowing power to $6,750 million. This was only a reprieve, however, since the accumulation of stocks, if continued for very long, would eventually have brought them to such levels that they could not have been stored, preserved or financed.[51]

Korean War Relieves the Situation

The situation was again relieved in a quite unexpected way. The outbreak of war in Korea set off a new wave of defense buying and a new inflationary upsurge in prices. CCC stocks and commitments were greatly reduced and by the middle of 1952 were down to levels which, though still large, seemed not to be unmanageable. Stocks amounted to just over a billion dollars and these together with other commitments reached a low in the second quarter of 1952 at about $1.5 billion.

The cotton inventory had been reduced sharply by the imposition of acreage allotments on the 1950 crop and a smaller yield on this reduced acreage. This action, as things turned out, was taken prematurely. United States cotton inventories, though seemingly large, were not adequate to offset both the increased demand and the reduced output.[52] Rationing of cotton to United States mills had to be resorted to and embargoes had to be placed on exports. As a result, cotton prices went to all-time highs. In some foreign markets, the price of cotton rose to over 90 cents a pound, more than twice the high price prevailing in the United States.

In the following year, acreage was greatly expanded and a new surplus problem was in the making. At the same time, the longer-term hold of the United States on foreign markets may very possibly have been weakened because it was unable to supply customers who, in the past, always had been able to depend on it as a source of supply. These developments were, of course, due in part to the unexpectedly strong demand which grew out of the Korean war. However, they point up the need for the maintenance of relatively large stocks of the major storable commodities in times when world conditions are very unstable, though not such large ones as have since come into being.

Re-emergence of the Surplus Problem in 1953 and 1954

Continuing high production and the easing off of war demand brought the problem of excessive carry-overs and heavy CCC commitments sharply to the fore in 1953 and 1954. Total loans and investments by CCC were estimated at more than $6 billion as of early February 1954, and were expected to go higher by the end of the crop year. The Secretary of Agriculture therefore requested and obtained an increase in the

---

51. In the meantime, farm prices had receded from an index of 285 (1910–14 = 100) to 249, which meant that heavy losses were almost certain to be incurred on the stocks held. *Ibid.*, p. 682.

52. Production declined from 16 million bales in 1949 to only 10 million in 1950.

borrowing power of CCC, to $8.5 billion, for meeting the legislatively established price guarantees on the 1953 and 1954 crops. This was not regarded as an amount sufficient to meet requirements for the 1955 crop.[53] To meet expected later demands on it, the Corporation's borrowing power was further increased, to $10 billion in August 1954.

The principal operations are in cotton, wheat, corn and butter. The year-end carry-over of wheat in the summer of 1954 amounted to 900 million bushels, which was more than a year's supply. The 9.4 million bale cotton carry-over was nearly double that of the preceding year and much larger than that of any year from 1945 on. The October 1 corn carry-over was at an all-time high of 918 million bushels and CCC was holding 506 million pounds of butter, 463 million pounds of cheese and 283 million pounds of dried milk.

Butter a Special Case

The heavy accumulation of butter in CCC stocks has presented a particularly serious problem. Here, the industry has been very severely affected by a major technological change. Butter is being replaced on an ever-increasing scale by the much cheaper margarines, and the public is rapidly accustoming itself to the use of margarine in place of butter. The Agricultural Act of 1949 required that the price of butter be supported at from 75 to 90 per cent of parity. As a result of very heavy pressure from the dairy interests, the Secretary of Agriculture supported the price of butter, until April 1, 1954, at 90 per cent of parity. Huge stocks of this semiperishable product have been accumulated by the government and there seems little prospect that a market will be found for them at any price that will come near to covering the CCC investment. In the meantime, very heavy costs for storage are being incurred and there is serious danger of deterioration in the quality of the stocks held.

The support price was reduced to 75 per cent of parity on April 1, 1954, but this still is so far above the price of margarine that there appears to be little prospect of checking the flow of butter into government hands or of reducing government stocks, except through sales at prices that will involve very heavy losses to CCC. Possibly even more serious is the fact that butter is being priced out of the market and margarine is taking its place in millions of American homes. As yet, no seemingly workable solution for this difficult problem has been put forward. Butter could, of course, be moved by eliminating price supports entirely and letting it seek its own level in a free market. This, however, implies such a drastic reduction in price as to be ruinous to those parts

53. See testimony of Secretary Benson, House Committee on Banking and Currency, *Increase Borrowing Power of Commodity Credit Corporation*, Hearings on H.R. 7339, 83d Cong., 2d sess., 1954, pp. 2–9.

of the dairy industry that are primarily dependent on butter as a source of income.

As of January 6, 1954, CCC commitments on butter covered 261 million pounds and amounted to $175 million. (Heavy sales to the government just before the April 1 reduction in support levels increased those holdings to 364 million pounds as of March 31, 1954.) CCC also had taken over, or was obligated to take over, 257 million pounds of cheese and 440 million pounds of dried milk. These involved an additional $177 million. Other heavy commitments, aside from those on cotton, cottonseed oil, wheat and corn, were for hay and pasture seeds ($37 million), linseed oil ($80 million), and wool ($64 million).[54]

Cost of the Program in Postwar Years

The losses and gains on the postwar price-support operations cannot be sharply segregated. A number of factors caused the cost of the program to seem smaller than it actually was. Some of them are measurable and some are not. There were gains on stocks held, particularly of cotton, which offset losses on other commodities. Some sales were made at higher than market prices, through transfer to other government agencies or subsidization from Section 32 funds. Gift shipments of wheat were made in such a way as to relieve CCC of burdensome stocks and to reimburse the Corporation for funds invested in them. The $500 million postwar price-support reserve took care of heavy losses that did not have to be made up by the usual type of transfer to restore CCC capital.

The $558 million loss under the International Wheat Agreement is also, in large part, chargeable to the postwar price-support program. Also, much of the amount spent out of Section 32 funds for price support, surplus removal and in other ways belongs in this category. The largest element of uncertainty lies in the heavy losses now in prospect on some $7 billion or more of stocks and commitments to purchase. These are practically certain to bring less than the amount invested in them but it is not possible at this time to estimate how large the losses will be.

Bearing in mind these qualifications, the restorations of capital authorized on the basis of annual audits, for the fiscal years 1949 through 1953, were as follows:

1949	$ 66,698,457
1950	421,462,507
1951	109,391,154
1952	96,205,161
1953	550,151,848
Total	$1,243,909,127

54. U.S. Senate Committee on Agriculture and Forestry, *Agricultural Outlook and the President's Farm Program,* Hearings, 83d Cong., 2d sess., January 18 and 19, 1954, p. 10.

Deducting the 1947 and 1948 repayments to the Treasury, which amounted to $66,636,502, the net restoration of capital for the period July 1, 1946 to June 30, 1953 was $1,177,272,625. This is in addition to the $500 million postwar price-support reserve fund, the $558 million subsidy on exports provided under the International Wheat Agreement, substantial amounts derived from Section 32 funds, and profits on procurement operations. Also, it does not take account of sales to other government agencies which, in accordance with congressional directives, were on the basis of cost to CCC, thus precluding some losses that might otherwise have had to be made up through capital restorations. Such overvaluation as there may have been on gift shipments derived from CCC stocks is not included. The actions taken in respect to these matters had, of course, other purposes than the easing of the strain on CCC or the support of farm prices. They did, however, lessen somewhat the amounts required for restoration of CCC capital. Taking account of such related activities as those mentioned above, the total costs attributable to price-support operations in these years amounted apparently to something in the order of $2 to $2.5 billion.[55]

CCC AS A STABILIZING INFLUENCE

The twenty-year experience with CCC, plus that gained earlier in the Farm Board stabilization operations, throws much light on the role this type of organization can and should play, and on the limitations and dangers inherent in operations of this kind. Such a corporation, if provided with large financial resources and a high degree of flexibility, and if wisely handled, can do much to stabilize both prices and physical supplies of farm commodities. Yet, if its activities are too rigidly prescribed and if it is assigned tasks for which it is not well suited, its continuing existence is jeopardized and it may constitute a threat to the agricultural price structure as a whole.

The cotton loans of 1933–34 demonstrated that a program like that of CCC can exert a steadying influence on prices and can provide valuable assistance in periods when markets are weak. The attempt thereafter to use CCC as a straight-out price-raising mechanism demonstrated with equal conclusiveness that loan rates that were substantially above market levels would check normal movement and pile up unwieldy stocks that might be a handicap in later operations. In this respect, the experience with the 1934–35 program was essentially the same as that of the Farm Board in 1931–32. The officials in charge were able to extricate

55. This, of course, is not by any means a clean figure. Other objectives, such as providing aid in the reconstruction of Europe and relief to India and Pakistan, were also involved. However, the figure does not take account of prospective losses on stocks now held except to the extent these may be reflected in the current methods of appraisal. It probably is much below the amount that will eventually have to be charged against the price-support activities of this period.

the Corporation from the untenable position created by the 12-cent loan of 1934 by paying a two-cent subsidy which enabled it to move a good part of its holdings into consumption and export. This was possible because funds derived from processing taxes were available for subsidizing sales. In the following year, the loan rate was reduced to more realistic levels and CCC was able to resume the type of function for which it is best fitted.

The 1933 corn loan was, to be sure, at a rate that was well above market prices. However, the Administration expected that economic recovery would raise prices and also that production would be reduced. Furthermore, no very large portion of the crop had to be put under loan in order to strengthen the market, since most of the corn crop would not be offered for sale but would be used on the farms where it was grown. The loan level established might have proved embarrassing had it not been for the very short crop of 1934. Nevertheless, the corn loan did set a pattern that gave promise of making a real contribution in the stabilization of feed supplies and the development of an "ever-normal granary" type of program.

CCC has been given large financial resources and mechanisms for adjusting production are now available. Nevertheless, the Corporation's freedom of action has been severely restricted in ways that constitute a serious threat to its continuing success and usefulness. No longer can loan rates be set at such levels as will, in the judgment of its directors and the Secretary of Agriculture, contribute to stability and moderate strengthening of prices. Instead, the Corporation has been required to provide loans and purchase commitments that virtually nullify its ability to provide stability over any considerable length of time.

Restrictions on Freedom of Action

The Agricultural Adjustment Act of 1938 specified that loans were to be in amounts ranging from 52 to 75 per cent of parity. Had these percentages been in terms of market price they would have been well within the range of normal commercial loans and probably too low to be of much use except as a mild aid to growers wishing to hold crops in anticipation of a stronger market later. Since parity prices were then so much higher than market prices, loans made at any rate significantly above the minimum percentages of parity specified would have meant putting them so much above market prices that normal movement would have been checked and large inactive stocks would have been acquired by CCC.

Even with the relatively low percentage of parity supports provided in these years, CCC holdings were becoming a serious problem around the end of the decade. This, of course, was due mainly to the wide gap between market prices and parity prices. In periods when demand is more active, prices in the market tend to be more nearly up to parity and higher supports in terms of percentage of parity can be provided without disturbing so drastically the normal movement of commodities.

To the extent that price supports can raise prices and still permit movement of the commodities, even though it be after they have been held for some time, supports of this kind can benefit producers. If they are so high that commodities accumulate in inactive and potentially harmful government holdings, the long-run result is not likely to be to the advantage of either farmers or the government. Under the conditions prevailing in the late 1930s, the levels of support provided were apparently about as high as they could be without seriously disturbing the flow of commodities into the hands of users rather than into government-owned stockpiles.

For example, the price to growers for cotton in 1937 was 8.4 cents per pound. The cotton support level of 1938, at 52 per cent of parity, was 8.3 cents, or approximately the market price of the preceding year. The corn support level of 1938, at 70 per cent of parity, was 57 cents as compared to a 51.8 cent market price for the preceding year. For wheat, the support level of 59 cents in 1938 (52 per cent of parity) was well below the market price of the preceding year (96.2 cents) but about 3 cents above the market in 1938.[56]

The levels of support provided in the 1938 act were not high enough to cause much difficulty so long as the Secretary of Agriculture could, at his discretion, keep them within the lower percentages of the ranges permitted. They were perhaps overconservative in not providing a level of support that could have been given with reasonable prospect of eventual liquidation of stocks acquired. Yet, the large cotton crop of 1937 had resulted in a very heavy carry-over which was causing some concern. Neither wheat nor corn was in long supply.

It was logical for CCC to step in, as it did in 1937, with a 53 per cent of parity loan (9 cents) to prevent a disastrous break in the price of cotton which almost certainly would have resulted had this support not been available, especially since the large crop was due partly to high yields. Cotton production in 1937 was almost 19 million bales as compared to 12.4 million in 1936 and 10.6 million in 1935. Nonrecourse loans at this level were not unmanageable though they would require skillful handling.

However, the Congress began in 1939 to apply restrictions which limited severely the ability of the Corporation to work out from under its heavy accumulations, particularly in cotton. One of these, an amendment passed in 1938 (52 *Stat.* 31, 67), provided that cotton could not be sold at a price lower than that which would reimburse the government

56. Support levels are as given in U.S. Production and Marketing Administration, *Parity Handbook*, Senate Doc. 129, 82d Cong., 2d sess., 1952. Prices quoted are average prices received by farmers as shown in *Agricultural Statistics, 1945*, pp. 9, 38 and 70.

for all costs incurred.[57] This meant that the price would have to be increased from year to year by enough to cover carrying charges and interest. Still more restrictive was the provision that not more than 300,-000 bales could be sold in any one month or more than 1.5 million bales in any one year.

High Mandatory Supports a More Serious Problem

Much more serious from the standpoint of stability was the sharp increase in the mandatory levels of support provided in later legislation. An act of May 26, 1941 (55 *Stat.* 203) required that loans to cooperators in the 1941 rice, tobacco, cotton, corn and wheat programs were to be made at 85 per cent of parity. Peanuts were added later. This level was later raised to 90 per cent and eventually, for the 1944 cotton crop, to 95 per cent. The Steagall commodities were also assured of support at 85 per cent of parity in 1941 and, later, at 90 per cent.

This stepping up of loan rates in terms of percentages of parity rather than of market price meant very high levels of support, insured heavy accumulations of inactive stocks by CCC and limited sharply its ability to manage the situation as a genuine stabilizing agency. For example, the increase in the support level for cotton, from 57 to 85 per cent of parity, raised it from 8.9 cents in 1940 to 14.02 cents in 1941, more than 4 cents above the 1940 market price of 9.89 cents. The support price on wheat was raised from 64 cents to 98 cents, as compared with a 1940 market price of 68 cents. Corn supports were raised from 61 cents in 1940 to 75 cents in 1941. The price received by farmers in 1940 was 61.8 cents, a price which itself was undoubtedly supported to some extent by the loan level of the preceding year.

These sharp increases in support levels, though partly a response to the emerging upsurge in war demand, were made in spite of mounting stocks of cotton, wheat and corn which were already causing grave concern to those in charge of the loan program. The magnitude of this increase of support levels from approximately market prices to some 25 to 45 per cent above them was not generally recognized at that time. In fact, the threat to the solvency of the program as a whole was largely concealed by the rapid increase in market prices that occurred so soon thereafter.

57. Various restrictions on the sale of stocks at less than support prices were written into the appropriation acts during the early 1940s. They were eased somewhat before the end of the war. The Surplus Property Act of 1944 authorized the sale of farm commodities for export at world prices, provided this did not result in a shortage of supplies for domestic use. In an act of April 12, 1945 (59 *Stat.* 50), policies governing the disposition of surpluses were spelled out more specifically. Mostly, they were not to be sold at less than parity. The Agricultural Act of 1949 set up permanent standards. Basics and storable nonbasics could not be sold at less than 5 per cent above the current support prices unless there was danger of spoilage or they could be converted to inferior uses. These restrictions did not apply to wool or to sales for export.

In the postwar years, this tendency for high loan rates to entice huge quantities of storable farm products into government holdings has become much more evident. The high postwar free-market prices which minimized government take-overs for many of the products kept this problem in abeyance much longer than was expected at the time the high support levels were originally written into the law. The situation now is more like that which caused the breakdown of the Farm Board stabilization corporations than at any time since 1932. The quantities held are much larger than those held by the stabilization corporations and the danger to the farm price structure is apparent.

Unbalance Likely to Continue

There are many more safeguards now, and the financial resources of CCC are much larger than those of the Farm Board. Machinery exists for cutting back production. Severe droughts could reduce stocks rapidly and a new upsurge of war demand could absorb surpluses. Nevertheless, the previous efforts to hold production in check have not been notably successful except in cotton and tobacco. The more powerful quota system now available for many of the crops can be used to check further accumulations if used rigorously enough. However, it is not likely to work well for corn, which does not, for the most part, move in the commercial markets. Also, sharp compulsory reductions in acreage create many problems in determining what to do with the cropland thus released for other types of production.

These problems are likely to be difficult for some years to come, whatever approach is made to them. A satisfactory solution cannot be achieved by continuing indefinitely to pile up inactive surpluses through the maintenance of prices that will not permit commodities to move freely into the domestic and foreign markets.

At some point, however high it may be, public and congressional opposition will force a halt in the granting of further funds, or stocks will become so cumbersome that facilities will be clogged. Furthermore, spoilage and the enormous costs of storage will subject the program to mounting criticism. If and when such a halt in further building up of stocks occurs, there is apt to be a serious and general break in farm prices as a result of the withdrawal of CCC support.

Over the longer run, it seems likely that the rapidly growing population will call for even larger production than is now available. Also, it is unlikely that the favorable production conditions of the years since 1936 will continue indefinitely. The problem appears to be one of bridging a gap in which production is likely to outrun market demand at the prices now being maintained.

Even for a much larger population, the production of some crops now seems clearly to be in excess of needs and some readjustments apparently will have to be made. This appears to be particularly true for wheat and possibly for rice. For many of the other commodities, the remedy may be to avoid excessive stimulation of production through high support prices until consumption can catch up. For cotton, the avoidance of surpluses is partly a matter of devising procedures that will enable American cotton to hold its position in the international markets. This also points up the need for a re-examination of price-support policies.

Moderately Heavy Stocks Desirable

In a world situation so unstable as that of recent years, it is apparent that stocks cannot safely be kept at the low levels that would result from complete reliance on the private profit motivations of farmers, millers, handlers and other business groups. Quite unforeseeable and heavy demands may arise from the outbreak of war. Unusually severe droughts or catastrophes to friendly or allied nations may give rise to pressing needs for surplus stocks.

However, the size of such stocks should not be determined by the chance accumulations resulting from rigid price-support operations. Stocks accumulated in that way are likely to become far larger than are needed under any reasonable criterion of safety. Also, they may at times be smaller than would be in the best interest of the nation and the industry. For example, the imposition of acreage controls on cotton in 1950 resulted in an acute shortage. Prices went to all-time highs, especially in foreign markets.

The high prices of 1950 apparently overstimulated production thereafter and this in turn has caused part of the troubles experienced in the years since, including those resulting from the sharp cutback in acreage in 1954. Furthermore, the position of American cotton in international markets was damaged, because of the doubts raised as to the dependability of American-grown supplies and the encouragement to foreign producers to expand their output. This outcome was, to be sure, partly a result of the sudden increase in demand that grew out of the outbreak of war in Korea. It does illustrate, however, the need for maintaining rather ample stocks in a period when both production and demand can change so quickly and so drastically.

Furthermore, trade between nations has been so severely disrupted by war and tension between the communist nations and the free world that customary stabilizing influences have been greatly weakened. World production as a whole does not vary greatly from year to year. Hence, if trade could be carried on freely, temporary shortages in one nation could usually be made up by shipments from some other country or a temporary surplus in one region might be needed in some other that had a temporary deficit. Such automatic adjustment cannot be counted on with world conditions as unsettled as they are at present.[58] Hence the need for liberal reserves of many of the important storable commodities. However, it is clear that such strategic reserves need not be as large as those now held. Smaller, though still adequate, stocks would be far more manageable and, if skillfully handled, could be used to some extent in stabilizing prices and absorbing temporary surpluses or meeting temporary deficits.

CCC Can Be an Important Asset

CCC can be an asset of great importance both to agriculture and to the nation, provided it is used in such a way as to perform the services for which it is best fitted. It can exert an important stabilizing influence but cannot, for any long period of time, serve as an outlet for vast quantities of products that cannot be sold at the prices it is required to charge.

Huge quantities of unused commodities held in storage constitute a national waste that sooner or later will result in severe repercussions that may bring about the destruction of a very useful instrument and at the same time deal a severe blow to the prosperity of agriculture. Relaxation of some of the restrictions on CCC and gradual liquidation of part of its holdings would undoubtedly reduce the danger of a more severe break later.

Such action is admittedly difficult. Some reductions in price are almost inevitable. However, a choice may have to be made between a series of relatively moderate readjustments and a severe crisis at a later date. A gradual shift to a stabilizing instead of a price-increasing function would perhaps be facilitated if the Corporation were to be placed under the direction of a semi-independent board with a good deal of freedom to use its vast resources in a variety of ways in stabilizing farm markets, strengthening farm prices where possible and safeguarding the public interest in respect to the adequacy and dependability of supplies. If such a function and structure were assigned to it, it could provide for agriculture a type of assistance somewhat similar to that provided for the nation's banks by the Federal Reserve System and the Federal Deposit Insurance Corporation.

The stocks now held need to be reduced, but how? Clearly they cannot be thrown onto the open markets without disastrous results. To find abnormal outlets for such vast quantities is by no means easy. Some will almost certainly have to be channeled into needy foreign areas. Some, no doubt, will go to inferior uses. Some should probably seek abnormal

58. Also, the danger of sudden and extensive cutting off of foreign sources through enemy action or shortage of ships is far more serious than in earlier times, though examples from the past are numerous. In World War I, Britain and France were dangerously short of wheat even though vast quantities were available in Australia. There were no ships to move it. In World War II, the United States was suddenly deprived of around a million tons of fats and oils normally available to it from the Pacific area.

outlets in this country. For example, surplus stocks of butter and cheese might perhaps be given to publicly supported institutions or sold to them at low prices.

All of these will mean losses to the national Treasury. However, the loss is already there though it has not yet been accepted and accounted for as a realized loss. The excess stocks are comparable to a merchant's unused and deteriorating inventory. It is a long-established principle of merchandising that such stocks must be moved and the loss taken before it grows larger. The chance circumstances which have enabled CCC to unburden itself from time to time in the past cannot be counted on to solve its problems continuously or in more normal situations. Hence, if present policies are continued, the problems are likely to become more difficult and the losses greater. Whatever the policy adopted in respect to maintenance of the prices of farm products, it should be so implemented as not to constitute a threat to the continuing usefulness of the Commodity Credit Corporation or a danger to the agricultural price structure as a whole.

THE EVER-NORMAL GRANARY IDEA

The disastrous drought of 1934 led to a good deal of interest in crop insurance as a way of easing the impact of disasters of that kind, and also of safeguarding the public against shortages in times of widespread drought damage. In various public addresses made in 1935 and 1936, Secretary Wallace suggested that both of these purposes might be served by adopting what he termed an "ever-normal granary plan." His proposal was that in years of good yields farmers turn over to a government agency specified quantities of wheat, cotton or other products as an insurance premium, and that in years of low yield they be indemnified, also in commodities rather than in money. Since the insurance reserves would be held in physical form rather than in money, presumably in bad years there would be stocks available to make up any deficits in overall supply. Thus both farmers and the consuming public would be protected to some extent against the ups and downs of production resulting from weather variations.

There had already been some attempt by private insurance companies and a few of the states to offer crop insurance of various kinds, but only in the form of cash premiums and indemnities. The protection they offered did not imply any attempt to carry reserves of commodities. There also had been some consideration of a national approach to the crop insurance problem. As early as 1923, the Senate Committee on Agriculture and Forestry discussed the possibility of providing some sort of government crop insurance. In 1928, the Secretary of Agriculture was asked to comment on the feasibility of setting up some workable plan of this kind. He reported that it was impossible to determine on the basis of data currently available whether such a plan would be practical.

The general idea of ironing out the ups and downs resulting from yield variations was implied in the provision for stabilization corporations which was included in the Agricultural Marketing Act of 1929. However, this objective dropped into the background as the stabilization corporations came to be used mainly to check the drop in prices that began in 1929. At that time, the overriding influence was a change in demand rather than in supply.

As supply factors came more into prominence, because of the efforts to control production and the very severe drop in production that occurred in 1934, there came to be more interest in developing some procedure to assure adequate supplies as well as protect farmers against loss. Secretary Wallace did much to arouse public interest in the idea by tying it to the biblical account of Joseph's accumulation of stocks in the seven fat years for use in the seven lean years. This whimsy, and the eye-catching title he hit upon, gave the plan wide popular appeal and created interest among urban people as well as farmers. The very dry season of 1936, coming so soon after the disastrous drought of 1934, gave the plan added impetus and provided a further demonstration of what could happen to farm incomes and national supplies in prolonged periods of subnormal rainfall.

Special Committee on Crop Insurance Set Up

During the summer of 1936, Wallace recommended that a program for crop insurance "in kind" be instituted as a supplement to the agricultural programs then in effect. Shortly thereafter, the President appointed a special committee to investigate the possibilities of such a plan. It made its report to him on December 23.[59] The committee reported that some of the private insurance companies had at various times undertaken to offer all-risk crop insurance but that their operations had not been successful and they had ceased to carry that type of risk. It recommended that a government crop insurance program be undertaken and that a start be made by offering coverage on the wheat crop of 1938. It proposed that the plan provide yield insurance but not price insurance. Since, where feasible, payments and indemnities were to be made in physical commodities rather than money, it was thought this would also provide a way of putting into effect the ever-normal granary idea.

The committee recommended that premium rates be determined on the basis of the loss experience of the individual farm and of the county or area in which the farm was located. Considerable amounts of data on individual farms had been collected in connection with the acreage control programs and the committee thought it feasible to formulate some

59. The committee consisted of Henry A. Wallace (chairman); Ernest G. Draper and Wayne C. Taylor, Assistant Secretaries of Commerce; A. G. Black, Chief of the Bureau of Agricultural Economics, and H. R. Tolley, Administrator of the Agricultural Adjustment Administration.

preliminary actuarial tables on the basis of these data. The recommendations included a proposal that the government subsidize the operation to the extent of carrying the cost of storage and the overhead costs of administering the program.

The justification advanced for this amount of subsidy was that there was a public interest in assuring greater stability of supplies and reducing special measures of relief for distressed areas in times of drought or other physical disaster. The committee also recommended that the crop insurance arrangement be closely tied in with the other farm programs and that participation in the crop adjustment and soil conservation programs be made a prerequisite for coverage under the crop insurance plan.

Congressional Action

The President forwarded the committee report to the Congress in February 1937. A bill substantially in accord with the recommendations contained in it was introduced and was passed by the Senate but failed to get House consideration in that session. The Congress did, however, pass a joint resolution, on August 24, 1937, which included language indicating approval of the ever-normal granary idea, though it also covered more broadly the general philosophy to which the Congress was then willing to subscribe.

In the Agricultural Adjustment Act of 1938, the crop insurance plan was incorporated as Title V, which is designated as the Federal Crop Insurance Act (52 *Stat.* 72). It was intended primarily as a means of alleviating distress caused by drought in the drier areas of the United States, particularly those engaged principally in wheat production. The act provided for a Federal Crop Insurance Corporation with a capital stock of $100 million subscribed by the United States. Management was placed in the hands of a board consisting of three employees of the Department of Agriculture. These were to be appointed by the Secretary of Agriculture and were to serve at his pleasure.

Main Provisions of the Act

The Corporation was authorized to insure wheat producers, beginning with the 1939 crop, against unavoidable losses in yield due to drought, flood, hail, wind, winterkill, lightning, tornado, insect infestation, plant disease and such other unavoidable causes as might be determined by the Board. Insurance was not to cover losses due to neglect, malfeasance of the producer or failure to reseed under conditions such that it is normal to reseed. For the first three years, contracts were to be limited to one year at a time. Indemnities were to be at 50 to 75 per cent of the recorded or appraised yield of the specific farm in a representative base period. The act made provision for some minor modifications of these arrangements in special situations.

Premiums and indemnities were to be paid in wheat or its cash equivalent. Though this was in accord with the ever-normal granary idea, it placed an added financial burden on the Corporation because of the difficulties inherent in these abnormal types of market operation. Premium rates, in practice, were determined by blending the yield experience of the individual farm and that of the county in which it was located. That procedure was not entirely successful and was modified in later years. An annual appropriation of $6 million per year for administrative expenses was authorized.

In June 1941, provision was made for similar insurance on cotton (55 *Stat.* 255).[60] The amount authorized for administrative expenses for the two programs was raised from $6 to $12 million per year. The Corporation was also directed to make studies and assemble data with a view to establishing an actuarial basis for insurance on corn.

During the 1942 crop year, some other changes were made. The list of hazards covered was enlarged so as to include losses caused by direct enemy action, or by our own forces in the defense of the country, and also those resulting from inability to obtain labor, fertilizer, machinery or insect poisons because of war conditions. The Corporation also began to accept, during the growing season, notes for payment of premiums on wheat. These became due at harvest time. Thus, the producer was able to pay his premium out of his insured crop and at a cash price per bushel commensurate with the sale value of the crop.

This to some extent decreased whatever small part the crop insurance program might have in carrying out the ever-normal granary idea. However, that phase of its program had already dropped into the background, partly because it was becoming apparent that the volume likely to be handled under the crop insurance program would not be large enough to be an important factor in national inventories and partly because this function was already being taken over by another agency.

CCC Had Already Become the Stockpiling Agency

Although the crop insurance program was originally put forward as the principal mechanism for maintaining a so-called ever-normal granary, it did not actually assume that role.

The loan and purchase program of CCC had already made it, in effect, the stock-stabilizing agency of the government, insofar as stabilization could be considered a primary objective. The stocks acquired and handled by it were so much larger than those contemplated by the crop insurance program that they would inevitably dominate the situation

60. In an act of March 25, 1939 (53 *Stat.* 550), some minor modifications were made. These included permission for the Secretary of Agriculture to make advances to farmers who were participating in the conservation program so they could pay their premiums when due.

regardless of what was done about those acquired by the insurance corporation.

So evident had this become by 1940 that the President of CCC felt warranted in commenting that CCC is the ever-normal granary.[61] This would have been true had CCC been permitted to continue operating along the lines initiated in 1933 and reasonably well adhered to until 1938. From 1939 on, when it was required to give continuous support to the market through loans and purchases, it was definitely forced out of the role of stabilizer and became an accumulator—so much so that a prominent economist referred to it as the "ever-abnormal granary."

The kind of stabilizing activity envisioned for the crop insurance program was predicated on comparatively free action of the markets. The crop insurance reserves were expected to rise and fall countercyclically in relation to yield variations, but there was not to be any continuing upward or downward trend in stocks held. If reserves became larger than the plan called for, because of losses smaller than those anticipated, premium rates would presumably be reduced. If they became too small, because of greater losses than were expected, premium rates would be increased. Thus the insurance program would be a price and quantity stabilizer but not a price-raiser.

If CCC were to be assigned the task of stabilizing prices and supplies and were given authority to handle its operations in such a way as to contribute to that objective, there can be little doubt that it is the most effective instrument yet devised for that purpose. It did function as a stabilizing influence in corn and cotton in 1933, and the action taken in cotton in 1937 was constructive and helpful. However, if it was to carry through consistently in a stabilizing function, it should have been permitted and encouraged to work these stocks down in an orderly way after the big 1937 excess had been acquired. Instead, it was not only forced to continue carrying them but, in addition, mandatory supports were shortly raised to levels that insured further accumulation instead of orderly liquidation. At the same time, similar problems were created in respect to wheat and corn.

This does not mean that CCC could serve the primary purposes for which the Crop Insurance Corporation was designed. Crop damage is likely to be local. Some groups of farmers may be seriously hurt even when the over-all supply and price situation is relatively satisfactory. A fully effective CCC stabilization program would not meet problems of this kind. There is evident need for some procedure to aid in minimizing the effects of the natural hazards faced by the individual farmer, if a suitable one can be devised.

In most years, losses of this kind do not have national significance. They cause serious difficulties for some farmers, but losses in one area are likely to be offset by good yields in other areas. One difficulty is that

61. Commodity Credit Corporation, *Report of the President*, 1940, p. 5.

some areas tend to be so continuously the victims of droughts and other hazards that premiums reflecting their actual loss ratios will be so high that farmers will not participate. In other areas, such losses are so infrequent that growers may refrain from taking insurance because the risk does not seem great enough to warrant the bother and expense.

First Crop Insurance Program, 1939–44

The results of the first five years of operation in crop insurance were not reassuring. Costs were high and not enough farmers participated to make it a significant part of the farm program. There was some adverse selectivity in the farms covered and the widely scattered and limited participation made for high costs of administration.

Most of the field work was handled by the county AAA committees and regional AAA administrators. This made for rather loose control of operations by the Crop Insurance Corporation and meant also that a good part of the field operation was carried out by men who had little previous experience in handling insurance and whose principal interest was in the crop adjustment, conservation and loan programs.[62]

During all of the first three years of the wheat insurance program, the Corporation paid out more in loss claims than it collected in premiums, even though national yields in those years exceeded the 15-year average by 3, 12 and 24 per cent. Possibly more disturbing was the fact that participation tended to be less in the high-premium (high-risk) areas than in those where production was more dependable.[63]

62. Most of these problems were soon recognized and efforts were made to overcome them. An outside committee of experienced insurance men was asked to review the program in the early summer of 1941. Its report, in the main, was favorable to the procedures then being used. It recognized the need for crop insurance and approved the corporate form of organization. It also thought that government subsidization of administrative expenses was warranted.

The committee stressed the need for contracts running for more than one year, in order to overcome adverse selectivity resulting from heavier participation in prospectively bad years. It recommended that termination be permitted only after a fairly long advance notice and that farmers participating in any of the wheat programs be required to carry crop insurance. It approved the handling of field operations through the county AAA committees, but felt there should be closer control by the Corporation over state crop insurance supervisors and closer supervision of the formulae and procedures used in checking yields. Mention was also made of the inadequacy of the data. The costs of the operation were said to compare favorably with those of private insurance companies.

63. G. F. Geissler, Manager of the Corporation, discussing in 1947 the causes of difficulty in these first years of operation, commented as follows:

". . . 75 per cent of the average yield is probably in many cases too high insurance protection, especially in view of the difficulties encountered in establishing an average yield for farms, on the basis of the records available. Records are inadequate and often no longer applicable when operating methods are changed. In the case of cotton, the amount of insurance was not only 75 per cent of the average yield but loss on cottonseed was protected in addition thereto.

"Added to the fact that the coverage was high, losses occurring early in the season were indemnified in full whereas neither the investment in the crop nor the value of the crop justified such large indemnities. Early losses were often more profitable to the

By 1944, the insurance program as a whole showed a loss of about $37 million, in addition to administrative expenses of about $30 million, though the years covered had been much better than average from a yield standpoint. The Congress discontinued the program in the Agricultural Appropriation Act of that year (57 *Stat.* 392, 418). The reasons given were that the insurance program was proving too expensive and that not enough farmers participated in it.[64]

Crop Insurance Program Reactivated in 1945

The crop insurance program was reactivated for 1945 and later years through an amendment to the act of 1938 passed on December 23, 1944 (58 *Stat.* 918). The amendment authorized insurance, on a nationwide basis, for wheat, cotton and flax planted in 1945. Experimental programs were authorized for a long list of other crops. The list included corn, dry beans, oats, barley, rye, tobacco, rice, peanuts, soybeans, sugar beets, sugar cane, timber and forests, potatoes and other vegetables, citrus and other fruits, tame hay and any other agricultural commodity, provided sufficient actuarial data were available. For 1945, the experimental program was to be limited to corn and tobacco. Not more than three other crops could be added in each year thereafter and then only for a three-year period. Such programs could not be undertaken in more than twenty counties for any one commodity.[65]

Other provisions were to go into effect in 1950. After that time, not more than 25 per cent of the premiums collected in the previous year could be used for administrative expenses in the operating year. From 1945 on, premiums were to be set at rates that would result in the accumulation of reasonable reserves against unforeseeable losses. From

---

insured than producing the crop, especially where the farmer could use the land for a substitute crop.

"Premium rates had to be based upon data that were available. These data proved to be less reliable than originally contemplated. In the case of cotton, records were based upon acreage in cultivation as of about July 1, whereas a large proportion of the losses have been paid on crops lost before July 1. In other words, there was no data on which cotton losses prior to July 1 could be estimated as the basis for the actuarial structure of cotton insurance.

"There was no provision in the law for refusing insurance on farms and in areas where the risk was so great or uncertain as to preclude sound insurance operations. Furthermore, there was no provision for minimum participation requirements in the law. Thus, operations were carried on in many areas where the volume did not justify the expense incurred, and probably also resulted in a lot of high selectivity, or only high-risk farms participating."

U.S. House Committee on Agriculture, *Crop Insurance,* Hearings, 80th Cong., 1st sess., 1947, p. 3.

64. President Roosevelt expressed disapproval of this action in signing the bill.

65. The amendment also enlarged the list of damages for which indemnities might be paid. Frost, fire, excessive rain, snow, wildlife damage and hurricanes were added. Insurance was limited to counties in which written applications were received from fifty or more farmers or one third of those normally producing the crop to be insured. Insurance could be extended to farms situated in local producing areas bordering on a county in which an insurance program was to be in effect.

1950 on, claims were to be paid on a prorated basis if they exceeded the amount of the premiums. These changes were designed to place the program on a self-supporting basis, except for costs of administration.

The Corporation's governing board also tightened up the insurance provisions in a number of ways. Indemnities on early-season losses were reduced, premium rates were increased and emphasis was placed on insurance to the extent of 50 per cent of normal yield rather than 75 per cent. Some farms were designated as uninsurable because of high or uncertain risks. Wheat contracts were sold for terms of three years and cotton contracts on a continuing basis, with prescribed cancellation provisions.

The Corporation also set up its own loss-adjustment organization and the method of determining premiums was changed.[66] The cumbersome arrangement of taking account of the loss history of the individual farm was changed to one of using a uniform rate for all farms in a county. On this basis, more reliable information could be obtained.

Situation Reviewed Again in 1947

During the years 1945, 1946 and 1947, the Corporation continued to show losses, principally on cotton. On wheat it registered a gain in each of these years, aside from administrative expenses, which were provided by the government. On tobacco it also operated in the black, and gained on flax in two of these years. There were deficits in the corn account in two of the years and large deficits on cotton in each of the three years. The over-all deficit for the three years was $32 million in addition to administrative expenses. (The surpluses, deficits and loss ratios for this period, by crops and by years, are shown in Table 35.)

New legislation which changed the whole approach to crop insurance was passed on August 1, 1947 (61 *Stat.* 718). The number of counties in which crop insurance might be offered was limited sharply. The depression emphasis on alleviation of distress in agricultural areas, which had characterized the earlier legislation, dropped into the background. The new objective, as stated in the legislation, was "to promote the national welfare by improving the economic stability of agriculture through a sound system of crop insurance and providing the means for research and experience helpful in devising and establishing such insurance."

Sponsors of the legislation hoped to encourage private companies to write some all-risk crop insurance. The act included a provision whereby the Federal Crop Insurance Corporation might reinsure crop risk policies written by private companies. No reinsurance of this kind has as yet been put into effect.

66. Federal Crop Insurance Corporation, *Annual Report, 1945*, p. 4.

TABLE 35

FEDERAL CROP INSURANCE EXPERIENCE, UNITED STATES SUMMARY,
1945–1947 [a]

Commodity		Year	Contracts in Force	Surplus or Deficit	Loss Ratio
Wheat		1945	14,390	$ 826,436	.44
		1946	305,428	8,882,442	.58
		1947	360,408	9,304,248	.59
	Total		680,226	19,013,126	.58
Flax		1945	31,131	573,232	.59
		1946	10,412	−534,634	1.07
		1947	35,613	1,547,162	.58
	Total		77,156	1,585,760	.65
Cotton		1945	96,231	−15,174,674	3.42
		1946	114,270	−37,066,429	3.49
		1947	122,212	−599,898	1.04
	Total		332,713	−52,841,001	2.55
Tobacco		1945	12,587	144,684	.79
		1946	13,891	472,402	.41
		1947	14,715	185,720	.74
	Total		41,193	802,806	.63
Corn		1945	10,603	−259,786	1.65
		1946	7,423	65,027	.83
		1947	6,886	−499,236	2.18
	Total		24,912	−693,995	1.58
Total, all commodities		1945	164,942	$ −13,890,109	
		1946	451,424	−28,181,192	
		1947	539,834	9,937,996	
Interest income				522,994	
Debt cancellation				−6,568	
Nonrefundable credits				5,308	
Reserve adjustment account				−406,432	
Operating results		1945–1947		$ −32,018,003	

Source: Federal Crop Insurance Corporation, *Report of the Manager, 1948,* pp. 9–10.

a. Data as of June 30, 1948.

The regular crop insurance program was put on an experimental basis and was limited to certain counties chosen because of their representativeness in the production of the crops insured. Though still limited and experimental, it has been moderately expanded in recent years. For 1948, insurance was to be made available on not more than seven crops, including wheat (200 counties); cotton (56 counties); tobacco (35 counties); flax (50 counties); corn (50 counties); and all others, 20 counties each. The minimum number of applicants was increased to 200 farmers or one third of the number of farms normally producing the commodity, whichever was smaller. The purpose was to get a larger and less selective group and to spread administrative costs over a larger number of farms. The composition of the Corporation's board of directors was changed to include two additional members experienced in the insurance business and not employed by the government, except as members of the board.

Insurance Program of 1948 and After

In accordance with the 1947 act, coverage in 1948 was reduced from 2,500 to 375 counties. Two types of insurance were tried experimentally, commodity-coverage insurance and monetary-coverage insurance. Under the first type, the indemnity is in terms of units of a commodity times its price at the time the indemnity is paid. Under the other, the coverage is expressed in dollars at the time the insurance is offered. Coverage on dry edible beans and oats was included, under multiple-crop policies. These were the first additions made from 1945 on, and this was the first time that multiple-crop policies were offered.[67] It was expected that the multiple-crop policy would make possible lower premiums than if each crop was insured separately. However, the Corporation has had serious losses under these policies, largely because a disaster to a given area tends to affect all crops severely.

An act of August 25, 1949 (63 *Stat.* 663) authorized a modest expansion of the program. For each year through 1953, the Corporation might offer coverage on wheat in up to 100 additional counties; on cotton in 28 additional counties; flax, 25 counties; corn, 25 counties; and tobacco, 17 counties. Multiple coverage was permitted in 50 counties with increases of 25 counties per year. Coverage may be extended to three new crops each year, with a maximum of 20 counties for each crop. After three years, these new crop coverages may be increased by ten counties a year.[68]

The new amendment also authorized the Secretary of the Treasury to cancel receipts for capital stock in the amount of the deficit incurred prior to 1948 when the more conservative policy was adopted. A pro-

67. Insurance on dry edible beans on a single-crop basis was also offered in four counties. In 1950, insurance on citrus was offered in two Florida counties but neither of them qualified for coverage in that year. Insurance was written in one county in 1951 and 1952.

68. The amendment also removed the provision (added in 1944) that losses be prorated on a reduced basis after 1949. It was felt that this would reduce protection too much in years of crop failure. The restriction on administrative expenses, to go into effect in 1950, was also rescinded. Coverage on tobacco was extended to include the period in which it is being cured and prepared for market.

gram operating deficit of $73 million, in capital losses, had been incurred in the years 1939 through 1947. The House committee stated that this deficit "should be charged off as part of the cost of developing crop insurance in (sic) a trial-and-error basis and that the experimental program on which the Corporation is now engaged should not be burdened with the deficits of the earlier Nation-wide program."

The question of expanding the insurance program came up again in 1953. Since the Corporation had been relatively successful in expanding on a modest scale, it was authorized to continue to add, but not to exceed 100 counties per year (67 *Stat.* 575—August 13, 1953). In adding new counties, the Corporation must consider the demands of the farmers for such insurance, the availability of crop insurance to commercial producers and the risk of loss to the Corporation.

Financial Record, 1948–52

The financial results of the program in the years 1948 through 1952, when it was on the new experimental basis, are shown by crops and by years in Table 36. Also included is a record of loss ratios, that is, of

TABLE 36

FEDERAL CROP INSURANCE EXPERIENCE, UNITED STATES SUMMARY, 1948–1952 [a]

Commodity	Year	Counties Partici- pating	Insured Units [b]	Surplus or Deficit	Loss Ratio
Wheat	1948	200	96,156	$3,570,000	.58
	1949	199	78,222	−3,497,000	1.45
	1950	283	107,097	4,107,000	.51
	1951	356	129,847	−472,000	1.04
	1952	390	140,371	1,874,000	.85
Total				5,582,000	.88
Multiple crop	1948	2	824	23,000	.06
	1949	7	3,028	115,000	.16
	1950	55	32,250	94,000	.93
	1951	95	39,844	−1,250,000	1.63
	1952	115	47,679	−4,026,000	2.33
Total				−5,044,000	1.78
Cotton	1948	53	22,024	806,000	.43
	1949	52	29,603	−1,532,000	1.97
	1950	80	69,887	−3,311,000	2.80
	1951	101	54,216	493,000	.82
	1952	98	40,128	1,157,000	.44
Total				−2,387,000	1.25

TABLE 36 *(continued)*

Commodity	Year	Counties Partici- pating	Insured Units [b]	Surplus or Deficit	Loss Ratio
Tobacco	1948	32	39,797	$370,000	.43
	1949	35	44,086	251,000	.66
	1950	52	93,130	574,000	.61
	1951	69	92,889	818,000	.49
	1952	82	95,786	333,000	.78
Total				2,346,000	.61
Corn	1948	36	16,518	361,000	.17
	1949	44	23,764	492,000	.16
	1950	73	36,868	− 170,000	1.23
	1951	98	42,097	− 1,458,000	2.31
	1952	99	40,893	1,011,000	.25
Total				236,000	.94
Flax	1948	48	17,255	752,000	.51
	1949	48	16,768	339,000	.62
	1950	63	17,026	291,000	.41
	1951	61	15,821	239,000	.49
	1952	59	13,128	105,000	.79
Total				1,726,000	.56
Beans, dry edible	1948	4	1,577	23,000	.29
	1949	9	3,184	34,000	.64
	1950	18	5,202	− 84,000	1.81
	1951	29	8,050	− 406,000	3.11
	1952	30	6,478	88,000	.56
Total				− 345,000	1.56
Citrus	1951	1	291	82,000	.00
	1952	1	202	54,000	.04
Total				136,000	.02
Total, all commodities [c]	1948	375	194,151	$5,904,000	.53
	1949	394	198,655	− 3,798,000	1.32
	1950	624	361,460	1,501,000	.90
	1951	812	383,055	− 1,954,000	1.10
	1952	874	384,665	596,000	.97
1948–1952				$2,249,000	.97

Source: Derived from data given in Federal Crop Insurance Corporation, *Report of the Manager, 1953*, pp. 10–11.

a. Data as of June 30, 1953.
b. Number of farms on which the insured crop was planted; includes duplication if both the landlord and tenant are insured. Insured farms on which no insured crop was planted are not included.
c. The total of counties participating includes duplications where more than one crop was insured in a county.

ratios between the indemnities paid and the amounts collected as premiums. If the ratio is 1.00, premiums collected and indemnities paid were equal. If it is more than 1.00, indemnities amounted to more than the premiums collected on that crop for that year, the last two digits indicating the excess of indemnity as a percentage of the amount collected in premiums.

For the operation as a whole, for this five-year period, the loss ratio was .97. Premium collections amounted to $79 million and indemnities paid to $77 million. The program can be considered modestly successful during these years. However, the Corporation has not been able to build up any substantial amount of reserves as would be considered necessary in orthodox insurance operations. The period covered was one of unusually good crops. A higher average amount of crop damage can be anticipated over a longer period. The principal continuing losses have been in the cotton and multiple-crop programs. If these programs could be put on a sounder basis, the over-all results would look moderately favorable.

The data given above do not include costs of administration. These have been heavy, but may be expected to decline, on a per farm basis, if more farmers participate in the program. Administrative expense provided, in addition to the capital stock, amounted to approximately $44.3 million for the years 1939 through 1947. For the years 1948–1952, it was roughly $24.7 million, or about $16 per farm per year for those participating in one or more of the programs.[69]

The crop insurance program has not yet had any large impact on American agriculture. A good deal of experience has been gained and the program appears to be on a sounder basis than in earlier years. Even when offered on a national basis, it has not reached much over a half million farms in any one year. Under the revised program, up to 1953, the largest number of farms served was 384,665 in 1952.

The program seems likely to find a continuing place in the great array of relatively unsensational government aids to agriculture, one which may prove useful and significant but not one which is likely to make large changes in the over-all farm situation. Its role will probably be comparable to that of many other long-sought government aids, such as grain inspection and control of stockyards and commodity exchanges, rather than to that of the major farm programs such as acreage control, marketing quotas, conservation and price supports.

As a means of carrying out an ever-normal granary program, if such a plan is seriously contemplated, crop insurance is not an effective instrument. If the ever-normal granary idea is to be put into effect, the Commodity Credit Corporation or some similar agency will be the logical and most effective one to use.

69. Subject to some duplication of figures on number of farms included, as indicated in footnote b, Table 36.

Chapter 11

Two Decades of Experience
What Conclusions Are Warranted?

THE FEDERAL GOVERNMENT has now been engaged for more than two decades in one of the most diverse and far-reaching efforts to aid agriculture that any nation has ever undertaken. Most of the devices proposed by agricultural spokesmen have been tried or at least have had sympathetic consideration. Experience has been gained under almost all conditions except those that might be considered normal.

This absence of knowledge about how the farm programs now authorized would work under more settled and stable conditions is perhaps the most serious handicap in deciding what kinds of activity to carry on in the coming years, when, it is hoped, the situation will be less "abnormal" than it has been in the decades just past. The period of principal activity has included the longest and most severe depression in our history. It has also included a period of about equal length in which prosperity has been at an all-time high and far above anything previously thought to be even remotely attainable. This in itself complicates the problem. What are reasonable expectations as to farm prices and incomes, real earnings of labor and profits to industry and commerce?

Wars put both labor and agriculture in strong bargaining positions because of the high and insistent demands that result from them. The unexpectedly long continuance of this high demand after World War II has no doubt caused both labor and agriculture, and probably business as well, to adopt goals that may be unrealistic under the conditions likely to prevail now that the war and postwar demand is slacking off. A period of inflationary upsurges in money incomes, such as those which wars tend to bring about, leads to the expectation of a continuing rate of increase in money wages and farm incomes that is larger than can be maintained without further inflation. If prices are to be stabilized and inflation controlled, the rate of increase in money incomes must somehow be brought into line with the rate of technological advance. That rate of increase is likely to be more modest than the one to which wage workers and farmers have become accustomed.

Much of the farm legislation now on the books is a product of the depressions of the 1920s and 1930s. Many of the ideas contained in it grew out of the efforts launched in behalf of agriculture in the 1920s.

431

These were stepped up in tempo and broadened in scope as a result of the body blow dealt the economy by the depression of the 1930s. In that period, they were carried much farther than any sizable group would have considered possible or desirable in earlier times. It is hardly conceivable that either of the major parties, in the years prior to 1930, would have chosen to go the road indicated by the NRA, the AAA or the Wagner Labor Relations Act. Without the gain in political power and know-how which the farm groups developed in the 1920s, it is very doubtful that so far-reaching a program for agriculture would have been launched even in the 1930s.

The 1940s brought war on a scale and of a duration which we had not known in nearly a hundred years. Agriculture almost at once showed its inherent preference for a free market and an unplanned economy. As soon as its terms of trade improved and the fear of low prices and limited outlets declined, it resisted vigorously the application of price ceilings on farm products, troubled itself not too much about rationing, and plunged ahead in an effort to produce in response to free-market price incentives pretty much in the traditional pattern.

However, even in the war years, the fear of depression was still strong, not only in agriculture but in many other parts of the economy as well. Farmer spokesmen demanded and obtained postwar guarantees that would assure them an outlet for their products at good prices. Agricultural administrators moved cautiously, out of fear of creating new surpluses, even when a more conservative outlook would have called for more strenuous efforts to build up stocks. Fortunately, the weather and other factors kept yields high. The large reserves that many thought should be maintained proved not to be badly needed, though larger stocks of wheat and corn would have been helpful in the early postwar years.

The agricultural legislation of the war years and most of that since has been of the "antidepression" type, though used principally as a means of maintaining a wartime level of prosperity for farmers. The fear of a return to 1930 conditions has continued strong, but the principal objective of much of the recent legislation has been the maintenance of high levels of demand and price rather than the prevention of serious depression. However, many seem to have assumed all too easily that, if price supports were lowered, agriculture would immediately return to the depressed conditions of the 1930s. Some have taken it for granted that, if price supports were only at 60 or 70 per cent of parity, prices would drop to that level. Yet most of the prosperity of recent years has not been a result of price supports but rather of strong demand in an essentially free market that has kept most farm prices well above support levels.

The time seems now to have arrived when we must, whether we wish it or not, look ahead and try to develop a farm program suited to conditions that do not reflect either the extreme anemia of the depression years or the robust demand of the 1940s. So long as the cold war lasts, heavy government spending will provide some artificial support to the economy. Any new outbreak of hot war of the traditional kind would, of course, put agriculture back in the happy position of having an outlet at high prices for almost any amount it may choose to produce. But a new war may not be like those of the past. It could be short, decisive and inconceivably devastating. In that case, the effect on the economy would undoubtedly be different.

More significant from the standpoint of plans relating to farm policy are such imponderables as the levels of employment and income in this country, the strength and receptivity of foreign markets and the possibility that we might encounter periods of devastating drought.

Whatever the future may hold, it seems reasonable to expect that we will not experience in the foreseeable future a depression so profound as that of the 1930s. There are now many safeguards and much know-how to forestall, or at least to alleviate, conditions that would lead us into a morass of such depth and persistence. It is almost equally certain that farmers will not have as favorable a period as that of the 1940s. The time is at hand when they, like other businessmen, will have to think more in terms of what the markets will take at reasonable prices and adjust their production accordingly. Scarcity prices and unlimited production do not go together in an economy geared for production on such a scale as ours now is.

Agriculture's Gains under Longer-Term Programs

The heavy emphasis of recent years on emergency and price-support programs has tended to obscure the very real gains agriculture has achieved through longer-term, more orthodox types of government aid. Some of these may in the long run prove to be more significant in their effects on American agriculture than those which are now so much in controversy. The depression of the 1930s was so severe that both the farmers and the public became willing to undertake far-reaching emergency and reform measures that would either have been unacceptable or would have come much more slowly in more normal times. The 1940s, in turn, were years of such vast and rapid change that farm and foreign-aid programs could be undertaken on a scale that would have been considered entirely unwarranted in most earlier periods.

But during these same decades, considerable progress was made in expanding and improving the kinds of aid to agriculture that had begun to take shape much earlier. These also looked to equalizing opportunities and real incomes in agriculture with those in other parts of the economy, but in slower and less sensational ways. As early as the last half of the nineteenth century, the federal government began to take account of the fact that the small-unit structure of agriculture, and the fact that its workers were so widely scattered, called for the fostering of some types of activity which, in other parts of the economy, could be undertaken without direct government assistance, through corporations, labor unions and so on.

The government-created protections for labor which have been built into the laws over the years, and especially during the past two decades, have enabled most of the urban workers to meet problems similar to those that farmers are concerned with. No longer is unrestrained and atomized competition allowed to determine the wages paid to labor, in most lines. Fringe benefits of many kinds have been sought and obtained, some through legislation and some by negotiation.[1] These assists from the government were, to be sure, superimposed upon a long and often violent struggle to achieve similar results through group action that was not fostered, directed or controlled by government. Farmers, too, have a long record of struggle to achieve their objectives without the aid of government, though they turned earlier to legislative remedies and, in recent years, have placed more reliance on them.

Contrasts in the Agriculture and Labor Movements

Though the agriculture and labor movements have elements of similarity, there are also significant differences between them. Much of the gain achieved by labor does not involve a direct drain on the federal Treasury. Higher wages and other benefits come by way of the market, except as they are extended to public employees. Agriculture, too, would prefer to achieve its higher income in the form of higher prices in the market rather than government payments, though the devices chosen have placed a considerable part of this burden on the public treasury rather than on purchasers in the market. But the biggest difference lies in the fact that, for labor, surpluses that result from wage rates that are out of line with those that would exist in a freer market tend to show up in the form of unemployment, whereas agricultural surpluses accumulate as government-owned stocks.

Another difference appears in the nature of the demand made on government in the event of a severe decline in employment or in farm prices. Unemployment insurance and other aids of this kind are in the nature of stop-loss floors, a means of getting along until conditions improve and a new job can be found. Though many farm leaders and others have often urged stop-loss floors as the appropriate guide in providing support for farm prices, the aim of the legislation of recent years has been to maintain prosperity prices. The cushion inherent in the gap between regular wages and unemployment or public relief has been removed in the case of agriculture. Hence, even a moderate recession in prices places a heavy burden on public funds.

1. For example, safety and sanitary provisions, prohibition of child labor, far-reaching statistical and analytical aids, unemployment insurance and public health facilities.

However, the difference is not so great as this comparison implies. Labor resists powerfully any reduction in regular wage rates if demand falls off, and lets the slack be absorbed by those who do not continue to be employed. Because of its characteristics, agriculture must take such a reduction in the form of a lower price, spread over the entire output. It cannot throw part of its group into unemployment at a lower rate of return. It does not follow, however, that agriculture as a whole is markedly worse off in a period of sharply reduced demand than labor as a whole. But the impact is not distributed in the same way.[2]

Business Meets the Problem in a Different Way

For the most part, business has relied less on direct government payments and legislation than either agriculture or labor. However, the variations in type and structure of business organizations are so great that few generalizations are warranted. For the larger industrial corporations, many of the services and controls for which agriculture and labor turn to government can be provided by the corporations themselves, because of the opportunities which the corporate structure and the nature of their business afford for assembling large-scale, corporation-controlled funds. Thus, they are able to support a very extensive research program, one which would be virtually impossible for agriculture with its small-unit structure.

Labor also has come to have control of very large funds and is able to carry on considerable amounts of research. Most of this, however, is of an operating type. Few large projects are undertaken. The nature of labor's problems does not call for the large investments in research that are required by many of the large corporations. Agriculture, too, is carrying on much more research in its own organizations than in the past, but this also is mainly of the day-to-day operating and legislative type.

Industry has a far greater incentive for supporting research privately than does agriculture. Its research results can be protected and used to its own advantage, through patents and trade secrets, to a far greater extent than can those of agriculture or labor. Research results in agriculture are likely to be brought quickly into general use throughout the industry. Thus, the benefits tend to be passed on to the public in lower costs and prices or improved quality. In industry, they tend to be restricted for limited use for a much longer time.[3]

2. For example, in the period 1929 to 1932, gross farm income fell from $13.8 to $6.4 billion, a drop of 54 per cent (U.S. Department of Agriculture, *Agricultural Statistics, 1952*, p. 618). Pay rolls in manufacturing industries fell from an index of 110.4 (1923–25 = 100) in 1929 to 46.7 in 1932, a drop of 58 per cent (*Statistical Abstract, 1942*, p. 389).

3. This does not mean, of course, that the public does not benefit from industrial research. Eventually, the results are passed on, but in the meantime they are presumably so handled as to result in a profit that justifies the expense.

Business and industry also are able to exercise privately some of the controls for which agriculture relies on the federal government. Private brands are established, market outlets are regulated and quality controls are maintained. In agriculture, the maintenance of specialized market research is virtually impossible except in a few highly organized, specialty lines. The above comments apply mainly to the larger corporate enterprises. There are, of course, many small or unorganized businesses for which both research and service facilities are markedly inferior to those available to either agriculture or labor.

Despite their peculiar advantages of structure, business and industry are by no means free of reliance on government. Not only are they coming to depend more on government action to support and stabilize their activities, but the amounts of government expenditure involved are very large. Antidepression construction activities, special tax and depreciation concessions, government purchases and a host of other kinds of government action contribute to the well-being of business, not to mention the very extensive activities carried on by the Department of Commerce and the very real advantages afforded by permission to operate as corporate entities, and the safeguards thrown around that type of organization. This aspect of the problem is far too extensive and complex for even the briefest analysis and summarization here. It is mentioned only to point out that government aid, in fact very expensive government aid, is not confined to agriculture.

Regardless of whether the farm groups do or do not receive more aid relatively than other groups, the pertinent questions are whether they need the amounts now being spent in their behalf and whether the programs now in effect are workable and in their best interest.

Effects as Well as Justification Must Be Considered

The price-support programs must be judged not only in terms of justice but also in terms of their effects and the practical problems they present. If they continuously call forth too large a volume of production which results in waste or the inescapable resort to give-away programs, they are bound to come under increasing criticism from the public, and the public is now predominantly urban. High wage rates for labor may take a comparable toll from the purse of the consumer but, for most products, the consumer has some choice as to whether he will or will not pay the price demanded. If the payment is made by way of taxes, he does not have that choice and is likely to be more critical, especially if the program leads to the diversion or waste of products he feels he has paid for and should have.

Some contend that if, in times of high employment, farmers do not find returns from farming comparable in over-all terms to those that might be achieved in other occupations, enough of the more mobile farm workers will shift out of agriculture so that real incomes will be somewhat comparable in the farm and nonfarm parts of the economy. This is, to some extent, the underlying logic of the acceptance of the 1910–14 base as a criterion for parity prices and incomes. Those years have been assumed to be a period when farm and nonfarm real earnings were roughly in balance in a free market.

However, such reasoning does not hold in short-run situations. Human abilities and money resources, once committed, are relatively immobile. Furthermore, in periods of abrupt change, especially in severe depressions, the alternative opportunities dry up and the choice is not there.[4] This provides a strong argument for emergency aid for agriculture but does not support the view that public aid should be provided continuously in such a way as to keep too many workers in agriculture or in any given type of agricultural production. The urban worker who thinks he should get more than he does, as most of them do, can try for a raise or can seek another job, but if his demands are higher than those the market will pay, he must either accept what he can get or be unemployed. The situation of the farmer in a relatively free market is somewhat similar.

Few will subscribe to the view that the farmer should be able to determine the price he will get and at the same time produce as much as he wants to. Urban businesses, even the largest of the corporations, cannot do that. They have more control over prices than the farmer has but not over price *and* volume. If a given level of price is to be maintained, the necessary adjustments in volume will eventually have to be made.

Some Programs Widely Accepted

Many parts of the government's farm program have become so well established that they do not need to be discussed at length here. Agriculture has, in fact, made long strides in achieving services and facilities comparable to those available to other economic groups. Farmers now have reasonably adequate mail service; electric power has been brought within reach of most farm homes; telephone service is improving and good roads are being made more and more widely available in the rural areas. Research and educational facilities in agriculture are probably as adequate as those available to most other industries. Farm credit facili-

4. The fact that agriculture produces more new workers than are required to maintain its own working force also gives rise to continuing inequality of return since there has to be enough differential between prospective earnings in farm and nonfarm occupations to cause workers to move from the one to the other. In the past, the barriers to movements of this kind, such as insufficient knowledge of alternative opportunities, distance and lack of suitable training for other jobs, have tended to cause more workers to stay on farms than were really needed and have resulted in markedly lower earnings for farm workers, especially in areas of high birth rate and poor opportunity. These factors are becoming less and less important as the population becomes more mobile, knowledge more general and industrial opportunities more widely dispersed. Also, the number of workers needing to shift out of agriculture is now much smaller in relation to the size of the nonfarm labor market.

ties have been brought to a high stage of development, and many of the more serious abuses and gaps in the marketing system have been eliminated through government action. Some progress has been made in overcoming or insuring against natural hazards.

The government has supplied these services to agriculture on a larger scale than for most of the nonfarm parts of the economy. However, many of them are so obviously in the interest of the general public, as well as of agriculture, that the question of continuing or not continuing them seldom arises. The policy questions raised are similar to those which come up in respect to almost all activities of government. Is the operation efficient? Should it have more support or less? Is it well organized and suitably coordinated with other activities having similar purposes?

Questions of this kind have been much discussed in congressional committee hearings both recently and in the past. However, the principal concern in recent years has been with the price and income problems which have been so widely discussed in the public press and elsewhere. Many of the reforms sought and obtained in earlier periods soon became relatively settled and noncontroversial, except for improvements and modifications.[5] The price- and income-support problems, on the other hand, have tended to become more controversial and to attract wider public interest.

Importance of Long-Term Gains

The importance of the long-term gains resulting from the more orthodox and less controversial types of program can best be appreciated by trying to imagine the conditions that would exist if they had not been achieved. For example, consider an agriculture with almost no specialized research, educational or extension facilities, except those provided privately by a few forward-looking individuals. Both history and the world of today afford many examples. For centuries during the Middle Ages, the farmers of western Europe continued to farm in almost the same way as their forefathers had done. In large parts of Asia, the Near East and Africa, and in other areas as well, agriculture has remained almost static for a thousand years or more.

Here would be the real danger of a drift toward peasantry that was so much publicized in the 1920s. If new technologies were not continually being introduced into agriculture, it would fall farther and farther behind the urban economy. If educational opportunities for farm young people were as limited as those of India, China or many of the

5. There are, of course, some important exceptions to this generalization, but few if any of the proposals made implied contributions from the federal Treasury to farmers as a group. The greenback and free silver campaigns, insofar as they were farmer movements, did imply large-scale government action in behalf of farmers but supposedly not at the expense of the federal Treasury. Some of the later demands for higher tariffs and for reductions in freight rates were of similar character but still did not involve direct government appropriations.

middle eastern countries, agriculture would not have the able and aggressive leadership it now has. More and more, its surplus of young workers would be dammed up in rural areas to compete for the limited opportunities afforded by such a society, or would have to seek outlets in the only kinds of nonfarm occupations that are available to ignorant and untrained workers.

The opening up of opportunities for broad-gauge, many-purpose education and the continuing flow of young people out of agriculture into nonfarm occupations is perhaps more significant than any other single influence in assuring, over any long period, a reasonable equality of opportunity between farmers and other economic groups. Part of this accomplishment, probably the most outstanding the world has known so far as farming is concerned, has come about through the efforts of farmers themselves. But much of it has been provided at federal and state expense. The cost is considerable but not high in comparison to that of making large-scale income transfers or in relation to the phenomenal achievements in the way of creating mobility, opening up alternative opportunities and raising the status and professional standing of agriculture and its leadership.

Educational opportunities, access to research findings and mobility of labor are, of course, by no means uniform throughout agriculture. Nor are they in nonfarm occupations. But a pattern of progress and equality of opportunity has been established. The need is for improvement in methods and wider availability rather than for any major change in this type of approach to the problem of equalizing rural and urban opportunities.[6]

The absence of rural free delivery of mail, of highways and of telephone and electric service would result in isolation, drabness and lack of contact in the rural areas. These handicaps have largely ceased to exist. Organization and facilities for intelligent group action by farmers in carrying on their own affairs, and for opposing abuses, are far more adequate than they were fifty years ago. Legislation, guidance and financing have been provided by government in such ways as to make it possible for farmers to conduct their business activities much as the most advanced urban groups do.

Credit Facilities Far Advanced

One needs to look back only forty years to be aware of the tremendous advance that has been made in providing for agriculture a credit system that is nearly as good as that of the most advanced of the urban indus-

6. This does not mean, of course, that facilities and methods should be identical in the urban and rural environments. All who are familiar with both rural and urban conditions are aware that there are, in many types of agriculture, educational values for young people that are not easily provided in urban environments. These, to some extent, counterbalance advantages that can be provided in the urban setting but are not easily supplied in rural areas.

tries. The cost of extending long-term credit to hundreds of thousands of small units makes borrowing rates somewhat higher than those of the large corporations, but not greatly higher. The advantages of long-term bonds and stability of financial arrangements have largely been achieved.

In the production credit field, much of the uncertainty that previously existed has been overcome or potentially eliminated. Government has facilitated and encouraged the development of a competitive system in this realm which goes far toward assuring agriculture against a repetition of the convulsive types of credit contraction that have injured it so severely in the past.[7] The provision of credit, both long term and short term, is highly competitive as between the government-sponsored cooperative system and the private banks, and agriculture seems not to be now in a disadvantaged situation so far as credit is concerned. It probably has better safeguards than most small-scale urban businesses, which are dependent almost wholly on the commercial banks.

In the fields of marketing and cooperative purchase of supplies, guidance, research assistance and financing are now provided in such a form and on such a scale that the way is open to many farm groups to handle their selling and buying operations in ways that are similar to those used by many of the more successful urban businesses. The road to full implementation of this approach is a long, slow and difficult one, but much progress has been made both by farmers operating without government aid and, more recently, with a substantial assist from the government.

For the low-income, underfinanced, high-risk farm operator, the facilities now afforded through the Farmers Home Administration, and previously provided by the Farm Security Administration, are almost certainly more liberal than those available to any comparable urban group.[8] This does not mean necessarily that they are as widely available and adequate as would be desirable. But a very long stride has been made in providing opportunity for this group of farmers to better its condition. It is the one that has had the greatest tendency to settle into a static, low-level situation.

Control of Abuses and Hazards

Much progress has been made in overcoming many of the difficulties that have in the past been of great concern to farmers. Manipulation of

7. This is on the assumption that the government could and would channel in new credit by way of the cooperative credit system or the commercial banks in the event of a severe and damaging contraction of private credit. This was done in the mortgage credit field in the 1930s. As yet, there is no specific provision for similar action in the production credit field, though it seems likely that some action of this kind would be taken if the need should arise on any large scale.

8. However, the urban FHA home-loan purchase program provides a similar type of aid on somewhat comparable terms so far as home purchase is concerned. It is not available for business loans. In agriculture, the two must be combined. In cities, they are usually separate.

prices and shady practices in the central markets have become much more difficult and dangerous than in earlier times. Here, both the farmer and the general public were helpless to take effective action. The government has therefore stepped in. Public control and regulation of commodity exchanges and stockyards have been brought to a relatively high stage of effectiveness. Adulteration, misbranding and misrepresentation of foods, drugs, insecticides and fertilizers have been outlawed and, to a considerable extent, brought under control.

Much progress has been made in standardization through grain and livestock inspection services, establishment of uniform grades and classes and regulation of containers and packaging. A continuing flow of market information has been developed and statistical and analytical services are now provided for farmers and others which are probably more comprehensive and adequate than those available to most other industries. Certainly they are the most highly developed of their kind to be found anywhere in the world.

Disease control, quarantines and other safeguards against natural hazards have helped materially in reducing losses but much remains to be done. Hazards of this kind constitute a very real disadvantage to which the farmer is peculiarly subject. His business is inherently vulnerable to disease and weather risks. The federal government is providing assistance designed to limit such losses and reduce risk so far as present knowledge and economic feasibility permit. It is also pushing forward research on such problems both at the federal and state levels. Weather hazards still pose a major problem. They are not to any large extent preventable. However, a serious attempt is being made, and has now been under way for fifteen years, to provide a workable system of insurance which may eventually ease the problem so far as the individual farmer is concerned.

Price Supports and Production Control

The price-support and production-control programs of the past twenty years are clearly the ones now of greatest interest to farmers and the general public. They are also much the most controversial parts of the over-all farm program. During recent years, analyses of these programs have occupied so exclusively the attention of economists and of writers for the public press that there has been some tendency to overemphasize their significance as solutions for the problems of agriculture. Their ability to create or maintain prosperity in agriculture may well have been exaggerated in the minds of farmers and of the general public.

The analysis here presented is designed neither to deprecate nor defend the price and control programs in effect now or in the past, but rather to afford a clearer view of what they have and have not been able to do and of ways in which they, or alternative procedures, can be made to serve better the longer-term interests of both farmers and the general public. Whatever amount the public may be willing to spend in bettering the relative position of agriculture in the economy, or may be forced to spend because of the political power of agriculture, it is clear that both the objectives sought and the relative merits of different ways of attacking the problem should be carefully weighed.

Price Supports Not Principal Cause of Recovery

Because agriculture was in deep depression in the 1930s and very prosperous in the 1940s, it has been easy to assume that the government programs evolved during the 1930s, and more fully worked out in 1938 and after, have been a dominant influence in the changes that have so evidently occurred. It would be unwarranted indeed to imply that their influence has been negligible, but the results have been spotty and often the types of action most highly publicized have not been the ones that had the most significant effects on farmers or their incomes. Both the reasons for the improvement in farm incomes and its significance are now becoming more clear than they could possibly be in the years when many of the programs undertaken were devised and launched.

The agricultural depression of the 1930s was not primarily a result of anything agriculture did or did not do. Except in the case of a few export crops, it was not importantly a result of overproduction. Over-all production, in fact, was remarkably stable in the years that were marked by one of the most severe declines agriculture has ever experienced. Over-all farm production stood at 102 in 1928 (1935–39 = 100). It dropped back to 99 in 1929 and to 98 in 1930 but rose to 102 in 1931 and dropped to 96 in 1932.[9] It did not again come close to 100 until 1937 and was down to 91 in 1935.

The overriding cause of the depression of the 1930s was a tremendous shrinkage in demand both here and abroad. There was apparent overexpansion in a few crops. Wheat production, for example, had been building up too fast throughout the world and some readjustment was needed.[10] World production of cotton had also increased markedly during the 1920s but only in comparison to the low outputs of the years 1915 to 1924. The 26.5 million bale crop of 1929–30 was only moderately higher than the 21 to 24 million bale crops of 1911–12 to 1914–15.[11] Most other crops were maintaining a rate of increase that was not much out of line with the rate of population growth.

With the severe drop in buying power which occurred in 1930–1932, it became apparent that production should be cut back, especially in

9. *Agricultural Statistics, 1952*, p. 660.
10. World wheat production (excluding Russia and China) had increased from around 3 billion bushels in 1921–1922 to nearly 4 billion in 1928–1929. *Agricultural Statistics, 1937*, p. 18.
11. *Ibid.*, p. 92.

wheat, cotton and hogs. Wheat and cotton were piling up in amounts that could not be sold, even at depression prices, and hogs were bringing such disastrously low prices that farmers could not be expected to find them tolerable even in a period of general and widespread depression. Many other farm commodities were bringing tragically low prices but most of them were less important either economically or politically than the ones mentioned above.

Farmers could not afford individually to make the adjustments needed in over-all output, particularly in these major crops. It was in this setting that the government crop adjustment programs were undertaken. Few will question seriously the need for some adjustment of output at that time. Whether the trouble stemmed from reduced demand or over-production, there was little to be said for continuing to produce commodities that could not be sold.

As an emergency device, acreage adjustment was logical. It would also have been logical in the overexpanded wheat industry of the early 1920s and again in the unbalanced wheat situation that has followed the abnormal demands of World War II and after.[12] Agriculture cannot, without government assistance, readjust downward quickly or without great hardship. Since the expansions of the World War I period and those made during and after World War II were in response to national need and partly a result of strong government encouragement, there was a clear justification for providing some government aid in making the unavoidable readjustment. This was less true in respect to the oversupply that developed in 1928 and 1929, but even here the catastrophic and unpredictable disaster that overtook the wheat growers unquestionably justified some action by the government to ease the situation.

Effectiveness of the Farm Programs of the 1930s

Planned production control did not bring prosperity or near prosperity to agriculture in the 1933–1936 period. The wheat and corn controls were only moderately effective and would not have raised prices materially unless continued for some years and strengthened. The carry-overs already in existence were sufficient to assure adequate supplies to the market even with a more rigorous cutback in production than that which was undertaken. The dominant influence on the supply situation, so far as wheat and corn were concerned, was the severe drought of 1934. This caused a far more drastic cut in output than anything contemplated by the AAA.[13]

12. Acreage allotments and marketing quotas for wheat and cotton were instituted for the 1954 crops, possibly a year later than would have best met the need for orderly readjustment.

13. The cotton and tobacco controls, under the much more rigorous Bankhead and Kerr-Smith Acts, were more successful but were not able to do more than reduce the severity of the depression in view of the weak demand in the markets of that period.

The ability of the adjustment programs to raise and stabilize farm prices did not get a full-scale tryout because of the abandonment of the original AAA program in 1936. But even with the more rigorous and comprehensive procedures authorized in 1938 and after, agriculture did not achieve prosperity or price balance with the rest of the economy. In terms of 1910–14 as 100, farm prices as a whole were up only to 95 in 1939 and the parity ratio for farm prices stood at 78 as compared to 100 in 1910–14.[14]

This was an increase of only 20 index points from the low point of 58 in 1932. The ratio had been higher in the meantime (88 in 1935, 92 in 1936 and 93 in 1937) but this was due mainly to the short crops of the drought years, the clearing away of stocks that kept the farm markets depressed in 1932 and 1933, and the mild business boom of 1937, which caused some strengthening of demand. Prices paid by farmers for commodities used in production and family maintenance moved up from a low of 102 in 1932 to 121 in 1939, an increase of 19 points as compared to 30 points for farm products (65 to 95).[15] Thus the price balance had improved somewhat but the prices of farm products still were low in comparison with those of nonfarm products.

In terms of income, rather than of prices, farmers were more favorably situated as compared to nonfarm workers. Salaries and wages in private industry dropped from $47.5 billion in 1929 to $24.2 billion in 1933, a decline of 49 per cent. They had recovered to $38 billion by 1939 (approximately 80 per cent of the 1929 level). Agricultural income fell from $6.8 billion in 1929 to $2.4 billion in 1932, a drop of 65 per cent. It had recovered to $5.2 billion by 1939 (about 77 per cent of the 1929 level).[16] The ratio of farm to nonfarm incomes was about 96 per cent of the 1929 ratio. It should be recognized, however, that farmers did not consider their price and income situation satisfactory in 1929, though there had been a substantial improvement over the depressed conditions of the early 1920s.

The point mainly stressed here is that the very diverse and extensive farm programs instituted in the 1930s had not in themselves been able to restore prosperity to agriculture in a period when nonfarm activity was low and demand weak. It is also true, however, that a very diverse

14. Prices received and paid by farmers here and below are as given in *Agricultural Statistics, 1952*, pp. 682, 684 and 685. The recovery in agriculture was also slowed down by the severe business recession of 1938. This, though a potent influence in keeping farm prices low, gives further evidence of the heavy dependence of farm prosperity on high levels of business activity rather than on the amount of government aid. The government aid provided in these years undoubtedly helped to reduce hardships in the farm areas but there is little evidence that either then or in other periods its influence was or would have been powerful enough to bring prosperity to agriculture when the rest of the economy was severely depressed.

15. *Ibid.*, pp. 682–85.

16. Data from U.S. Bureau of the Census, *Statistical Abstract of the United States, 1943*, pp. 384–85. These data are subject to numerous qualifications. They do, however, give some indication of the relative rates of recovery in agriculture and for a somewhat comparable working group consisting mainly of nonfarm workers in private industry.

and extensive array of nonfarm government programs had not succeeded in bringing prosperity or even a "normal" level of activity in the nonfarm economy.

Depression Programs Provided Needed Help

Though the programs of the depression years did not accomplish all that was hoped for, the kinds of aid given were neither useless nor insignificant. In periods of such general hardship, aid must be given even though it is only ameliorative rather than curative. The vast outlays for relief and public works were, in the main, necessary and helpful in a desperate situation. So also were many of the aids provided to agriculture. The point is rather that neither farmers nor workers generally should place their principal reliance on special-aid programs of this kind as a road to satisfactory incomes and living conditions in more normal times.

Help can be given, but serious economic illnesses can usually be overcome only gradually through the process of general economic recovery. The sick man must have medical assistance and suffering must be relieved, but medication, even of the most drastic type, is not a satisfactory substitute for the maintenance of health.

Much has been learned about the possibilities of preventive economic action. In the event of a new onset of depressed conditions, more powerful and direct procedures appear to be available, and they probably would be used much earlier than in the 1930s, when corrective action had to be devised and experimented with after the crisis had developed. However, the depression was almost world-wide and no action that could have been taken by the United States would have been likely to restore health to the great export markets which were so important in the agricultural situation.

Chance factors still were very important. Some of those in the farm sector helped to ease problems that would have been much more difficult had the course of events been different. If the droughts of 1934 to 1936 had not occurred, agriculture probably would have been plagued by heavy stocks and depressed prices almost all through the decade, unless much more drastic controls on output had been put into effect. Even with the substantial improvement in balance between supplies and available outlets that occurred in the middle 1930s, the problem of unbalance was arising again in the closing years of the decade.

Had it not been for the large stocks taken over by the government in the late 1930s, thus reducing the amounts offered in the market, farm prices would undoubtedly have been lower and the apparent recovery less significant than it was. But the problem had only been deferred, not solved. The stocks were still in existence and available for sale. In part, however, this accumulation of stocks was an early manifestation of war influence. The outbreak of war in 1939 reduced even further the low level of farm exports that had prevailed in the earlier years of the decade.

Thus, in part, the stock accumulations were a logical and necessary stabilization activity in a war situation. Government action to provide temporary outlets for storable commodities when markets are sharply contracted because of outside influences may well be justified if not carried to extremes.

Nevertheless, continuing purchase of excess supplies soon builds up stocks that create more problems than they solve. In a period when demand falls suddenly, action to take goods off the market and immobilize them can give time for making necessary adjustments of production. But if adjustments are not made and the stocks continue to pile up, they may become a serious threat to the farm price structure as a whole. At best, they do not solve the problem since it is still there, along with that of excess stocks. Sooner or later the necessary adjustments in output have to be made, usually with the added complication of stocks to be worked down.

Prosperity in the 1940s

The prosperity of agriculture in the 1940s derived its strength from a phenomenally high demand, not from production controls or price supports. This strong demand, though indirectly a result of war activity, was based primarily on full employment and abnormal exports, with full employment the predominant influence.

The importance of full employment can hardly be overemphasized. Even though we ignore the war period itself, if national income and business activity could be kept at the levels prevailing in the years since 1946, much of the farm problem would be solved, once needed adjustments are made. There can be little doubt that a domestic consumer demand as high as that of the present would more than take care of the amount of unbalance that was appearing in the late 1930s, granting a moderately strong foreign demand for such major export crops as wheat, cotton and tobacco.

The levels of support in effect at that time were modest, possibly lower than could well be provided in periods of reasonably strong demand. The excessive accumulations, except those of cotton, were absorbed, chiefly in domestic markets, as available workers became employed and national income rose. United States per capita food consumption soon moved up to a level some 10 to 12 per cent above that of the late 1930s.[17] The volume of exports was abnormal from 1941 through 1949 but mainly for a relatively small number of products, particularly wheat, dried eggs, dried milk and some types of pork products. Some of the highest levels of prices reached were for products that were not exported in important amounts. The markets were especially strong for meats and fluid milk, which did not move importantly into the export markets.

17. See *Agricultural Statistics, 1952*, p. 811.

With a rapidly growing population, if full employment can be maintained, domestic requirements should in a few years be adequate to absorb at good prices the amounts of farm products now being produced, except for a few commodities in which severe distortions resulting from the war period or from sudden changes in demand still have not been ironed out. Thus, the problem is partly that of checking or slowing down further expansion until demand can catch up with production capacity. This would imply currently a program of disposal through abnormal outlets of part of the existing accumulation of stocks, some easing down of the price stimuli which now seem to be resulting in a larger output than is needed, and measures for quick adjustment in the acreages of crops that still seem to be on an overexpanded war and postwar basis.[18]

1942–1948, Control of Inflation the Principal Problem

From the time of our entry into the war, the principal problem was not that of holding farm prices up but rather that of holding them down. Temporary gains to agriculture could be achieved by allowing farm prices to rise above parity. Farm representatives contended that this was only fair in view of the long period in which farm prices had been low. However, the urban worker who had been unemployed could equally well contend that no controls should be applied to wage rates since he, too, was entitled to a catching-up period.

There can be no doubt that letting food prices and wage rates seek their own level in a free market would have been extremely inflationary and also a serious handicap to the war effort in a mobilization as complete as that of World War II. If stabilization of prices and wages is to be undertaken, it must be rigorous and across the board. Only in that way can an enormous ballooning of war costs be avoided and, in all probability, a major deflation when the war ends.

Though agriculture tends to profit temporarily in an inflationary period, there is reason to doubt that its long-term interests are best served by encouraging such a development. Inflation tends to raise sharply many of the fixed costs of agriculture, notably transportation rates, taxes and the cost-price structure for things bought by farmers. If we can judge by past experience, it is much more difficult to hold farm prices up when the inflationary pressures ease off than for other groups to maintain the prices of their goods and services. Thus, agriculture may find itself saddled with a greatly inflated cost structure, and its competitive position in foreign markets weakened, without having received in return anything of lasting value. Its long-term interests appear to be best served by a relatively stable general price level. During the war years, both agricul-

18. This comment pertains primarily to commercial markets. It does not include "give-away" programs. To the extent that these are contemplated, either as a continuing part of our foreign policy or as a means of easing the problems of transition here and abroad, they would presumably be paid for domestically in dollars and hence would provide a larger market than that implied above.

ture and labor were in a strong position politically and economically. Labor seemingly showed greater restraint in its demands for temporary gains.

Had agriculture been willing to accept the general principle on which the price and wage stabilization of the war years was based, except for some catching up which appears to have been a justifiable demand, the more prominent controversies of the war period could have been avoided. Prices received by farmers had risen from 95 in 1939 (1910–14=100) to 158 in 1942, an increase of 66 per cent. The parity ratio then stood at 105.[19] Gross farm income had risen from $10.4 to $18.6 billion, an increase of more than 78 per cent.[20] This larger increase in income was due to increased production. The corresponding rise in realized net income was from $4.3 to $8.8 billion, an increase of just over 100 per cent.

Average weekly earnings of production workers in manufacturing industries had advanced from $23.86 in 1939 to $36.65 in 1942, an increase of 54 per cent.[21] The heavy expenditure of government funds for food subsidies, which was strongly opposed by the farm groups, was made largely to hold food prices stable and thus to ease pressure for breaching the wage stabilization line roughly established by the "Little Steel" formula, which permitted, for most types of normally employed workers, increases of up to 15 per cent over the levels prevailing in 1940.[22]

The issue was whether farm prices should be rolled back enough to hold the cost of living line or whether nonfarm workers should pay enough more out of their increased earnings to cover the increased cost

19. *Agricultural Statistics, 1952,* p. 682.
20. *Ibid.,* p. 698.
21. *Statistical Abstract, 1953,* p. 214. While the figures given above do not reflect the over-all change in wage rates, they are probably the most dependable and the most appropriate for use in such a comparison. Substantially higher rates were paid in the war industries. However, the taking of these jobs meant in many cases a shift in location for the worker, the learning of a new trade, and the acceptance of poorer and more expensive living accommodations. Higher rates were necessary to entice workers, including some not normally in the labor force, into these essential industries.

Farmers were in place and could undertake a stepped-up program of production without changing their locations or ways of life. This was true also for many of the factory workers. The farmer often gained a distorted view of the situation, for which some of the Department of Agriculture presentations are not without blame. Graphs showing the increase in *total* earnings of nonfarm workers as compared to total returns to farmers were given wide publicity. This formulation of the relationship ignored the fact that there had been a great increase in the number of nonfarm workers employed while the number of workers on farms had decreased slightly. Total employment had risen from about 45 million in 1939 to 55.8 million in 1942. Unemployment had dropped from an estimated 8.7 million to virtually zero. The number employed in agriculture declined from 10.7 to 10.4 million. See U.S. Bureau of the Census, *Historical Statistics of the United States, 1789–1945,* p. 65.

22. Many workers were, however, earning more than 15 per cent above their 1940 rates because of overtime at overtime rates, steadier employment, and through evasions of the stabilization formula. Note above that average weekly earnings in factory work had increased by 54 per cent.

of food. The farm groups contended that wage workers could well afford to absorb this increase in food costs, which no doubt was true. However, labor was not likely to acquiesce in such a solution without demanding relaxation of the controls on wages.

The government compromised by adopting the very controversial rollback program of April 1943. Farm prices were allowed to remain undisturbed and the government paid subsidies to processors, handlers and producers to enable them to continue the higher prices to farmers while still avoiding significant further increases in the prices paid by consumers. These subsidies, like any that are extended to the population as a whole, proved very costly. More than $4 billion of government funds went into them and, in general, inflationary pressures were increased rather than decreased. The amounts could have been absorbed either by the farmers or by the consumers without serious hardship. The solution arrived at was a result of political pressures, not a reflection of the desires of the administrative officials concerned.[23]

Postwar Guarantees

The postwar guarantees provided in the act of 1941 and the Steagall Amendment can be defended on at least two grounds. One, they were designed to assure willingness of farmers to make the investments necessary for relatively full production during the war years. In this respect, they were not materially different in principle from the concessions made to industrialists whereby they were assured of returns adequate to cover costs and a right to claim very rapid depreciation on their facilities after the close of the war. Two, there was reason from the standpoint of both farmers and the public to provide insurance against a disastrous break in farm prices such as that of 1920. Such a period of assured support could give time for readjustment to a peacetime pattern and volume of production.

Labor was also given some assurance against a severe setback when the war ended, and a longer-term commitment as well. The Employment Act of 1946, though not passed until after the war ended, had been under consideration for some time. The very general concern over the possibility of a severe postwar slump made it virtually certain that some kind of stabilizing legislation would be enacted.

The Employment Act did not provide such definite and direct assurance as that contained in the farm legislation. Nevertheless, the implied commitment of federal funds was probably at least as large, even when considered in terms of the relative sizes of the farm and nonfarm parts

23. For a fuller account of this controversy, see M. R. Benedict, *Farm Policies of the United States, 1790–1950,* Twentieth Century Fund, New York, 1953, pp. 420–30. The food subsidy program was not wholly one of price stabilization. In part, it was used as a means of stimulating production, particularly of dairy products. More than a billion dollars of it was for that purpose.

of the economy. The act constituted acceptance of a policy of using to the fullest extent possible the resources of the government to assure continuing high employment. Presumably this meant heavy deficit spending in the event of a severe decline in employment and the use of other measures as well.

Contrary to expectations, conditions in the postwar period were such that neither of these guarantees had to be used to any extent. After only a brief period of readjustment, the economy moved into a period of high employment and active demand. Buying power was high, not only as a result of full employment at high wages but also because of large amounts of buying power carried over from the war period in the form of savings.

This high level of business activity made for an extremely strong domestic market for the products of agriculture. Demand was further strengthened by the large, artificially financed export market provided through the British loan and the grants and loans made under the policy known as the Marshall Plan. Farm prices not only maintained their wartime levels but went much higher. Standing at 206 (1910–14 = 100) in 1945, they moved up to 234 in 1946, to 275 in 1947 and to 285 in 1948. Not until 1949 was there any hint of the kind of postwar slump that had been so much feared.

A significant readjustment did get under way in 1949 and the farm price index dropped to 249. However, the parity ratio was still up to 100[24] and the adjustment then being made cannot be regarded as an unhealthy one. Some retreat from the extremely high prices of the war and postwar years was inevitable, and it was desirable that it be taken in moderate steps rather than for the industry to continue to be over-stimulated until it built up a situation in which a much more severe setback was likely.

The situation of agriculture had also been strengthened by the fact that production remained high in these years. As a consequence, the returns to farmers reached levels never before approached, even when allowance is made for changes in the price level. Gross farm income exceeded $34 billion in both 1947 and 1948. This compares with the pre-World War II peak of $17.7 billion reached in 1919, which was also in a period of very marked postwar inflation. Yet, the number of workers on farms was lower than at any time since 1910 and earlier.[25]

There was trouble in a few lines, mostly minor crops and products, such as fruits that were heavily dependent on foreign markets that had been disrupted or cut off, dried eggs, dried milk and so on. These problems were eased substantially by the opportunities afforded for exports under the foreign-aid programs. Even cotton stocks, which had been a problem from 1938 through 1946, were quickly reduced and

24. Until then, it had been above 100 in every year from 1942 on and had reached 115 in 1947. See *Agricultural Statistics, 1952*, p. 682.
25. Except for a slightly smaller number in 1944 and 1945. There were about 3 million fewer workers on farms in 1948 than in 1910. See *Agricultural Statistics, 1953*, p. 565.

were down to very modest levels by 1947. The principal problem was in potatoes, which were being produced at a rate far in excess of needs because of the high support levels established in the war years and the very rapid technological advances which brought about a doubling of yields in some areas and very large increases in others.

Adjustment Checked in 1950

The adjustment which had got under way in 1949 was checked and, in fact, thrown into reverse by the outbreak of war in the summer of 1950. Farm prices again moved up, reaching 256 in 1950 and 302, an all-time high, in 1951. The 1951 parity ratio stood at 107. Prior to this new upsurge in prices, there were indications that farmers themselves were beginning to make some of the adjustments needed. Wheat acreage planted was down from 84 million in 1949 to 71 million in 1950. Corn acreage was reduced from 87 to 83 million. Cotton acreage was cut more severely, probably too much in view of the demand that developed later. This came about as a result of acreage allotments and quotas which were applied to the 1950 crop. Potato acreage was down about 40 per cent from the levels of the war years but yields were far above normal and production continued to be excessive.

The 1950–51 upsurge in prices caused a re-expansion of acreage in wheat and cotton and contributed to the surplus problem which developed in 1953 and 1954. Wheat acreage was increased to 77.5 million in 1952 and to 78.5 million in 1953. The harvested acreage of cotton was up in 1951 to 26.8 million as compared to 17.8 million in 1950 and remained above 25.5 million in 1952.

As a consequence, the readjustments that most people expected would have to be made in the years just following the war have been deferred for nearly a decade. By 1953, it became evident that some crops were being produced in amounts that could not be sold at satisfactory prices even with a strong domestic demand and a gradually reviving foreign market. Stocks began to pile up and a planned readjustment was initiated for several of the major crops for the year 1954. Acreage allotments and marketing quotas were placed on wheat and cotton and acreage allotments were assigned for corn. Tobacco has continued under the rigorous controls of earlier years.

In part, the heavy accumulations of 1949–50 and 1953–54 were due to the continuance of the long run of good yields which has lasted almost without a break since 1937. If a year or two of poor crops were to occur, the transition to a more balanced production and stock situation might perhaps be made more easily than if yields continue high. However, readjustments in some lines must be made sooner or later. Wheat production, for example, has been geared to an export outlet of 400 to 500 million bushels per year, but exports had declined to about 215 million bushels by 1953–54, and they may go lower, if we can judge by the volumes taken in earlier peacetime periods.

Wheat Problem Not Wholly One of Prices

The problem in wheat is not wholly one of unduly high prices. There appears to be more wheat available and in prospect than can be moved into consumption except possibly through gift and loan programs. It is very doubtful that a continuing commercial outlet for as much as 300 million bushels of U.S. wheat per year can be found even at prices much lower than those now prevailing in the world markets. It seems more realistic to think in terms of a usual flow of exports in the order of 150 to 250 million bushels than of one as large as that of recent years. This, however, is in terms of something approximating current world prices. If the United States wishes to export as much as 200 to 300 million bushels of wheat and at the same time to maintain U.S. prices at current levels, that apparently can be done only by continuing the very expensive export subsidy program now being carried out by means of the International Wheat Agreement or one of similar type.

A gradual withdrawal of the United States from the export market would undoubtedly strengthen the world market price for wheat, but it seems entirely likely that Canada, Australia and Argentina, and the consuming countries, could and would expand production enough to take care of the export market the United States is now supplying without raising world market prices enough to wipe out the current differential between United States and world prices. In other words, it does not seem likely that any practical adjustment the United States could make would support world wheat prices at the levels now maintained in the United States.

The acreage cuts put into effect in 1954 brought production roughly into balance with the then current levels of domestic consumption and export but were not large enough to cause a reduction in the stocks held. Unless there should be a year or two of poor yields, or a new war demand, it is probable that abnormal outlets will have to be devised if these stocks are to be worked down significantly in the near future.

If the current levels of price support are to be maintained, it seems apparent that subsidies on exports will have to be continued even if a solution is found for the excess-stock problem. Furthermore, acreage and market controls will have to be continued at least until a new pattern of crop production involving less acreage in wheat becomes rather well established. The current adjustment is in the direction of a more normal level of wheat acreage, not a temporary action to clear up an acute situation and one which can be abandoned once the oversupply has been reduced.

The current level of price support for wheat will induce farmers to plant more acreage than is needed to meet prospective domestic and foreign demand. If these prices are to be maintained, production will have to be held in check. Such a plan will, of course, mean a lower gross return to wheat farmers for wheat because of the smaller volumes produced. Some decision will have to be made either to ease down price supports so as to provide less stimulus for wheat production or to maintain some kind of two-price program, letting farmers produce as much for export, or for inferior domestic uses, as they find attractive at the prices they can obtain. The only alternative is to continue rigorous controls on output and the expensive export subsidy program now being used. It may be that a combination of two or all three of these devices will be needed for a time.

Continuing accumulation of stocks through CCC purchases cannot provide any lasting solution. Furthermore, it tends to build up a more and more serious threat to the well-being of the industry and to the farm price structure generally. The sooner a more appropriate and longer-term policy can be adopted the better. CCC loans, purchases and holdings can do much to steady the situation in periods of temporary surplus. They can maintain needed emergency reserves and can aid in transition programs. They cannot provide, for any long period, an outlet for commodities that are produced continuously in substantial excess of the amounts the market will take.[26]

Cotton Presents a Different Set of Problems

The United States has long been the major supplier of the world's cotton markets. Hence, what is done with respect to cotton will have

---

26. The above comments pertain to the commercial markets. To the extent that the United States chooses to undertake, temporarily or continuously, give-away or special-concession programs for aid to needy people abroad, larger amounts can be used. This, however, involves many problems which cannot be discussed here. Not the least of them would be the willingness of other countries to accept such donations, the willingness of our people to make them and the danger that they may be interpreted as attempts to interfere in the political affairs of other nations.

Furthermore, aside from the humiliations inherent in accepting charity from a rich neighbor, other countries are understandably reluctant to become dependent upon a flow of supplies that is geared to the need of another nation to unburden itself of stocks rather than to the continuing needs of the receiving country. Such gifts also are subject to the whims of a foreign legislative body over which the recipients have no control.

There is much to be said for seeking abnormal outlets as a means of easing down the excess stocks now held and affording other nations an opportunity to meet emergency needs or initiate needed reforms. The actions of this kind that were taken in the years following the war are almost universally regarded as having been constructive, practical and humane.

However, there is almost equally general agreement that such measures, though appropriate in times of great need, may if continued undiscriminatingly actually weaken the economies of the recipient nations by causing them to place excessive reliance on outside help. The longer-term storage policy should apparently be such as to make possible U.S. aid in meeting desperate and temporary needs abroad. Public sentiment almost certainly would favor such a policy. It is unlikely that it would support any continuing, large-scale give-away program.

more bearing on what happens in other parts of the world than what is done in regard to wheat. Also, U.S. cotton production was not expanded during the war years. Carry-overs were heavy both here and abroad but these were quickly and substantially reduced in the years immediately following the war.[27] The problem is similar in many ways to that of the 1930s.

During the late 1930s and again in the recent postwar years, U.S. cotton prices were held higher than they would have been had there been no government intervention. Foreign growths could be sold at slightly under the U.S. price and the burden of carrying unsold stocks rested mainly on the U.S. government. The prices thus maintained in the world market were high enough to provide a significant stimulus to foreign cotton producers.[28] Foreign production moved up from around 11 million bales in the early 1930s to a 15– to 18–million-bale level in the middle 1930s. This about offset the cutbacks made in the United States and resulted in a world production that was comparatively stable, except for the big crops of 1936 and 1937.

Foreign production, like that of the United States, dropped back during the war years. However, it moved up strongly in the years following 1949 and provided well over half the world supply in 1950 and 1951.[29] So long as the United States maintains a well-known and legislatively established price, foreign growths can be sold at slightly lower prices and still reap most of the advantages of the U.S. control programs. However, there still is a marked preference for U.S.-grown fiber and the maintenance of a strong foreign outlet for U.S. cotton is obviously of great importance to American growers.

It may be that the United States could maintain or nearly maintain its place in the world markets by making only moderate adjustments in its program. There apparently should be enough flexibility in its marketing operations to permit the moving of a normal portion of its export cotton into world markets in most years. This might not ordinarily require any very marked price concessions. It would imply keeping the American market flexible enough so that it could meet ordinary types of competition. Until 1948, the over-all world production of cotton did not show any significant upward trend. World production did expand in the years 1948 to 1952 but even then was about the same as in the years 1929

27. For data, see *Agricultural Statistics, 1952,* p. 80.

28. Here the dependence of the world market on U.S. supplies was so great that at most times the U.S. price had to be met or nearly met in order to obtain supplies. Hence the action taken in the United States affected importantly the whole world market. For wheat, the United States does not occupy this dominant position and its influence on the world markets for most other farm products is even less significant.

29. Foreign production moved up from about a 12-million-bale level in 1947 and 1948 to 16.9 million bales in 1950 and 19.2 million in 1951. U.S. production was down to 9.9 million bales in 1950 and expanded again to 15.1 million bales in 1951. It ranged from 8.6 million bales to 16 million in the years 1946 through 1949. See *Agricultural Statistics, 1953,* p. 68.

through 1933. The United States itself accounted for more than half of the 3-million-bale increase of world output in 1949.

Part of the postwar gain in the relative position of foreign-grown cotton has no doubt been due to the dollar shortage and the tendency for the consuming countries to buy in soft-currency areas. This influence appears to be receding and possibly can be offset to some extent by increased sales effort—for example, by making American supplies available in convenient locations abroad and by improving short-term credit arrangements. However, there is need for U.S. exporters to be able to meet competition in a businesslike way. This implies less rigidity both in prices and in the regulations governing the release of stocks held by the government.

The maintenance of a smooth and continuous flow of cotton into the markets, both foreign and domestic, is of great importance to the future of the cotton industry. Once machinery has been adapted to other types of cotton, and when new trade channels have been developed and foreign acreages expanded, it is extremely difficult to recapture markets that have been lost.

Competition from Synthetics

Possibly even more important is the great increase in the substitution of synthetic fibers for cotton, silk and wool. United States annual consumption of rayon, acetate and other synthetic fibers has grown from less than 10 million pounds in 1920 to nearly 1.5 billion in 1950–1952.[30] However, this increase in the use of synthetic fibers has not resulted in any significant decrease in the per capita consumption of either cotton or wool. It has been added on. Per capita consumption of cotton was in excess of 30 pounds in both 1950 and 1951. It never reached this figure in the period between 1919 and 1940. Consumption was higher in the war years, ranging from 32 to 41 pounds, but this increase apparently was largely a result of high military requirements.

A more important consideration is what the synthetics may do to the foreign markets for cotton. There the increase in the use of synthetic fibers has also been notable, especially in the years between 1948 and 1951. With dollars hard to get, there are strong incentives for other countries to turn to synthetics, many of which can be made from raw materials that are available either domestically or in other soft-currency countries.

Once factories for the production of synthetic fibers have been built, and markets for the product developed, this much of the market for cotton has virtually been lost forever. It is obviously in the long-run interest of cotton growers, therefore, to avoid forcing this type of change-

30. *Ibid.*, p. 80.

over by pricing themselves out of the market or by policies that lead to uncertainty about the dependability of U.S. supplies.[31]

This does not necessarily mean that the United States should strive to regain as large a place in the world markets for cotton as it once held. Cotton has traditionally been a plantation crop. Much of our dominant position in world cotton production resulted not only from climatic and soil factors but also from low wages and low standards of living for cotton farmers and cotton workers. The possible alternative uses for this labor and these resources in the United States appear to be favorable enough to warrant some shift away from our past heavy reliance on cotton in some areas, unless increased mechanization should make possible much lower real costs than have prevailed in the past.

It may be in the national interest as well as that of the cotton producers to move toward a lower volume of cotton production and in so doing to improve the returns to the people who work in cotton both here and abroad. There is need for much study and careful thought both about the direction our cotton program should take and the kind of cotton economy we want to aid in developing.

Whatever longer-term policy is adopted, it seems apparent that there is immediate need for introducing more flexibility into the pricing arrangements, particularly for export cotton; for aggressive and realistic sales policies in the markets abroad; and for less reliance on CCC purchases and loans as a method of supporting prices. Here, as in wheat, continuing acquisition of costly, immobile stocks cannot provide any permanent solution and may set the stage for a disastrous price break.

The Butter Problem

The amounts of money committed in the butter price-support program are a large though not a major factor in the current heavy commitments of the Commodity Credit Corporation. While the problem presented by these heavy stocks of a costly and semiperishable product is extremely perplexing, a still more baffling one is that of devising a more permanent program.

The butter industry is in the throes of a major technological and consumption revolution. A growing population in which per capita milk consumption is high has caused vast areas that formerly depended on income from butter and cheese to turn to the production of fluid milk for the urban markets. If there were no margarine industry, the dairy industry as now constituted could not supply our present population with as much butter as it would desire. Some sort of substitution or abstention would be necessary.

At the same time, a new and much cheaper product of similar type

31. That is, by policies that may lead to such severe curtailments that regular customers cannot be supplied in some years. This applies to situations such as that of 1950 when the abrupt and drastic cutback in cotton production helped to bring about a severe shortage and very high prices throughout the world.

has become available. The consumption of margarine has grown from 230 million pounds in 1931 to more than 1.2 billion in 1952.[32] Per capita consumption moved up from 1.8 pounds to 7.8 pounds. During the same period, butter consumption declined from 2.2 billion pounds to 1.4 billion and per capita consumption fell off from 18.0 pounds to 8.7 pounds. Part of the change is due to a change in dietary habits. Total per capita consumption of the two spreads is now only about 16.5 pounds as compared to nearly 20 pounds in 1931. In part, this difference has been made up by increased use of other edible oils. The amount of such products used has grown from 4.8 pounds to 8.8 pounds, an increase of 4.0 pounds per capita. This constitutes, in the main, an additional shift to butter substitutes.

Total milk production grew from 89 billion pounds in 1924 to 115 billion in 1952.[33] The sales of whole milk rose in the same period from 26 billion pounds to 77 billion. Thus, the dairy industry as a whole, and in particular the fluid milk phase of it, has shown a strong and consistent growth. The principal problem is in the dairy areas that depend mainly on returns from butter. Considerable amounts of butter are made from excess milk supplied to distributors of fluid milk. Fluid milk consumption is rather stable within the year but milk production varies considerably. Since the producers of milk to be sold for consumption as fluid milk or cream must be able to supply the market in periods of low production, they must have large supplies in some seasons of the year and these must be disposed of in other ways. Much of this "Class II" milk is made into butter.

However, neither these producers nor the distributors are primarily dependent on the returns from butter. Their principal income is from sales of fluid milk and cream. Even in the by-product field, there are other outlets such as ice cream, cottage cheese, casein and dried milk. Hence, though a marked reduction in the price of butter would be to their disadvantage, it would not constitute an economic disaster as it does for dairy farmers in the areas that specialize in butter production.

Effect of Price Supports on the Industry

The price-support legislation passed during and after the war provided for support of the price of butter at from 75 to 90 per cent of parity. Until April 1954, the price of butter was supported at 90 per cent of parity. This was a higher price than the market would pay and still absorb the entire output.[34] As a consequence, even in this period of high buying power, large quantities of butter have been bought and stored by the

32. *Agricultural Statistics, 1953*, p. 150.
33. *Agricultural Statistics, 1952*, p. 471, and *ibid., 1953*, p. 405. This omits milk sold to other farmers for local delivery.
34. In the computation of parity, the relation of butter prices to the prices of other commodities is derived from an earlier period when margarine was not an important competitor.

government. It cannot be kept indefinitely. Butter deteriorates much faster than wheat, cotton and other nonperishables.

More serious from the standpoint of the butter producers is the fact that more and more people are turning to margarine because of its lower cost and are becoming confirmed margarine users. Butter is being priced out of the market and the outlook is for a declining rather than an increasing volume of consumption. If butter is to be kept generally on American tables, it apparently will have to be priced at a level that will enable it to compete with margarine.

This does not mean, of course, that it would have to sell at the same price as margarine. There still is a strong preference for butter and it has some qualities that margarine does not have. Undoubtedly it could all be moved at prices substantially above those for margarine but not at as large a differential as that which has existed in recent years. Furthermore, there is a very real chance that the younger generation now growing up, if confined largely to the use of margarine, may not have any strong preference for butter. Hence the market for butter might decline still further in the years to come.

The support price for butter was reduced to 75 per cent of parity on April 1, 1954. However, the price was still enough above that of margarine to make it unlikely that the entire output could be sold through normal channels. The government also was faced with the difficult problem of finding ways of moving into consumption the stocks already held.

Alternative Solutions

Government purchase and storage of butter obviously is not a satisfactory method of aiding the industry. It almost certainly will have to be abandoned in the not distant future. Alternative solutions are difficult and perplexing both for the butter producers and the industry. Farmers have long been encouraged to turn to dairying as a stable and constructive type of farming. Very heavy investments have been made in herds, barns, silos and other dairy equipment. These things cannot be changed easily or quickly, and very large numbers of thrifty, able farmers are dependent on dairy products for their incomes.

Part of these resources can be turned to cheese production, an excellent substitute for meat, which occupies so large a place in the food budgets of most families. It is probable that some of the adjustment will be in this direction, but it cannot come rapidly. Government stocks of cheese acquired under the price-support program have also been increasing, though they do not constitute as severe a problem as the butter stocks.

The total civilian consumption of cheese has doubled since 1924 and per capita consumption has risen from 4.5 to 7.7 pounds.[35] American

35. *Agricultural Statistics, 1953,* p. 496.

per capita consumption of cheese is low compared to that of European countries. Dietary changes of that kind take place only slowly and probably cannot be readily brought about. Nevertheless, the government might, as part of its dairy program, consider giving aid and stimulus to some shift in this direction. However, this may not be an easy way out as it seems likely that the repercussions of the declining butter market will force some readjustments in the price of cheese and that current levels of support for cheese cannot practically be maintained through government purchase and storage.

It is unlikely that the clock can or will be turned back very much as far as the shift to margarine is concerned. A large segment of the farm population is being affected by an important technological revolution. One part of this revolution, the shift to production for the fluid milk markets, has on the whole proved beneficial to those farmers who were able to take advantage of it. They do not constitute a major problem so far as the margarine situation is concerned.

For the others, there appears to be justification for providing some government aid in making the kind of transition that probably is inevitable. It seems equally clear that high price supports and a top-heavy storage program are not only impractical for the government but are not likely to be in the longer-run interest of the butter producers themselves.[36] Direct payments on a declining scale might be considered as a means of easing the transition. If used, they should be accompanied by positive programs designed to facilitate and encourage shifts to the kinds of production patterns that probably will eventually emerge. Continued propping up of an industry that appears to be faced with a major readjustment is not likely to prove satisfactory either to the public or to the farmers concerned.

In the meantime, steps need to be taken as promptly as possible to move the stocks in storage in such a way as to disturb the markets as little as possible. Among the possibilities are sales to public institutions, export programs, and special drives and incentives to increase domestic consumption. The dairy industry will not benefit from a repetition of the procedures which led to such widespread condemnation of the potato program and resulted in virtual abandonment, at least for the time being, of efforts to aid in making the adjustments needed.

Programs Relating to Minor Crops and Fluid Milk

It is not feasible to summarize here all of the many price-support programs undertaken or authorized under legislation now in effect. Most of them are described and analyzed in preceding chapters and in the more

---

36. This is not meant to imply that well-considered storage programs cannot be used to advantage at times. Short-term stabilizing purchases have been helpful in some situations. They have not been successful as ways of keeping prices far above the levels at which the market would absorb the product.

detailed analyses presented in the companion volume on commodity programs. Many of them are smaller in scale and hence, whatever their merits or demerits, do not involve such large commitments of federal funds. Neither do they constitute so serious a threat to the over-all structure of farm prices. For most of the programs, the price guarantees are less rigid and more opportunity is afforded for realistic management of the industry problems involved.

Probably the most significant price-support programs, in terms of dollar volume, are those relating to fluid milk, sugar and wool. Each of these involves problems that are peculiar to itself and unlike those pertaining to the major field crops discussed above. The fluid milk market has to a large extent been stabilized by means of federal and state marketing agreements and legislation and by somewhat similar organizational arrangements not sponsored by either federal or state governments.[37]

In the main, the aim has been to introduce stability in an industry that, without comprehensive organization, either private or governmental, would almost inevitably become so chaotic that action of some kind would have to be taken. There has been some criticism of the monopoly characteristics of the program and complaints about the levels of price maintained. However, because of its nature, it does not give rise to a major fiscal problem for the federal government. The direct input of federal funds is negligible. The issue, if there is one, is that of equity as among consumers, producers and distributors and as between producers who are in or outside the system.

It may be, however, that weaknesses in the program have been to some extent concealed by the rapid increases in consumption that have marked the past decade and by the prevailing high level of prosperity. A considerable degree of stability has been achieved in this set of conditions. Would the program work as well in a period of declining demand, or would prices tend to be kept too high in terms of fairness to consumers and the best interests of the industry as a whole?

The pricing process that has been developed is administrative in character rather than competitive and hence subject to the same kinds of mistakes that such procedures are prone to in both private and government business. Political considerations would enter in more strongly, however, since decisions would not be so exclusively in the hands of governing boards and administrators as in the case of private corporations. The procedures now almost universally used in the industry seem

37. It is significant that the governmentally sponsored or administered programs in fluid milk are very similar to those that have grown up in markets where the organizational arrangements are wholly private. The price structures in the two types of market are much alike. This does not mean, of course, that either type of market is free of monopoly influences. In most markets of any size where there is neither federal nor state control, both producers and distributors are highly organized and the pricing arrangements are more like those arrived at by labor unions bargaining with employers than those prevailing in most competitive markets for farm products.

likely to make adjustments possible in the event of a sharp decline in demand for fluid milk and in such a way as not to threaten disaster to the organizational arrangements. More milk would be consigned to secondary uses and returns to producers would be reduced. Prices to consumers for fluid milk might be held higher than many would consider appropriate and reasonable. However, an outlet for such manufactured by-products as butter, cheese and ice cream would apparently exist at some price and the industry would not be likely to run into the problem of unmanageably large stocks, except temporarily in such products as casein and dried milk for which the quantities the markets will absorb are limited.

This is on the assumption that the industry would dispose of its manufactured by-products at free-market prices if necessary. To the extent that the government chooses to support their prices through a purchase and storage program, carried out largely in behalf of producers in the areas dependent on income from manufactured dairy products, the problem would become one for the government rather than for the fluid milk industry.

Continuance of the current program in respect to butter, cheese and dried milk does, of course, involve heavy government outlays, part of which arise by way of the fluid milk industry. A retreat from existing levels of price support for manufactured dairy products might be expected to increase pressure from outside producers for entry to the fluid milk markets. New technological developments also may contribute to such outside entry into the fluid milk markets through channels other than those of the regular fluid milk marketing agencies. For a fuller analysis of this large and complex problem, see Chapter 11 of the companion volume on commodity programs.

Sugar, Wool, Meats, Poultry and Rice

Two of the major products, sugar and wool, are deficit commodities in the United States. Both have long been prominent in congressional discussions of farm problems. There are strategic, as well as political, considerations in respect to them. For both of them, the United States is heavily dependent on offshore supplies in the event of war. The programs relating to them involve significant governmental costs but in less direct forms than for most of the products discussed above. However, they do not lend themselves to any brief and simple set of conclusions. Discussion of them is therefore deferred to Chapters 7 and 8 of the volume on commodity programs.

The growers of many of the other commodities have made considerable progress in adjusting to postwar markets, provided employment and national incomes continue at their present high levels. Problems persist in some of the fruit industries, particularly dried fruits and citrus. The beef cattle industry has experienced a severe readjustment in prices, but this was in relation to the very high level of the early postwar years.

Meat animals as a whole are still in fairly good situation in terms of parity, even with parity computed according to the new formula, which results in a higher parity for these products than when the old formula is used.[38] However, this level for meats is due to the fact that hogs are substantially above parity while beef cattle and calves are below parity. The cattle industry is in the process of liquidating an abnormally high inventory. The relationships between cattle and hog prices seem likely to change during the next few years as cattle inventories are reduced and hog production is increased.[39] In general, the beef cattle producers apparently prefer to rely on competitive market prices rather than on government programs. This has been their attitude almost all through the period here under review.

The poultry and egg industry has, for the most part, reverted to free-market operations and appears to have made its adjustment without major difficulties. The greatly expanded dried egg industry was given support through government purchases for some years after the war but adjustments have now been made and this phase of the industry seems to be less of a problem than it was in 1949 and early 1950. Some assistance in the form of price-support purchase programs has been given to the turkey industry but this also seems now to be getting into better balance.

Rice production still is out of balance, and new marketing agreements for a number of the perishables have been considered from time to time. In the main, the approach to these problems looks more in the direction of stabilizing the industries concerned than toward direct price raising through government action. For some of them, assistance has been provided out of Section 32 funds and school lunch funds. As a whole, they do not bulk large in the over-all farm problem that is currently of such large congressional and public interest. If the problems relating to cotton, wheat, corn, butter, sugar and wool can be solved, the others do not appear to be unmanageable.

CONSERVATION AND CONSERVATION PAYMENTS

Aside from the price-support programs discussed in the preceding pages, there has been more controversy over conservation policy and organization than on any of the other long-term programs relating to

38. As of March 15, 1954, the parity price for beef cattle (under the new formula) stood at $21.20 per hundredweight. The price received was $16.00. Hogs were $24.70 as compared to a parity price of $20.80. See U.S. Department of Agriculture, Agricultural Marketing Service, *Statistical Summary,* April 15, 1954.

39. The hog-corn ratio—that is, the ratio between the price of hogs per hundredweight and the price of a bushel of corn—then stood at 18 as compared to a long-term average of slightly more than 12. This meant that it was very profitable to feed relatively cheap corn to high-priced hogs. As a consequence, hog production, in terms of live weight, was increased about 9 per cent in 1954.

agriculture. As now carried on, conservation also involves heavy expenditure of federal funds.

The conservation activities for the farming areas fall mainly into two categories, one a program consisting mainly of education and technical assistance, the other a program involving cash payments to farmers for carrying on specified types of soil-conserving activity. The first and earlier of the two has been developed through the Soil Erosion Service and its successor the Soil Conservation Service (now the Agricultural Conservation Program Service). The second program was originally handled by the Agricultural Adjustment Administration and later by the Production and Marketing Administration. It is now under the Agricultural Conservation Program Service.

The general objective of both types of program is widely accepted among both farmers and nonfarmers. Controversy centers mainly around the questions of how much to spend and how the work should be organized. Between 1936 and 1953 there were, in effect, two separate federal organizations with similar but not identical objectives. In addition, the state extension services have developed a strong interest in the problem and are to some extent rival claimants for funds and leadership in this field.

Rivalries and, in some cases, frictions have developed because of the divided responsibilities and because of differences not only in the methods used but in the objectives sought. Charges of duplication of effort, lack of coordination and excessive expense have been frequent both in the Congress and on the part of the farm groups. Rivalries between farm organizations for control or influence have also played a part in the controversy. A far-reaching system of soil conservation districts has been developed. It does not follow county lines and its principal ties have been with the Soil Conservation Service. The conservation payment program is handled on a county basis. The agricultural extension services, which have strong ties with the state and national farm bureau federations, are organized on a county basis.

Some farm organizations favor continuance of direct supervision from Washington and place primary emphasis on the soil conservation districts as the agencies to work through at the local level. Others favor the transfer of most of the funds to the states and placing on the state agricultural extension services the main responsibility for carrying out the program of education and technical assistance.

These differences are to a considerable extent problems within agriculture. They do not, in the main, involve questions of the desirability of carrying on conservation work. The general public is not importantly concerned with them except as rivalries and lack of coordination may increase the expense, change the emphasis, or decrease the efficiency of a program which, for the most part, has the approval of farmers and the public at large. It would appear therefore to be principally a problem for agriculture itself rather than a problem of broad national policy in which the general public is likely to take an important interest.

The other phase of the soil conservation program, namely, paying farmers for making soil-conserving types of change in their farming operations, is of broad national interest, not only because it involves large public expenditures but because of the principles underlying it. This program was initiated in 1936 as a substitute for the original Agricultural Adjustment Act, much of which was invalidated by the Supreme Court on January 6th of that year. It was designed in part to continue payments to farmers for reducing the acreages of the major cash crops and also to provide income supplements to increase the over-all returns to farmers. The payments also, of course, were intended to encourage farmers to make soil-conserving changes in their farming operations and to provide funds that would enable them to do so.

At that time, farmers were in desperate circumstances and even these modest supplements to their incomes were of considerable importance to them. Also, there was a good deal to be said for almost any orderly plan that would get more money into circulation. Furthermore, farmers could undoubtedly be made more aware of the conservation problem, and the adoption of soil-conserving practices could be speeded up by providing direct financial incentives.

Small income supplements of this kind are not now as important to farmers as they were in the middle 1930s, and much more powerful mechanisms for controlling acreages and marketings have been provided. Direct financial incentives for introducing and maintaining soil-conserving practices are probably less needed now than they were then. This raises the question whether the conservation idea now has become sufficiently well established that farmers will continue to use good practices even if they are not paid for doing so.

A Long-Established Trend Reversed

The soil conservation movement as a whole has brought about one of the most significant planned changes American agriculture has ever experienced. The nation's soil resources had been deteriorating almost from the time the lands were first settled. The importance of this trend was little recognized and few farmers knew how to check or control such losses even when they were aware of them. Education, technical assistance and financial incentives all were needed. The reversal of a major national trend of this kind is a slow, expensive and difficult task. Much progress has been made, but there still is much to do.

The program can be carried forward at a slower pace from here on or it can be speeded up, depending on how much the public is willing to spend on it at a given time. Now that farmers have become more aware of its importance and of its significance in improving their own individual returns, it may be that emphasis should shift more toward education concerning the problem and providing needed technical assistance rather than to continue to provide direct cash incentives on the scale previously maintained.

The situation is not uniform over the country. Some areas and some farmers almost certainly need both financial aid and financial encouragement if they are to bring about the kinds of changes needed. Subsidies may not be important, from a soil conservation standpoint, in areas where farmers have already become keenly aware of the problem and are financially able to carry out protective and soil-improving practices. Furthermore, soil-conserving expenditures lend themselves well to expansion and contraction in periods of low or high economic activity. Financial aid and even direct income subsidies may be justified in periods of acute depression, and perhaps in depressed areas at other times, though they would not be appropriate and possibly even would contribute to instability in periods when inflationary forces are dominant.

Results of the Program

There is no way of placing a value on the results achieved. They can be stated only in qualitative terms. An awareness of the problem has been created. Millions of farmers are making a conscious effort to check erosion and to improve the productivity of their farms. More than one and a quarter million of them are operating in accordance with detailed individual farm plans worked out in cooperation with soil conservation specialists and agricultural extension personnel. It can be said that a good start has been made and a new trend has been established. The task should be easier from here on, but the kinds of help given and needed are becoming more specific and detailed.

The initial stages of so far-reaching a change as the one here discussed have called for more governmental effort than should be needed as the plans and practices become more fully developed and established. If the amount of personnel assigned was adequate in the initial stages of the program, it should be more than adequate when the program has become well established and detailed farm plans have been developed and widely accepted. It seems doubtful that a stage has yet been reached in which the intensity of educational and technical effort can safely be relaxed.

Most students of the problem agree that fully effective conservation work calls for the working out of a conservation plan for each individual farm. While much progress along these lines has been made, the task is still far from complete and revisions and improvements will be needed almost indefinitely. This seems to indicate that the time has not arrived when any marked diminution of effort would be in the public interest, except for such economies as can be achieved through better coordination of effort and avoidance of duplication.

The distribution of effort by areas presents a more difficult problem both technically and politically. It is evident that some areas are much more subject to damage from erosion than others and that far more work is needed to restore them to productivity. The technical problems to be dealt with are much more complex in some places than in others. Some types of agriculture on some types of land can be rather easily and quickly brought under a reasonably adequate and effective conservation plan. Others are very difficult to bring to this condition. To the extent that political considerations can be eliminated, it would seem logical and in the public interest to give the national administrators of the program considerable discretion as to the relative intensities of conservation effort to be applied in various areas. Eventually it should be possible to reduce somewhat the over-all amount of effort and public expense involved.

Publicly Owned Lands Present Other Problems

A large amount of land, particularly in the West, is owned by the federal government itself. Until the latter part of the nineteenth century, it was rather generally assumed that nearly all of the lands owned by the federal government would eventually pass into private ownership. Most of the land legislation of the first century of national existence looked in that direction. Near the beginning of the present century, concern over the rapid disappearance and deterioration of forest lands led to the adoption of a policy of retaining in public ownership and under public management large areas of the forest land still held by the government. That policy has persisted for more than half a century and seems to have strong public support, though it is challenged from time to time.

The very long-term public interests involved and the difficulties in the way of developing suitable organization, financing and incentives for management of such lands in a way that will maximize their social product in all types of use seem to argue strongly for retention of the established basic policy. The more enlightened policies adopted in recent years in the management of privately owned forest lands may raise a question as to the merit of continuing indefinitely to expand the area of public ownership and control.

It seems clear, however, that where important supplemental values such as watershed protection and recreation are involved, maximum total production in terms of all values concerned can be achieved only through public ownership. This would seem to argue for selective acquisition or sale of lands with a view to having in public ownership those forest lands for which the total social product will thus be maximized, and leaving to private ownership those for which it can be shown that private ownership can and will achieve results comparable or superior to those likely to result from public ownership.

If this policy—essentially the policy that has been in effect for a half century or more—is accepted, the principal issues center around the problems of amount and stability of local community income derived from such lands, in the form of in-lieu payments, and equitable terms of sale for the stumpage sold to private operators. A logical policy to work toward would seem to be one in which payments to the local communities would be equivalent to and as stable as those which would result from private ownership of the resource. The policy obviously should include reasonably flexible provisions for acquiring or releasing lands by purchase, sale or trading in such a way as to permit blocking up of both public and private lands for efficient operation. Such a policy, efficiently implemented, would seem best suited to the capturing of all or most of the public values concerned without sacrifice of any important and legitimate private values.

Management of Grazing Lands

For most of the federally owned grazing lands, the problem is of a different kind. Here there are not, in most areas, important supplemental returns which can be captured only through public ownership. Presumably, the lands could be operated as effectively and in much the same way if they were privately owned. The problem is more largely one of practical results.

This vast, nonforested public domain has apparently not been sufficiently attractive as an investment to induce private acquisition on any large scale. Its productivity is very low. Some of it is so nearly worthless that it will almost certainly remain in government ownership regardless of the policy adopted. Until recently, when it was not under either government or private management, this land was deteriorating and important public values were being lost. The question now is whether, if thrown open to private purchase, it would be taken over and handled constructively or would revert to its former unmanaged status.

Though there is significant difference of opinion on this point, there appears to be a growing feeling among livestock growers that their interests may be better safeguarded through orderly public management and development of this resource than through private acquisition, provided they can maintain reasonably stable tenure and a reasonable amount of local control. They are thus relieved of the heavy capital outlay that would be required under private ownership yet are in a position to operate in much the same way as though the lands were held privately. Some public and local values are conserved in that the intrusion of small, ill-advised types of farming operation tends to be avoided and the size of units can be kept reasonably well adjusted to economic realities. There is, however, some restraint on the increase in size of operation that obviously is desired by some of the more successful ranchers.

From the standpoint of the local communities and the general public, the underlying principle is similar to that relating to forest lands. If the local communities are to find such a system satisfactory, they will expect to derive public revenues from the lands roughly comparable in amount and dependability to what they would receive if the lands were privately owned. Payments to the federal government over and above the amounts to meet this obligation should, it would seem, be roughly equivalent to what the lands would rent for if privately owned. For the government to accept less involves continuous subsidization of the particular individuals who are granted grazing rights and increases pressure from those who are not able to obtain grazing permits.

It does not follow, however, that all of this net rent should be drained out of the communities concerned. The government may choose to use a good part of it for some time to come in building up the resource. Such a policy would mean that the fees charged would have to be more nearly equivalent to the market value of the forage provided than they are at present.

Consistent Policy Needed

Even more important is the need for a more consistent and uniform policy in the methods of supervision and fees charged with respect to federal lands of similar type but under the jurisdictions of different federal agencies. The differences, both in intensity of use and in fees charged, as between the Forest Service and the Division of Range Management, are striking. This does not mean that either levels of use or charges should be identical. Multiple-use considerations bulk much larger in some of the grazing areas managed by the Forest Service than for most of those controlled by the Division of Range Management. Also, there are differences in value which stem from differences in location or timing of the forage resources made available. There does not appear to be reason, however, for any marked difference in underlying principle as both agencies are managing a publicly owned land resource.

The interest of both the public and the users requires that the resource be preserved and built up. At the same time, fairness both to the public and to the competing producers who operate on privately owned lands requires that the forage be paid for at approximately its true commercial value. Acceptance of this principle does not make the solution of the problem easy. There are wide differences of opinion as to the intensity of use that can be permitted without deterioration of the resource and also about the value of the forage provided. Presumably the facts on both of these points will become more clear and less controversial as a result of further research and experience. There is evidence, too, that the ranchers themselves are becoming more and more interested in the maintenance and improvement of these resources as they become more aware of the importance of such practices to their longer-term well-being and economy of operation.

Stability of Tenure Important

Clearly, there is need for further study and consultation on procedures for stabilizing the livestock industry dependent on these range resources. This calls for continuity of access, that is, some type of continuing tenure, together with equitable provisions for exit and entry of users. There does not appear to be at this time any generally accepted conclusion as to how the various conflicting views on this highly controversial problem can best be reconciled.

The building up of a stable and efficient livestock-producing unit requires investment in facilities and effective organization. Any sudden change in the access to federally owned range lands tends to destroy values thus built up. On the other hand, it is hard to defend a plan whereby private individuals may acquire a salable and transferrable right to the use of publicly owned lands. The traditional procedure of transferring public lands to private individuals through homesteading has given the transferees private ownerships for which the accretions in value could be captured by the person holding title to the land. However, if use rights to publicly owned land came to have any large sale value, it would presumably be an indication that the charge made for grazing rights is unduly low in relation to their value.

Though comprehensive conclusions in regard to this complex and difficult problem are not attempted here, some generalizations do seem warranted. Reasonable stability of tenure for the individual livestock grower must be achieved if the industry is to be efficient and the community and family life of the area are to be on a satisfactory basis. Charges should be equitable as between the owners of the land (in this case the public) and the users. Fees probably should be more flexible than they are at present so as to take account of changing prices for the livestock produced and the quality of the range. The number of head permitted to graze must be varied in accordance with weather and range conditions, if the range resource is to be maintained in reasonably adequate condition. Incentives must be provided not merely for maintenance of the resource but for improvement of its quality and carrying power.

Associated with these problems is that of determining what kinds and sizes of unit will be permitted or fostered. The interests of the local communities apparently will be furthered by a pattern of operation that consists of a considerable number of moderate-sized units rather than a few large ones. The social life of the users also seems likely to be better if units are not extremely large. At the same time, it is not desirable from the standpoint of either the users or the communities to create or maintain units so small that they are inefficient and cannot provide a fairly high level of family income.

Land Classification Needed

The program of classifying lands for best use should be continued and strengthened. A clearer picture of the suitabilities of the various public lands for various uses has long been needed and is essential for wise decisions about what to do with them. Orderly and considered decisions on this matter are the best assurance against costly mistakes which may open to private operation areas that do not lend themselves to the type of farming chosen or that tend to become problem areas if opened up for crop farming. On the other hand, lands that can be put to a higher use by transfer out of government ownership should, in most cases, be made available for private purchase unless there are important reasons for not doing so.

Whatever decisions are made currently as to type of use or ownership should not be unduly rigid. Conditions change. Lands which are suited to private ownership or operation at one period may be less so in a later period. Other lands, which at one time will not be managed or conserved except through government ownership, may become suitable for private ownership and management as the economy develops. Some areas which have become severely eroded or deforested under private operation, or on which production is too hazardous for successful farming operations, may well be acquired and managed by government either temporarily or permanently. Neither private nor public interests are best served by perpetuating types of land tenure and operation that lead to progressive deterioration of the land itself and of the work opportunities of those living on it. Thus, a long-time program should contemplate transfers both into and out of public ownership as conditions warrant. The time is past when continuing and indiscriminate alienation of lands from government ownership is appropriate either from a public or a private standpoint.

Scattered public and private land holdings should be regrouped through exchange, purchase or sale in such a way as to encourage and facilitate the creation of economically efficient units of management, both private and public. This means that the illogical checkerboard pattern of land ownership in some of the western states, a survival from the railroad-building period, should be cleared up as rapidly as possible.

Reclamation and Forest Conservation

For reasons which are readily apparent, this study does not attempt either detailed analysis or conclusions in regard to the reclamation and forestry programs. While both programs have some bearing on problems of agricultural policy, the connection is not very direct and the effects on the well-being of agriculture as a whole are minor. The development of farm lands was at one time a major function of the Bureau of Reclamation and is still an important part of its work. However, the production of power has now come to be a dominant phase of its activity, one which impinges on agriculture in many ways but which is, in the main, part of a broader public problem. The agricultural production involved is of great significance regionally and locally but does not importantly affect the over-all output of agriculture nationally or the policies relating to it.

Forestry policy also touches on agricultural policy at many points but in its broader aspects is a separate national problem rather than one that has a prominent and direct bearing on the problems here under consideration. For both forestry and reclamation, the brief summaries presented in Chapter 9 are designed mainly to show the relationship of the agricultural conservation programs to the over-all approach to the problem of conservation of natural resources and to indicate relative costs for these different types of conservation activity.

The Cost of the Program

It is easy to build up large totals for any type of federal expenditure if the period covered is long enough. Question may well be raised as to the warrant for presenting such cumulative data. This is water over the dam. Decisions were made in respect to many different types of problems and in settings that ranged from the depths of the most devastating depression in the nation's history to the peak of its greatest prosperity. Obviously, the most useful and pertinent information is that on what the farm program is costing now and what it is likely to cost in the future. The first of these can be shown. The second will, of course, depend on the course of events and on decisions as to the kind of program to be carried out in the future.

Nevertheless, there is wide interest in the global figures covering the farm programs of 1933 and after. Over-all figures are frequently given in the public press. Often they are incorrect, irresponsible, or so general that no clear view of the problem can be derived from them. Furthermore, the period from 1930 on does represent as a whole a continuing attempt to make a planned change in a major segment of the national economy. It has involved efforts to change the distribution of national income, to check a long-established downward trend in the productivity of soils and, at the same time, to create and develop new services designed to improve the efficiency of agriculture and the condition of farm people.

As we come closer to the present, cost data are inevitably less significant and reliable. For example, the government owns or has commitments on more than $7 billion worth of farm commodities. The prices at which these can be sold and the losses that will have to be taken cannot be determined at this time. Knowledge about the realized costs and losses of earlier years will throw some light on these problems, though only in a general way.

The conditions in which the liquidation of current stocks will have to be carried out will almost certainly be different from those of any previous period. Unless things change materially from what now seems likely, liquidation will not have to be undertaken in a period of deep depression and low demand. Neither is it likely that a rapidly rising price level, such as that of 1941 to 1948, will enable the government to work its way out with little or no loss.

Much more difficult is the problem of presenting equally important data on the credit side of the ledger. This, in fact, cannot be reduced to similarly specific figures. The best that can be done is to describe as accurately and fairly as possible the results of the programs and the purposes for which they were undertaken. The subjective valuations placed on these results will vary almost from person to person. Some will regard a given result or objective as vastly more important than another, while others will hold it in much lower esteem.

It is not the purpose of this study to render pontifical judgments on these matters, but rather to present as fully as possible the whole body of information both on costs and results so that the members of Congress, the farm groups and the general public may, it is hoped, reach decisions that will be wiser and more constructive than if such information were not at hand.

Some judgments as to the merits and demerits of various parts of the program are inevitably implied or expressed. Their acceptability must depend largely on the extent to which they accord with the criteria used by the majority of the people of the United States, or at least of the representatives chosen by them. However, the interpretations made have not been pulled out of thin air. They have been subjected to scrutiny and criticism by many people both in and outside the government. Differing views have been considered and carefully weighed. Final decision as to the data and interpretations to be included has, of course, been the responsibility of the research staff. It is believed, however, that the value judgments implied are reasonably well in keeping with those of very large parts of the public for which the study has been made.

Realized Costs of Agricultural and Related Programs

During the spring of 1954, the Department of Agriculture released a comprehensive summary of the costs of the various farm programs for the period 1932 through 1953.[40] This had been long in preparation and unquestionably provides the most accurate and complete summary of

40. U.S. Department of Agriculture, *Realized Cost of Agricultural and Related Programs, by Function or Purpose, Fiscal Years 1932–1953*, February 1954.

such expenditures available or likely to become available. The results given vary somewhat from those shown in earlier chapters of this volume since the two were worked out independently and often with different inclusions and exclusions or different classifications. However, in broad outline, the two appear to be in substantial accord.

The compilation of the Department of Agriculture groups the expenditures into six main categories, aside from "Wartime Consumer Subsidies on Agricultural Commodities" and "Other Special Activities Not a Part of the Agricultural Programs of the Department," which are presented separately. The six main categories of the agricultural program series and their costs for the period 1932 to 1953 are shown in Table 37.

TABLE 37

REALIZED COSTS OF AGRICULTURAL AND RELATED PROGRAMS, BY FUNCTION OR PURPOSE, FISCAL YEARS 1932–1953

(Millions)

Type of Program	Cost [a]
Total	$16,921.0
Programs primarily for stabilization of prices and farm income	7,510.4
Programs primarily for conservation of resources	4,589.1
Credit and related programs for electrification and telephone facilities, and farm purchase, maintenance, operation and housing	1,756.3
Research and education	1,189.7
Other, chiefly school lunches, marketing services, control and regulatory activities	1,531.3
Programs primarily for wartime, defense and other special needs	344.2

Source: U.S. Department of Agriculture, *Realized Cost of Agricultural and Related Programs, by Function or Purpose, Fiscal Years 1932–1953,* February 1954.

a. These figures do not include losses not as yet realized, for example, those which may result from CCC stocks and commitments in existence as of June 30, 1953.
The basis for the costs reflected in this table is as follows: (1) for activities financed from appropriated funds, the expenditures less receipts arising from the activities so financed; (2) for noncorporate loan funds, the losses on loans and the net interest cost or income; (3) for Commodity Credit Corporation and Federal Crop Insurance Corporation corporate funds, the net gains or losses from operations and the interest cost to the Treasury on government-subscribed capital; and (4) for corporations of the farm credit system, the interest cost to the Treasury on government-subscribed capital and payments made by the Treasury on account of reductions in interest rates on mortgages less dividends and franchise taxes paid to the Treasury. Interest cost to the Treasury on noncorporate loan funds and on government-subscribed capital of corporations has been computed on the basis of the average rate on the public debt paid by the Treasury in each of these years.

Stabilization of Prices and Farm Income

For the programs designated as primarily for stabilization of prices and farm income, a breakdown of costs by type of activity is shown in Table 38. A more complete summary of this phase of the program by type and by years is given in Appendix B.[41]

41. Also, for a careful and more detailed analysis of these costs, see Frederick D. Stocker, "Costs of Federal Programs to Stabilize Agricultural Prices and Incomes," U.S. Agricultural Research Service, *Agricultural Finance Review,* November 1953, pp. 37–52.

TABLE 38

REALIZED COSTS OF PROGRAMS PRIMARILY FOR STABILIZATION OF PRICES
AND FARM INCOMES, FISCAL YEARS 1932–1953

(*Millions*)

Type of Program	Cost
Total, 1932–1953	$7,510.4
Commodity Credit Corporation Program operations Price-support programs	1,110.1
Supply, foreign purchase, commodity export, and other CCC activities	(−319.8) [a]
Administrative and other general costs	299.6
International Wheat Agreement [b]	558.1
Removal of surplus agricultural commodities [c] (Section 32 programs)	1,567.6
Sugar Act	(−296.1) [a]
Federal crop insurance	157.8
Acreage allotment payments under the agricultural conservation programs	2,354.8
Other, including Agricultural Adjustment Act of 1933, parity payments, and other adjustments and surplus removal programs	2,078.3

Cost by Fiscal Year

Year	Cost	Year	Cost
1932	$297.8	1943	$512.0
1933	75.1	1944	402.1
1934	(−48.8) [a]	1945	50.1
1935	178.7	1946	23.7
1936	469.9	1947	(−51.2) [a]
1937	442.9	1948	116.8
1938	227.2	1949	328.7
1939	589.8	1950	486.9
1940	746.8	1951	624.3
1941	766.0	1952	306.2
1942	634.8	1953	330.6

Source: U.S. Department of Agriculture, *Realized Cost of Agricultural and Related Programs, by Function or Purpose, Fiscal Years 1932–1953,* February 1954.

a. Excess of credits; deduct.
b. The expenditures under this program are for payment of the difference between the price specified in the International Wheat Agreement and the domestic market price of wheat. The program is essentially international in nature and is included in this classification with the kinds of items to which it most nearly relates.
c. Excludes cash payments for school lunch programs.

TABLE 39

Realized Costs of Conservation Programs, Fiscal Years 1932–1953

(*Millions*)

Type of Program	Cost
Total, 1932–1953	$4,589.1
Agricultural conservation programs [a]	3,500.7
Soil Conservation Service programs [b]	616.5
Forest Service programs [c]	421.7
Flood prevention program	50.2

Cost by Fiscal Year

1932	$19.8	1943	$254.3
1933	12.4	1944	270.1
1934	6.9	1945	328.2
1935	8.5	1946	338.5
1936	13.5	1947	411.3
1937	90.3	1948	313.4
1938	131.2	1949	255.2
1939	168.3	1950	330.2
1940	259.5	1951	344.9
1941	177.5	1952	333.4
1942	179.3	1953	342.4

Source: U.S. Department of Agriculture, *Realized Cost of Agricultural and Related Programs, by Function or Purpose, Fiscal Years 1932–1953*, February 1954.

a. Excludes acreage allotment payments.
b. Includes the purchase of 9,643,738 acres of submarginal land at a total cost of approximately $60,061,000.
c. Includes the purchase of 14,450,711 acres of land at a total cost of approximately $68,532,000.

Conservation

During the same period, the cost of the conservation programs administered by the Department of Agriculture amounted to $4,589.1 million. These costs, by year and by type of activity, are given in Table 39. This summary does not include conservation expenditures made by the Bureau of Reclamation, the Tennessee Valley Authority or the Army's Corps of Engineers. For a more complete breakdown, see Appendix B.

Credit

The various farm credit program costs incurred in the period 1932–1953 amounted to $1,756.3 million. This does not include costs and receipts for the federal land banks, intermediate credit banks and seed loan program for the years 1916–1932. These are included in the summary given in Chapters 5 and 6. The data given are on the basis of realized costs, not expenditures. Thus, the loan funds provided through the Rural Electrification Administration (about $2.5 billion), the Federal Farm Mortgage Corporation (about $800 million) and those of the

Farm Security and Farmers Home Administrations and related programs (about $3 billion) are not included except as to amounts written off, the cost of money to the government and interest payments.

Administrative expenses, losses and other subsidies, such as those paid out to cover reductions in interest charges to federal land bank and Farm Mortgage Credit Corporation borrowers, are included. The interest subsidy, which is here included as part of the cost of the farm credit program, accounts for a considerable part of the difference between the $506 million shown here and the amounts given in Chapter 5. The realized costs by program for the various phases of the credit program are shown in Table 40.

TABLE 40

REALIZED COSTS OF FARM CREDIT PROGRAMS, FISCAL YEARS 1932–1953

(*Millions*)

Type of Program	Cost
Total, 1932–1953	$1,756.3
Lending programs:	
Rural Electrification Administration [a]	99.8
Farmers Home Administration	83.2
Farm Credit System	506.0
Grants and other expenses, including salaries and expenses related to the above lending agencies	1,067.3

Cost by Fiscal Year

1932	$24.0	1943	$97.2
1933	26.3	1944	68.8
1934	45.1	1945	44.6
1935	60.7	1946	43.5
1936	136.7	1947	47.4
1937	227.6	1948	35.3
1938	183.7	1949	(−18.4)[b]
1939	152.6	1950	33.8
1940	142.8	1951	42.2
1941	133.1	1952	47.2
1942	126.3	1953	55.8

Source: U.S. Department of Agriculture, *Realized Cost of Agricultural and Related Programs, by Function or Purpose, Fiscal Years 1932–1953,* February 1954.

a. These costs are determined on a net realized cost basis but also have been determined on an accrual income and expense basis. On the second basis, the REA would have a net gain of $45.5 million. Similarly, the costs of the Farmers Home Administration and the Farm Credit Administration can be determined on this alternate basis. (For the difference in the two methods of ascertaining cost, see *Realized Cost of Agricultural and Related Programs,* p. 2, and Appendix B.)

b. Excess of credits; deduct.

Research and Education (*Federal*)

The costs for research and education, including federal aid provided to the state agricultural extension services and also the research expenditures of the Department of Agriculture itself, amounted to $1,189.7 million for the years 1932–1953. These costs were divided as follows: for research, $724.7 million, and for extension work, including payments to the states, $465 million.

Federal expenditures on these activities have grown rather consistently over the years but do not show the ups and downs that are so evident in most of the other series (see Appendix B). That is, they were not greatly increased in the depression years or reduced in the years following the war. The costs by fiscal years are as follows (in millions):

1932	$30.7	1943	$50.4
1933	28.0	1944	47.7
1934	24.7	1945	49.1
1935	24.9	1946	55.5
1936	35.8	1947	64.5
1937	37.9	1948	69.6
1938	40.5	1949	83.7
1939	44.2	1950	88.9
1940	49.4	1951	87.5
1941	50.4	1952	87.4
1942	51.1	1953	87.8

Other Programs

The costs for school lunches (not including foods paid for with Section 32 funds), for marketing services and for control and regulatory activities have amounted to $1,531.3 million for the years 1932–1953. Of this, $690 million was for school lunches and $841.3 million for marketing services and control and regulatory activities.[42]

Wartime, defense and other special need programs accounted for $344.2 million, most of it in the years 1944 through 1950.

Over-All Cost

For the programs summarized above, the total costs for the period 1932–1953, as given by the Department of Agriculture, amounted to $16,921 million. It should be noted that this is not all for price and income supports. Approximately $7,510 million of it falls roughly in that category. The remainder is for a great variety of other activities, many of them of almost as much concern to society in general as to agriculture itself.

In addition, there were expenditures listed under the heading Wartime Consumer Subsidies on Agricultural Commodities in the amount of $4,245 million, mainly in the years 1943 through 1946. For reasons

42. For year-to-year data, see Appendix B. The $841.3 million for marketing services and control and regulatory activities includes other minor expenses such as those for staff offices of the Department of Agriculture for which segregated data are not available.

already mentioned (see pp. 294–301), it is impossible to determine specifically who were the beneficiaries of these subsidies. This decision depends to a large extent on the attitude taken as to the level at which ceiling prices on farm products should have been applied. In any event, it was an expenditure specifically related to the prosecution of the war and not now of much interest except historically. It was not a part of the continuing price-support program.

There were also very large expenditures of a more general nature though administered by the Department of Agriculture. These were principally procurement activities relating to lend-lease, UNRRA, Mutual Security and other foreign-aid programs. They were carried out with funds transferred from the agencies responsible for the programs. Some of them did help to relieve the Commodity Credit Corporation of excess stocks and contributed to other price-support objectives. That, however, was not their primary purpose. Expenditures of this kind, administered by the Department of Agriculture, have amounted to $16,214.7 million.

Costs by Commodities

A breakdown by commodities for the cost of programs carried on primarily for the stabilization of prices and farm income is also of interest. These costs are shown in Table 41, by commodity groups. For a complete list see Appendix B, which also includes more detailed footnotes explaining and qualifying the figures used in this and earlier sections.

Current Cost of the Program

The current cost of the program is, of course, far more important in considering present-day problems than the long record of past expenditures discussed above. Data are presented for fiscal 1953, the latest year for which data are available. (See Table 42.) Most of them are accurate and dependable. For one category, price-support costs, it must be recognized that property was being acquired and commitments were being or had been assumed on which realized losses and costs may eventually be much higher than those shown. The 1953 data reflect only those costs which became realized costs in the fiscal year ending June 30, 1953. For price-support activities, they do not reflect accurately the current costs of the program and are probably much too low.

THE PROBLEM AHEAD

The people of the United States have now gained experience with farm programs of various kinds over a period of nearly a hundred years. Farmer discontent has often been important politically, and some of the national policies we now have grew out of these movements. Until the 1930s, few of them involved heavy drains on the federal Treasury.

TABLE 41

REALIZED COSTS OF PROGRAMS PRIMARILY FOR STABILIZATION OF PRICES
AND INCOMES, FISCAL YEARS 1932–1953

(*Millions*)

Commodity Groups	Cost
Total commodities	$7,279.8
Basic commodities, total	4,668.7
Corn [a]	1,113.8
Cotton	1,564.9
Peanuts	137.9
Rice	35.9
Tobacco	94.6
Wheat	1,721.6
Designated nonbasic commodities, total	1,054.6
Butter	158.8
Cheese	28.7
Milk	113.9
Potatoes	635.8
Wool	104.6
Other	12.8
Other nonbasic commodities, total	1,556.7
Eggs	331.6
Flaxseed and linseed oil	72.0
Sugar	(−280.3) [b]
Other [c, d]	1,433.4

Source: U.S. Department of Agriculture, *Realized Cost of Agricultural and Related Programs, by Function or Purpose, Fiscal Years 1923–1953,* February 1954.

a. Includes cornmeal and AAA corn-hog program.
b. Excess of credits; deduct.
c. For details and specific commodities, see Appendix D.
d. Nonallocable costs amounted to $230.6 million additional and thus account for the difference between the total shown here and the $7,510 million total used earlier.

TABLE 42

REALIZED COSTS OF AGRICULTURAL AND RELATED PROGRAMS, BY FUNCTION
OR PURPOSE, FISCAL YEAR 1953

(*Millions*)

Type of Program	Cost
Total	$962.2
Stabilization of prices and farm income	330.6
Conservation of resources [a]	342.4
Credit and related programs	55.8
Research and education	87.8
School lunches, marketing, control and regulatory programs	140.2
Other special programs	5.4

Source: U.S. Department of Agriculture, *Realized Cost of Agricultural and Related Programs, by Function or Purpose, Fiscal Years 1932–1953,* February 1954.

a. For Department of Agriculture programs only.

During the past twenty to twenty-five years, we have had experience with a considerable number of programs which involved much more positive and direct action by the government and were much more expensive than the ones undertaken in earlier periods. In them, the government plays a different role from any that would have been considered suitable before 1930. In the early 1920s, agriculture was depressed and out of step with other parts of the economy. In this period and the one immediately following, the farm groups became more fully organized and much more articulate. The more severe and general depression of the 1930s created a willingness on the part of farmers, and the public as well, to go much farther in the direction of government control over economic relationships than would have been acceptable to them in earlier periods, even those in which there were vigorous farmer protest movements, as in the 1870s and the 1890s.

During the early and middle 1930s, the new program was looked upon as largely an emergency approach to a desperate situation. Even as late as 1940, it seemed to many, possibly to most people, a reasonable and somewhat experimental effort to overcome some of the widely recognized handicaps of agriculture in an economy that was becoming more highly organized and less flexible. Agriculture was to be given some aid in exercising the kinds of control that had become common in other types of business, and further progress was to be made in extending to farmers services and facilities that were already widely available to urban people.

The magnificent response of farmers to the national need during the war years created a generally favorable attitude toward the aspirations of agriculture and its desire for protection against an acute reaction such as that which followed World War I. There was little public opposition to official guarantees that prices would be supported at relatively high levels for a reasonable period following the cessation of hostilities.

Thereafter, agriculture entered its greatest period of prosperity, instead of the depression it had feared. The need for readjustment of output was postponed at least until 1949, but was beginning to take shape at that time. It was again deferred as a result of the unexpected inflationary and demand developments that grew out of the outbreak of war in Korea. Since then weaknesses in the current program have reappeared and new policies are being widely and actively discussed. Adjustments will apparently have to be made, either in the levels of price support or in the volumes of production or possibly in both. The decisions to be made are important and far reaching. Possible approaches to them are discussed in the succeeding comments of the special consultative committee appointed to review the study here presented and to draw from it such conclusions as it considers warranted. The committee also makes such recommendations as seem to it appropriate.

COMMITTEE REPORT

Chapter 12

Report of the Committee on Agricultural Policy

THE POLICY problems relating to agriculture are controversial and complex. In presenting this brief statement about them, this committee does not contemplate a comprehensive review of all phases of the relation of government to agriculture. Many of the government activities that affect agriculture, and through it the well-being of the nation, have been taking shape for nearly a hundred years. The comprehensive study to which this report is appended describes in considerable detail the nature of the over-all farm program, how it came into being, and the reasons for it. Much of this program has been carefully considered in the step-by-step process by which it emerged. Large parts of it have stood the test of time and of repeated and careful scrutiny by the Congress and other groups and agencies.

The purpose here is to indicate how government farm policy can best be fitted into over-all policies so as to be in the national interest as well as just and helpful to agriculture. The policies proposed are designed to enable agriculture to make its fullest contribution, not only to its own well-being, but to a dynamic, progressing national economy, in ways that will deserve the full support of the public at large.

The national economy is now, and has been for some years, operating at a relatively high level of activity. We are not now in a period of severe depression of the sort that gave rise to many of the farm programs we have today. Neither are we faced with a war emergency and the abnormal requirements growing out of it. Instead, the problem is one of sizable surpluses and excess capacity that seem likely to cause continuing trouble unless steps are taken to deal with them realistically and to bring agricultural production into better balance with the effective markets available. Some of these maladjustments are part of the inevitable aftermath of wartime and postwar developments which have affected the demand for farm products from the United States. Some have been created, or at least aggravated, by actions taken by the government itself.

The problems of most consequence, so far as commercial agriculture is concerned, are the overexpanded wheat industry, the rapid deterioration in the economic position of manufactured dairy products, and the lack of balance between production and effective demand for some of the other farm products. Accompanying and growing out of these is the very serious problem of excess stocks accumulated in the hands of the

Commodity Credit Corporation as a result of the price-support policies of recent years.[1]

The proposals set forth in the following pages are designed to eliminate the dangers that seem to us inherent in the overrigidity of the policies and programs of the past few years, some of which cannot be overcome without further remedial legislation. There is urgent need to make changes in those features of the existing program that may prove unstabilizing and dangerous to the longer-term well-being of agriculture. This should be accomplished as rapidly as can be done without causing severe dislocations in the agricultural economy.[2]

Agriculture Has Served the Nation Well

Attention is focused here on what we regard as needed changes in a far-reaching program which, on the whole, has achieved widespread farmer and national support. Since recommendations for change imply criticism, we stress the fact that we are *not* presenting the case for the program or emphasizing its accomplishments. To do so would be repetitive and would require more space than is available for this committee's report. However, we do call attention to the fact that American agriculture, on the whole, has served the nation well. Its record under the farm programs of the past two decades does not compare unfavorably with that of other groups in the national economy, either in accomplishments or in over-all costs for the gains achieved.[3]

1. The Commodity Credit Corporation is the government-owned corporation to which the Congress has assigned the duty of carrying out such agricultural price-support loan and purchase operations as the Congress authorizes. It makes nonrecourse loans on designated storable farm products held under seal on farms or elsewhere in accordance with regulations prescribed by the Corporation. The borrower may repay the loan and reclaim the product or, if he chooses, may surrender the product at the end of the loan period and be absolved from any obligation to pay the difference between the amount advanced and the market value of the product, if the market value is less than the amount loaned. Thus the loan is, in effect, a purchase commitment which establishes a price floor for the commodity but does not obligate the borrower to surrender it if he chooses later to pay off the loan and use or sell the commodity.

Ordinarily, if the price continues to be less than the amount of the loan, the commodity eventually passes into the hands of the Commodity Credit Corporation, thus adding to the stocks held by it. If the price rises above the loan level, the collateral is usually reclaimed by the farmer and sold or used by him. The Commodity Credit Corporation also engages in many other activities, such as direct purchases in the market to strengthen prices, procurement of commodities for other government agencies, and rotating of stocks. Under the legislation now in effect, it is the primary price-supporting mechanism of the Department of Agriculture.

2. It should be noted at the outset that this report deals principally with commercial agriculture, that is, with that part of agriculture which, though it consists predominantly of family farms, is concerned mainly with producing for the market. For these farms, price policy is a central issue. The report does not discuss, except incidentally, the problems of the million or more low-production farms which have little to sell even though farming may be a full-time occupation for the farm families that operate them. The report also does not deal with the agricultural labor problem. Many of the conditions which affect agricultural labor, especially the migrant workers, need early consideration, but they could not be dealt with in the time and space available here.

3. That is, if we think in terms of the over-all costs to consumers rather than only of

Throughout the difficult period of the 1930s and since, agriculture has provided an abundant supply of foods, fibers and other commodities, not only for our own use but for the war and postwar needs of other nations whose welfare was of vital consequence to us. Agricultural efficiency has been increased enormously. One of the most difficult problems, except in the war years, has been that of keeping agricultural prices up to what the Congress regarded as a fair return to farmers rather than that of holding them down to prevent hardship to consumers. Few other nations of the world have comparable records with respect to abundance of supplies, moderateness of food prices and smallness of the proportion of the population required to provide the food and fiber needed.

The problems we stress here relate therefore to defects in the program, to dangers inherent in it, and to keeping its cost as low as possible without sacrificing gains that are of enough significance to warrant the costs involved. We are also concerned with the maintenance of the dynamic qualities that have put American agriculture in the forefront among the agricultural economies of the world. We emphasize particularly the need for adjustments that will keep the programs well adapted to the varying conditions of different periods and that will result in the best use of the human and other resources employed in agricultural production. A period of great prosperity or of normal activity does not necessarily call for the same kinds and amounts of government action as one of severe depression. It is also apparent that peacetime needs are not the same as those of a war or postwar period.

Obviously, it cannot be expected that any group will be wholly in accord as to the kind of program needed. The attempt here has been to find as large an area of agreement as possible but not to vitiate conclusions by making them so general and innocuous that they conceal the differences that exist. For that reason, disagreements that could not be reconciled and differences in emphasis are recorded as signed footnotes. In part, these stem from differences in basic philosophy concerning the role of government in human affairs. Hence, some of the proposals made will be found acceptable or not acceptable as they accord or do not accord with the general philosophy of the individual reader or committee member.

---

costs borne by the federal government. As pointed out repeatedly in various parts of the research report, gains to labor, business and other groups tend to come by way of markets, rather than through government appropriations. They are, however, paid for by the consuming public, though in the form of prices for goods and services rather than in taxes.*

* It should be noted, however, that, although the consuming public supports labor in the form of prices for goods and services rather than in taxes, the consumer has an opportunity to refuse to pay certain prices, to substitute lower-cost items or to refrain from buying the goods and services. There is no such freedom of choice in regard to the payment of taxes.—LOUISE L. WRIGHT

The Older Farm Programs

Until about 1930, the principal types of government aid to agriculture were, in broad terms, the following:

1. Aid in providing educational facilities that would improve the technical efficiency of agriculture, raise its professional and occupational status and broaden the opportunities available to young people in the rural areas. Incidentally, this proved also to be a means of increasing the competence of part of the labor force available to the nonfarm industries, since many agriculturally trained young people move into nonfarm occupations and professions. The broadening of educational opportunities for rural young people, partly through federal aid to the land-grant colleges, rural high schools and the agricultural extension services, has also helped to improve and equalize agricultural opportunities as compared with those in other occupations, by facilitating the outflow of excess population from agriculture.

2. Help in providing a research arm designed to increase agricultural efficiency. This has made it possible for a smaller and smaller portion of the total population to supply the demand for farm products.

3. The provision of considerable amounts of regulatory, service and credit assistance which agriculture could not well provide for itself, because of its small-unit structure and wide dispersion. Many of these activities benefited consumers and business as well as farmers. More and more generally, similar types of assistance are being provided for consumers and small-unit segments of the nonfarm economy, for example, food and drug regulation, small-business financing, insurance of bank deposits, public health programs and home-loan financing.

These types of assistance to agriculture have not been displaced in later years. In fact, they have been expanded and improved and are virtually unchallenged as a significant and appropriate phase of governmental activity. Their importance to agriculture and to society as a whole is very great, but we omit further discussion of them here. They are not highly controversial and their nature and significance are described in considerable detail in Chapter 3.

Change in Emphasis and Scope After 1930

As a result of the severe depressions of the 1920s and 1930s, a much broader and more intensive program of governmental aid to agriculture was undertaken. In the early 1930s, the steps taken were largely of an emergency and anti-depression type. However, they very soon came to have longer-term objectives such as the conserving of soils, maintaining the prices of farm products, improving the lot of disadvantaged groups in agriculture and providing protection against natural hazards.

During World War II, the objectives of the farm program were greatly modified. Efforts were made to increase output in nearly all lines rather than to hold it down. However, the means used were much the same as those which had been developed earlier for dealing with depression conditions. Income and price maintenance had a part in the program, but this feature was not strongly stressed. The price maintenance provisions enacted during the war years, for application after the war, were intended mainly as a stabilizing factor in an expected difficult period of readjustment rather than as a means of increasing prices during the war years themselves.

Since the end of 1948, production-maintaining objectives have not been prominent features of the farm program, except in the period around 1950 when the Korean war led to renewed emphasis on increased output. Neither have the policies adopted been in the nature of insurance against disaster conditions. Instead, they have consisted, in the main, of an effort to avoid adjustments in prices and production that would normally be expected to result from the slacking off of abnormal kinds and amounts of demand.

In part, the resistance to price adjustment has been based on the widely held view that, even in a period of high economic activity, the free markets will not provide prices for farm products that are equitable in relation to nonfarm prices. This view is based partly on the parity formula, which came to be so widely used as a criterion of equity between farm and nonfarm groups in the 1930s and 1940s, and partly on the contention that free-market prices are not the major determinants of the returns to many groups in other parts of the economy, notably to corporate enterprises and to labor. Corporations can and do exercise control over output and establish prices by administrative procedures, and labor unions arrive at wage rates and working conditions through collective bargaining.[4]

We do not attempt here to explore the merits of these contentions. They are discussed more fully in Chapter 11 and in Appendix A. What we do wish to stress is that the objectives of national farm policy have not always been the same and that government activities relating to agriculture should now be re-examined to see whether they are well suited to present conditions and whether they are consistent, workable and defensible.

INCENTIVES, STABILITY AND EQUITY AS GOALS IN FARM POLICY

The incentives provided to agriculture, by way of the markets or otherwise, should be such as to insure supplies of food and fiber for a growing population in amounts and kinds consistent with the demands

4. The statements made above are, of course, an oversimplification of a very complex situation. It is so described as a means of highlighting major tendencies, and of emphasizing the need for formulating plans better suited to present needs than those which had to be adopted hastily in dealing with two of the most hectic and fast-moving decades in our history.

of a prosperous and expanding economy and in accord with such volumes of exports and imports as appear to be in the national interest.

Stability and Progress

In addition, the industry should be aided in achieving a degree of stability that will protect it against extreme variations in prices and incomes. However, stability in a static sense should not be a goal. Agriculture, in its own interest and that of the public as well, should continue to be a dynamic industry, changing as the needs and opportunities for change arise. This means that a particular pattern of production should not be frozen and that the fact that a given kind and amount of production and a certain number of families or farm units have been customary in the past should not be justification for measures designed to perpetuate patterns of production and organization that may have become obsolete.

While stability of the agricultural economy is the point stressed here, it is recognized that agriculture alone cannot be stabilized unless the economy as a whole is kept reasonably stable. Assuming general acceptance of the need for maintaining an active and expanding national economy, and vigorous efforts to achieve that goal, the aim with respect to agriculture should be to ease the impact of abrupt changes that affect severely the incomes of sizable groups of agricultural producers. Past experience has demonstrated that some parts of agriculture can be in great distress even when the national economy is relatively prosperous. Droughts, technological changes and sudden shifts in demand can create regional and single-industry problems that warrant both emergency aid and help in bringing about needed adjustments.

The federal government has, in the Employment Act of 1946, pledged itself to use all means available to it to assure the maintenance of high levels of employment and a prosperous and productive economy.[5] This is a pledge to agriculture as well as to those not in agriculture. The maintenance of high buying power in the economy as a whole is undoubtedly the most important single factor in agricultural prosperity and is logically a primary objective in farm policy as well as in national policy. The experience of the 1930s demonstrates that no amount of special programing can make agriculture prosperous if the rest of the economy is in severe depression.

Special Aid Warranted in Time of Depression

If steps designed to maintain prosperity and high employment generally are not taken, or if they prove unsuccessful, emergency programs

5. In our free, competitive, dynamic economy, government cannot "assure the maintenance of high levels of employment and a prosperous and productive economy." It can continually strive to maintain an atmosphere congenial to that objective.
—QUENTIN REYNOLDS

in both the farm and nonfarm sectors are appropriate. The federal and state governments give some assurance to nonfarm people that if severe hardships arise in spite of their efforts to prevent them, some aid will be given, through unemployment insurance, work relief, old-age assistance and so on. These are not guarantees of satisfactory levels of income; they are aids designed to prevent extreme hardship. Agriculture has every right to expect comparable aid, though in different forms, when it encounters hardships that are beyond its control, for example, extreme declines in prices, widespread droughts or unusually severe and sudden adjustments which necessitate large-scale changes in land use and types of farm organization.

However, it is unlikely that either public sentiment or national interest will justify maintaining fully satisfactory returns to any one minority group if other large groups are in distress. All will have to share in the adjustments and hardships that must be faced, but the situation should be kept as equitable as possible. In nonfarm activities, the major impact is likely to be in the form of large-scale unemployment. Farmers, for the most part, will not become unemployed. Instead, they will be faced with the problem of low prices and continuing high costs. The government should approach this problem on two fronts: through efforts to expand nonfarm employment and through efforts to maintain farm prices and incomes. If successful, such types of action will supplement and strengthen each other.

We concede that any long-term program must recognize the possibility of depressions, but we do not accept the view that depressions are inevitable. Many new procedures for maintaining and strengthening economic activity have been devised during the past two decades, and we have learned much about how to use them. We do not think it either necessary or probable that economic activity will again sink to the low levels that characterized the tragic years of the 1930s.

As a consequence, we believe the farm program of the future should contemplate constructive aid in maintaining and strengthening agriculture as part of an active and progressing economy. It should not be distorted by undue preoccupation with fears of a severe depression which may never happen. If depression should come, precedents are at hand whereby much quicker and more effective actions could and should be taken than those of the early 1930s. This means, in our judgment, the development of a program that will aid in meeting problems as they arise, one that will look to continuing betterment of farm living and income and one that will not be self-defeating because of undue rigidity of goals or methods of operation.

Government Obligation to Aid in Readjustment

When programs designed to meet abnormal national needs cause severe distortions in the agricultural economy, as in wartime, the national government has an obligation to assist in the transition to a more balanced pattern of output in the succeeding period and should accept that responsibility.[6] Such a policy is in the interest not only of farmers but of the public as well. It is an effective way of assuring all-out production when war needs are large and tends also to lessen the shock to the national economy from readjustments that have to be made to get production back into balance with peacetime demand.

Such types of aid, however, should not be of such a nature or so long continued as to perpetuate the unbalance in the agricultural economy. They should be accompanied by positive programs designed to provide opportunity and incentives for changes in production that will bring output into line with demand in the national and international markets, plus such amounts of farm products as may be required for other programs that may be agreed on.

Equitable Returns to Agriculture

The question of what constitutes an equitable return to agriculture in times when no major adjustments or distortions are involved is not a simple one, nor is it likely that any simple conclusion in regard to it can achieve wide acceptance. Many farmer spokesmen contend that, even in "normal" times, other groups are able to exercise restraints on the free play of market forces that give them price and income advantages over farmers, since farmers are not able to bargain collectively or to regulate output.

This, like all broad generalizations, is only partly true. In some lines, notably fluid milk, farmers have developed mechanisms that are somewhat similar to those used by organized labor and by industry. It is also important to recognize that the farmer is an entrepreneur, not an employee. He assumes certain risks and also has the possibility of making more as well as less than some expected amount, whereas the employed worker agrees on a specified wage which constitutes a maximum as well as a minimum return to him. Nevertheless, both labor and industry have greater control than farmers do over the prices at which their services and products are put on the market.

We recognize and assume that the opportunities in agriculture should be comparable to those in other occupations requiring similar abilities and qualifications. However, the methods by which such equality of return can best be achieved are different in agriculture than in urban employment. They are more like those available to the small-business entrepreneur.

In terms of equity, it would seem that farmers should have opportunity, within reasonable limits, to act jointly in adjusting their output

6. As originally conceived, the post-World War II price guarantees were of this nature, though they were not adequately supplemented by positive programs of readjustment.

so as to put smaller quantities on the market at higher prices if they choose to do so.[7] They may not find such action helpful as a long-run solution to their problem. Extreme restrictions on output may not prove to be profitable or to be good business from the farmer's standpoint. Even in most types of industry, rigorous adherence to a price objective, without regard to the effect on volume of sales, does not accord with good business policy.

If such power is to be granted, there must be assurance that it will not be used to the disadvantage of the public as a whole. Though the restraints on collusive action by industrial firms to restrict production, in order to raise or maintain prices, undoubtedly are frequently evaded or nullified, long-established public policy specifies that such restraints shall not be applied to the detriment of the public interest. This implies that the Congress, if it authorizes government aid in restricting agricultural production or marketings, is under obligation to specify the conditions in which such procedures can be used and to place limits on action of that kind.

It may well be that when the major maladjustments in acreage and stocks have been eliminated, most farmers will find they prefer freedom to make individual adjustments, both up and down, to the rigidities that are inherent in any governmental program for control of production. Governmentally imposed restrictions on acreages and marketings seem better suited to the correction of major maladjustments than for use in ordinary times.[8]

Whether through government action or individually or collectively, farmers will eventually find it necessary to adjust their output to amounts the markets will absorb at prices they are willing to accept. Government accumulation of stocks, with no longer-term objective than that of taking them off the farmers' hands, cannot be continued for very long. Such a program is self-defeating as well as socially undesirable. Stocks of that kind are not actually disposed of; they pile up, creating pressures like water behind a dam. Eventually something must give, and the result is likely to be a full-scale breakdown of the price structure for the commodity. In the meantime, heavy costs for storage are incurred, deterioration takes place and farm resources are used for purposes that are useless or worse.

Occupational Mobility and the Problem of Equity

Almost all through our history, one of the factors in improving the balance between farm and nonfarm incomes has been the movement of young workers out of agriculture and into urban occupations. In most

7. I can only say "no" to this sentence. Moreover, I am more than uneasy about this discussion of equitable returns.—T. W. SCHULTZ

8. I do not concur with this statement about acreage restrictions, as I shall explain in a later footnote.—T. W. SCHULTZ

periods, the rural areas have produced more workers than were needed to supply their own labor requirements.

During the past decade, this factor has become more effective as an equalizer than in earlier periods because of (1) greater mobility of the population and increased awareness of alternative opportunities, and (2) the changing relative sizes of the farm and nonfarm labor markets. The United States has long had a mobile population as compared to most other countries. However, some labor groups and some areas have been notable exceptions. During recent years, the growing use of automobiles and the extensive development of highways have brought a great increase in workers' contacts with other areas and occupations. Still more important were the labor-recruiting activities and high wages of the war period and the extensive reshuffling of population that resulted from wartime military service. Thousands of young men who had not previously been away from their home communities enough to have much knowledge of other work opportunities have settled in new locations or changed their occupations.

The other major influence, that of the changing relative sizes of the farm and nonfarm labor markets, has affected the situation more gradually but nevertheless at a rate that is striking and very significant. As late as 1870, more than half the national labor force was engaged in agriculture. By 1952, only about 12 per cent of the total employed working population, in the age group 14 years and over, was in agriculture. This means that a relatively large percentage shift of farm workers into urban employment now produces a much smaller percentage increase in the nonfarm working force than in earlier periods. Suitable adjustments in the size of the agricultural labor force are therefore more feasible than they were only a few decades ago, provided there is a high level of employment in the economy as a whole. For example, a shift of 10 per cent of the agricultural working force out of agriculture and into urban occupations would add less than 2 per cent to the nonfarm labor force.

Such adjustments, even today, occur too slowly and too incompletely to maintain full equality of returns and opportunities in the farm and nonfarm parts of the economy. However, if freedom of choice to work either in agriculture or out of it can be achieved and maintained, real incomes to farmers should not long remain far out of balance with real incomes in comparable nonfarm occupations, even though urban workers and industries may have somewhat more direct control over prices and incomes than have farmers.[9]

9. In commenting on the equality of returns to farm and nonfarm groups, I find no mention of the fact that the nonfarm worker is usually dependent upon his cash income for a place to live and something to eat. This is seldom true of the farm groups. There is an important psychological difference which should be taken into account in any equating of the two groups.—LOUISE L. WRIGHT

The kinds of occupational shift described above are now and have been in the past mainly in the younger age groups. The older, more established farm operators and farm workers cannot readily change their occupations or, in most cases, their locations. But it is not necessary that they do so if adequate mobility and freedom of choice can be maintained for those parts of the farm population best suited for making adjustments of that kind.[10]

There are some maladjustments in production and price relationships at the present time. These are partly an aftermath of war-expanded production and partly a result of the price policies pursued by the government in recent years. However, we do not find factual support for the view that the trading position of agriculture is now less favorable than it was in 1910–1914, except for the influence of the stocks held by the Commodity Credit Corporation and some continuing excess in production capacity. If the problems associated with these elements in the situation can be solved, there is reason to think that agriculture's relationship to the nonfarm part of the economy, even in terms of free-market trading, would now be at least as favorable as it was in the 1910–1914 period. In those years, the nonfarm economy was far less active and the nonfarm labor market much less receptive than now.[11]

In times of depression, the situation is different. Agricultural workers do not then have ready access to another and much larger labor market, and they may even find their industry burdened with displaced workers from the nonfarm occupations. This argues strongly for stand-by arrangements that can provide prompt and vigorous help when it is much needed. In such times, neither the public interest nor that of agriculture calls for a shift of human and material resources out of agriculture. The maladjustment is on the demand side, not on the supply side. Primary emphasis should therefore be on restoring a healthy demand and at the same time avoiding disruption of agriculture's own essentially sound production program. But if agricultural production continues to exceed the amounts that can be sold at prices farmers and the Congress regard as acceptable, even in times of very high economic activity, and if unneeded stocks

10. This kind of shift seems now to be occurring on a fairly large scale and may come to be an important factor in maintaining balance between farm and nonfarm incomes, if employment continues high in the nonfarm economy. In the period 1950–1954, the estimated population living on farms in the age group 18 to 24 declined by 623,000, or nearly 26 per cent. The number of males declined by almost 31 per cent. In contrast, the number of males in the age group 25 to 44 was down only 13.5 per cent, and the change in the 45 to 64 age group was about the same. (Data from U.S. Bureau of the Census and U.S. Department of Agriculture, Agricultural Marketing Service, *Estimates of the Farm Population of the United States, April 1950 to April 1954,* Series Census-AMS [P-27], No. 20, September 3, 1954.)

11. I fear this paragraph will be seriously misconstrued. For supplies to clear farm product markets on ahead, the terms of trade—say, old parity—are likely to be in the neighborhood of 85 compared to 100 for 1910–14. But this change by itself does not imply that the real returns to farm people will be either lower or higher than in other occupations requiring comparable abilities and skills.—T. W. SCHULTZ

build up, it is apparent that government action which continues to over-stimulate the industry tends to aggravate the problem rather than to solve it.

Government Has a Role to Play

In the suggestions made, we recognize that government has an impor-tant role to play in stabilizing and strengthening the agricultural economy, but we favor as much reliance on automatic adjustments in the market as is consistent with the goals suggested.[12] We believe that the farmers of the United States want, and that the general welfare requires, an agricultural economy in which there will be as much freedom of action as is consistent with the maintenance of reasonable stability and equality of opportunity between farming and other occupations. The contribution which can be made by the wisdom and managerial ability of some five million farm operators should not be sacrificed through too much reliance on regulation and centralized planning, which inevitably draw on rela-tively small numbers of brains and create inefficiencies and inconsist-encies in an economy as diverse and complex as ours.

Most of the adjustments needed are not uniform but instead should vary from farm to farm, depending on the particular situation. They can best be brought about through full use of the vast reservoir of managerial ability that exists in the farmers of the United States. Such action, par-ticipated in by millions of farmers, brought about many of the great shifts and readjustments of the past: the shift out of wheat, beef cattle and sheep in the New England area; the development of the great dairy and livestock industries of the Middle West; and the grain and specialty-crop industries of the Plains area and the Far West. Farmers, through their individual action, brought into use mechanized agriculture, hybrid corn, improved breeds of livestock, and many other new developments.

When large and general adjustments need to be made quickly, gov-ernment can and should step in with both aid and guidance. Here, planned and standardized types of adjustment have a place during the period in which the change is being made but are not likely to be satisfac-tory as something to live with permanently. Of this type are the cutbacks in wheat acreage and production that are usually needed after any great war, the adjustments to a major change in technology and demand such as that now facing the butter industry, and the kinds of adjustment long

12. A distinction of the first order of importance is needed at this point, namely, that between accepting prices as they are made in the market as supply and demand now function, and trying to regulate, or more particularly supplement, the operations of the markets we now have in such a way as to bring about a set of prices that will help to keep supply in balance with demand. To take the most obvious case, as the markets and supply and demand now function, we continue to have the ups and downs of the hog-corn and cattle cycle, an overexpansion of output following new developments in tech-nology, and a failure of production to contract following a major shift in consumption or loss of foreign markets.—JOHN D. BLACK

needed in the older cotton areas which were occurring too slowly until the government stepped in with assistance and leadership designed to help bring them about.

Problems that are too large to be handled effectively or quickly by farmers acting individually may arise in peacetime as well as in war periods, for example, the overexpansions in wheat and cotton that occurred around 1930. Major changes such as those relating to soil conservation may also require large-scale government aid and guidance if deterioration tends to grow and feed on itself rather than to be corrected through individual or group action.

In addition to the kinds of maladjustment mentioned above, there are, of course, many continuing problems within agriculture itself on which government action of one kind or another is needed if sound and forward-looking solutions are to be achieved in any reasonable length of time. These are covered in part in the conclusions and recommendations following, but primary emphasis is given to the price-support and related problems that currently are of major interest.

IMMEDIATE AND PRESSING PROBLEMS

What to Do about the Wheat Situation

One of the most pressing problems requiring attention at this time is that of how to restore balance and healthy trading arrangements in wheat. The wheat problem also illustrates, in rather extreme form, many of the problems faced by the producers of other farm commodities and by the government. Since all of the commodity programs cannot be discussed in similar detail without burdening the report unduly, the wheat situation is discussed at some length as an example of the kinds of difficulties that arise in dealing with several of the major storable farm products.[13] For most of the others, production and available outlets are more nearly in balance and the adjustments needed can be made with less difficulty.

Wheat production is now substantially greater than the amounts that can be disposed of for human use either here or abroad. United States requirements for human use and seed are in the order of 600 million bushels a year. Present indications are that not much more than 200

13. A somewhat similar situation is developing in the rice industry. Some of the proposals for dealing with it are much like those that have been put forward as solutions for the wheat problem. Both wheat and rice are widely used, storable cereal grains and both have been greatly expanded in the period since 1940. The rice problem is not discussed separately here, partly because of its similarity to the wheat problem and partly because the number of growers affected is much smaller. United States rice production increased from about 24.5 million bags in 1940 to more than 58 million in 1954. For the growers directly concerned, the problems are fully as acute as those relating to wheat, but they do not have such far-reaching importance for the agricultural economy as a whole and the acreages involved are very small in comparison with those used in the production of wheat.

million bushels a year can be exported, even with export subsidies and liberal policies in respect to sales made in conjunction with foreign-assistance programs. Since production has been running at close to or well above a billion bushels per year, wheat stocks are continuing to pile up even though they are already so large that they constitute a serious problem.

Piling up unneeded stocks of wheat under government loan or ownership is at best only a temporary solution for the kind of problem which now faces the wheat industry. Sooner or later, unless acreage is held down very rigorously, these stocks will become so large that storage facilities will be overtaxed or the Congress will not make funds available for adding to them. If that should happen while production is as high as it now is, and with no alternative plan to turn to, the result might be serious demoralization of the wheat market. It is essential, therefore, that production be adjusted and a freer flow of wheat developed in time to prevent a catastrophe of that kind. The longer the unbalance continues, the greater will be the danger of an outcome that will be harmful to wheat growers as well as expensive to the government.

The overexpansion in wheat is largely a result of the abnormal demands of the war and postwar years and of the overstimulating effect of the postwar price-support program. It is our opinion that government aid in correcting maladjustments of that kind is warranted. The government itself played a major role in bringing about the distortions that now exist. However, such aid should be in a form that will help to correct the maladjustment rather than to perpetuate it.

Size and Nature of the Problem

During and after World War II, wheat acreage was greatly expanded, from 63 million to 84 million (acres seeded in 1939 and 1949). Production increased from 741 million bushels in 1939 to 1,359 million in 1947, and to 1,295 million in 1948. Though the amount produced was moderately lower in the years 1949 through 1951, it was up again to 1,291 million bushels in 1952 and remained high in 1953 (1,169 million bushels). Acreage restrictions and less favorable weather in the spring wheat area brought the total output down to 959 million bushels in 1954 (November 1 estimate), but production remained high in the winter wheat areas in spite of the curtailment of acreage.

Wheat production has been at a rate of more than a billion bushels in every year since 1943, except 1951 and 1954 when it was close to that figure. Even with the acreage controls applied in 1954, the volume produced exceeds domestic flour requirements by 300 to 400 million bushels. The excess must find its outlet as exports, as feed or as additional government stocks.

Until 1949, the large crops grown were needed and the government encouraged the acreage expansions and other measures required to achieve them. Most of the increase of the years prior to 1949 was shipped out of the United States. Exports rose from 48 million bushels in 1939 to 503 million in 1948. The war and postwar volume of exports is far above what can reasonably be expected as a continuing peacetime outlet for wheat not needed in the United States. It seems apparent, therefore, that, if wheat production continues to exceed domestic flour requirements and the amounts really wanted and needed by other countries for human consumption, part of its outlet will have to be as feed or in other lower-grade uses, unless the already top-heavy government stocks are to be increased still further.

Set-Aside Only a Temporary Stopgap

The set-aside provided in the Agricultural Act of 1954 is at best a temporary stopgap.[14] The wheat to be set aside, even under the most liberal of foreign-aid programs and with substantial concessions for diversion to lower uses, will not be easily disposed of. In the meantime, it involves heavy storage costs and some deterioration. It is likely also to become increasingly a depressing factor in the over-all market for wheat.

Substantial Reserves Needed

Though we stress the dangers that may result from excessively large stocks, we do not advocate a reduction of wheat reserves to the amounts that would be carried commercially by the grain trade. In the present unsettled condition of world affairs, and with the possibility that there may be years of severe drought and low output, we are of the opinion that the national interest requires a usual carry-over of some 400 to 500 million bushels of wheat.[15] This is a larger reserve than the trade will carry on a commercial basis. Therefore, even if changes are made which result in more normal functioning of the markets, the government still should play a part in the management of reserves.

14. The Agricultural Act of 1954 (approved on August 28) provides that portions of the stocks held by the Commodity Credit Corporation are to be set aside for disposal outside the normal channels of trade. The commodities thus segregated are to be disposed of through donations for famine relief abroad, sale or barter for strategic materials, donations to school lunch programs, transfer to national stockpiles and in various other ways which will keep them out of the regular commercial markets. The purpose is to bring about a reduction in the top-heavy holdings of the Commodity Credit Corporation without disturbing unduly the markets for new crops coming on. The commodities thus set aside are not to exceed $2.5 billion in value, and the maximum amounts of various commodities that can be so handled are specified. The largest single item is wheat, which is limited to 500 million bushels. Others specified are cotton, cottonseed oil, butter, nonfat dry milk solids and cheese.

15. Current estimates indicate that, even with a possible further reduction of 100 million bushels in wheat production in 1955, the carry-over on July 1, 1956 may still be close to one billion bushels. See U.S. Department of Agriculture, *The Wheat Situation*, August 30, 1954, p. 3.

However, holdings of that kind should be treated as strategic reserves, not merely as a place to dump wheat that has nowhere else to go. Amounts not needed as a national strategic reserve should be moved into consumption here or abroad as soon as that can be done practically. Production should be adjusted to what can be put to effective use under some orderly plan of disposal. To do otherwise is to continue to use human and material resources wastefully and at great expense to the public. It also increases the danger of a severe price break later on.

Present Program Distorts Quality and Price Differentials

The wheat program now in effect tends to treat all wheat as a single commodity, though actually it is not. The production and use patterns are very complex and some of them are thrown badly out of balance under a program that fails to take account of customary price and quality differentials.

The carry-over of hard red spring wheat, though larger than normal, would not be a serious problem if the markets were operating freely.[16] Most of that type of wheat, except the off-grades, is used for domestic flour production. Little is exported and the supply frequently is supplemented by imports from Canada. Neither the public interest nor that of the spring wheat growers will be furthered by drastic curtailment of production in the hard red spring area or by policies that encourage the substitution of less desirable types of wheat in the uses for which this type is best suited.

The durum wheats also do not present a problem. The current level of carry-over is, if anything, low rather than high, largely because of very low yields in 1954. There does not appear to be any logical reason for acreage cutbacks in this type of wheat at this time.

The soft white wheats, especially those produced in the Pacific Northwest, present a different kind of problem. The domestic use of these wheats is largely in flours suitable for making crackers, pastries, noodles and so on. They are not bread wheats. However, they have in the past enjoyed a substantial and growing export demand, particularly in the Orient, a demand which may be damaged by a pricing program that fosters the substitution of other export wheats. There has also been an increasing tendency for other types of wheat to be substituted for Pacific Northwest white wheat in some domestic markets where it has in times past sold at a premium.

Overproduction and excessive carry-overs (in relation to the amounts produced) are serious problems in the white wheat area. There is need

16. The July 1, 1954 carry-over of hard red spring was 206 million bushels (preliminary estimate). This was roughly double what might be regarded as normal, though the carry-overs of this type of wheat have varied so widely, even under free-market conditions, that no very precise estimate of a normal carry-over can be made. However, no large change in the acreages grown would be needed to bring this type of wheat reasonably well into adjustment.

for price adjustments that will permit vigorous merchandising of this wheat in the uses and markets for which it is best suited and possibly for an increase in the amounts used as feed.

The principal wheat problem is in hard red winter, which is grown mainly in the southern and Central Plains states. Nearly two thirds of the July 1954 wheat carry-over was of this type.[17] It is here also that the largest expansion of acreage has occurred. Hard red winter is the principal export wheat grown in the United States, but it is also used extensively in the manufacture of domestically used bread flour. From one half to two thirds of the current volume of production is used in our own bread flour industry. Since there is no significant difference in type or quality between the wheat exported and that used in domestic flour production, there is no way of classifying part of it as export wheat, for sale in a different market, and part as wheat for domestic consumption, except on an arbitrary, proportional basis.

The other principal type, soft red winter, has accumulated to some extent but does not constitute a major problem. Such amount of cutback as may be needed in this type probably would come about fairly quickly through the action of farmers themselves if support prices were moderately lower. In the areas where these wheats are mainly grown (chiefly in and near the Corn Belt) alternative crops are more generally available and the individual farmer is not so exclusively dependent on wheat as his chief source of income.

No Easy and Simple Solution Available

From the above comments, it is apparent that there is no quick, easy way of solving the wheat problem. Many of the plans put forward have, in fact, oversimplified the problem and have proposed unrealistic solutions. This has come about in part from the tendency to look upon wheat as a single commodity, which it obviously is not.

A uniform cutback on all types of wheat clearly is not in the interest either of all wheat growers or of the public. Furthermore, a simple domestic allotment plan that would assign uniform percentages of all of them to domestic use or export would not be likely to prove equitable or practical. The major adjustments needed, either in the amount of wheat grown or in the uses to which it is put, are in the hard red winter and white wheat areas.

Price Differentials Based on Quality, Type and Location

A first essential in achieving a healthier situation in the wheat markets is to devise a plan whereby the prices received will reflect the preferences of the users, thus preventing overstimulation of the less desired types

17. The estimated carry-over as of July 1, 1954 was 663 million bushels as compared to a total carry-over of 1,007 million bushels.

and qualities and understimulation of those which will best meet the needs of consumers. Realistic geographic price differentials also should be restored as soon as possible so as to avoid arbitrary and artificial interregional shifts in production.

One way of meeting this problem would be to let each type of wheat find its own relative level of price in a free market and to provide whatever subsidy is felt to be warranted on a flat or graduated per bushel basis. This would encourage production of the most desired types and grades and would tend to lessen the emphasis on types less desired or needed. It would also eliminate the flat and rigid type of price support, which inhibits movement into export or feed markets.

The input of federal funds could be about the same as, or smaller or larger than, the amounts now being spent on the program, as the Congress might decide. The cost of the present program is indeterminate since no one can say what losses will have to be taken on the stocks now held or financed by the government. Current subsidies, however, are costing in the order of $200 million a year and the losses on stocks will eventually have to be added to them.

Export Markets Will Not Absorb All of the Excess

A mere shift to a subsidy on domestically used milling wheats, letting the remainder go for export, would not solve the problem. The world market will not absorb, at any acceptable price, the amounts of wheat that would be thrown on it if all of the excess not required for domestic flour production were to be suddenly channeled into it. Furthermore, very serious international repercussions would result. Some reasonable control over amounts exported through commercial channels must be maintained, at least for some time to come.

The alternative to such controls may well be a marked increase in embargoes or tariffs against U.S. wheat on the part of some of the consuming nations, such as Britain, and growing friction with competing export countries such as Canada, Argentina and Australia. Even an unsubsidized free-market approach, which is normally considered appropriate and internationally acceptable, would be likely to cause trouble if put into effect suddenly and without consultation with the receiving and exporting countries concerned. The aim should be, however, to move in the direction of restoring the stabilizing influence of a freely operating world wheat market.

The International Wheat Agreement, under which the United States now has commitments running until 1956, is principally a method of subsidizing U.S. wheat exports without undue disturbance to the world market and with the acquiescence of competing suppliers. As now constituted, it is not a solution to the problem and is not likely to become one. Several of the consuming nations, including the United Kingdom, and some of the important exporting nations are not signatories. There is every reason, however, for continuing consultation with other wheat-using and wheat-supplying nations. To throw the international wheat market wide open at this time would bring about a chaotic situation that would be detrimental to all concerned, and might result in even more severe restrictions than now exist.

A large expansion of shipments for relief or through abnormal methods of financing also does not offer prospects of a satisfactory and continuing solution to the problem. Other nations, like our own, are reluctant to accept heavy shipments from abroad merely because some other country wants to get rid of them. This is especially true if in-shipments tend to disturb or demoralize local markets. Such supplies cannot be depended on as a continuing resource. Hence, if they tend to destroy or weaken an industry on which the receiving country is heavily dependent, it may find itself later in a worse situation than if it had not accepted the shipments at all.

These considerations should not, of course, preclude the use of excess U.S. stocks to the fullest extent feasible in alleviating catastrophes or advancing constructive programs in situations where both the giving and the receiving country are in accord as to the ends to be sought. Such methods of disposing of foodstuffs not readily salable in the normal channels of trade have frequently been proposed, and there is wide interest in this type of solution for the surplus problem we now have. However, the excess reserves now held will apparently provide ample amounts for carrying out programs of that kind to the extent that they are found feasible and desirable. A continuing program of shipments for relief and of sales at concession prices, or for blocked currencies, does not appear to be a practical way of dealing with surpluses that may arise in the years ahead. Though the United States and the receiving countries may look with favor on such procedures as a temporary solution for pressing current problems, neither the United States nor the countries presumably benefited look upon them as a satisfactory substitute for healthier, more soundly based international trading arrangements.

Suggested Lines of Attack on the Problem

The complexity of the problem makes it inappropriate to present detailed or dogmatic proposals for its solution. We do, however, suggest certain types of approach to it which in our judgment warrant serious consideration and further exploration. These are as follows:

1. The markets for wheat should at the earliest practical time be freed sufficiently so that customary, use-based price differentials for the various types and grades can be reflected in the prices paid to growers. Until that is done, desirable types of adjustment will be inhibited or slowed down, the production of less needed types of wheat will be over-

stimulated and that of types for which there is an actual or potential food market may be unduly restricted or discouraged.

No large adjustment is needed in the hard spring area and, as of now, none at all in the durum wheats. Supports for these types should be at such levels as will let them move normally into the uses for which they are suited, except for such strategic reserves as may be needed. The loans made should be at levels that will provide financial aid for farmers who want to hold wheat but not so high as to constitute purchase commitments.

This implies no marked reduction in loan levels for these types of wheat other than the amounts authorized in existing legislation when it comes fully into effect, that is, such adjustment as will come about from using the modernized formula in figuring parity prices and some degree of flexibility in adjusting the percentages of parity at which loans will be made. Except for off-grades, the markets will apparently absorb most of these types of wheat at parity or above. For the durum wheats, prices are now much above parity, partly because of the low yields of 1953 and 1954.

Hard red winter production is overexpanded, in terms of bread use either here or abroad. A first step in orderly adjustment, for this type of wheat, is to remove entirely the support on the lower grades which should move into feed use and probably will eventually have to be so used, even if they are for a time taken over by the government. For the better grades, the loan level should be so related to that for hard red spring that the price differentials between them can be established by the trade, in terms of actual use-value for flour production and exports for food use.

That would mean lower supports for this type of wheat in order to encourage freer flow into available markets, some reduction in the amounts grown and more diversion to feed use. This is on the assumption that current excess stocks, which are mainly in this type of wheat, would be immobilized and disposed of through abnormal channels so as not to place unwarranted burdens on the growers in the years ahead.

Since there is no difference in quality or type between hard red winter wheat used in domestic bread flour production and that exported for similar uses abroad, supports on the bread quality hard red winter will apparently have to be the same whether the wheat is to move into domestic use or into export. Until the industry becomes better adjusted, some provision should be made for transitional controls and possibly for subsidies on export wheats. This would probably require that the government, for a time, stand ready to absorb some further amounts of such wheat if necessary. The amounts released for export, except low-grade feed wheat, should be specified in negotiations with other wheat-exporting countries so as not to break or seriously depress the world market.

This rather moderate downward adjustment in support level, plus the removal of supports on the poorer grades, would, it is hoped, result in sufficient readjustment in production and use to overcome in the course of four or five years much of the maladjustment now existing in the winter wheat industry.[18] If not, some further reduction in support levels might have to be considered. The situation should be kept under study with a view to modifying the program from time to time in such a way as to carry out an orderly retreat from the present overexpanded situation in this type of wheat.

For the Pacific Northwest white wheats, seldom used in bread production, a first step should be a downward adjustment in the relative support levels so that these wheats can compete effectively in both the domestic and foreign markets. Serious inroads on the domestic markets for them are being made by the soft red winter wheats of the Middle West and part of a fairly large potential foreign market is being lost. At the same time, production is being overstimulated. Excess stocks have become relatively about as serious in the Pacific Northwest as in the hard red winter area.

Here, also, considerable amounts of wheat will probably have to move into feed use. The solution appears to lie largely in the removal of supports on the lower grades of wheat, in order to encourage their use as feed instead of channeling them into government holdings, and enough reduction of the support level on the better grades to enable them to compete effectively in the markets for which they are well suited.

For the soft red winter wheats, we suggest that the level of support might well be reduced to about that on corn, thus encouraging their use for feed and a rather sizable reduction in acreage. Under the conditions prevailing in the soft red winter areas, it seems likely that such a reduction in support levels would result in a rather quick shift to other crops. Here, the alternatives are numerous and relatively attractive.

2. If support levels are reduced or price differentials increased as suggested above, or even if the present program is continued, we recommend that effective aid be given to individual farmers in working out the kinds of changes in farming that will enable them, with as little hardship as possible, to make the adjustments that apparently will have to be made in the not distant future whatever kind of program is adopted. Where such adjustments put a severe strain on the resources and incomes of the farmers concerned, we favor liberal aid in the form of special credits and, if necessary, special payments during the transition period. Aid should be given, preferably in the form of conservation payments, in those situations where readjustment involves reversion to grass farming following overexpansion of wheat in marginal areas. Some of these

18. If the agricultural legislation enacted in 1954 is allowed to go into effect by coming Congresses, the gradual shift to modernized parity in 1956 will mean relatively lower parity standards for wheat, corn and cotton. Higher standards have already been established for the livestock products generally. The setting of 75 per cent floors, as provided in the flexible support provisions of the act, will also make possible lower support levels for wheat, corn and cotton. These measures are, it must be admitted, generally in the right direction.—JOHN D. BLACK

lands are likely to be forced out of grain production if dry years occur, and the best and safest long-time use of them may be in grass and live-stock farming. Such changes may require five to ten years. The program adopted should recognize that fact.

3. We see no escape from some continuing limitation on acreage until wheat production and use can be brought into better balance than they are now. Further additions to inactive stocks should be considered only as a last resort, and even then should be kept to the lowest practical minimum. Cutbacks in acreage should not be uniform in all areas. It is not logical to force acreage reductions in areas that are not producing materially in excess of market needs or where an adequate adjustment can be brought about by special conservation payments or otherwise. This problem can, we believe, be met by assigning allotments and quotas by regions and types, with greater cutbacks on those types of wheat that are in heaviest oversupply. Growers who find it profitable to grow wheat for feed use on acreage in excess of allotments should be permitted to do so provided it is possible to maintain adequate control over the use made of the product.

4. It would not be in the interest either of U.S. wheat growers or of foreign producers and consumers to flood the world market and throw it into chaos. The aim should be to move gradually in the direction of a freer and more stable world market without creating a situation in which state trading and severe restrictions on trade will be re-emphasized.

Under present conditions, the export of wheat is largely under government control because of the export subsidies required to bridge the gap between the artificially supported United States price and that prevailing in the world market. If price differentials such as those suggested above are permitted to develop, it may become more attractive to export some types and grades of wheat without subsidy. In that case, it might be necessary for a time to maintain government control over exports by means of licenses or otherwise. Such action should, of course, be taken only for the purpose of steadying the situation until a better balance can be achieved and should be carried out by mutual agreement on the part of the principal consuming and supplying nations.

5. The International Wheat Agreement should, we believe, be allowed to expire when it next runs out, in 1956, and should be replaced by a suitable agency for continuing consultation by the principal wheat-using and wheat-supplying countries.[19] As a means of steadying the situation until the markets come into better balance, the United States might well announce in advance, probably after consultation with other exporting nations, the amounts it will put on the international market so as to remove the fear that a large part of our heavy reserves will suddenly be released and cause a chaotic situation in the world market. Such a

19. In my view it would be preferable to continue attempts to effect agreements on both price and quantity through the International Wheat Council.—ANDREW STEWART

commitment should not, of course, be so inflexible as to preclude additional shipments if widespread droughts or other emergency developments make larger exports desirable as a means of furthering widely accepted national and international objectives.

6. We commend in principle the idea of immobilizing a good part of the excess stocks now in hand until they can be moved into abnormal outlets. To the extent that they can be used in carrying out or facilitating foreign-aid and relief programs without creating undue repercussions, that should be done. The possibility of channeling some of these stocks into lower-grade uses, such as feed, should also be kept under continuing study, and action along this line should be taken whenever it can be done constructively and without undue disturbance to the market. This will require some relaxation of the restrictions on sales by the Commodity Credit Corporation and acceptance of the losses involved. However, these losses have already been potentially incurred and unless there should be war, or a very severe and prolonged drought, they will eventually become realized costs, probably on a larger scale than if action is taken now.

7. It will be apparent from the above discussion that we do not see a likelihood that any simple two-price, domestic allotment, export subsidy, foreign-aid or blocked-currency program will provide an adequate solution to the wheat problem. Exports cannot be increased enough to take up the slack in the near future, whether through export subsidies, by free-market sales or by shipments made in conjunction with foreign-aid programs. In 1953–54 we were able to export, even with heavy subsidies, only about 217 million bushels. Foreign-aid shipments might perhaps absorb more wheat than in the past, but resistance to them appears to be strong in the receiving countries, except when crop failure and famine cause them to be urgently needed.

These reservations apply even more significantly to the prospect of heavy purchases with blocked currencies. Resort to blocked-currency transactions would have been appropriate in the early postwar years, and may still be useful in some cases, but the need for action of that kind has declined. Most of the importing countries would not now choose to buy on that basis except when threatened with very severe exchange difficulties.

We also point out that any program that treats all wheat as "wheat" and calls for arbitrary segregation of parts of it for given uses or outlets, without taking account of variations in type and grade, is almost certain to be found unrealistic and unworkable. This is true as well of the more extreme proposals for drastic reduction or elimination of price supports. Such action could result in chaotic conditions and serious depression in the wheat areas. The problem now with us is a result of influences that extend back for more than a decade, and of great changes that have come about in land use and methods of farming. It will have to be dealt with on a step-by-step basis, but it is of crucial importance that the steps taken be in the right direction.[20]

The Cotton Problem

Internationally, the cotton situation is not far out of balance. Moderate changes in the existing program would, we believe, result in the absorption in most years of the amounts of cotton available for export. Other cotton-producing countries are running into high costs and would probably cut back production at prices even moderately below those now prevailing. The existing maladjustments are largely between regions within the United States.

We suggest that the cotton loan program be put on a bona fide loan basis moderately lower than that now provided so as to make possible businesslike handling of U.S. cotton in the domestic and international markets. This would mean stabilizing the market through loans to producers but avoiding the use of an announced, fixed price that provides an open invitation for other countries to dispose of their entire surplus at prices slightly below the U.S. minimum price, thereby placing on the United States government the burden of supporting cotton prices throughout the world.

It has been stated on good authority that a decrease of as little as 3 cents a pound on cotton would get us into balance and enable us to sell as much as 16 million bales. During much of the time since 1943, the level of cotton prices has not been due in any important way either to price supports or acreage controls. Thus, there is a body of experience to go on. Except in 1950 and 1954, there were no acreage controls. The controls applied in 1950 seem not to have been needed and probably were harmful to the industry. The suggestion made does not therefore imply a drastic change in the procedures used during most of the past ten years.

Whatever plan is followed, it should facilitate the flow of cotton into the markets in such a way that dangerously unstabilizing carry-overs

20. This rather long treatment of the U.S. wheat problem has many elements of strength. It does not lump all wheats together but treats them as different commodities as is long overdue. It seeks to find the market value of each type of wheat. My belief as to the underlying economic characteristics of wheat leads me, however, to modify or to place more stress than this statement does upon the following: (1) Acreage allotments are not only unnecessary, they are a nuisance all around. (2) Until carry-over stocks held by the U.S. government are down to 500 million bushels or less, the government should schedule its export sales of wheat for a year ahead and it should announce this schedule (dates and amounts to be sold for twelve months ahead) on or about July 1st in order to reduce the great uncertainty which U.S. stocks now create in the world market for wheat. (3) Much more wheat should be produced for and used as feed than is envisaged in this statement. (4) The production adjustments required to approach equilibrium are not as difficult as implied. And (5) the long-run competitive position of U.S. wheat, in view of the cost-reducing advances in techniques of production that have been achieved, is much stronger, even in competing for a larger share of the world market, than one might infer from this statement.—T. W. SCHULTZ

will not be built up. The Commodity Credit Corporation should be given more latitude in the disposal of cotton stocks held by it than it now has. It would then be in a position to carry out more effectively the stabilizing function for which it is designed. Detailed instructions written into law as to the amounts of cotton that can be sold in any given period and the price at which it can be released tend to prevent orderly handling of stocks and to reduce the effectiveness of the Commodity Credit Corporation as a stabilizing agency.

Other steps designed to facilitate more aggressive selling of American cotton can be helpful in some situations. In some cases, more adequate short-term credits might well be made available to foreign mills and other buyers, and stocks held abroad could perhaps be larger than in recent years, with a view to making the purchase of American cotton attractive and convenient for foreign buyers. If government aid is needed in carrying out programs of these kinds, we favor providing it. Some steps in this direction have already been taken. Public Law No. 30, approved May 21, 1953, authorized the Export-Import Bank to provide insurance against loss or damage to tangible personal property located in friendly foreign countries, where the loss results from hostile or war-like activities in time of peace or from internal strife.

To the extent that strong merchandising policies and the maintenance of a free flow of cotton into the consuming markets will not result in prices that growers consider adequate, the solution should be sought in readjustments in cotton production such that a better balance will be achieved. The competition from synthetic fibers and foreign growths is, of course, a factor in how high a level of prices cotton growers may find it in their interest to maintain through restrictions on production.

The lack of balance between cotton-growing regions in the United States is partly a result of the government programs undertaken in the past. The upsurge of demand in 1950 was accompanied by a sharp reduction in U.S. production, which was largely a result of the acreage allotments applied in that year. Cotton prices went to record highs and as a result the acreages grown in the western part of the cotton belt were greatly expanded. The high prices received for the 1950 crop gave impetus to a shift that was already well under way. Even in areas where some reduction in acreage would be in order on strictly economic grounds, there has been some tendency to maintain acreage as a means of protecting or enlarging acreage bases which growers felt might be to their advantage in succeeding years.

It is apparent that a major, and probably irreversible, interregional shift in cotton production is occurring in the United States. Government policy should look in two directions: (1) to avoiding action that will overstimulate cotton production in the West, thus intensifying the problem of adjustment in the eastern areas, and (2) to facilitating adjustments in the older cotton areas that will help them to move in the direction of a well-adjusted relationship to the newer western areas.

In other words, the goal to be sought should be an orderly and gradual adjustment to the underlying comparative cost situations in the various regions. Some of the newer cotton-producing areas of the United States can undoubtedly compete profitably with any cotton-producing areas in the world. The program should aim at enabling them to do so as fast as this can be done without undue hardship to the older cotton areas. This means helping the older areas to move forward with the type of adjustment already well under way there and the adoption at the earliest practical time of a price policy that will permit U.S. cotton to move freely in the world market.[21]

The Corn Situation

Corn is primarily an item of agricultural supply; it is not produced mainly for sale as corn. Ordinarily no more than 20 to 30 per cent of the corn crop is sold. Even that figure is somewhat inflated for recent years, since considerable amounts of the corn listed as "sold" were surrendered to the Commodity Credit Corporation under the nonrecourse loan program and hence were not a genuine sale for current use. More than two thirds of the crop is used on the farms where it is grown. For this part of it, the price maintained is largely hypothetical, since the farmer is charging himself a higher or lower price on a home-produced cost factor and is showing, in a bookkeeping sense, a smaller or larger profit on the product he actually sells, mainly hogs and beef cattle, neither of which is under a price-support program.

The level of price support is significant, therefore, with respect to (1) that portion of the crop actually sold in an ordinary market sense (this goes mainly to other farmers), and (2) the amount of loan that can be obtained from the Commodity Credit Corporation. On the corn sold in the market, growers do benefit from the maintenance of a higher price. However, this gain is realized principally by a limited number of growers in the cash-corn areas. It is not widely distributed over the corn-growing area as a whole.[22]

21. I concur with these recommendations for cotton for I interpret them to say that in view of the prospective value of cotton, if the loans on cotton were about three cents a pound lower than they are, the "decks would clear," because cotton would then move freely into both domestic and foreign channels and no acreage allotments would be needed or, in any case, should not be employed. Like wheat, cotton represents a complex set of commodities some of which are overpriced relative to others as loans are still being determined.—T. W. SCHULTZ

22. Many farmers probably believe that governmental action which raises the market price of corn is an advantage to corn producers even though they feed all their corn, because they believe the higher price of corn is reflected in higher prices for hogs. There is undoubtedly a relationship between the prices of hogs and corn. However, the causal effect normally runs in the opposite direction. In the absence of government action, the price bid for corn is a result of the prices obtainable for hogs and beef cattle and of the number on feed in relation to the amount of corn available. A corn price-support and

For corn put under loan to the Commodity Credit Corporation, the specific loan level is not highly important if the corn is to be used eventually by the borrowing farmer. Moderate variations in the loan rate affect only the maximum amount that can be borrowed against it. A higher or lower loan level does, of course, change the amount received by the grower if the loan is not repaid and the corn is taken over by the Commodity Credit Corporation. However, corn taken over in that way creates a problem for the government and possibly eventually for the corn growers themselves, if government stocks become so large as to be an element of weakness in the structure of corn prices.[23] Stocks that are in excess of those needed for stabilizing the livestock industry are hard to dispose of without breaking the market. Growing corn for sale to the government is at best a temporary expedient and one not greatly needed in periods when employment and demand are at high levels.[24]

The corn areas have done remarkably well in adjusting to the rapidly changing conditions of the past two decades, and the price and storage programs adopted have, on the whole, worked better than for most of the other farm products. This is partly due to the internal flexibility of the corn-livestock economy. Corn can be sold either as livestock or as corn. Also, it can be stored. Furthermore, corn acreage can be diverted to roughage or to other cash crops, and vice versa. These characteristics of the industry have enabled it to take in stride the very drastic changes in supply and demand factors that have occurred since 1930.

A major and prolonged depression was followed by a period of high war demand and inflation. At the same time, a technological revolution brought into general use far more efficient methods of production. Mechanization of field work has gone forward at an extremely rapid rate, and hybrid seed corn, which results in much higher yields, is now used on more than 95 per cent of the acreage in the Corn Belt. Commercial fertilizers are being used more extensively and more intensively and are of growing importance as a yield-increasing influence.

On the whole, the corn economy has accommodated itself to these

storage policy that takes corn out of the market may have a temporary strengthening influence on livestock prices. However, if production is not reduced and if the corn is eventually released and fed, the over-all effect is not likely to be great. Such action may, in fact, stimulate corn production enough so that the effect of the operation over a period of years may be to make livestock more plentiful and thus to reduce average prices of livestock for the period as a whole.—CALVIN B. HOOVER

23. Such maladjustments in corn production and use do not lend themselves to correction through production control. Efforts to control corn production by means of acreage allotments have not been effective. The allotment program has been a nuisance to growers and a source of considerable administrative expense without accomplishing the purpose for which it was intended.

24. Furthermore, the maintenance of an artificially high price brings about readjustments in the feed-purchasing areas which affect the surplus corn areas. It tends to encourage the growing of corn and other concentrates to replace corn which has traditionally been purchased from other areas. With rising freight costs, this kind of shift is likely to damage permanently markets which corn growers in the Corn Belt might otherwise find profitable in most years.—QUENTIN REYNOLDS

large fluctuations in demand and supply better than could have been anticipated. No longer ago than 1932, the acreage (harvested) was 110 million acres. For some years now it has been about 80 million acres, fully 27 per cent less. Regional and type-of-farming shifts have gone forward which have improved the location of the crop. Most important of all, whereas in the 1930s most of the corn-producing area was receiving very low returns for the labor, land and capital used in corn production, because of excess capacity in the industry, there is no such maladjustment currently. The returns on the resources used in growing corn, including those for labor and management, have been for some time on a par with returns to comparable factors in industry.

On only four occasions since 1932 have the amounts of corn put under loan and purchase agreements exceeded 5 per cent of production. In 1933, 11.2 per cent of the crop was pledged. Though much larger than normal, the stocks carried over proved a valuable asset in the season following because of the severe drought of 1934. In 1938 and 1939, the amount of corn put under loan rose to 11.8 per cent of production. Though generally regarded at that time as too large, the stocks held by the Commodity Credit Corporation turned out to be very useful in meeting wartime needs for feed and food. In 1948 and 1949, the amounts put under loan rose again to more than 10 per cent of production, but stocks did not become burdensome since the high demand and inflation resulting from the Korean war made liquidation feasible. The most recent period of heavy commitment was that of 1953 and 1954, with a little less than 15 per cent of production being placed under loan and purchase agreements in 1954.

Though the record on the whole is a good one, some changes in the corn price and storage program are needed. The relatively easy liquidation and readjustment of stocks that occurred in 1934 and again in 1942–1945 and in 1950–51 were largely a result of fortuitous factors that cannot be counted on to correct at the right time such maladjustments in corn stocks as may arise in the future. The very severe drought of 1934 was one of the worst in our history, and the war demands of 1942–1945 and 1950–51 cannot be looked on as normal types of stock readjustment and Commodity Credit Corporation operation. The changes in the program that appear to be needed can be made fairly easily because of the generally good condition of the corn economy and the fact that the price supports for corn are not far out of line with those needed for maintaining a healthy balance between supply and demand in this very basic part of the farm economy.

A logical price support for corn, based on supply and demand considerations, would point to a loan that would be in the order of 5 per cent lower than that of 1954. With loans available at about that level, there would be no need for acreage allotments and they should not be employed. A storage program is needed to compensate for variations in corn yields caused by weather and also to carry such reserves as may be considered appropriate for meeting variations in demand such as those which might arise in the event of war. A loan program of that kind would also, of course, provide a convenient method of financing some of the stocks held for use within the year and of rotating stocks held for relatively long periods.

This would mean using the Commodity Credit Corporation, or some similar organization, as a holder of reserve stocks that should be larger than those the trade will carry on a commercial basis and that can at times be carried longer than is customary in commercial operations. For most periods, an October 1 carry-over in the order of 600 to 800 million bushels would apparently be adequate to meet probable variations in yield or demand. However, the size of carry-over needed should be kept under continuing study to assure its adequacy and at the same time avoid the expense of maintaining an unnecessarily large reserve.

Operation of the corn-loan program on this basis would make it a genuine stabilizing influence both for the corn growers and for the livestock industry. The readjustments implied would be mostly within agriculture itself and would be largely in terms of cost and return computations for different enterprises on individual farms rather than modifications of the over-all return to Corn Belt farmers.

The policy suggested would be a return to a program more like that of the 1930s than the one of recent years, but with a more positive effort to stabilize feed supplies and the livestock industry. It would call for loan rates high enough to meet the needs of growers who actually contemplate reclaiming the corn on which the loans are based. It would also place a floor under the corn price structure that would give protection against disastrously low prices. It would not encourage the growing of corn that is not needed by the livestock industry. For it to work well, the length of the period in which such loans can be carried should be increased. Usually a short-crop year will not follow immediately after one of heavy oversupply.[25]

No Easy Solution for the Butter Problem

The butter situation presents quite different problems from those discussed above. A substitute product has become available at much lower prices and demand has shifted. During World War II, the dairy industry of the United States was not adequate to meet the sharply increased demand for fluid milk and at the same time supply as much butter per capita as the people of the United States had been accustomed to using. As a result and because of its lower price, margarine has come to be widely used and seems likely to hold or even increase the portion

25. I find the first three and the last paragraphs on corn somewhat off key with the heart of the analysis. I concur fully with the main body of the statement, aside from the four paragraphs mentioned.—T. W. SCHULTZ

of the market it supplies. The problem has been postponed to some extent by heavy government purchases which have absorbed temporarily considerable amounts of butter that could not be moved into consumption without a serious break in butter prices. However, this type of program is at best an expedient and should be used, if at all, only to give time for more fundamental solutions to the problem.

The most severe impact is on those areas where butter is the principal product. Lower prices for butter and other by-products are a disadvantage to dairymen in the fluid milk areas, but they do not constitute, for them, a major catastrophe. The fluid milk industry has been expanding rapidly and has absorbed the output of many of the dairy areas that formerly relied on butter and cheese as their main sources of income. With a rapidly increasing population and a high level of fluid milk consumption, this part of the dairy industry does not appear to be faced with adjustment problems so serious that they cannot be handled within the industry itself. The fluid milk markets are in fact continuing to reach out into the butter- and cheese-producing areas in a way that will, to some extent, ease the impact of the decline in butter use for some of them. However, some increase in competition, in the form of larger outputs of cheese, canned milk and other manufactured products, can be anticipated as the butter areas seek to shift to other products as a means of meeting their problem.

The maintenance of butter prices by government purchase and storage is tending to contract still further the per capita consumption of butter and to encourage the use of butter substitutes, thus losing some of the advantage of the long-established preference for butter. Butter has, we believe, qualities that make most consumers willing to pay more for it than for margarine but not as much more as the current margin between the two. As a consequence, more and more people, especially in the younger age groups, are becoming accustomed to margarine as the customary spread for bread and in other uses.

We believe the industry would be well advised to undertake aggressive selling of butter and to play up strongly its very real merits as a food. It should be priced competitively, that is, with a realistic differential, and an attempt should be made to recapture some of the ground lost.

Government aid in the form now being given is costly and is likely to meet with increasing public criticism. More important, it affords no real solution to the problems of the butter industry and is likely to leave them unsolved or possibly even more acute than if the program had not been undertaken. Butter is not a storable commodity in the sense that wheat, cotton, rice and tobacco are. Its quality declines much more rapidly and, if released for food use, butter that has deteriorated in quality would seriously damage the butter market. Poor butter should not be sold for human consumption even in the export markets. It is likely to give American butter a bad name and make future sales more difficult. The butter purchase and storage program should therefore be recognized for what it is, a poorly conceived expedient for dealing with a very complex problem.

We believe there is warrant for public aid in making adjustment to a technological change of such far-reaching significance as the one the butter industry is now faced with, especially since the public agencies themselves have long encouraged a shift to dairy farming as a sound and desirable change in types of farming and since considerable effort was made to expand the dairy industry in the war years. We recognize, however, that, even with the most realistic and helpful plans that can be devised, the industry has several years of painful and difficult readjustment ahead of it.

Prompt and intensive study should be given to the kinds of adjustment that will be needed and the directions they should take. Educational aid should be provided and, if needed, special credit facilities and possibly some incentive-type subsidies to help in speeding up the changes that are found likely to be necessary or desirable.

We are now subsidizing the butter industry in a way that is futile and harmful to the industry. If subsidies are to be used, we think the money so spent could accomplish more if handled in such a way as to provide positive aid in making needed adjustments. We suggest careful exploration of the possibility of providing, in the primary butter-producing areas, a declining direct-payment program which would aid butter producers during the time adjustments are being made.

In programs designed to speed adjustment, particular attention should be given to areas where reasonably attractive alternatives exist and where production is thus likely to be more sensitive to price changes. It may be that demand will be strong enough to absorb at moderately good prices most of the butter from areas that have few or very limited alternatives. It is suggested, too, that the possibility of increasing the consumption of alternative products manufactured from milk be fully explored. Some increases of that kind would apparently be consistent with national nutritional objectives. We do not, of course, assume that such adjustments as could be made along these lines would be large enough to provide a full solution to the problem.[26]

THE ROLE OF THE COMMODITY CREDIT CORPORATION

The price problems discussed above center largely in the Commodity Credit Corporation, since it is the principal agency used in carrying out the current price-supporting activities. The need for a government agency

26. I feel that the net effect of the discussion of the corn and dairy problems is to make solution of them sound much easier than it will in fact prove to be. Needed reduction of wheat acreage will tend to enlarge production of livestock feeds, including corn. Necessary reduction of butter production (and cheese, which is not mentioned, in spite of the fact that storage stocks have topped 300 million pounds) will tend to flood the fluid milk market and various meat lines. Barring a lucky drought this year and/or next, I would expect the pressures in the group of related Midwest and Southwest agricultural products—grain-dairy-meat—to be rather severe for the next few years, and the flexible lowering of support levels to be imperative.—EDWIN G. NOURSE

that could help in stabilizing the agricultural industry was recognized as early as 1929, and the idea has been incorporated in both Republican and Democratic legislation during the past twenty-five years. The relatively small-scale and fumbling attempts made by the Federal Farm Board demonstrated some of the limitations on action of that kind. The Commodity Credit Corporation program of 1933–1939, operating under a different set of conditions, showed in a more positive way some of the things that can be done by an organization of the CCC type. In fact, the success of these operations was, in part, the reason for the tremendously larger resources and responsibilities that were assigned to CCC in the years that followed. The Corporation also carried out many very useful operations during World War II.

In 1933–34 the Corporation demonstrated that it could, within reasonable limits, help to stabilize both supplies and prices of corn. The success of this operation was in part a result of the quick succession of years of oversupply and very low prices and a year in which output was severely reduced by drought. Nevertheless, the type of action taken was appropriate at that time, provided loans were not put at unrealistically high levels.

During the 1930s the cotton loan program tended to strengthen and steady the market without checking unduly the movement of cotton into domestic and foreign markets, except in 1935 when the 12-cent loan proved to be too high. The action taken in supporting prices on the unexpectedly large 1937 crop was logical as a means of preventing demoralization in a market that obviously would not absorb the amounts of cotton available. The difficulties that arose later, in connection with this and subsequent crops, were largely an outgrowth of the restrictions placed by the Congress on the release of these stocks and failure to make adequate adjustments in the amounts produced in succeeding years.

Almost from the time the Commodity Credit Corporation began to absorb cotton and other commodities in the late 1930s, businesslike handling of these stocks has been prevented by legislative restrictions placed on its operations. For cotton, CCC sales from the heavy stocks acquired in 1937 and after were for a number of years limited to 1.5 million bales a year and to 300,000 bales in any one month. Nearly all through the period since 1938, CCC has been prohibited from selling at less than parity most of the commodities held by it. Sometimes the level at which sales could be made was put as high as 105 per cent of parity. At other times, the requirement was that the commodity could not be sold for an amount less than the total accumulated costs on it. This meant in nearly all cases a price substantially above that at which farmers had chosen to surrender the commodity to the government rather than to try to sell it in the open market.

When it is recalled that CCC's mandate over most of the period was to support prices of storables at 90 per cent of parity, the restrictions placed on liquidation of stocks were such that, except in a period of continuing inflation, some stocks could not be moved at all. It is this inability to release commodities that has led to the top-heavy holdings now owned by or under loan from CCC.

Some exceptions have been made, notably the wartime sales of CCC-owned wheat for feed purposes, approximately at the price of corn, and the relief and foreign-aid shipments made in recent years. Granting that the sale of such stocks must be handled with extreme caution if serious damage to the price structure is to be avoided, it is no solution to a problem of this kind to force continuing accumulation until the stocks become so large that they constitute a much more serious threat to the price structure than if the crops had been sold on a year-to-year basis.

The CCC loan, purchase and storage type of program is not well suited for aiding the producers of perishable products and should not be so used. For these commodities, including such semiperishables as butter and cheese, other kinds of programs should be devised. If products that deteriorate rapidly in storage are bought and held, the ultimate cost is certain to be large, the public reaction bad and the results unsatisfactory.

For the storables, CCC can, within moderate limits, make a significant contribution to agricultural stability. It can be helpful in strengthening prices and providing needed crop credit in a form that is not likely to be available from other credit agencies. Some risks of price decline that commercial credit agencies cannot afford to assume can be taken in that way and may be well justified, even if losses are encountered in some years.

Heavy stocks that result from high yields or temporarily ill-adjusted production can well be carried over and liquidated gradually so as not to disturb the markets unduly. Adequate safety reserves also can and should be maintained. However, the reservoir that is full cannot absorb a flood. A stockpile that is overloaded cannot serve effectively as a shock absorber in times when help is most needed.

We are now in a period of relatively high economic activity and high demand. It is a time when, from the standpoint of stabilization objectives, the stocks of most commodities should be rather moderate. Yet, the stocks held are now at all-time highs and commitments are expected to go higher within the year. Storage facilities are full to bursting in spite of the large increases in capacity that have been and are being made. Storage alone is costing the government in excess of half a million dollars a day. This is not a situation that offers promise of genuine, large-scale help if agriculture should run into more serious difficulties in the years ahead.

The unbalance is most serious in the case of wheat. We recognize that this has resulted largely from the tremendous changes that have occurred in the available outlets abroad. It is not a situation related in any important way to the levels of economic activity in this country. A special and relatively long-term program will be needed for the solution of it. For most of the other commodities, top-heavy stocks seem not to be appropriate in a period like the present.

In summary, it seems clear that the support of prices through non-recourse loans at levels well above those at which the commodities can be moved is self-defeating and constitutes a serious danger to the well-being of agriculture. The stocks held should, as soon as practicable, be brought down to approximately the level of reserves needed in the national interest, except for temporary increases to take care of abnormally large crops.

If this is not done, both commitments and stocks may eventually reach levels such that the Congress will be unwilling to authorize further additions to them.[27] If accumulation were to be suddenly discontinued, agriculture might find itself in a serious situation. Ominously heavy stocks would be hanging over the market and could result in a severe price break that could have a very adverse effect on farm prices generally.

Even if the stocks held were not released, they would continue to absorb public funds in the form of storage costs at a rate of close to $200 million a year, which might better be used for aiding agriculture in other ways. Furthermore, deterioration and waste would be taking their toll and adding to the ultimate cost. Steps should be taken at the earliest possible time to put the Commodity Credit Corporation in a position such that it can give effective and sizable help if any serious situation arises.

STRENGTHENING THE EXPORT MARKETS

In 1951, crops from some 52 million acres were exported from the United States. Since that time, the volume of exports has dropped by almost half. Such a decline brings pressure not only on the producers of export crops but also, as a result of acreage diversion, upon the producers of other agricultural commodities as well. It is highly important, therefore, that all of agriculture recognize the vital nature of the steps which must be taken to develop and promote international trade. The alternatives are a progressive restrictionism in agriculture, which is not likely to prove workable, or progressive economic attrition, which will affect adversely the whole agricultural economy.

Though a good deal of progress has been made in freeing currencies, reducing barriers to trade, and regaining the stabilizing influence of freely operating international markets, there still is much to be done before American farm products can move freely into world markets in

27. I would stress the point that some day soon the taxpayer may rebel against paying taxes to subsidize the farmer so that he may charge high prices which the same taxpayer has to pay as a consumer. At the same time, the taxpayer has to see his taxes used to buy and store food which is, in the end, spoiled or wasted.—LOUISE L. WRIGHT

such a way that the ups and downs of production in the various countries can be spread widely instead of being concentrated in individual countries. The international markets still are much distorted by the nationalistic policies and disturbances that grew out of the war and depression periods.

Generally speaking, our agricultural export industries, such as wheat, cotton, rice, soybeans and fresh and processed fruits, are highly efficient. In the absence of such handicaps as exchange restrictions, import quotas and bilateral trading, the U.S. producers of such commodities can compete effectively in world markets on a profitable basis. It must be recognized, however, that even with an improved world-trade situation, the peacetime trade in some of these commodities, especially wheat, cannot be maintained at the high levels which resulted from wartime and immediate postwar demands.

If foreign trade in American farm products is to be put on a stable and dependable basis, primary emphasis must be on measures that will contribute most effectively to the re-establishment of multilateral international trade on the broadest possible basis. Of primary importance is the restoration of free currency convertibility between the major trading nations of the free world. As a first step in achieving convertibility it is essential that we strive to demonstrate to the other nations of the free world the willingness of the United States to accept a high level of imports into this country. Aggressive rather than reluctant cooperation in the development of multilateral trade will be required if real progress is to be made in time to preserve maximum freedom in the movement of American agricultural products into export markets.

In some quarters, there is considerable emphasis on the use of a number of extraordinary devices for maintaining a high volume of exports of farm products. Such devices include the sale of surpluses for non-transferable balances in foreign currencies, the barter of farm surpluses for strategic materials, the donation of farm surpluses as a form of foreign aid, two-price systems and the use of open or concealed export subsidies.

Some of these procedures are authorized in existing legislation and will no doubt be found helpful in some situations. In the main, however, their use tends to becloud the issues and prevent the adoption of the broader measures which are required if our export trade is to be pushed back toward the pattern of multilateral trade that is essential for the maintenance of a free, dynamic economy.

The trade problem is not one that can be solved quickly through some specific short-term action. At best, the achievement of strength and balance in this important phase of our market will require some years of vigorous and carefully planned effort. Some temporary and interim measures almost certainly will be needed, but these cannot, in the long run, provide as satisfactory a solution as a comprehensive, freely operating world market and should not be allowed to become a substitute for it, if that can be avoided.

Consequently, our program with respect to world trade should be strong, consistent and continuing. Also, we should use imagination and vigor in developing programs that will increase consumption abroad. Such measures, if they are to be of lasting significance, must look to a continuing and constructive increase in the demand for U.S. products, not merely to the disposal of temporary surpluses that the United States or other nations may wish to get rid of.[28]

THE GOVERNMENT-SPONSORED CREDIT PROGRAM

The farm credit programs sponsored or carried on by the federal government are of two principal types, each handled through a different set of organizations.[29] The cooperative credit system centers mainly in the Farm Credit Administration. It has been designed primarily to provide a commercial type of credit without substantial government subsidy. Emphasis has been on conservative loans that can be made at low rates of interest because of the small risk involved. It is largely borrower-owned and borrower-controlled. Modest government subsidies were provided in establishing it and some subsidy is still provided to the banks for cooperatives and the production credit corporations. The system is, in the main, a strictly business organization for channeling credit into commercial agriculture at as low a cost as possible and in forms suited to the agricultural industry.

This group of credit agencies has reached a high stage of development

28. This section on "Strengthening the Export Markets" as the title suggests is a wholly one-sided treatment of the role of U.S. agriculture in international trade. Only the interests and gains of farmers as exporters are stressed. Not a word appears on the serious inconsistency between U.S. farm (price) policy and the much needed and desired freer trade policy.—T. W. SCHULTZ

The program with respect to world trade should take into consideration the fact that the technical assistance programs may, in some instances, deprive the United States of markets because of increasing self-sufficiency and, on the other hand, an increased standard of living, which is the goal of the technical assistance programs, may develop new demands for American products. The United States will be better able to make far-reaching plans if it continues to work with the Food and Agriculture Organization and with other international agencies concerned with the food supply of the world.

—LOUISE L. WRIGHT

29. It will be noted that the Farm Credit Administration is still referred to as a "government-sponsored" credit agency even though the federal land banks have paid off the capital advanced by the government to get them started, and the production credit associations are well on the way to achieving that goal. This does not mean, however, that they are government-sponsored only in the sense of having been helped by the government to get started. The government in effect still stands behind them and will come to their rescue if another severe depression occurs, just as it did in the early 1930s. Without this protection, the debentures sold to finance the loans made by the Farm Credit System would not find as ready a market as they do. Even without a severe general depression, the production credit associations do not now have sufficient capital to make the loans needed in the event of bad crop years and the like, with the result that certain areas have to be declared disaster loan areas and provided for by special measures.—JOHN D. BLACK

and has functioned effectively.[30] The capital structure of the banks for cooperatives appears to warrant study and some gradual modification.[31] The production credit *corporations* were set up as a means of providing government capital and supervision for the local associations (production credit *associations*) through which farmers borrow from the intermediate credit banks. The production credit associations are now established, going concerns. More than 80 per cent of them have retired the government capital advanced to them. The amount of supervision and aid now needed by them could apparently be supplied by means of a simpler organization with smaller capital and less overhead. These points are more fully discussed in the research report. (See pp. 156–61.)

The principal unfilled need, so far as the Farm Credit Administration is concerned, is for larger amounts of longer-term intermediate credit. We are of the opinion that the production credit associations could provide better service to American agriculture than they now do. The production credit system was originally intended as a means of providing loans written to cover periods approximating those required for carrying out the operation contemplated, and falling due at such time as liquidation of the loan from earnings could be anticipated. For some of the most important types of constructive intermediate-term investment, such as farm reorganization, conservation improvements, farm wood lot development and the building up of livestock enterprises, loans need to be set up on the basis of from one to several years.

This is not the type of loan most commonly provided by the production credit associations. Over most of the country, the associations tend to provide loans that are much like those supplied by commercial banks, which are heavily dependent on bank deposits for their loan funds. The intermediate credit system was set up specifically to relieve agriculture of its heavy dependence on loans derived from bank deposits, since loans of that kind may be reduced sharply in a time of credit stringency.

The funds supplied to the production credit associations by the intermediate credit banks need not be subject to this type of instability since the loan funds used are derived from fixed-term debentures sold by the

30. It is my belief that government-sponsored and government-aided rural credit agencies should be complementary to rather than competitive with private credit enterprises. The several lending services now gathered under the Farm Credit Administration have rendered invaluable help to agriculture in situations in the past in which conventional credit agencies were blind to farmers' needs or callous about serving them. The continuance of this service in the future as a yardstick or a pace-maker is needed, but the Farm Credit Administration should not be regarded as an end in itself and compete for a maximum share of the rural credit business—particularly at any sacrifice of sound (but broad-gauged) credit standards. The policy should be to withdraw from any area in which private lending agencies are able and willing to render adequate service, but be ready to re-enter or expand operations in times of emergency or newly arisen need.

—EDWIN G. NOURSE

31. A number of the cooperative groups have recently proposed legislative and other actions designed to bring about the retirement of the government capital in the banks for cooperatives and to make them borrower-owned.

intermediate credit banks. If necessary, these could be issued on a longer-term basis than they now are. We suggest the desirability of exploration, by production credit association directors and the Farm Credit Administration, of the possibility of supplying a larger volume of genuine intermediate credit for types of agricultural development that are not now being carried out on as large a scale as they might well be.

Farmers Home Administration Loans

The other principal feature of the credit program is that which centers in the Farmers Home Administration. Here the purpose is to provide a higher-risk, smaller-scale type of credit designed to meet the needs of farmers who are not eligible for regular commercial loans such as those supplied by the Farm Credit Administration and the commercial banks, and also to give assistance to beginning farmers who are unable to make the large investments required to get started in present-day commercial agriculture. Disaster loans of various kinds are also supplied through that agency.

The FHA program grew out of a number of emergency and experimental programs directed principally to the needs of small-scale and low-income farmers. Much of the program of the 1930s (under the Resettlement Administration and the Farm Security Administration) was undertaken to meet acute emergency conditions. That emphasis is not now prominent, except in specific drought or other disaster situations. More general emergency lending based on economic disaster rather than physical disaster could become important if a severe agricultural depression should again occur. In that event, the Farmers Home Administration would be the logical mechanism for loans of the subcommercial type, except possibly the refinancing of mortgage loans, which was handled effectively through the land bank system in the 1930s.

In more normal times, the Farmers Home Administration is mainly engaged in efforts to improve the efficiency and living conditions of farmers who for one reason or another are in poor status in terms of tenure, capitalization, size of farm or efficiency of operation. The loans made by it involve more risk than those made by the Farm Credit Administration and usually involve less collateral. They also require much more in the way of individual supervision and educational work. Most of the funds used are appropriated by the Congress instead of being borrowed in the commercial money markets as are those of the Farm Credit Administration.

The committee recognizes the need for loans of that type. The FHA loan program constitutes the principal effort of the federal government to raise to a more satisfactory economic and tenure status the one to two million low-income farmers, who have tended to be bypassed both by the upsurge in farm prosperity in the 1940s and by the farm programs designed mainly for farmers engaged in commercial agriculture and hence not well suited to the needs of these smaller-scale, subsistence-type farmers.[32] For these farmers, appropriate loans accompanied by effective supervision and help in farm planning offer the best prospect for advancement to more satisfactory incomes.

This does not mean that we assume that all of them can or should be helped in that way. The loan program should be selective in terms of types and groups of farmers who can be effectively aided by programs of these kinds. For many of the younger farmers in areas where such farms are numerous, out-movement from agriculture to other occupations should be encouraged and facilitated. However, many of the older farmers of this group are not of an age or so situated that transfers to other occupations or locations can be made practical or attractive.

These low-production farms do not contribute importantly to the over-all volume of commercial farm products, but they do provide the living and working environment for about a third of the farm families of the United States. They are heavily concentrated in certain regions, particularly in the southeastern states and in portions of northern Michigan, Wisconsin and Minnesota. Recent studies indicate that the proportion of such farms is not large in most other parts of the United States. It is these farmers who, in general, are most out of line with other groups in the economy so far as income is concerned. Their situation reflects most

32. Available data and much of the analysis in this report lead me to conclude that the prosperity of the 1940s was shared by all areas and major groups on farms in the United States. Perhaps we have given too little attention to the growth of off-farm work, which constituted an important way in which a considerable proportion of the people living on farms shared in the prosperity of the 1940s. Those who emphasize the large amount of poverty among farm operators use as evidence the large percentage of low money incomes reported by farm people in various surveys. The 1950 decennial census, for example, shows that 35 per cent of the families and unrelated individuals reported money incomes for 1949 of less than $1,000. (U.S. Bureau of the Census, *Census of Population: 1950*, Vol. II, Characteristics of the Population, Table 57.) It is helpful in appraising the meaning of such data to note that even for states such as California and Iowa 24 and 16 per cent respectively of the families and unrelated individuals reported incomes of less than $1,000.

For many reasons, such data provide a very inadequate basis for judging how many people have been bypassed in a general advance or are living in poverty. Many people for one reason or another understate income when replying to questions in a survey; incomes of any one year for many people, especially farm people whose incomes vary a great deal from year to year, are not typical, so there are many fewer very poor and somewhat fewer very rich than the data for any one year indicate. In addition, these incomes relate solely to money and take no account of the fact that farm dwellings are provided as well as a considerable part of the food and fuel used, and that the use of the automobile for family living is in large measure considered a farm expense to be deducted in estimating net money income.

Valuable evidence on how different farm areas have shared in the prosperity of the 1940s is provided by the farm-operator family level of living indexes for the counties of the United States prepared by Dr. Margaret J. Hagood of the U.S. Department of Agriculture. I have examined these indexes in various ways; and in my opinion changes in them are closely related to changes in the average income of consumer units living in them. There does appear to be some tendency for the indexes to overstate the economic advance from 1940 to 1950 of the poor compared to the well-to-do counties. Nevertheless these indexes provide conclusive evidence that all major farm areas shared appreciably in the prosperity of the 1940s. In spite of this trend some areas must still be classed as "low-income."—MARGARET G. REID

sharply the problem of inequality within agriculture (except for the farm labor group, which is not discussed in this report).

For this group of farmers, we regard the Farmers Home Administration production and subsistence loan program as of primary importance. For them, credit accompanied by special aid in the form of planning assistance and supervision is, we believe, the quickest and most effective way of bringing about needed improvements. It constitutes a type of assistance that is specially tailored to their needs and resources.

We urge that considerable stress be put on the type of program designed to enlarge farms that are too small for efficient operation, by means of government loans and through insured private loans.[33] For reasons more fully discussed in the research report, this procedure seems to offer one of the best prospects for significant and continuing betterment of the farming opportunities of considerable numbers of farmers whose farms are too small.[34]

For farm-purchase loans, we stress the insured 90 per cent loan in preference to a large expansion of the government-financed, tenant-purchase loan program.[35] The latter program, though it has been relatively successful, involves a considerable element of selectivity and does

33. At the same time, however, we should avoid creating new crops of farm operators lacking the capacity and executive ability required for successful farm operation. Such individuals will be using their talents more profitably as employees than as proprietors. We should also avoid perpetuating or creating farms that are so poor or so small that they do not offer prospect of providing an acceptable standard of living.
—QUENTIN REYNOLDS

34. As for family-type farming, the effects of the great changes of recent years have been generally favorable. More and more of the family-type farms are now large enough and have resources enough to enable the families to make a good living and educate their sons and daughters and start them on the way toward good lives of their own. The family-type farm of today needs two to three times as many acres as in the 1910-20 decade. The censuses of the ten years from 1940 to 1950, however, show only a small increase in the average farm size in this country—from 177 to 215 in total acres, and from 53 to 64 in crop acres. There is evidence of some consolidation in the size-group 30 to 1,000 acres and also in the smaller units. This often takes the form at the start of additional rented land. The greatest increase in the number of farms of 500 to 1,000 acres has occurred mostly in the semiarid and arid grain and ranching areas of the West. This is even more true of the 20 per cent increase in the number of farms of 1,000 acres or more. In the Great Plains area, an efficient family-type grain farm using a diesel tractor unit needs around 2,000 acres of cropland.—JOHN D. BLACK

35. Important in this connection are the effects which the increasing use of power machinery and technology generally may be having on land tenure, particularly on tenancy and family-type farming. As for tenancy, the proportion of farms rented has declined sharply since 1940. If the leasing systems now in use were well devised from the standpoint of use of the land and helping younger farmers to climb the agricultural ladder, we could, to advantage, have even a larger percentage of rented farms than the 28 per cent reported in the 1950 census. Farmers' sons with relatively limited means are indeed fortunate if there are adequate farms available for rental under good leasing arrangements in their communities. However, two aspects of this problem do require attention. One is the greatly increased amount of working capital now required to start farming even under a share lease, especially with a balanced crop and livestock system. The other is the incorporation in the lease of provisions for conservation practices such as pasture improvement, green manuring, cover crops, contour cultivation, sod waterways and the like.—JOHN D. BLACK

not reach those most in need of help in achieving farm ownership. Neither is it likely to be on a large enough scale to affect the tenancy situation very significantly. Insured loans on a 90 per cent of value basis, if such a program can be carried out successfully, could expand almost indefinitely and would provide loan arrangements for agriculture roughly comparable with those available to urban home buyers with little capital.

Loan procedures and funds for rural housing improvement on middle-range commercial farms and on small farms are not as yet satisfactorily developed. The problem is complicated by the close interrelation between the farm as a business and the home as a residence and also by the limited availability of architectural and craft services in rural areas. It should be given further study.

Rural Electrification and Rural Telephone Service

The financing, leadership and technical assistance supplied by the Rural Electrification Administration, in conjunction with earlier and concurrent developments on the part of the private power industry, have brought about a situation in which the great majority of the nation's farms are now supplied with central-station electric power. With some $2.5 billion of government loan funds already invested in these enterprises, it would appear that the undertaking should be largely self-supporting from now on and should not need further large net inputs of federal funds. However, the increasing load of many of the lines is making necessary a considerable amount of additional investment for heavying up power resources and transmission lines. The government should either make available additional capital for this purpose or adjust repayment rates in such a way that the REA cooperatives can finance expansion and improvement out of earnings. Aid should be continued in extending more widely the availability of rural telephone service, which is being financed in a similar way.

CONSERVATION

The conservation of soils has become a very important feature of the farm program. Since full exploration of the activities relating to it would require much more time and effort than this committee has been able to give to them, we confine our comments to a few points which, in our opinion, should be given special consideration in the shaping of conservation plans for the future. These are as follows:

1. We are convinced that both the farmers and the general public are in favor of a vigorous and continuing program designed to carry forward the excellent start that has been made in conserving and improving the soils and other natural resources of the United States.

2. Important public as well as private returns are involved. Hence, there is warrant for public participation in the program by direct con-

tribution of funds to those parts of it in which the public interest extends beyond or is much more important than the private gains to individuals.

3. Even in those parts of the program where gains to the individual are presumably sufficient to warrant carrying out the program, the public interest is, we believe, sufficient to warrant providing at public expense a vigorous and effective program of conservation education, and the supplying of a substantial amount of technical aid and guidance in developing and carrying on conservation activities. This applies not only to farm lands but to privately owned timber and range lands as well.

4. Technical assistance, in the farm areas, should consist largely of aid in working out long-term whole-farm and community plans, plus aid and counsel in carrying them out. In doing this, the farm-planning activities of the conservation specialists should be brought into closer collaboration with the farm management work of the agricultural extension services with a view to developing farm plans that will not only be adequate from a conservation standpoint but will be so designed as to improve farm profits to the fullest extent feasible without sacrificing unduly the soil conservation objectives.[36]

To this end, we urge much more emphasis on appropriate farm management and economic training for a sufficient portion of the extension personnel to make such a joint effort practical and effective. This means that special provision should be made for intensive in-service or graduate training in farm management and economics for those extension workers who are expected to take an active part in working out soil-conserving and profit-maximizing farm plans. The training and experience of most of the field personnel in agricultural extension is inadequate for carrying out its part of the type of program here advocated.

5. We are of the opinion that the conservation payment program can and should be modified substantially now that it is well under way. This program was originally designed to: (1) aid in bringing about adjustments in the acreages planted to cash crops; (2) supplement farm incomes; and (3) induce and enable farmers to undertake soil-conserving practices which they were unlikely to carry on otherwise, either from lack of understanding and interest or from lack of financial resources to carry them out.

The conservation payment program unquestionably gave much impetus to the soil conservation movement and helped to create the widespread interest in it that now exists. At the time it was started, even the small payments per farm were important to a severely depressed industry in which these small income supplements were much needed. Such special aids and inducements are appropriate and effective in initiating and stimulating planned changes of that kind. If continued

36. The Eighty-third Congress appropriated $7.5 million for a greatly expanded program of aid to farmers in the economic planning of their farm businesses. This is in accord with the recommendation here presented but may imply expansion at a faster rate than can be carried out in view of the scarcity of qualified personnel.

indefinitely, they become, mainly, thinly spread subsidies to many farmers who are already using good soil-conserving practices.

Such amounts as the Congress is willing to appropriate for soil conservation activities of this kind should be provided on a selective basis, that is, for special intensive efforts to restore and build up badly deteriorated areas and for aid and encouragement to farmers who are financially unable but otherwise competent to undertake the kinds and amounts of conservation activity needed.

6. In cases where there is need for severe readjustment in the acreages of given crops, in connection with allotments and quotas, special payments may be warranted for a time to encourage the shift of unused acreages to soil-conserving uses with a view to keeping them out of all types of commercial use for a limited period. This obviously should be merely a temporary aid to farmers faced with unusually severe adjustment problems, not a continuing handout of funds for maintaining a distorted pattern of agricultural production.

7. Aid of a kind similar to that outlined in (4) above should be made available for improving and increasing the productivity of small-scale forest holdings, including those on farms.

8. Major expenditures for conservation structures not only on farms but more especially in the larger irrigation and flood-control programs should, so far as possible, be handled on a countercyclical basis; that is, enlarged in times of low economic activity and reduced when times are good and labor rather fully employed.

9. We do not attempt to suggest policy in respect to the forest, range and reclamation activities since, in the main, these lie outside the farm policy field which this committee has undertaken to consider. Full exploration of them would require both more extensive and more intensive study than this committee has been able to give to these problems. We do urge, however, that much-needed classification of all of the federally owned lands be completed as soon as is practicable, and that the administration of them be assigned as promptly as possible to the specialized agencies best fitted to manage them in an efficient and businesslike way. This means that managed forest lands should be assigned to the Forest Service and open grazing lands, where feasible, should be administered by the Division of Range Management.

School Lunch and Food Stamp Programs

The School Lunch Program is primarily a means of improving nutrition for school children rather than a significant factor in the farm program. The amounts taken are not large enough, in most cases, to have a measurable effect on the prices of the commodities used. However, in the fluid milk field, where the surplus is comparatively small, school lunch use of milk may have an appreciable effect on the market.

On the whole, this program and any food stamp plans considered should be judged on the basis of their effectiveness and desirability as aids to consumers, not as a way of solving the farm problem. For reasons more fully discussed in the research report, we are of the opinion that the school lunch subsidy as now handled is spread too thinly to be of major importance in improving the diets of needy and undernourished children. Although excellent results are reported in some districts, the program as a whole needs revision. We recommend, therefore, that it be so modified as to provide a larger amount of aid in areas and to individuals where such aid is genuinely needed and that such federal effort as is put into the program elsewhere emphasize technical assistance and counsel in improving the effectiveness and quality of locally supported school lunch programs.

Though the outlet that can thus be provided for farm products that are temporarily in excess supply is not a large one, we recommend close and continuing cooperation between the Department of Agriculture and school authorities in using to the fullest extent practical temporary surpluses, particularly of perishable farm products. Where such products can be used without detriment to the over-all objectives of the School Lunch Program, public costs will be reduced and a modest contribution will be made to the betterment of diet and the channeling into constructive use of farm products that may otherwise go to waste.

There is also a continuing interest on the part of nutritionists and others in the possibility of improving the diets of other groups as well as those of school children. While the general level of nutritional adequacy is high throughout the United States, there are undoubtedly a good many people in disadvantaged groups, particularly among the aged, the handicapped and broken families, who still are not able to buy food adequate for their needs. In a nation where recurring surpluses of farm products present problems, this anomaly should, of course, be reduced to the lowest practical level. We suggest, therefore, the need for continuing study of this problem and attempts to deal with it through special programs, including further experimentation with the use of food stamps.

If such programs are again undertaken, they should be oriented mainly to the needs of consumers rather than to the solution of the farm surplus problem, but, as in the case of school lunches, they should be so handled as to help dispose of farm surpluses—particularly of perishable products—wherever that can be done practically and without detriment to the program.[37]

37. I am in favor of full use of the productive resources of the American economy and am optimistic about the steadily increasing productivity in all industries as a means of raising consumption levels. I would like to see more adequate diets, more adequate schools, and more adequate libraries, hospitals, medical service, parks, and many other things. My knowledge of the Food Stamp Plan of the late 1930s and early 1940s, plus my knowledge of consumption levels and behavior of consumers and sellers, makes me

Food stamp and other similar programs would not affect at all the accumulations of such products as wheat and cotton and could affect the corn situation only indirectly, through such small increase in the consumption of corn-using livestock as might result. However, such programs could be more important in stepping up the consumption of dairy products and of other perishables in times when there is an over-supply of them.

It should be recognized that any generalized aid in the form of sub-sidized prices on food for large numbers of people is bound to be very expensive and might involve budgetary drains running into hundreds of millions annually. Consequently, any program of nutritional aid should be selective and directed specifically toward well-identified groups that are not able to buy adequate diets with the incomes available to them.

Moreover, programs of the food stamp type present difficult adminis-trative as well as budgetary problems. To learn more about these diffi-culties, an experimental program might well be adopted and tried out on a small scale. Screening of applicants, of course, should be done by some agency other than the Department of Agriculture. Such an experi-mental program should be tried out now to gain information that could be useful if a full-scale depression should develop.[38]

A DYNAMIC, FORWARD-LOOKING PROGRAM NEEDED

We have dealt mainly with the more pressing problems, many of them holdovers from the disturbances that grew out of the depression and war decades. The crops and enterprises principally discussed account for roughly half the output of American agriculture. Most of the livestock industries and many of the others have made good progress in adjusting to new levels of demand and to the conditions now prevailing. On the whole, those agricultural industries which have not been under price-support programs in the years since 1948 have fared at least as well as those in which postwar adjustments have been retarded by government action.

---

doubt very much that a food stamp program is a desirable means of achieving the broad goals of greater well-being.—MARGARET G. REID

38. Nothing in the foregoing points out cogently enough that by all means the most effective way of reducing surpluses in the United States is to get a considerable amount of the production and consumption of food products shifted from foods for direct human consumption to foods of animal origin. From six to seven times as much land is needed to produce a given number of food calories in the form of meats, eggs, milk and dairy products as to produce them in the form of wheat, sugar, vegetable fats, potatoes, and beans. Beef production is the most land-using of all by a wide margin. To shift produc-tion to foods of livestock origin is not enough—consumption must be shifted at the same time. Higher incomes and fuller employment for the low-income fraction of our popula-tion contribute to this end, but that will not occur fast enough to meet the needs of the situation. A program is needed first of all in education directed toward a more rapid revision of diets in this direction. Well-directed school lunch programs fit effectively into such an educational effort. But more direct and more immediate measures are war-ranted in the present emergency.—JOHN D. BLACK

We recognize, however, that most of the commodities for which price supports have not been provided are consumed domestically. Hence, they have not been subjected to the severe strains growing out of changes in foreign demand that have had so large a part in creating problems in the export-crop areas. However, even for products of this latter type, solutions will not be found by continuing to postpone adjustments that must eventually be made. Instead, the programs adopted should look to positive and constructive aid in bringing both demand and supply into better balance. This means efforts to revitalize foreign demand as well as to bring U.S. production into better balance with amounts that can be disposed of.

If solutions can be found for the major problems discussed in the preceding sections of this report, most of the more serious war-engendered maladjustments will have been worked out. This does not mean, of course, that there will be no problems left to solve. Growers of any of the commodities mentioned may be in difficulties in any given year or sometimes over a period of several years. If serious and widespread depression should occur, more direct and extensive programs than those here suggested should be undertaken quickly and vigorously.

There are also, of course, many continuing and more fundamental problems in agriculture which will require consideration in the years ahead. For example, though much progress has been made in developing a sound and effective conservation program, much remains to be done and some changes in methods and organization are undoubtedly needed. The problem presented by the two million or more small, low-production farms has by no means been solved, and the problem of hired-farm labor has scarcely been touched.[39, 40]

Some major adjustments in types of farming and interregional shifts in production are still before us, and some agricultural areas have been bypassed in the march of progress. They will need special types of aid if they are to achieve conditions and opportunities that are in keeping with those of the rest of the economy. Also, there are pressing problems to be dealt with in some of the minor crop areas, particularly those which produce tree and vine crops and have long been heavily dependent on foreign markets as an outlet for their products.

Problems of these kinds have been touched on only briefly in this report. Many of them undoubtedly will come under closer scrutiny in the coming years and should be considered by other, more specialized groups. The most urgent problem before us now is to establish a sound

39. We recognize the importance of these problems but have not undertaken to discuss them at length in this report. The problem of low-production farms is currently under study in the Department of Agriculture and is of sufficient importance to warrant a separate report dealing mainly with it, instead of being tacked on as a minor appendage to a report that deals principally with the programs relating to commercial agriculture.

40. While I am in accord with much of the content of the report here presented, it is my view that it does not take sufficient account of the needs and problems of the small, family farm group, which I regard as the backbone of the nation.—Obed A. Wyum

basis for continuing progress in dealing with the longer-term problems in agriculture and for meeting special problems as they arise. If that can be done, there is reason for confidence that American agriculture will continue strong and virile and that reasonably adequate solutions will eventually be found for most of the farm problems that now concern us.

Jesse W. Tapp, *Chairman*	Margaret G. Reid
John D. Black	Quentin Reynolds
Harry B. Caldwell	Theodore W. Schultz
Calvin B. Hoover	Andrew Stewart
Donald R. Murphy	Louise Leonard Wright
Edwin G. Nourse	Obed A. Wyum

Supplementary Statement of Harry B. Caldwell and Donald R. Murphy

While the preceding policy statement makes some admirable suggestions about shifts in farm policy, it fails to come to grips with the major issue. As things stand now, farmers are again plagued with surpluses clear across the board. These surpluses seem likely to be a continuing problem. Declining exports, lucky weather and improvements in technology have pushed production of many farm products far ahead of demand.

Moreover, the increases in population will not automatically solve this problem. Production in agriculture is increasing faster than population. The policy of "hold on and hope for the best" won't work.

What does the farm policy outlined do for this situation? Not enough. Many of the improvements suggested would be helpful, but on the whole the result would seem to be lower returns to farmers for several years at least.

The policy statement would seem to recommend shifting the present surplus of crops into livestock, and shifting the present "surplus" of farmers into town.

But what happens if we change the crop surplus into a livestock surplus? (One example is putting part of the wheat crop into feed instead of into exports or domestic use.) Then we simply transfer surplus problems from one sector to another. Nothing is cured.

What about the "surplus" of farm people? If some farmers can earn a better living in town than on the farm, they had better move. But what jobs are available? What training will be needed? What help in moving and job hunting will be required?

For the long pull, there is a good deal of sense in shifting the crop surplus into a livestock surplus. Our growing population won't eat more wheat; it will eat more meat and drink more milk. But we can't turn surplus wheat into hogs and then go off and forget about the hogs.

What is plainly needed is a program to improve diets and stimulate consumption both at home and abroad. We should be experimenting boldly with food stamps, with expanded school lunches, with better marketing devices and with other methods to keep abundance from being a curse both to producers and to the national economy. To the extent that this takes time or proves inadequate, farmers must have assistance in adjusting operations to market demand.

We should also explore the possible development and uses of some device such as a two-price plan so that our farmers can compete in the world market. If we have a price-support program, which supports farm prices above the world market price, we shall lose world markets on export crops, unless we subsidize exports or maintain a genuine two-price program. A price-support program to insure domestic producers a better income is no reason for depriving them of the right to sell on the world market at competitive prices. We do not favor export dumping or encroachment on the market of others, but we should allow our producers to supply as much of the world market as they normally would have supplied in the absence of a price-support program on export crops.

The policy statement gives a disproportionate amount of attention to the government surpluses now in storage. The storage problem is actually several problems. In corn, we had a carry-over in 1954 of approximately 900 million bushels, or about three months' supply. There is nothing here to cause alarm, except possibly that the reserve is so small.

Wheat is in excess supply and some of the remedies suggested, such as renting marginal land, are badly needed. But wheat keeps pretty well, and the problem can be dealt with gradually.

The pressing storage problem is in the field of dairy products. By terrifically bad collective judgment, we support the prices of dairy products by buying and storing butter, cheese and dry skim milk. The answer here is to abolish purchase and storage of dairy and other livestock products as a way of supporting prices, and to shift over to a program of production payments whenever supports are ordered.

In general, what the policy statement seems to lack is a realistic sense of the immediate pressure of farm surpluses and of the urgent need to deal with this problem effectively and quickly in order to keep farm income in balance with the income of the rest of the economy.

HARRY B. CALDWELL
DONALD R. MURPHY

APPENDICES

APPENDIX A

THE PARITY CONCEPT AND ITS RELATION TO THE FARM PROBLEM

IN RECENT YEARS, most of the controversy about farm policy has centered around the level of price support, not the question of whether farm prices should be supported at some level. The bench mark most commonly used is "parity price" as defined and redefined from time to time in the legislation of the past twenty years. Efforts have also been made to develop a "parity income" approach as a substitute for or supplement to the parity price criterion. Since the parity idea has had so large a place in the establishment of farm policy goals, it is important that it be more clearly understood and that its limitations as well as its advantages be recognized.

The advantage of having some way of measuring changes in price relationships is obvious. An index number is a device for measuring the percentage change in a variable or group of variables such as prices, incomes, amounts of production and so on, as compared to what they were in a base period which is taken as 100. Much of the analytical work relating to agriculture and to other parts of the economy could not be carried on without resort to index numbers of many kinds.

In most types of analysis, index numbers serve a purpose much like that of the readings on a thermometer. That is, they are ways of measuring what is happening. If the price, employment or production level measured falls sharply or rises rapidly, an attempt is likely to be made to correct the situation that caused it to change. That, however, is a policy decision. The index itself should be purely and simply a measuring device. As such, it should be made as accurate and logical as possible without reference to the policies based on it.

It would be unwarranted to imply that index numbers reflecting price relationships are as precise and dependable as the expansions and contractions of the mercury column in a thermometer. They are at best approximations to the changes they are designed to measure. Because of this, there has been a continuing effort in the U.S. Department of Agriculture to refine and improve the methods of measuring the relationship between agricultural price levels and incomes and those in other parts of the economy.

Most index series are modified from time to time as better data, more adequate methods of computation or more suitable definitions of the things to be measured are developed. The base periods used are changed and brought up to date as conditions change. Index numbers become markedly less dependable as the length of time covered by the index increases, especially if the weightings used are not changed.

However, the procedure followed in respect to the parity index for agriculture differs from that in most other parts of the government. No other index is defined by law. Except for the farm price and parity indexes, the items to be included or excluded and the base periods to be used are determined by the statisticians responsible for preparing the indexes rather than

532

by the Congress. In a few cases where important government or business policies are based directly on such indexes, the Congress does from time to time give some attention to the procedures used. The principal series of this kind, aside from those relating to agricultural price relationships, is the consumers' price index, commonly referred to as the "cost of living" index, which is prepared by the Bureau of Labor Statistics.

For the index series used in showing the relation of agricultural prices and incomes to those in other parts of the economy, the Congress itself has from time to time written into the laws various changes and requirements that affect the levels of price or income shown. These changes, and the way in which the parity idea came into use as a guide in farm policy decisions, are described briefly in the sections that follow.

Origin of the Parity Idea

The idea of parity for farmers has been expressed in two principal ways, one broad and general, the other very specific. The first is that, everything considered, farmers should receive an annual return over a period of years for their skill, energy and capital comparable to that of the people who produce the things farmers buy. In other formulations, this concept has been modified and broadened in various ways, to include the idea of equality of opportunity, reasonably equivalent services and living conditions and so on. At times, it has been expressed in still broader and more vague forms, for example, in terms of the "farmer's share" of the national income and the "farmer's share" of the consumer's dollar.

Even before any effort was made to define parity income or parity prices, much of the government aid provided to agriculture looked in the direction of equalizing farm and nonfarm opportunities. Federal aid was provided in establishing agricultural research and educational facilities, and help was given in controlling marketing abuses, providing better rural mail service and so on. The government has since carried this type of aid much further, by developing special farm credit arrangements, setting up a rural electrification and a rural telephone program, improving farm-to-market roads and in various other ways.

The other, more specific, formulation of the parity idea came later and has led to much more controversy. It emerged in the early 1920s and led to the long and vigorous struggle for adoption of the McNary-Haugen plan. The criterion then proposed was that farm prices, to be "fair," should be such that farmers could purchase with a given quantity of a farm product the same amount of nonfarm commodities as they had been able to buy, on the average, before the outbreak of World War I. The first specific formulation of the idea was presented to the public in 1922, in a pamphlet entitled *Equality for Agriculture,* prepared by George N. Peek and Hugh S. Johnson.[1] Their version of price parity for agriculture was included in the first McNary-

1. The formula presented in *Equality for Agriculture* provided for relating changes in the wholesale prices of the specified farm products to changes in the wholesale price level of all products using as a base the period 1906–1915. In an addendum to the second edition, computations from the Department of Agriculture were presented on a 1905–1914 base, and it was stated that farm prices for farm products and retail prices for the things farmers buy would be the appropriate data to use if they were available. The 1905–1914 base was the one specified in the McNary-Haugen bill of 1924.

Haugen bill, introduced in 1924. The assumption back of it was that the prices of farm products and those of nonfarm products had been roughly in balance in the period just prior to 1914 and that the re-establishment of these price relationships would be fair to both farmers and consumers.

The wholesale price index of all commodities, as constructed by the Bureau of Labor Statistics, was taken as a measure of the general price level, the prices being stated as percentages of the prewar average, which was given a value of 100. In like manner, the average price for each farm commodity in the prewar period was given a rating of 100. If, in later years, the all-commodities index stood at, say, 150, the price for any given farm product, to be on a fair exchange basis, should be 50 per cent higher than its average price in the prewar years. This was called its "ratio price." The term "parity" was not used in that period.[2]

Parity Idea Not Written into Law Until 1933

The idea that farm prices should be brought up to a prewar relationship with the general level of prices, or to some other criterion of equity, was prominent in almost all of the discussions of the farm problem during the middle and late 1920s and early 1930s but did not gain legal recognition until 1933. From 1924 on, more emphasis was given to the idea of "making the tariff effective for agriculture." In the later versions of the McNary-Haugen bill the objective was so stated and the ratio price concept was omitted. This was partly a concession to criticisms of the first McNary-Haugen bill and partly a tactical adjustment resulting from the fact that farm prices had moved up in 1924 and 1925 to where they were about on a par with the general level of wholesale prices for all commodities, which was

2. The "ratio price" described above was slightly different mechanically from that which later came to be known as "parity price," mainly because subsequent refinements of data made possible a more precise formulation of the idea. In the meantime, Dr. G. F. Warren had begun to construct and popularize price indexes in which he used the five prewar years as a base. He converted the Bureau of Labor Statistics wholesale price index from a 1913 to a 1910–1914 base. For the base prices of farm products at the farm, he used monthly averages for August 1909 to July 1914. See G. F. Warren, *Prices of Farm Products in the United States,* U.S. Department of Agriculture, Bulletin 999, 1921.

In 1928 the Department of Agriculture constructed a new index series for prices paid by farmers. This was for the prices of things actually bought by farmers, mostly at the retail rather than the wholesale stage. The annual collection and publication of such data had been started in 1910. This new index, based on prices for the years 1910–1914, provided a better measure of the prices actually paid by farmers than did the index of wholesale prices. It displaced the index of wholesale prices as a measure of changes in the money cost of commodities bought by farmers. The all-commodities index includes the prices of farm products as well as those of commodities bought by farmers and it does not reflect changes in the spread between wholesale and retail prices.

The weightings used in constructing the index of prices received by farmers were revised in 1934, from the relative quantities sold in 1918–1923 to those sold in 1924–1929. A further revision was published in 1944, and in 1950 both series were revised and adjusted to a common base period, January 1910 to December 1914. For more detail, see the excellent article by B. Ralph Stauber, Nathan M. Koffsky and C. Kyle Randall, "The Revised Price Indexes," *Agricultural Economics Research,* April 1950, pp. 33–62. See also U.S. Agricultural Marketing Service, *Agricultural Prices,* January 1950 and January 1954. For a discussion of changes made prior to 1940 and their significance, see John D. Black, *Parity, Parity, Parity,* Harvard Committee on Research in the Social Sciences, Cambridge, 1942, Chapter 5.

the yardstick then used. Thus, the case for government action to eliminate a large disparity between farm and nonfarm prices was weaker than it had been in the early part of the decade.[3]

In the meantime, the Department of Agriculture had adopted the practice of publishing "ratio prices" for the various farm commodities. The idea that the ratio price was the "fair" price for any given commodity came to be more and more widely accepted by farmers and by many of the members of Congress and thus became an accepted goal in the drive for farm relief legislation.

The very severe price break of 1929–1932 put the prices of farm products so far below their ratio prices that almost no one questioned the need for raising them. The efforts of the Farm Board proved ineffective in restoring pre-existing price relationships, and in the latter part of the Farm Board period interest shifted to the control of production as a method of raising prices.

When the Roosevelt administration took over in 1933, the production control approach was adopted and interest shifted back to the idea of re-establishing "fair exchange" relationships between farm and nonfarm prices. If prices were to be raised through government action, there was need for some statement of the objectives of such action and for placing limits on the amount of price increase that would be permissible. The Agricultural Adjustment Act of 1933 established such goals and limitations. It stated that it was the intent of the Congress to:

> . . . establish and maintain such balance between the production and consumption of agricultural commodities, and such marketing conditions therefor, as will re-establish prices to farmers at a level that will give agricultural commodities a purchasing power with respect to articles that farmers buy, equivalent to the purchasing power of agricultural commodities in the base period.

Since this could not be accomplished all at one time, the administrators of the act were directed to take steps designed to:

> . . . approach such equality of purchasing power by gradual correction of the present inequalities therein at as rapid a rate as is deemed feasible in view of the current consumptive demand in domestic and foreign markets.

The consumers' interest was recognized by a provision that farm production should not be readjusted in such a way as to:

> . . . increase the percentage of the consumers' retail expenditures for agricultural commodities, or products derived therefrom, which is returned to the farmer, above the percentage which was returned to the farmer in the prewar period, August 1909–July 1914.

3. The proponents of the McNary-Haugen type of legislation were seeking not only to make as good a case for farm legislation as they could, but also to devise a formula that might be more acceptable to the Congress and the Administration than the one they had first presented. Peek, like most of the members then in Congress, had strong protectionist leanings. He also was thinking, rather vaguely, of a procedure that would result in prices that would cover cost of production plus a profit, an idea which was much discussed in that period. He assumed that if farmers could obtain the world price plus the tariff, and if the tariffs were set at appropriate levels, they would as a matter of course receive prices that would cover their costs of production.

Thus the attainment of parity prices for farm products had come to be officially accepted as a major objective in the government's farm programs. However, the term actually used in the legislation was "fair exchange value" rather than "parity." [4]

The base period for determining fair exchange value for all farm products except tobacco was specified as the prewar period, August 1909 to July 1914. For tobacco, a postwar base period, August 1919 to July 1929, was to be used. This became a precedent for shifting other commodities to postwar bases at various times thereafter. There had been a considerable increase in the demand for tobacco as a result of the much wider use of cigarettes that developed in the war and postwar years. Base periods for the two leading tobacco types (flue-cured and burley) were later shifted to 1934–1939. These changes resulted in a "fair exchange" or "parity" price for tobacco that was substantially higher than if the prewar base had been used.[5] Under provisions of the Agricultural Adjustment Act amendments of 1935, potatoes and some other commodities were shifted to postwar bases. The base period for potatoes was made the same as that for tobacco.[6]

The exception made in the case of tobacco in 1933 was based on the contention that great changes had occurred in the tobacco industry in the years following 1914 and that the use of a 1909–1914 base would be illogical. Also, tobacco farming had long been notorious as an industry of low incomes and bad living conditions.[7]

Further changes were made in 1937, with respect to milk under marketing agreements and orders. If minimum prices were to be fixed, the Secretary of Agriculture was directed to establish prices at such a level as would reflect the prices of feeds and other economic conditions which affect the supply and demand for milk and its products in the marketing area. Thus, by the late 1930s, the parity prices for a number of farm commodities had been shifted from a prewar to a postwar base, but only in cases where this resulted in a higher parity price. No steps were taken which looked to reducing parity prices of commodities for which the costs of production had declined.

Taxes and Interest Included in 1935

The August 1935 amendment to the Agricultural Adjustment Act provided for a change in the method of computing equivalent purchasing power or

4. There was some discussion also of the idea that parity income would be a more appropriate objective. However, no attempt was made at that time to devise mechanisms for using income parity as a goal in adjustment activities.

5. The net result of these changes, and of changes in the prices of things bought by farmers, is that parity prices based on 1934–1939 are now 43 per cent higher for flue-cured tobacco and 66 per cent higher for burley than if they were calculated on the basis of 1909–1914 as 100.

6. The milk base was shifted to the postwar period under an amendment to the provisions relating to marketing agreements and orders. For some commodities, adequate prewar data were not available. In such cases, the Secretary of Agriculture was authorized, in entering into marketing agreements, to use the 1919–1929 base period or that portion of it for which satisfactory data were available.

7. Tobacco prices have in fact been maintained at markedly higher levels in recent years, in terms of the 1909–1914 base, than those of other farm products. The tobacco price index has been above 400 in every year since 1949, whereas the average for all farm products ranged from 256 to 302. U.S. Department of Agriculture, *Agricultural Statistics, 1953*, p. 602.

"fair exchange value." [8] Thereafter, the index showing prices paid by farmers was to reflect also "current interest payments per acre of farm indebtedness secured by real estate and tax payments per acre on farm real estate, as contrasted with such interest payments and tax payments during the base period" (for all commodities having a prewar base).

This change had the effect of raising the parity index from the time of its adoption through 1941 but has resulted in a lower parity index in the years since 1941.[9] The over-all effect has not been large. However, it constituted a first step in the direction of a broader concept of parity than the one put forward in the 1920s. The Peek-Johnson plan contemplated only that farm-produced commodities would have an exchange value in relation to nonfarm commodities that would be as favorable as that of 1909–1914. The inclusion of interest and taxes, and later of farm wage rates, looked more to keeping the prices of farm products in line with farm production costs, including services as well as purchased commodities.

Income Parity—A New Approach

An income approach to the concept of farm parity was introduced in the Soil Conservation and Domestic Allotment Act of 1936, though the underlying principle was similar to that of "fair exchange value." In the earlier formulations of the parity idea, it was assumed that if farm and nonfarm prices were kept in the same relationship as in 1909–1914, incomes also would bear approximately the same relationship to each other as in that period. This, however, did not take account of the sharp changes in relative volumes of production that occurred in the early 1930s. Agricultural production continued to be relatively high but industrial production fell to very low levels. Consequently, if farm prices had been in the same relationship to nonfarm prices as in 1909–1914, agriculture, with its high level of production, would have had a substantially larger income relatively than the non-farm groups with their much reduced volume of output.

8. Farm organization leaders were using "parity" as a means of expressing this price relationship at least as early as 1933. The concept itself, though not by that name, dates back even beyond the 1920s. See James H. Shideler, "The Development of the Parity Price Formula for Agriculture, 1919–1923," *Agricultural History*, July 1953, pp. 77–84.

9. The index of taxes payable per acre rose rapidly during World War I and in the 1920s. It stood at 117 in 1914 (1910–1914 = 100) and had increased to 281 by 1930. As of 1930, the index of prices paid for commodities bought by farmers was 140. By 1940, taxes had been reduced to an index of 189, and the index for prices of commodities bought was 122. From 1945 on, taxes increased rapidly, reaching a level of 353 in 1952. (*Parity Handbook*, Senate Document No. 129, 82d Cong., 2d sess., 1952, p. 19, and *Agricultural Statistics, 1953*, p. 604.) The index for prices of commodities bought by farmers was then 273. Consequently, as of the present, the inclusion of taxes in the index of prices paid by farmers raises the cost index and hence the computed "parity" prices of farm products.

The index for interest payable per acre was 116 in 1914. It rose to 261 in 1923 and declined thereafter to 74 in 1946. It was 107 in 1952. Thus, the inclusion of interest payments in the parity formula, since they are relatively much lower than the prices of commodities bought by farmers, operates to lower the index of farm costs and, hence, the "parity" prices based on the formula. (Note: The data relating to these items differ in the two sources used. Recent revisions, as published in *Agricultural Statistics, 1953*, put both the interest and tax indexes at substantially higher levels than those published in the *Parity Handbook* in 1952.)

The idea of parity income had been in the background all along and was strongly implied in the earlier legislation, but was not set up as a working guide until it was included in the act of 1936. In that act, the income phase of the policy objective was stated as follows:

> . . . re-establishment, at as rapid a rate as the Secretary of Agriculture determines to be practicable and in the general public interest, of the ratio between the purchasing power of the net income per person on farms and that of the income per person not on farms that prevailed during the five-year period August 1909—July 1914, inclusive, as determined from statistics available in the United States Department of Agriculture, and the maintenance of such ratio.

The use of an income parity standard was brought under study and was the subject of numerous conferences in the Department of Agriculture. However, it did not come into use as a practical working guide because of the difficulty of applying it to individual products. Adequate data and methods for applying parity on an income basis had not been developed, and have not been worked out in the years since. Though the Department of Agriculture has continued its studies of the relation of farm and nonfarm incomes, that approach has not had much practical importance in the working out of the various farm programs. The programs have been set up almost exclusively in terms of commodities and the problem has remained of how to relate these in a practical way to the achievement of an over-all balance between farm and nonfarm incomes.[10]

Price Parity the Principal Criterion After 1938

From 1938 on, the Congress and the farm organizations turned more and more to emphasis on parity prices rather than parity incomes.[11] Price parity was more specific and more easy to understand. It was also easier to measure and use in administering farm programs. Furthermore, with the decline in farm prices that occurred in 1938 and 1939, the use of a parity price criterion resulted in a substantially higher income goal than if the comparative income criterion had been used.[12] The Congress resumed the practice of

10. The parity income concept itself was modified slightly in the Agricultural Adjustment Act of 1938. Income parity was there defined as "that per capita net income of individuals on farms *from farming operations* that bears to the per capita net income of individuals not on farms the same relation as prevailed during the period from August 1909 to July 1914." (Italics added.) This meant dropping out such parts of the incomes of people living on farms as were not derived from farming operations.

11. In the Agricultural Adjustment Act of 1938, the terms "parity price" and "parity income" were used in the legislation itself, to describe this relationship for which, up to that time, other expressions had been used.

12. The short crops of 1934–1936, plus some general recovery and inflation, brought farm prices up to 92 and 93 per cent of parity in 1936 and 1937. Income parities, including government payments, were higher: 107 in 1935, 99 in 1936, and 107 in 1937. Though the index of farm prices fell from 122 in 1937 to 97 in 1938 and to 95 in 1939, incomes held up better because of the larger volume produced and the amounts received in the form of government payments. The parity price index fell about 20 per cent while the parity income index fell about 10 per cent. Yields have been higher in most years since 1940 than in the 1930s. Consequently, the reversion to a parity price criterion in the late 1930s and after has meant establishing higher goals than if an income criterion had been used (if percentages of parity were the same).

formulating its directives to the Secretary of Agriculture in terms of price parity and has continued it in the years since.

After the outbreak of World War II, proposals to shift the over-all parity base to 1935–1939 received some consideration. The primary objection to this was that the persistence of a high level of unemployment and a low level of exports had resulted in accumulation of stocks of most of the basic commodities and relatively low prices for them. The demand for cigarette tobacco was an exception. In 1940 the Congress took account of the increase in demand for the tobaccos used in the manufacture of cigarettes and shifted the base for burley and flue-cured types to August 1935–July 1939, leaving the other types on the 1919–1929 base. While the justification claimed for this change was the upward trend in demand for these types of tobacco, the action was criticized by many as special-favor legislation for a few farmers.[13]

As time passed, questions arose concerning the price bases to be used for new crops, such as soybeans, and for older nonbasic crops for which economic conditions had changed greatly since the 1909–1914 base period. The Steagall Amendment to the Price Control Act of July 1941 provided for administrative discretion in establishing "comparable prices" for such "nonbasic" commodities. It provided that the "comparable price" should be determined and used "if the production or consumption of such commodity had so changed in extent or character since the base period as to result in a price out of line with parity prices for basic commodities."

It was further declared to be the policy of the Congress to support the nonbasic commodities at a fair parity relationship with others insofar as funds would permit. The method developed for determining "comparable prices," briefly, was to adjust the average price for the nonbasic commodity in a chosen recent period by relating it to the parity price of the basic commodity in the same period so as to establish a base price to which the current parity index could be applied.

Obsolescence of the 1909–1914 Base

During the late 1930s and throughout the war period, price parities based on 1909–1914 relationships (for the basic commodities other than milk and tobacco) continued to be used and were not seriously challenged in popular and congressional discussions of price problems. However, statisticians and economists had become increasingly critical of the continuing use of the 1909–1914 base period, which by then reflected price relationships of a quarter of a century earlier. Relative costs and relative demands for the various farm products had changed significantly in the meantime. Farm tractors and other larger-scale machines had come into general use and the amounts of labor required to produce many of the major field crops had been

13. The upward movement of tobacco prices was due in some measure to controls on production that were applied to tobacco in some of those years. Production controls on tobacco were more effective than for most other crops. Tobacco acreage was cut back sharply in 1934 and 1935 and remained low in 1936, though there were no direct controls in effect in that year. The acreages grown increased again in the late 1930s and by 1939 were about the same as in 1929 and 1930. However, the increased demand of this period brought the over-all average of tobacco prices to levels that were above those of 1929, except in 1939. The extent and significance of the restraints on tobacco acreage were not the same for all types, and controls were not used in some of the years.

greatly reduced. Most of the livestock enterprises had not experienced comparable gains in production efficiency.[14]

This meant that, if prices were actually maintained at or near parity in all lines, there would be strong incentives for farmers to expand production of such things as wheat, corn, cotton and rice, rather than of livestock and truck crops. But demand was tending to shift in the opposite direction. Increased amounts of livestock products and of truck and fruit crops were wanted by American consumers, while the demand for wheat and cotton, crops heavily dependent on export markets, was falling off, except in the war years and immediately thereafter.

Economists and nutritionists criticized the continuing use of the old base period as pointing in the direction of misuse of national resources, with overexpansion in some lines and underexpansion in others. Statisticians objected on other grounds, mainly technical; that is, that the use of a base period so far in the past tended to vitiate the usefulness and dependability of the index figures.[15]

Criticisms of the old base and the patchwork of modifications mounted with the prospect of a need for postwar adjustments. The Secretary of Agriculture, Clinton P. Anderson, stated the views of the United States Department of Agriculture in a speech in November 1945, at Memphis, Tennessee.

> . . . we definitely know [he said] that if a historical base is used, changing conditions sooner or later will make any fixed set of prices unacceptable to farmers and nonfarmers alike. And this happens, no matter how reasonable the relationship between farm and nonfarm prices may have been in the base period. The fact is that production factors in agriculture and industry shift so much and so rapidly that no price relationship is permanently stable. People's wants, their methods of living, their methods of working—and the number of people themselves—continually change and make new patterns.
>
> As a matter of objective history, parity price bases have been changed and amended so much in the past 15 years that they are now a patchwork of special provisions. Even a Philadelphia lawyer could not explain just why the parity price of a particular commodity is what it is.
>
> We know from past experience that parity prices don't necessarily produce parity income.
>
> During World War II parity income . . . could have been produced by farm prices below parity.[16]

14. There were also other types of increases in production efficiency that affected costs unevenly. For example, the introduction of hybrid corn had increased yields and reduced per bushel costs markedly. Wheat yields were being improved by means of better strains, increased use of fertilizer and so on. Improvements were also being made in the methods of producing livestock and truck crops, but in most cases these did not reduce costs as fast or as much as those which resulted from increased mechanization.

15. Some economists also challenged the assumptions underlying the whole idea that prices based on the relationships of the 1909–1914 period were inherently "fair" and right. They contended that the period 1909–1914 was one in which farm prices, as compared to nonfarm prices, were abnormally favorable and that price relationships within agriculture were not as well adjusted in that period as the parity formula implied. See, for example, Joseph S. Davis, "Price Disparities and Parities," in *Journal of Farm Economics*, April 1933, pp. 251–54. For a contrary view, see remarks by O. C. Stine, in *ibid.*, pp. 254–59.

16. *Journal of Farm Economics*, February 1946, p. 390, quoted from the address "Equality for Agriculture" at the meeting of the National Association of Commissioners, Secretaries and Directors of Agriculture, Memphis, November 12, 1945, pp. 5, 6 and 11.

The Master of the National Grange, Albert S. Goss, at the annual meeting of the Grange in November 1945, briefly summarized the situation as he viewed it:

> . . . The formula does not recognize the constantly changing demand between commodities, and should be modernized.
>
> The results are so erratic that the Congress has authorized the Secretary of Agriculture to establish "comparable prices" when the formula produces indefensible results. Thus, we abandon the principle of parity and rely on the judgment of one man. On some items, the Congress has even changed the base period. Obviously, every commodity so adjusted throws the rest of the formula out of balance.[17]

Farm Economic Association Report on Parity

The American Farm Economic Association appointed a committee in 1945 to prepare an outline of a price policy for American agriculture for the postwar period. The committee's report on parity concepts was published in the *Journal of Farm Economics* for February 1946.[18] Subsequently, a report "On the Redefinition of Parity Price and Parity Income" was presented at the annual meeting of the Association in September 1947.[19]

In its report on parity concepts, the committee summarized its objections to the parity formula and the policies based on it in a series of eight points, of which the first four were:

> 1. By adopting a historical base period as the yardstick for the support price of specific commodities, the parity-price formula freezes the functional and otherwise self-adjusting price mechanism. The historical base leads to rigid maintenance of accidental price relations that existed under an entirely different situation. Prices, and even more so price relations, are the most powerful instrument for directing and allocating manpower, brainpower, and man-made resources (such as capital and research) as well as natural resources. Even the economic solutions applied by the Soviet Union and Nazi Germany have not refuted this economic axiom.
>
> 2. In allocating productive resources and people, the only alternative to relative prices that we have available is the direct order of the government. Political command cannot fail to result eventually in decrees as to who can farm, and where, and how, and who must leave the farm.
>
> 3. The parity formula disregards the progress made in farm technology which in recent years substantially reduced the production costs of some commodities, but has left at former levels the production costs of others. Therefore, some parity prices are too high, others too low, for a balanced agricultural production sensitive to the relative demand in the market for specific products, and to shifts in that demand.
>
> 4. The parity formula does not make allowance for the improvement in the quality of goods and services which the farmer buys. Many of the goods used in production have not changed in price or at least have not risen in price, but the quality and performance he obtains gives him far

17. Address delivered by Albert S. Goss at the 79th annual session of the National Grange, Kansas City, Missouri, November 14, 1945.

18. Pp. 380–97.

19. See Proceedings Number, *Journal of Farm Economics*, November 1947, pp. 1358–1377.

more for his money. This is notably so for motor cars, tractors, and other power equipment.[20]

The Committee on Redefinition of Parity Price and Parity Income, reporting about a year later, restated criticisms of the currently used price parities and commented favorably on a suggestion that a moving average of price relationships in an immediately preceding period be substituted for the fixed bases then being used.[21] However, a majority of the Committee believed that the parity price approach should be abandoned, and that, in the event of a recurrence of severe depression, farm incomes should be supported by means of income payments.[22]

Parity Formula Modified in 1948 and 1949

The problems created by the continuing use of the original parity formula came in for a good deal of discussion in the period when new, longer-term farm legislation was being considered to take the place of the postwar price

20. *Journal of Farm Economics*, February 1946, p. 391. The other four points had to do with policies based on the parity formula. They were as follows:

"5. Production controls in the form of acreage quotas are ineffective for most of the crops. During the period before the war, the system of controlling the crop through acreage restrictions broke down for nearly all crops. The farmer shifted the restricted crops to more productive land, used more fertilizer, better seed, and better methods of cultivation. The high support price gave him the incentive to produce on fewer acres as much as his too easily underrated ingenuity and resourcefulness would allow.

"6. Thus the parity formula has actually been instrumental in subsidizing excess production simply to fill public granaries. While the nation has reason to desire a sufficient cushion between years of poor and bumper crops, to avoid running out of the physical volume of supplies, the rigid parity-price formula abuses the granary system merely for the sake of fixing prices, irrespective of what happens in the market.

"7. Unchanged support prices in the market in view of overloaded granaries violate the rule of good common sense. The domestic consumer and the foreign importer take their cue for heavier or lesser buying just as much from the price as the farmer does his for production. If prices continue high while granaries overflow, the consumer continues to economize and consumes as little as his budget permits and only what he absolutely needs. The industrial manufacturer, processor, or converter does the same. If substitutes of similar quality but lower in price are available, he will use those. Manufacturers of substitutes will be greatly encouraged by the maintenance of the fixed price of the product against which they compete. Thus parity prices actually undermine the market position of some of the American farmers' staple crops—for example, cotton.

"The worst feature of all is that government price supports which keep prices above the free market price levels tend to restrict consumption.

"8. Fixed parity prices do similar harm to American agriculture in the foreign market by pricing its export products out of the range of the importing countries. As a result, America's farmers must reduce their output and farmers in other countries will tend to fill the gap. Such renunciation of otherwise possible exports is a net loss of income to the farmer, to our nation, and to other nations.

"At the outset of this report, the Committee stated its belief in creating through public policy a certain minimum degree of social security for the farmer. But we are convinced that the parity price formula and related methods of price support are an approach which will become the more untenable as the overlapping war boom and the relief period subside. We believe, moreover, that failure to revise and reorient the parity policy without much further delay will inflict immeasurable damage upon American agriculture and this nation's whole economy." (*Ibid.*, pp. 391–93.)

21. This idea had been put forward by Albert S. Goss in the address cited above and had been discussed in various other connections.

22. "On the Redefinition of Parity Price and Parity Income," *Journal of Farm Economics*, Proceedings Number, November 1947, pp. 1358–1374. See also "A Dissenting Comment" by O. V. Wells, in *ibid.*, pp. 1374–1377.

supports, which were scheduled to expire at the end of 1948. In the new act (the Agricultural Act of 1948), passed in July 1948, provision was made for a new or "modernized" parity formula which was to become effective on January 1, 1950. However, general use of this formula for agricultural products was delayed by subsequent legislation.[23]

Though the use of direct government payments as a method of supporting prices was included in the act, proposals for using income payments in times of depression as a substitute for continuously available price supports were rejected. Forward announcement of price supports was authorized, but a proposal for forward pricing based on estimated requirements and necessary prices was not accepted.

Since the modifications provided in the Agricultural Act of 1949 were written into the law before Title II of the act of 1948 became effective, the changes made by the two acts combined are treated as one in the discussion that follows. The new legislation left unchanged the basic idea that the over-all relationship between the prices of things farmers sold and the prices of things bought by them was fair and reasonable in the period 1909–1914. This over-all relationship was therefore to be maintained. The most important change was one which would establish "parity" prices for the *individual* agricultural products on the basis of their relationships in some later period rather than on those of the 1909–1914 period. But the average for all of them was still to bear the same relationship to the average of the prices of things bought by farmers as that which existed in 1909–1914.

The new base used was to be a moving average of the ten years immediately preceding the one in which the computation was made. That is, for computations made in 1951, the base period would be the years 1941 through 1950; in 1952, it would become the period 1942 through 1951, and so on.

An "adjusted base price" for each commodity was to be computed as illustrated in the following example: If, in the most recent ten-year period, the average of the prices received by farmers was 235 per cent of what it was in 1909–1914, the "adjusted base price" of any particular farm commodity would be 100/235 of what its price actually had been in the most recent ten-year period. This might be the same as or higher or lower than the average price of the commodity in the period 1909–1914. If in the meantime the index of prices paid by farmers had increased to 287, as compared to 100 in 1909–1914, the "adjusted base price" for the commodity would be multiplied by 2.87. This would give its parity price under the "modernized" formula. In simpler form, this meant multiplying the average price of the commodity for the most recent ten-year period by 287/235, or 1.22.

This can be shown more clearly by taking a specific case. The price

23. The new formula was contained in the bill passed by the Senate and was intended for immediate adoption. The House bill retained the old formula, and also the 90-per-cent-of-parity levels of price support provided in the wartime legislation. In the conference committee, the two bills were combined, but with a provision that the House bill (Title I) and the old parity formula would be in effect for the year 1949 and the Senate bill (Title II), which included the "modernized" parity formula, would become effective January 1, 1950. The "modernized" formula specified in the Agricultural Act of 1948 did not come into effect intact as additional changes were made in the Agricultural Act of 1949, which was passed before Title II of the act of 1948 became effective. For a fuller description of these developments, see M. R. Benedict, *Farm Policies of the United States, 1790–1950,* Twentieth Century Fund, New York, 1953, pp. 473–84.

received by farmers for wheat averaged $0.884 per bushel for the years 1909–1914. If the prices of things bought by farmers had increased by 187 per cent (that is, to an index of 287), the parity price under the old formula would be arrived at by multiplying $0.884 by 2.87, which would give a parity price of $2.54. Under the new formula, using the assumed figures given above and a price of $1.74 per bushel as the average received by farmers in the most recent ten-year period, the computation would be as follows: 100/235 x $1.74, or $0.74, would be the adjusted base price per bushel (instead of $0.884, the actual base period price). This figure multiplied by 2.87, or $2.12, would be the parity price for wheat as computed by the "modernized" formula. This is lower than the parity price computed according to the "old formula" ($2.12 as compared to $2.54) because the price of wheat has been lower in recent years, as compared with the prices of other farm products, than it was in 1909–1914.

A reverse situation is found in computing the new parity for a product like beef cattle. The price of beef cattle during the most recent ten-year period was higher in relation to other farm products than in the period 1909–1914. Under the old formula, the parity price for beef cattle would be 2.87 times the price received in the 1909–1914 base period, that is, 2.87 x $5.23, or $15.00 per hundredweight. Under the "modernized" formula, the average price received in the most recent ten-year period, here taken as $17.30, would first be multiplied by 100/235, which gives an "adjusted base price" of $7.36 instead of $5.23, which was the actual average for the years 1909–1914. This "adjusted base price" multiplied by 2.87 gives a figure of approximately $21.10, which would be the parity price for beef cattle under the "modernized" formula. Under the modernized formula, if both cattle and wheat were selling "at parity," the incentive for shifting out of wheat and into beef cattle would be greater than if both were at parity under the old formula.[24]

Farm Wage Rates Added in 1949

Two changes were made in the "modernized" parity formula by the Agricultural Act of 1949. The most important was that thereafter the index of changes in wage rates paid to hired farm labor was to be included in computing the index of prices of things bought by farmers. During the 1940s, farm wage rates had increased more rapidly than the prices of commodities. Consequently, the inclusion of wages paid in the prices of things bought by farmers raised the cost index and thereby raised the computed "parity prices" for farm products. As of that time, the effect of this change was to raise the index of prices required for them to be at parity by some 5 to 8 points (about 3 per cent).[25]

24. For a more extended discussion of these computations and other features of the parity formula, see *Parity Handbook*.

25. Wage rates for hired farm labor stood at 101 in 1914 (1909–1914 = 100). They had risen to 241 by 1920. Thereafter, they dropped back to 88 in 1933 and were up only to 129 in 1940. During the 1940s, farm wage rates rose rapidly. By 1952, the index had reached a level of 502 in terms of the 1909–1914 base.

The act of 1949 also directed that wartime payments made directly to producers be included in the ten-year averages of prices received by farmers for the commodities on which such payments were made. This resulted in higher parity prices for some commodities, mainly milk (at wholesale) and butterfat.

Though the computations required seem cumbersome and complicated, the idea back of these changes is relatively simple. The relationship between the *average level of all farm prices* and the average level of prices paid by farmers was to be the same as in 1909–1914. But the relationships between the prices of the *individual* farm commodities was to be that of the ten-year period just prior to the year for which the computation was made, not that of 1909–1914. Hence, if the price of a given farm commodity had risen relative to the prices of other farm commodities, its new parity would be higher by a proportionate amount. If its price had declined relatively, because of reduced demand or lower costs of production, or both, its parity price under the new formula would be lower than under the old formula.[26]

Transitional and Blocked Parities

Since the price supports on basic commodities provided by law were at 90 per cent of parity, the changes described above would have meant sudden and rather sharp reductions in the levels of support for some commodities if put into effect all at once. For example, the reduction in the support level on wheat as of January 1952 would have been from $2.205 per bushel (90 per cent of $2.45) to $1.908 (90 per cent of $2.12). To avoid unduly severe reductions of this kind, the Agricultural Act of 1948 stipulated that the parity price of any commodity for which price supports were provided, if lower under the new formula, would be reduced by 5 per cent per year (of its parity under the old formula) until its price under the new formula would be higher than the parity price so reduced. Thereafter, its parity price would be figured according to the "modernized" formula.

The Agricultural Act of 1949 retained the transitional parity price provision for "nonbasic" commodities but directed that, for the four-year period beginning January 1, 1950, the parity price for any "basic" commodity "shall not be less than its parity price computed in the manner used prior to the enactment of the Agricultural Act of 1949." The four-year period was later extended to six years (by legislation passed in 1952). This was a political compromise and not in accord with the parity principle to which the Congress had subscribed repeatedly over the preceding years. It meant that adjustments could be made only if they raised the parity goal, not if they lowered it, even though the lower parities so established might be in accord with the principle on which the parity price criterion is based.

The retention of the old formula for such of the basic crops as would have a higher parity price under that formula than under the new one had the effect of increasing the average level of farm prices required to put farm

26. The relatively simple explanation here presented is subject to a number of qualifications. Few of the farm prices were actual free-market prices in the period 1942–1951. Wheat tended to be overpriced because of war demand and abnormal methods of financing. The prices of some commodities were being supported by the government while others were being held down (during part of the war years). Subsidies affected the prices of some of them. Furthermore, even though the introduction of the moving-average idea will presumably iron out some of these abnormalities, the government price supports provided all through the succeeding years cause distortions that tend to prevent the new formula from reflecting accurately the price differentials between the different farm commodities that would have existed in an entirely free market. The new formula brings parity prices more closely into line with relative values in the market but still provides only a rough approximation to free-market price relationships.

prices "at parity" with the prices of things farmers buy. That is, under this mixed-formula arrangement, the "parity" prices for some of the commodities would be increased while the parity prices of others (still under the old formula) could not be reduced to give an average that would be comparable to that resulting from the use of either formula by itself.[27]

No further change was made in the legislation relating to parity until 1954, except for the postponement of the full adoption of the "modernized" formula. The Agricultural Act of 1954 provides that, beginning in 1956, the modernized parity formula shall go into effect gradually on those basic commodities not now computed on that basis, but reductions are not to exceed 5 per cent per year of the parity price as computed by the old formula. In other words, the 1954 act establishes a new transition period, for basic commodities, beginning in 1956. The over-all effect of the postponements has been to delay by six years the full transition to the new method of computing parities.

27. The new formula, even when used by itself, has resulted in a higher parity index in most of the recent years, largely because it includes farm wage rates, which were not in the old formula.

The parity indexes for farm products as a whole as figured by the two methods are as follows: [a]

Year	New Formula	Old Formula	Year	New Formula	Old Formula
1910	97	96	1932	112	124
1911	98	100	1933	109	119
1912	101	100	1934	120	128
1913	101	102	1935	124	128
1914	103	102	1936	124	127
1915	105	107	1937	131	132
1916	116	125	1938	124	126
1917	148	148	1939	123	123
1918	173	173	1940	124	124
1919	197	198	1941	133	132
1920	214	202	1942	152	150
1921	155	165	1943	171	161
1922	151	164	1944	182	168
1923	159	167	1945	190	172
1924	160	167	1946	208	192
1925	164	169	1947	240	231
1926	160	167	1948	260	250
1927	159	165	1949	251	244
1928	162	167	1950	256	252
1929	160	165	1951	282	274
1930	151	159	1952	287	280
1931	130	140	1953	279	278

a. *Parity Handbook*, p. 18, through 1951 (with later revisions). Data for 1952 and 1953 supplied by the U.S. Department of Agriculture. Simple average of 12 monthly figures, 1910–1914 = 100.

As of 1954, parity prices for about two thirds of the farm commodities were being computed in accordance with the new formula. However, the law required that several of the principal field crops such as wheat, corn and cotton be computed by the old formula, as this results in a higher parity index. The effect of the change in formula on the parity ratio in some years can be illustrated by the data for 1950. In that year, an average level of farm prices that would have been at parity under the old formula would have been 98.4 per cent of parity under the new formula. In 1953, the two methods of computation resulted in about the same parity index.

THE PARITY CONCEPT—PROBLEMS INVOLVED

The underlying idea of equality of income and opportunity in farm and nonfarm occupations is relatively simple, but when an attempt is made to measure these relationships, especially if far-reaching government programs are based on such measurements, a good many technical and controversial problems arise. Some of these have been touched on in the main text of this volume and also in the report of the project committee. The literature pertaining to the subject is voluminous. Even a general summarization of it would require much more space than can be provided in an appendix of this kind.[28] The purpose here is to provide a basis for intelligent consideration of the problem by the lay reader, not to deal exhaustively with it, especially in respect to technical matters such as items to be included or excluded, methods of computing indexes, their reliability and so on.[29]

The parity concept should be distinguished from the question of levels of support for farm prices. The government, or the farm groups, or others, could undertake to measure the relative levels of farm and nonfarm incomes and the relative changes in various groups of prices even if there were no price-support program at all. Such measurements of price and income movements are widely used in analytical work and many business and governmental decisions are based on them.

For example, if the index of employment or of wholesale prices shows a sharp decline, the government may decide to expand and ease credit or to undertake large-scale highway or building programs; or, if prices appear to be rising too rapidly, it may contract credit and cut back on government expenditures. Actions of that kind, though involving some measure of planned management of the economy, are more in keeping with the operation of a freely adjusting, dynamic economy than are those which seek to maintain some specific relationship between prices for different groups of products.

A decision to maintain a given relationship, as among the prices of different farm products or between farm and nonfarm prices, implies a move in the direction of a more fully planned economy since, for such a decision to be effective, production must be planned and controlled as well as prices, unless prices are to be supported in some other way than by means of the market. It has some tendency to block adjustments that would otherwise occur and to encourage the use of resources for types of production that are not the ones most desired by consumers.

Income Comparisons

For many reasons, farm and nonfarm incomes cannot be compared directly in money terms. The elements included are quite different both in

28. For a partial list of pertinent literature, see note 33 and the footnotes in the text.
29. There are, for example, differences of opinion among competent students about the appropriateness of including such items as cost of living expenditures, taxes and so on. These differences relate mainly to underlying principles. They do not affect importantly the parity indexes derived. The methods used in introducing new commodities, or dropping those which are no longer important, and changes in weightings, have much more effect on the indexes finally arrived at than does the inclusion or exclusion of such items as those mentioned.

kind and amount. For this reason, indexes of *change* in relative money incomes are much more significant than direct comparisons of dollar incomes. For example, housing is, in the main, a noncash item in farm expenditures whereas, either as rent or as payments on homes purchased, it is likely to be a very substantial item in the cash budget of the urban worker. Many farm families produce at home a good many food items that the urban worker customarily pays for in cash on a month-to-month basis. Transportation to and from work and expenses for eating, and in some cases for sleeping, away from home tend to bulk larger in the budget of the city worker, though the farmer usually has other kinds of expenses not borne by the urban worker that may offset them.

Other less tangible values and costs are involved. The farmer, in most cases, works under his own direction. His home surroundings tend to be more roomy and secluded but often are lacking in some of the amenities available to most city workers. Educational and entertainment facilities vary as between the two environments, with each having some advantages and some disadvantages. Most operating farmers have more job security than urban wage workers have, and their work is likely to be at a less exacting pace and less monotonous. These differences cannot be measured in dollars and cents and, in fact, have different values for different people.

Still more important is the difference in the make-up of the two groups. Neither of them is homogeneous. In both settings, there are fully employed, partly employed and virtually unemployed groups. The skills, judgment and effort required may be higher or lower in one group or another. Farmers, in general, take more risks than urban wage workers do, but they have a possibility of unexpectedly large as well as unexpectedly small incomes.

Probably the most defensible comparison that can be made is that between commercial farm operators, excluding large-scale farms, and employed factory workers of all grades. Nearly a third of the 5.4 million farms enumerated in the 1950 Census of Agriculture were not classed as commercial farms. The farms in this low-income and "other" group were mainly part-time, abnormal and residential farms, and those on which farming operations were so small or poor that they could be regarded virtually as subsistence-type farms. Some were farms on which there had been crop failures in the year of enumeration.

These noncommercial farms, which accounted for only about 2 per cent of the value of all farm products sold, constituted 30 per cent of all of the farms enumerated. Their average income from farm products sold was only $338. Thus, they cannot properly be regarded as full-time, effective commercial farms. If they are included in the total number of farms used in computing average income per farm from sale of farm products, the result is, of course, a gross distortion of the figure for average income to actual commercial farmers. There are similar unrepresentative groups in the nonfarm economy. To include them in computing average nonfarm incomes causes similar distortions, though they may be either smaller or larger than those for the farm groups.

Though these qualifications make direct dollar comparisons of farm and nonfarm incomes difficult and unsatisfactory, the rates of change in the incomes of the two groups, as shown by index numbers for cash returns, do provide a way of judging how they are faring as compared with each other.

However, such comparisons are more meaningful and precise if made between large, fairly homogeneous urban groups and the earnings on efficiently operated commercial farms than if the very diverse fringe groups both urban and rural are included. The farms classified as commercial in the 1950 census numbered about 3.8 million and accounted for about 98 per cent of the value of farm products sold in 1949.[30] If 98 per cent of the value of farm products sold is divided by 3.8 million, the resulting return per farm is, of course, much larger than if 100 per cent of the value of farm products sold is divided by the entire 5.4 million places classed as farms.[31]

Price Comparisons May Not Reflect Relative Incomes

The comparisons of prices from period to period for things sold by farmers and those bought by them may not reflect relative incomes of farm and nonfarm people at all accurately. If farm output is high and prices are also high, the result is a high total income. But if production has to be cut back sharply to maintain high prices, or if high prices are a result of poor yields, the farmer may not be any better off with high prices and a low volume of output than he would be with lower prices and a higher volume of output. The same is true for urban labor. High wage rates do not assure high average per capita incomes if there is a large amount of unemployment.

If the comparison sought is true parity of return as reflected in some accepted base period, income comparisons are far more significant than price comparisons. Farm prices held at or near parity in a depression period, without controls on production, would put agriculture in a highly favored position, so much so that the public would not be likely to find such action acceptable.

30. The sizes of farm operation classed as commercial and noncommercial must, of course, be made arbitrarily in tabulating census returns. However, the classifications used have been arrived at after much consultation with interested groups and individuals. The lowest income group classified as "commercial" farms by the census is that in which the value of farm products sold in 1949 was within the range $250 to $1,199. Farms where the operator worked more than 100 days at off-farm work and those where the income of the farm operator and members of his family received from nonfarm sources was greater than the value of farm products sold were excluded as not being representative of this group. For data and explanation, see Bureau of Agricultural Economics, Bureau of Human Nutrition and Home Economics, and Bureau of the Census, *Farms and Farm People*, A Special Cooperative Study, June 1953, especially pp. 3–12.

31. Though the ratio between farm and nonfarm prices and incomes is the most commonly used measure of relative returns to farm and nonfarm groups, there are other indicators that help in providing an understanding of the economic condition of agriculture. One of these is the valuation placed on farm real estate. At the peak of the post-World War I boom in 1920, farm lands and buildings were valued at $66 billion. By 1933, this valuation had dropped to $30.6 billion. It had recovered only to $33.6 billion by 1940 but rose thereafter to a high of $93.7 billion in 1952. It dropped off to $92.3 billion in 1953 (*Agricultural Statistics, 1937*, p. 391 and *ibid., 1953*, p. 555). This indicates that the level of prices and incomes in the 1940s and early 1950s was sufficiently attractive to cause active bidding for farm lands. The farm foreclosure rate, which stood at about 18 per thousand in 1934, had fallen to only 1.2 per thousand in 1953. (U.S. Farm Credit Administration, *Farm Foreclosure Sales, 1950*, July 1951, p. 1, and *Agricultural Statistics, 1953*, p. 557.) The rapid upsurge in land prices, the large reduction in mortgage debt and the low foreclosure rate indicate a high level of farm prosperity in the period since 1940, which, of course, has a bearing on the extent of the need for special financial aid on any broad scale. While the over-all level of farm prosperity was high, there were, of course, some areas and some groups that were not sharing in this prosperity and were in need of assistance.

In such a period, the incomes of urban workers as a whole, and of urban business, would be substantially reduced because of heavy unemployment and smaller production and sales.

There are also marked differences in the kinds and rates of quality change in the two groups of commodities and services. For the most part, farm products continue to be of about the same kind and quality from period to period. A bushel of wheat or a pound of pork or a dozen eggs now is about the same as it was in 1920, or in 1910, or in 1900. This is not true for many of the things farmers buy. Items like clothing, food and tobacco have shown little change, but automobiles, tractors, combines, corn cultivators, refrigerators, electric irons, stoves and washing machines have been greatly improved. Taxes, which are included in the parity formula, do not now pay for the same things as they did in 1910–1914.

If these differences in quality could be measured and taken into account, it is possible that farm prices would now be at parity or above instead of 88 per cent of parity as shown (for September 15, 1954) by the current methods of computation.[32]

Parity Not a "Normal" or "Necessary" Price

Economists define a "normal" or "necessary" price, in a free market, as the price required to bring forth enough production to keep supply and demand roughly in balance over fairly long periods. There has been some tendency to confuse "parity price" with this idea of a normal or necessary price. This it clearly is not. Parity price as now defined will, in many lines, bring forth more production than can be sold at that price.

Parity price is more in the nature of a goal or "desired" price than something that occurs naturally in the market. In this respect, it is similar to the wage worker's goal of "a living wage." A "living wage" is not a precise sum, and it does not stay the same from period to period. If wage workers had attained only the levels of real income they regarded as a living wage twenty years ago, they would be getting far less than they do now. As wages approach what was formerly considered a living wage, the "living wage" itself is raised to constitute a new goal. This is probably desirable, but it means that the living wage as defined in any particular period is seldom attained in that period.

The situation in respect to parity prices for farm products is somewhat similar. So long as farm prices were far below parity as then defined, congressmen and farmers were quite content to go along on a definition of parity in terms of exchange relationships between prices of *commodities* bought and *commodities* sold. The same amount of wheat, for example, should exchange for the same number of wagons, or the same amount of clothing or machinery.

But as the parity ratio approached 100 in the middle 1930s, parity was redefined to include interest and taxes. Again in 1949, when the parity ratio

32. Such quality changes are not measurable in precise terms and cannot be taken into account practically in computing numerical indexes. However, they should be kept in mind in interpreting data purporting to show relative price changes of farm and nonfarm products. The price comparisons shown by the indexes now used tend to overstate the disparities in buying power as between the two types of commodities.

had been above 100 for several years, other modifications were made, through the inclusion of the cost of farm labor and the retention of the "old formula" in computing parities for some of the commodities. It is hardly to be expected that the definition of parity will remain unchanged if there seems to be a possibility of achieving a higher goal by establishing a different method of computation. Here, as in the case of labor, there need be no serious objection to the setting of a continually advancing goal, provided it is recognized as a goal and not as something the government is obligated to translate into reality as of a given time.

Parity and a Dynamic Economy

The maintenance of a full parity price on each individual commodity is clearly not consistent with dynamic progress in the agricultural industry as a whole. The relative demands for different commodities do not remain the same from period to period. Neither do the relative costs. Many examples can easily be cited. In the 1940s, billion-bushel wheat crops were wanted and desperately needed. Now a wheat crop of 800 to 900 million bushels would be ample. The demand for meat and milk is increasing, as a result both of a growing population and of a desire for better diets. Furthermore, most groups have enough buying power to purchase better diets, which was not true in some earlier periods. On the other hand, the per capita demand for potatoes, bread and some kinds of fruits is declining.

On the supply side, wheat, corn and rice can be produced with much fewer hours of labor per acre and per bushel than in 1909–1914 or even in much more recent periods. Such products as wool and mutton, or beef cattle, continue to require about as much labor as in early periods and may even come to require more outlay as wage rates increase and grazing lands become relatively less abundant.

Much of the unreality of price parity relationships as between farm products has been eliminated by the changes in methods of computing parity prices that have been introduced in recent years, though there still are some distortions arising from the fact that neither demand relationships nor cost relationships were the same in the 1940s as they are now.

Agriculture's Trading Position

Even under the "modernized" parity formula, the over-all price and income relationships of the 1910–1914 period have continued to be used as a guide in determining what constitutes a "fair" return to farmers as compared to the prices and incomes received by people in other occupations. That period is now so far in the past and conditions have changed so much that most students of the problem regard it as an unsatisfactory standard to use. Actually, there seems to be no solid foundation for the contention that agriculture's trading position is now less favorable than it was in 1909–1914, except for maladjustments that have resulted from the war and postwar periods.

If these maladjustments in stocks and production capacity could be overcome, it would seem that agriculture's free-market position should now be at least as good as it was just prior to World War I and that it would not be necessary to reach back so far in the effort to devise some reasonable standard of equitable returns. The nonfarm economy is far more active and prosperous than it was in 1910–1914 and the nonfarm outlet for farm people is relatively much larger. The agricultural labor force now amounts to less than 10 million people, while the nonfarm labor force consists of more than 50 million. Consequently, shifts out of agriculture and into nonfarm employment, in order to achieve higher returns, are much more feasible now than they were in 1910–1914.

The trading position of agriculture would, of course, be different if a serious depression should occur. Farmers could not then shift out of agriculture easily, and their prices and incomes might go very low. If, in such times, agriculture maintains a needed volume of production, it at least should not suffer more income reduction relatively than those parts of the economy that cut back production and employment in order to maintain prices and wage rates, thus contributing heavily to unbalance and low levels of activity in the economy as a whole. These considerations obviously should be taken into account in deciding on national policy, but the criteria to be used in establishing price and income policies for agriculture should not now be based on the relationships of a period that is more than forty years in the past.

Farmers naturally will continue to try to improve their relative position in the economy and to obtain a larger per capita share in the continually growing national income. Conflicts of interest are inevitable as labor, business, public employees and other groups seek to do the same thing. In this struggle, agriculture has certain handicaps and also certain advantages. It is not so easily organized into tightly knit, well-disciplined organizations as are labor and many types of business. On the other hand, it occupies a strategic position politically and, thus far at least, it has been able to obtain very substantial assistance from government in achieving its goals. However, its political power and influence are bound to decline as the number of farm voters decreases in proportion to the number of nonfarm voters. The goals established should be reasonable, forward-looking and of such a nature that they can command widespread public support.[33]

33. The foregoing discussion omits consideration of many of the technical problems of price and income measurement. For those who wish to explore these further, the following sources will be helpful.

Though the literature on the subject is very voluminous, much of it is now out of date and only of historical interest. Among the articles and publications of particular interest are the following:

American Farm Economic Association. Committee on Redefinition of Parity Price and Parity Income, Report, *Journal of Farm Economics,* November 1947, pp. 1358–1374
Black, John D. *Parity, Parity, Parity,* Harvard Committee on Research in the Social Sciences, Cambridge, 1942
Davis, Joseph S. "An Evaluation of the Present Economic Position of Agriculture by Regions and in General," *Journal of Farm Economics,* April 1933, pp. 247-54
Parity Handbook, Senate Document No. 129, 82d Cong., 2d sess., 1952
Randall, C. Kyle. "Parity Prices," U.S. Bureau of Agricultural Economics, *Agricultural Economics Research,* January 1949, pp. 1–4
Sheppard, Geoffrey S. "What Should Go into the Parity Price Formula?" *Journal of Farm Economics,* May 1953, pp. 159–72
Shideler, James H. "The Development of the Parity Price Formula for Agriculture, 1919–1923," *Agricultural History,* July 1953, pp. 77–84
Stauber, B. Ralph, Koffsky, Nathan M., and Randall, C. Kyle. "The Revised Price Indexes," *Agricultural Economics Research,* April 1950, pp. 33–62

Stine, O. C. "Parity Prices," *Journal of Farm Economics,* February 1946, pp. 301–05

Turning the Searchlight on Farm Policy, A Forthright Analysis of Experience, Lessons, Criteria, and Recommendations, The Farm Foundation, Chicago, 1952

Wright, K. T. "Basic Weaknesses of the Parity Formula for a Period of Extensive Readjustments in Agriculture," *Journal of Farm Economics,* February 1946, pp. 294–300

For a more complete listing, see *Parity Price, Comparable Price, and Parity Income,* a Selected Bibliography compiled by Orpha Cummings, Librarian, Giannini Foundation of Agricultural Economics, University of California, Berkeley, processed, 2d edition, March 1951.

APPENDIX B

U.S. DEPARTMENT OF AGRICULTURE COMPUTATION OF COST OF FARM PROGRAMS, 1932–1953

THE DEPARTMENT OF AGRICULTURE released, in the spring of 1954, a compilation of the costs of the various agricultural programs by fiscal years for the period 1932 through 1953.[1] That summary is here reproduced in Tables 1 through 5. The data shown in the preceding chapters of this study were worked up independently and differ in some respects from those prepared by the Department of Agriculture. There are differences in the categories used and, in some cases, in items included or excluded. However, the two are in substantial accord on most main items. The Department of Agriculture release provides undoubtedly the most comprehensive and accurate summary available and is also a convenient source of data on specific programs and commodities.

There are, of course, many ways of presenting data of this kind. The Department's summary, very properly, uses categories established by legislation and in government accounting. They are not in all cases the same as those used in grouping activities according to type, function or economic effect. Consequently, interpretations of them will vary among different users, depending on the purpose of the analysis, the type of analytical approach used and the views held as to what types of items are properly regarded as debits and credits.

For the tables here shown, the Department uses the general designation "Realized Cost of Agricultural and Related Programs, by Function or Purpose." Figures given are for fiscal years, that is, for periods ending on June 30 of the years shown in the tables. The basis for the costs reflected in the tables is as follows: (1) for activities financed from appropriated funds, the expenditures less receipts arising from the activities so financed; (2) for noncorporate loan funds, the losses on loans and the net interest cost or income; (3) for Commodity Credit Corporation and Federal Crop Insurance Corporation corporate funds, the net gains or losses from operations and the interest cost to the Treasury on government-subscribed capital; and (4) for corporations of the farm credit system, the interest cost to the Treasury on government-subscribed capital and payments made by the Treasury on account of reductions in interest rates on mortgages less dividends and franchise taxes paid to the Treasury. Interest cost to the Treasury on noncorporate loan funds and on government-subscribed capital of corporations has been computed on the basis of the average rate on the public debt paid by the Treasury in each of these years.

In releasing the data here shown, the Department called attention to the difference between data presented on a realized cost basis and those reported

1. Published in U.S. Senate Committee on Agriculture and Forestry, *General Farm Program,* Hearings, 83rd Cong., 2nd sess., Part I, 1954, pp. 74–89.

on an accrued income and expense basis. The Department's statement in regard to this is as follows:

Relationship of Realized Costs to Statements of Accrued Income and Expenses for Noncorporate Lending Programs

The financial aspects of the noncorporate lending programs of the Rural Electrification Administration and the Farmers Home Administration, which are reported on this statement on a realized cost basis, are also susceptible of being reported on an accrued income and expense basis. Records for these programs are maintained and reports are made on the accrued basis pursuant to regulations covering business-type Government operations. To illustrate the differences involved in these two concepts, the following tabulation, using the REA as an example, shows the results from the beginning of the REA programs through the fiscal year 1953 on the accrual basis compared with the realized costs reflected in this statement.

Lending Operations of REA from Inception to June 30, 1953

	Accrued Income and Expense Basis	Net Realized Cost Basis
	(Millions of Dollars)	
Interest income	234.0	150.9
Expense:		
Interest expense	185.9	250.7
Provision for possible losses on loans	2.5	—
Net income	45.5	xx
Net expense	xx	99.8

The principal differences in the two bases are as follows:

(1) Interest income. The accrual basis includes interest earned but not collected. A substantial part of the difference is due to the inclusion on the accrual basis of interest deferred under the law during the first five years of a loan but properly accounted for as accrued interest earned although it is not due or payable. The realized cost basis includes actual collections of interest.

(2) Interest expense. The accrual basis includes only the interest actually charged to REA on funds borrowed from RFC (in the earlier years) and from the Treasury, under borrowing authorizations provided by Congress. The realized cost basis includes as interest expense the amount resulting from applying to the average total of loans outstanding in each year the average interest rate paid by the Government for the funds it borrowed in that year.

(3) Provision for possible losses on loans. The accrual basis includes projected or anticipated losses based on the best estimate that could be made at the end of the fiscal year 1953. The realized cost basis, which takes into account only those costs that have actually come about, does not include any anticipated losses on loans.

TABLE B-1. REALIZED COST OF AGRICULTURAL AND RELATED

		1932	1933	1934	1935	1936	1937	1938	1939	1940
1	*Programs Primarily for Stabilization of Prices and Farm Income:*									
2	Commodity Credit Corporation:									
3	Program operations:									
4	Price support programs	—	—	—	—	8.7	5.3	0.4	4.6	7.4
5	Supply, foreign purchase, commodity export, and other CCC activities	—	—	—	—	—	—	—	—	—
6	Administrative and other general costs	—	—	0.6*	0.9*	11.7	3.9	2.1	3.0*	8.7
7	International Wheat Agreement a	—	—	—	—	—	—	—	—	—
8	Removal of surplus agricultural commodities b	—	—	—	—	32.2	35.2	35.2	211.6	143.9
9	Sugar Act	—	—	—	—	—	—	27.4*	6.5*	25.2*
10	Federal crop insurance	—	—	—	—	—	—	—	4.4	7.7
11	Acreage allotment payments under the Agricultural Conservation Program	—	—	—	—	—	313.6	217.4	350.7	380.2
12	Other, including Agricultural Adjustment Act of 1933, parity payments, and other adjustment and surplus removal programs	297.8	75.1	48.2*	179.6	417.3	84.9	0.5*	28.0	224.1
13	Total	297.8	75.1	48.8°	178.7	469.9	442.9	227.2	589.8	746.8
14	*Programs Primarily for Conservation of Resources:*									
15	Agricultural Conservation Program (exclusive of acreage allotment payments)	—	—	—	—	0.5	55.1	88.8	119.8	202.0
16	Soil Conservation Service programs c	0.2	0.2	0.1	0.2	3.5	21.0	24.2	25.7	30.9
17	Forest Service programs d	19.6	12.2	6.8	8.3	9.5	14.2	17.9	21.4	24.3
18	Flood prevention program	—	—	—	—	—	—	0.3	1.4	2.3
19	Total	19.8	12.4	6.9	8.5	13.5	90.3	131.2	168.3	259.5
20	*Credit and Related Programs for Electrification and Telephone Facilities, and Farm Purchase, Maintenance, Operation, and Housing:*									
21	Lending programs:									
22	Rural Electrification Administration	—	—	—	—	—	0.2	0.7	1.3	—
23	Farmers Home Administration	13.7	13.2	13.7	14.5	9.5	14.5	12.2	17.7.	11.4
24	Farm Credit System	5.4	6.5	22.3	33.5	49.9	55.2	60.0	61.1	58.5
25	Grants and other expenses, including salaries and expenses related to the above lending programs	4.9	6.6	9.1	12.7	77.3	·157.7	110.8	72.5	72.9
26	Total	24.0	26.3	45.1	60.7	136.7	227.6	183.7	152.6	142.8
27	*Research and Education:*									
28	Research	20.6	18.1	15.3	15.6	18.4	20.9	22.6	25.7	30.2
29	Extension Service, incl. payments to States	10.1	9.9	9.4	9.3	17.4	17.0	17.9	18.5	19.2
30	Total	30.7	28.0	24.7	24.9	35.8	37.9	40.5	44.2	49.4
31	*Other, Chiefly School Lunch, Marketing Services, Control and Regulatory Activities:* ·									
32	School lunch program e	—	—	—	—	—	—	—	—	—
33	Other	23.9	22.2	18.0	37.1	41.5	34.7	35.6	33.7	32.8
34	Total	23.9	22.2	18.0	37.1	41.5	34.7	35.6	33.7	32.8
35	*Programs Primarily for Wartime, Defense, and Other Special Needs*	—	—	—	—	—	—	—	—	—
36	Total, above items	396.2	164.0	45.9	309.9	697.4	833.4	618.2	988.6	1,231.3

° Excess of credits—deduct.

a. The expenditures under this program are for payment of the difference between the price specified in the International Wheat Agreement and the domestic market price of wheat. The program is essentially international in nature, and is included in this classification with the kinds of items to which it most nearly relates.

b. Exclusive of cash payments for school lunch programs.

PROGRAMS, BY MAJOR CATEGORIES, 1932–1953 (*Millions of Dollars*)

1941	1942	1943	1944	1945	1946	1947	1948	1949	1950	1951	1952	1953	Total	
														1
														2
														3
34.0	69.1*	49.9*	5.9*	29.4	30.1*	71.9	125.4	254.7	249.2	345.6	67.4	61.1	1,110.1	4
—	0.1*	2.0	12.4*	5.8	35.9*	242.7*	38.4*	4.7*	2.7*	1.6	1.3	6.4	319.8*	5
2.2	9.6*	12.1	10.4	26.1	33.2	13.9	6.5*	15.9	48.1	42.0	34.6	55.3	299.6	6
—	—	—	—	—	—	—	—	—	75.6	180.4	171.3	130.8	558.1	7
226.1	196.3	112.0	63.4	24.9	19.2	78.4	51.2	75.6	96.6	46.0	37.5	82.3	1,567.6	8
30.0*	32.7*	0.6*	21.3*	32.9*	5.2*	7.4*	13.1*	23.3*	14.5*	14.8*	21.8*	19.4*	296.1*	9
9.8	14.8	14.6	18.1	2.9	21.5	36.9	1.8*	0.4*	9.6	4.6	8.7	6.4	157.8	10
326.7	332.5	218.1	193.1	—	22.5	—	—	—	—	—	—	—	2,354.8	11
197.2	202.7	203.7	156.7	6.1*	1.5*	2.2*	—	10.9	25.0	18.9	7.2	7.7	2,078.3	12
766.0	634.8	512.0	402.1	50.1	23.7	51.2*	116.8	328.7	486.9	624.3	306.2	330.6	7,510.4	13
														14
132.7	136.6	212.0	226.6	278.9	275.3	329.2	230.6	167.6	237.2	275.5	262.0	270.3	3,500.7	15
23.0	23.4	23.4	25.1	28.2	34.6	43.1	41.3	47.9	52.8	52.1	56.0	59.6	616.5	16
18.9	17.8	18.5	18.3	21.0	28.0	36.4	37.7	33.8	33.5	9.8	7.6	6.2	421.7	17
2.9	1.5	0.4	0.1	0.1	0.6	2.6	3.8	5.9	6.7	7.5	7.8	6.3	50.2	18
177.5	179.3	254.3	270.1	328.2	338.5	411.3	313.4	255.2	330.2	344.9	333.4	342.4	4,589.1	19
														20
														21
2.5	1.0	1.9*	4.4*	1.9*	0.9*	2.5	6.5	9.7	14.4	20.2	23.2	26.7	99.8	22
9.3	7.1	0.3*	9.8*	7.6*	2.6*	4.9*	4.6*	4.8*	3.2*	5.4*	5.3*	5.1*	83.2	23
51.5	50.9	48.1	43.2	18.1	9.4	7.3	7.0	f52.3*	11.2*	8.0*	7.8*	2.6*	506.0	24
69.8	67.3	51.3	39.8	36.0	37.6	42.5	26.4	29.0	33.8	35.4	37.1	36.8	1,067.3	25
133.1	126.3	97.2	68.8	44.6	43.5	47.4	35.3	18.4*	33.8	42.2	47.2	55.8	1,756.3	26
														27
31.2	31.6	30.9	28.2	29.7	31.6	37.1	42.4	52.6	56.8	55.2	54.8	55.2	724.7	28
19.2	19.5	19.5	19.5	19.4	23.9	27.4	27.2	31.1	32.1	32.3	32.6	32.6	465.0	29
50.4	51.1	50.4	47.7	49.1	55.5	64.5	69.6	83.7	88.9	87.5	87.4	87.8	1,189.7	30
														31
—	—	1.0	33.7	45.4	56.6	77.5	68.4	75.0	83.2	82.8	83.6	82.8	690.0	32
30.9	31.1	31.0	35.8	36.3	40.3	48.5	40.5	48.1	52.8	55.2	53.9	57.4	841.3	33
30.9	31.1	32.0	69.5	81.7	96.9	126.0	108.9	123.1	136.0	138.0	137.5	140.2	1,531.3	34
—	5.3	14.1	73.8	54.7	31.1	31.3	41.3	45.9	31.5	1.6	8.2	5.4	344.2	35
1,157.9	1,027.9	960.0	932.0	608.4	589.2	629.3	685.3	818.2	1,107.3	1,238.5	919.9	962.2	16,921.0	36

c. The amounts shown include the purchase of 9,643,738 acres of submarginal land at a total cost of approximately $60,061,000.
d. The amounts shown include the purchase of 14,450,711 acres of land at a total cost of approximately $68,332,000.
e. Includes costs under the National School Lunch Act and Section 32 funds used for cash payments for school lunch programs.
f. Includes $9.3 million representing the cumulative net loss of capital subscribed to the Regional Agricultural Credit Corporations- which were liquidated in 1949.

TABLE B-2

WARTIME CONSUMER SUBSIDIES ON AGRICULTURAL COMMODITIES, 1942–1953

(*Millions of Dollars*)

Year	Paid by Reconstruction Finance Corporation	Paid by Commodity Credit Corporation	Total
1942	0.9	8.3	9.2
1943	23.4	145.5	168.9
1944	570.4	390.1	960.5
1945	626.3	741.7	1,368.0
1946	924.8	845.1	1,769.9
1947	3.0*	22.4*	25.4*
1948	0.1	4.0*	3.9*
1949	. . .	2.2*	2.2*
1950	. . .	0.1	0.1
1951	. . .	0.3	0.3
1952	. . .	0.3*	0.3*
1953	. . .	0.1*	0.1*
Total	2,142.9	2,102.1	4,245.0

* Excess of credits—deduct.

TABLE B-3

OTHER SPECIAL ACTIVITIES NOT A PART OF THE AGRICULTURAL PROGRAMS
OF THE DEPARTMENT, 1932–1953

(*Millions of Dollars*)

Year	Special activities conducted by the Department under transferred funds as a service for other agencies (chiefly for purchase of commodities for Lend-Lease, UNRRA, Mutual Security and other foreign-aid programs)	Government procurement of agricultural commodities for foreign-aid programs other than through the Department of Agriculture	Total
1932	2.1	. . . .	2.1
1933	3.1	. . . .	3.1
1934	32.1	. . . .	32.1
1935	161.8	. . . .	161.8
1936	72.3	. . . .	72.3
1937	64.0	. . . .	64.0
1938	26.1	. . . .	26.1
1939	30.0	. . . .	30.0
1940	20.6	. . . .	20.6
1941	20.9	. . . .	20.9
1942	698.4	. . . .	698.4
1943	2,031.2	. . . .	2,031.2
1944	2,139.9	. . . .	2,139.9
1945	1,382.1	. . . .	1,382.1
1946	1,610.8	. . . .	1,610.8
1947	579.1	. . . .	579.1
1948	744.6	. . . .	744.6
1949	1,018.4	1,425.9	2,444.3
1950	611.4	1,236.3	1,847.7
1951	447.6	741.8	1,189.4
1952	331.8	312.4	644.2
1953	118.7	351.3	470.0
Total	12,147.0	4,067.7	16,214.7

TABLE B-4. SUMMARY OF REALIZED COST OF AGRICULTURAL AND RELATED PROGRAMS PRIMARILY FOR

| | | | Commodity Credit Corporation | | | | Inter-national Wheat Agreement | Removal of surplus agri-cultural com-modities [b] |
		Total	Price support programs	Supply, foreign purchase, commodity export and other CCC activities	Administra-tive and other general costs	Total		
1	*Basic Commodities:*							
2	Corn (including cornmeal and AAA corn-hog program):							
3	Program expense	1,375.8	70.9			70.9		18.4
4	Miscellaneous receipts	0.6*						
5	Processing taxes (net)	261.4*						
6	Total, Corn	1,113.8	70.9			70.9		18.4
7	Cotton:							
8	CCC price support:							
9	Upland cotton	268.2*	268.2*			268.2*		
10	Puerto Rican cotton	0.1	0.1			0.1		
11	Cotton export differential	41.4	41.4			41.4		
12	Cotton-rubber barter	11.1*	11.1*			11.1*		
13	Total, CCC price support	237.8*	237.8*			237.8*		
14	Other cotton programs:							
15	Program expense	2,059.4		ꜰ 12.5		12.5		ᵍ 348.9
16	Miscellaneous receipts	9.5*						
17	Processing taxes (net)	247.2*						
18	Total, Cotton	1,564.9	237.8*	12.5		225.3*		348.9
19	Peanuts:							
20	Program expense	142.9	92.6			92.6		26.8
21	Miscellaneous receipts	1.3*						
22	Processing taxes (net)	3.7*						
23	Total, Peanuts	137.9	92.6			92.6		26.8
24	Rice:							
25	Program expense	35.4	1.5			1.5		6.6
26	Processing taxes (net)	0.5						
27	Total, Rice	35.9	1.5			1.5		6.6
28	Tobacco:							
29	Program expense	186.4	1.6*			1.6*		18.1
30	Miscellaneous receipts	23.3*						
31	Processing taxes (net)	68.5*						
32	Total, Tobacco	94.6	1.6*			1.6*		18.1
33	Wheat (including wheat cereal and wheat flour):							
34	Program expense	1,981.9	95.1	ꜰ 1.2		96.3	546.5	133.2
35	Miscellaneous receipts	15.4*						
36	Processing taxes (net)	244.9*						
37	Total, Wheat	1,721.6	95.1	1.2		96.3	546.5	133.2
38	Total, Basic	4,668.7	20.7	13.7		34.4	546.5	552.0

STABILIZATION OF PRICES AND FARM INCOME, BY COMMODITY GROUPS, 1932–1953 [a] (*Millions of Dollars*)

Sugar Act	Federal crop insurance	Acreage allotment payments under the Agricultural Conservation Program	Agricultural production programs (principally acreage allotments and marketing quotas) [c]	Parity payments	Retirement of cotton pool participation trust certificates	Agricultural Adjustment Act of 1933 and related Acts	Removal of surplus cattle and dairy products [d]	Agricultural Marketing Act Revolving Fund, and payments to stabilization corporations for losses incurred [e]	Other	
										1
										2
	0.4	441.0	8.9	347.5		488.7				3
						0.6*				4
						261.4*				5
	0.4	441.0	8.9	347.5	—	226.7				6
										7
										8
										9
										10
										11
										12
										13
										14
	67.8	771.2	21.1	279.7	1.3	416.7		140.2		15
			7.7*			1.8*				16
						247.2*				17
	67.8	771.2	13.4	279.7	1.3	167.7		140.2		18
										19
		6.2	13.6			3.7				20
			1.3*							21
						3.7*				22
		6.2	12.3			—				23
										24
		11.7	0.4	5.6		9.6				25
						0.5				26
		11.7	0.4	5.6		10.1				27
										28
	3.0*	85.0	19.8	6.1		62.0				29
			21.2*			2.1*				30
						68.5*				31
	3.0*	85.0	1.4*	6.1		8.6*				32
										33
	1.8	351.2	22.0	328.2		354.6		148.1		34
			15.4*							35
						244.9*				36
	1.8	351.2	6.6	328.2		109.7		148.1		37
	67.0	1,666.3	40.2	967.1	1.3	505.6		288.3		38

TABLE B-4 (continued)

| | | | Commodity Credit Corporation | | | | | |
		Total	Price support programs	Supply, foreign purchase, commodity export and other CCC activities	Administrative and other general costs	Total	International Wheat Agreement	Removal of surplus agricultural commodities [b]
39	*Designated Nonbasic Commodities:*							
40	Butter	158.8	48.7			48.7		110.1
41	Cheese	28.7	25.0			25.0		3.7
42	Milk	113.9	62.8			62.8		51.1
43	Potatoes	635.8	478.1			478.1		131.6
44	Wool	104.6	92.2			92.2		
45	Other	12.8	1.0			1.0		11.3
46	Total, Designated Nonbasic	1,054.6	707.8			707.8		307.8
47	*Other Nonbasic Commodities:*							
48	Eggs	331.6	189.7			189.7		141.9
49	Flaxseed and Linseed Oil	72.0	66.2			66.2		5.8
50	Sugar:							
51	Sugar Act program:							
52	Sugar payments	819.9						
53	Sugar taxes	1,135.2*						
54	Net total, Sugar Act	315.3*						
55	Other sugar programs:	111.2	16.5			16.5		
56	Processing taxes (net)	76.2°						0.1
57	Total, Sugar	280.3*	16.5			16.5		0.1
58	Other:							
59	Program expense	1,452.0	109.4	20.0		129.4		506.9
60	Miscellaneous receipts	18.4*						
61	Processing taxes (net)	0.2*						
62	Total, Other	1,433.4	109.4	20.0		129.4		506.9
63	Total, Other Nonbasic	1,556.7	381.8	20.0		401.8		654.7
64	Total, all commodities	7,279.8	1,110.1	33.8		1,143.9	546.5	m 1,514.4
65	Interest cost:							
66	Interest payments	272.5			261.7	261.7	10.8	
67	Imputed interest cost [n]	71.5			31.9	31.9		
68	Interest income	174.0*			149.3*	149.3*		
69	Other costs not allocable to specific commodities [o]	63.4		ᵖ 353.6°	155.3	198.3°	0.8	53.2
70	Receipts not allocable by commodities	2.8*						
71	Realized cost	7,510.4	1,110.1	319.8°	299.6	1,089.9	558.1	1,567.6
72	RECAPITULATION: Commodity totals:							
73	Program expense (before deduction of miscellaneous receipts and taxes)	9,385.1	1,110.1	33.8		1,143.9	546.5	1,514.4
74	Miscellaneous receipts	68.5*						
75	Sugar taxes	1,135.2*						
76	Processing taxes (net)	901.6*						
77	Total, commodities	7,279.8	1,110.1	33.8		1,143.9	546.5	1,514.4
78	Other amounts not allocable by commodities	230.6		353.6°	299.6	54.0°	11.6	53.2
79	Realized cost	7,510.4	1,110.1	319.8°	299.6	1,089.9	558.1	1,567.6

TABLE B-4 (continued)

Sugar Act	Federal crop insurance	Acreage allotment payments under the Agricultural Conservation Program	Agricultural production programs (principally acreage allotments and marketing quotas) [c]	Parity payments	Retirement of participation cotton pool trust certificates	Agricultural Adjustment Act of 1933 and related Acts	Removal of surplus cattle and dairy products [d]	Agricultural Marketing Act Revolving Fund, and payments to stabilization corporations for losses incurred [e]	Other	
										39
										40
					*					41
										42
		26.1								43
								12.4		44
								0.5		45
		26.1						12.9		46
										47
										48
										49
										50
										51
819.9										52
1,135.2*										53
315.3*										54
		3.6				91.0				55
						76.2*				56
315.3*		3.6				14.8				57
										58
	1.9	658.8				0.2	76.6	78.2		59
						5.4*			13.0*	60
						0.2*				61
	1.9	658.8				5.4*	76.6	78.2	13.0*	62
315.3*	1.9	662.4				9.4	76.6	78.2	13.0*	63
315.3*	68.9	2,354.8	40.2	967.1	1.3	515.0	76.6	379.4	13.0*	64
										65
										66
	13.7							25.9		67
	0.7*							24.0*		68
19.2	75.9	q	r 6.8	49.5	0.1	56.2				69
						0.1*			s 2.7*	70
296.1*	157.8	2,354.8	47.0	1,016.6	1.4	571.1	76.6	381.3	15.7*	71
										72
819.9	68.9	2,354.8	85.8	967.1	1.3	1,426.5	76.6	379.4		73
			45.6*			9.9*			13.0*	74
1,135.2*										75
						901.6*				76
315.3*	68.9	2,354.8	40.2	967.1	1.3	515.0	76.6	379.4	13.0*	77
19.2	88.9		6.8	49.5	0.1	56.1		1.9	2.7*	78
296.1*	157.8	2,354.8	47.0	1,016.6	1.4	571.1	76.6	381.3	15.7*	79

Note: Details may not add to totals shown due to rounding.
* Represents income or minus expenditures.
For notes see page 571.

TABLE B-5. DISTRIBUTION OF REALIZED COST BY COMMODITIES, WHERE POSSIBLE, OF

		Total	Commodity Credit Corporation				International Wheat Agreement	Removal of surplus agricultural commodities
			Price support programs	Supply, foreign purchase, commodity export and other CCC activities	Administrative and other general costs	Total		
1	Almonds	1.7						1.7
2	Apples	81.5						81.5
3	Apricots	1.3						1.3
4	Barley	10.1	10.1			10.1		
5	Beans	60.6	35.0			35.0		25.1
6	Beef	1.5						1.5
7	Beets	1.0						1.0
8	Blackberries	0.1						0.1
9	Butter	158.8	48.7			48.7		110.1
10	Cabbage	5.1						5.1
11	Carrots	1.3						1.3
12	Castor beans	0.2	0.2			0.2		
13	Cattle and dairy products	76.6						
14	Cauliflower	0.1						0.1
15	Celery	0.5						0.5
16	Cheese	28.7	25.0			25.0		3.7
17	Cherries	2.2						2.2
18	Citrus	0.1*						
19	Citrus (juice and salad)	0.1						0.1
20	Coffee	0.6						0.6
21	Corn, cornmeal and corn-hog program:							
22	Corn	869.6	70.9			70.9		0.9
23	Cornmeal	17.5						17.5
24	Corn-hog program:							
25	Program expenses	488.7						
26	Miscellaneous receipts	0.6*						
27	Processing taxes (net)	261.4*						
28	Total, corn-hog	226.7						
29	Total, Corn	1,113.8	70.9			70.9		18.4
30	Cotton:							
31	CCC price support program:							
32	Upland cotton	268.2*	268.2*			268.2*		
33	Puerto Rican cotton	0.1	0.1			0.1		
34	Cotton export differential	41.4	41.4			41.4		
35	Cotton-rubber barter	11.1*	11.1*			11.1*		
36	Total, CCC price support program	237.8*	237.8*			237.8*		
37	Other cotton programs:							
38	Program expenses	2,059.4		f 12.5		12.5		g 348.9
39	Miscellaneous receipts	9.5*						
40	Processing taxes (net)	247.2*						
41	Total, Cotton	1,564.9	237.8*	12.5		225.3*		348.9
42	Cottonseed and products	13.6*	15.3*			15.3*		1.7
43	Cranberries	1.2						1.2
44	Dairy products	0.5						
45	Dates	0.4						0.4
46	Eggs	331.6	189.7			189.7		141.9
47	Figs	2.6						2.6
48	Filberts	0.6						0.6
49	Fish	1.2						1.2
50	Flax	21.8	0.4			0.4		0.2
51	Flaxseed and linseed oil	72.0	66.2			66.2		5.8
52	Fruits and vegetables	5.6						
53	Fruits, dried	14.9	14.9			14.9		
54	General depleting crops	627.5						
55	Grain	83.0		i 12.0		12.0		
56	Grain sorghums	41.4	35.4			35.4		6.0

PROGRAMS PRIMARILY FOR STABILIZATION OF PRICES AND FARM INCOMES, 1932–1953 ª (*Millions of Dollars*)

Sugar Act	Federal crop insurance	Acreage allotment payments under the Agricultural Conservation Program	Agricultural production programs (principally acreage allotments and marketing quotas) c	Parity payments	Retirement of cotton pool participation trust certificates	Agricultural Adjustment Act of 1933 and related Acts	Removal of surplus cattle and dairy products d	Agricultural Marketing Act Revolving Fund, and payments to stabilization corporations for losses incurred e	Other	
										1
										2
										3
										4
	0.3							0.2		5
										6
										7
										8
										9
										10
										11
										12
							76.6			13
										14
										15
										16
	0.1*									17
										18
										19
										20
	0.4	441.0	8.9	347.5						21
										22
										23
										24
						488.7				25
						0.6*				26
						261.4*				27
―	―	―	―	―	―	226.7	―	―	―	28
	0.4	441.0	8.9	347.5		226.7				29
										30
										31
										32
										33
										34
―	―	―	―	―――	――	―	―	―	―	35
										36
	67.8	771.2	21.1	279.7	1.3	416.7		140.2		37
			7.7*			1.8*				38
						247.2*				39
―	67.8	771.2	13.4	279.7	1.3	167.7	―	140.2	―	40
										41
										42
								0.5		43
										44
										45
										46
										47
										48
										49
	3.3*	24.5								50
										51
								5.6		52
		h627.5								53
										54
								71.0		55
										56

TABLE B-5 (*continued*)

			Commodity Credit Corporation					
		Total	Price support programs	Supply, foreign purchase, commodity export and other CCC activities	Administrative and other general costs	Total	International Wheat Agreement	Removal of surplus agricultural commodities
57	Grapes	0.5						0.5
58	Grapefruit (fruit and juice)	27.8	1.7			1.7		26.1
59	Hay	8.0		⌡8.0		8.0		
60	Hemp and hemp fiber	21.5	21.5			21.5		
61	Hides (miscellaneous receipts)	13.0*						
62	Hominy grits	3.5						3.5
63	Honey	12.2	0.9			0.9		11.3
64	Hops	1.7	1.0			1.0		0.7
65	Lard	19.3						19.3
66	Lemons (fruit and juice)	0.4						0.4
67	Livestock	0.1						
68	Meat, miscellaneous	0.2						0.2
69	Milk	51.1						51.1
70	Milk, dried	62.8	62.8			62.8		
71	Multiple crops	5.0						
72	Naval stores	1.4	1.4			1.4		
73	Nuts	0.3						
74	Oats	1.4	1.4			1.4		
75	Oats, rolled	3.4						3.4
76	Olive oil	0.4	**			**		0.4
77	Onions	2.9						2.9
78	Oranges (fruit and juice)	51.6						51.6
79	Peaches	10.0						10.0
80	Peanut butter	1.7						1.7
81	Peanuts:							
82	Program expenses	142.9	92.6			92.6		26.8
83	Miscellaneous receipts	1.3*						
84	Processing taxes (net)	3.7*						
85	Total, Peanuts	137.9	92.6			92.6		26.8
86	Pears	11.9						11.9
87	Peas (Canned, dried and fresh)	3.2	0.9			0.9		2.3
88	Pecans	3.8	**			**		3.8
89	Pineapples	0.1						0.1
90	Plums	0.6						0.6
91	Pork	66.0						66.0
92	Pork and beans	2.1						2.1
93	Potatoes	635.8	478.1			478.1		¹131.6
94	Potatoes, sweet	4.0	0.1			0.1		3.9
95	Poultry	0.3						
96	Prunes	36.6						36.6
97	Raisins	33.1						33.1
98	Rice:							
99	Program expenses	35.4	1.5			1.5		6.6
100	Processing taxes (net)	0.5						
101	Total, Rice	35.9	1.5			1.5		6.6
102	Rye:							
103	Program expenses	0.4	0.2			0.2		
104	Processing taxes (net)	0.2*						
105	Total, Rye	0.2	0.2			0.2		
106	Seeds:							
107	Program expenses	5.6	4.9			4.9		
108	Miscellaneous receipts	5.4*						
109	Total, Seeds	0.2	4.9			4.9		
110	Shortening, vegetable	0.1						0.1
111	Soup	0.9						0.9
112	Soybeans	4.4*	4.4*			4.4*		
113	Spinach	0.3						0.3
114	Squash	0.1						0.1

TABLE B-5 (continued)

Sugar Act	Federal crop insurance	Acreage allotment payments under the Agricultural Conservation Program	Agricultural production programs (principally acreage allotments and marketing quotas)c	Parity payments	Retirement of cotton pool participation trust certificates	Agricultural Adjustment Act of 1933 and related Acts	Removal of surplus cattle and dairy products d	Agricultural Marketing Act Revolving Fund, and payments to stabilization corporations for losses incurred e	Other	
										57
										58
										59
										60
									13.0*	61
										62
								**		63
										64
										65
										66
								0.1		67
										68
										69
										70
	k 5.0									71
										72
								0.3		73
										74
										75
										76
										77
										78
										79
										80
										81
		6.2	13.6			3.7				82
			1.3*							83
						3.7*				84
		6.2	12.3			—				85
										86
										87
										88
										89
										90
										91
										92
		26.1								93
										94
								0.3		95
										96
										97
										98
		11.7	0.4	5.6		9.6				99
						0.5				100
		11.7	0.4	5.6		10.1				101
										102
						0.2				103
						0.2*				104
						—				105
										106
								0.7		107
						5.4*				108
						5.4*		0.7		109
										110
										111
										112
										113
										114

TABLE B-5 (*continued*)

| | Total | Commodity Credit Corporation | | | | International Wheat Agreement | Removal of surplus agricultural commodities |
		Price support programs	Supply, foreign purchase, commodity export and other CCC activities	Administrative and other general costs	Total		
115 Sugar:							
116 Sugar Act program:							
117 Sugar payments	819.9						
118 Sugar taxes	1,135.2*						
119 Net total, Sugar Act	315.3*						
120 Other sugar programs, including sugar beets:							
121 Program expenses	111.2	16.5			16.5		0.1
122 Processing taxes (net)	76.2*						
123 Total, other sugar	35.0	16.5			16.5		0.1
124 Total, Sugar	280.3*	16.5			16.5		0.1
125 Syrup	0.4						0.4
126 Tangerines	1.1						1.1
127 Tobacco:							
128 Program expenses	186.4	1.6*			1.6*		18.1
129 Miscellaneous receipts	23.3*						
130 Processing taxes (net)	68.5*						
131 Total, Tobacco	94.6	1.6*			1.6*		18.1
132 Tomatoes	3.8						3.8
133 Tung oil	0.1	0.1			0.1		
134 Turkeys	33.4	**			**		33.4
135 Vegetables	42.7	**			**		[1]35.9
136 Walnuts	13.8						13.8
137 Wheat, wheat cereal and wheat flour:							
138 Wheat:							
139 Program expenses	1,870.4	95.1	[f]1.2		96.3	546.5	21.7
140 Miscellaneous receipts	15.4*						
141 Processing taxes (net)	244.9*						
142 Total, wheat	1,610.1	95.1	1.2		96.3	546.5	21.7
143 Wheat cereal	4.5						4.5
144 Wheat flour	107.0						107.0
145 Total, Wheat and wheat products	1,721.6	95.1	1.2		96.3	546.5	133.2
146 Wool	104.6	92.2			92.2		
147 Total, all commodities	7,279.8	1,110.1	33.8		1,143.9	546.5	[m]1,514.4
148 Interest cost:							
149 Interest payments	272.5			261.7	261.7	10.8	
150 Imputed interest cost [m]	71.5			31.9	31.9		
151 Interest income	174.0*			149.3*	149.3*		
152 Other costs not allocable to specific commodities [o]	63.4		[p]353.6*	155.3	198.3*	0.8	53.2
153 Receipts not allocable by commodities	2.8*						
154 Realized cost	7,510.4	1,110.1	319.8*	299.6	1,089.9	558.1	[b]1,567.6
RECAPITULATION:							
155 Commodity totals:							
156 Program expense (before deduction of miscellaneous receipts and taxes)	9,385.1	1,110.1	33.8		1,143.9	546.5	1,514.4
157 Miscellaneous receipts	68.5*						
158 Sugar taxes	1,135.2*						
159 Processing taxes (net)	901.6*						
160 Total, commodities	7,279.8	1,110.1	33.8		1,143.9	546.5	1,514.4
161 Other amounts not allocable by commodities	230.6		353.6*	299.6	54.0*	11.6	53.2
162 Realized cost	7,510.4	1,110.1	319.8*	299.6	1,089.9	558.1	1,567.6

TABLE B-5 (*concluded*)

Sugar Act	Federal crop insurance	Acreage allotment payments under the Agricultural Conservation Program	Agricultural production programs (principally acreage allotments and marketing quotas)c	Parity payments	Retirement of cotton pool participation trust certificates	Agricultural Adjustment Act of 1933 and related Acts	Removal of surplus cattle and dairy products d	Agricultural Marketing Act Revolving Fund, and payments to stabilization corporations for losses incurred e	Other	
										115
										116
819.9										117
1,135.2*										118
315.3*										119
										120
		3.6				91.0				121
						76.2*				122
		3.6				14.8				123
315.3*		3.6				14.8				124
										125
										126
										127
	3.0*	85.0	19.8	6.1		62.0				128
			21.2*			2.1*				129
						68.5*				130
	3.0*	85.0	1.4*	6.1		8.6*				131
										132
										133
										134
		6.8								135
										136
										137
										138
	1.8	351.2	22.0	328.2		354.6		148.1		139
			15.4*							140
						244.9*				141
	1.8	351.2	6.6	328.2		109.7		148.1		142
										143
										144
	1.8	351.2	6.6	328.2		109.7		148.1		145
								12.4		146
315.3*	68.9	2,354.8	40.2	967.1	1.3	515.0	76.6	379.4	13.0*	147
										148
										149
	13.7							25.9		150
	0.7*							24.0*		151
19.2	75.9	q	r6.8	49.5	0.1	56.2				152
						0.1*			*2.7*	153
296.1*	157.8	2,354.8	47.0	1,016.6	1.4	571.1	76.6	381.3	15.7*	154
										155
819.9	68.9	2,354.8	85.8	967.1	1.3	1,426.5	76.6	379.4		156
			45.6*			9.9*			13.0*	157
1,135.2*										158
						901.6*				159
315.3*	68.9	2,354.8	40.2	967.1	1.3	515.0	76.6	379.4	13.0*	160
19.2	88.9		6.8	49.5	0.1	56.1		1.9	2.7*	161
296.1*	157.8	2,354.8	47.0	1,016.6	1.4	571.1	76.6	381.3	15.7*	162

Note: Details may not add to totals shown due to rounding.
* Represents income or minus expenditures.
** Less than $50,000.

Notes to Tables B-4 and B-5

a. The distribution by commodities is necessarily estimated in most instances since accounting records were not required to be maintained on an individual commodity basis.

b. Exclusive of cash payments for school lunch programs.

c. The amounts indicated hereunder are principally for salaries and expenses for fiscal years 1947 to 1953 in connection with acreage allotments and marketing quotas on the commodities shown. Prior to 1947, such work was handled as a part of the Agricultural Conservation Program, and administrative expenses for this work were not maintained separately from administrative expenses of the Agricultural Conservation Program. Accordingly, amounts for acreage allotments and marketing quotas for 1946 and prior years are not included in this statement.

d. Program conducted under the Jones-Connally Act.

e. Represents principally losses incurred on loans made from the revolving fund by the Federal Farm Board to stabilize the prices of wheat and cotton. A large portion of such losses resulted from donations authorized by Congress to the American Red Cross, without reimbursement to the fund, of wheat and cotton acquired in stabilization operations.

f. Represents cost of commodity export program on cotton and wheat exclusive of export differential on cotton owned or pooled by CCC.

g. Includes $163.2 million for cotton price adjustment.

h. Breakdown by commodity is not available. In general, row crops were considered to be soil-depleting if grain or forage was removed from the land. In addition, small grain crops harvested for grain or hay fell into this category.

i. Represents cost of the storage facilities program which applies primarily to the cost of providing local and emergency storage for corn and wheat in the earlier years of the Corporation's program.

j. Represents net loss on sales of hay for feeding in Drought Emergency areas in 1953.

k. This item applies to a type of insurance which covers several crops on the farm and on which indemnities are paid only for crop deficiencies based upon the total value of the insured crops.

l. Includes $25.6 million and $4.9 million applicable to potatoes and vegetables, respectively, in incentive payments under the 1943 Agricultural Conservation Program.

m. Includes $163.2 million cost applicable to the cotton price adjustment programs and $30.5 million in incentive payments under the 1943 ACP program. An item of $12.1 million of program cost, which cannot be allocated to individual commodities, is included in "Other costs not allocable to specific commodities" below.

n. Interest computed for each year on the basis of the average rate on the public debt paid by Treasury in that year.

o. Consists of administrative expenses and other general costs or income not distributable by specific commodities.

p. Includes charged-off accounts and notes receivable of $1.8 million and the net realized gain on the supply and foreign purchase programs which are identifiable by broad commodity groupings as follows:

Supply		Foreign Purchase	
	(Millions)		*(Millions)*
Cotton and linters	$ 1.9*	Cotton	$ 5.9*
Grains and seeds	76.0*	Fats and oils	38.9*
Oils (bulk)	0.9*	Foodstuffs	5.7*
Tobacco	4.8*	Other	0.2
General commodities purchase	185.8*		
Processed and packaged commodities	39.1*	Total	$50.3*
Other	3.4		
Total	$305.1*		

These programs were separate from the major activity of the Corporation and were undertaken as a means of supplying the requirements of Government agencies, foreign governments, and relief and rehabilitation agencies, and to meet domestic requirements. The gain of $185.8 million reflected under general commodities purchase resulted from the establishment of sales prices at a level which would prevent losses to the Corporation on the supplying of commodities and products thereof to meet the requirements of the U.S. Armed Services, Lend-Lease participants, foreign governments, relief agencies, etc., during World War II.

q. No administrative or other general costs are included for these acreage allotment payments. The program was conducted as a part of the Agricultural Conservation Program and records of administrative and other nonpayment costs were not maintained separately for acreage allotment payments as distinguished from payments for conservation practices.

r. Represents activities to assure production of crops in short supply and assistance to farmers in obtaining equipment and materials necessary to achieve the production required by the Korean mobilization.

s. Represents receipts from liquidation of the Federal Surplus Commodities Corporation.

INDEX

INDEX

[The letter "t" following a page number, as in 205(t), indicates that the reference is to a tabulation only, and not to a text discussion.]

Sirup: diverted to relief channels, 282; surplus purchases, *1936,* 284(t); costs of stabilization programs for, *1932–1953,* 568–69(t)

Smith-Hughes Act (1916), 59

Smith-Lever Act (1914), 58

Soap: exports by Commodity Credit Corporation, *1941–1952,* 304(t)

Soil conservation, *see* Conservation, soil

Soil Conservation Act (1935), 330, 331

Soil Conservation and Domestic Allotment Act (1936): provisions, 252–54; conservation payment program, 251(t), 327, 331–32; relation to Soil Conservation Service program, 331–33; funds spent on agricultural adjustment program, 249; surplus removal provisions, 283; parity income approach, 537–38

Soil conservation districts: established, 327; described, 331; state contributions to, 334n; conflict with TVA system of approach, 349; conservation method, 374–76, 463; local representatives, 375–76; mechanism for long-range conservation program, 377

Soil Conservation Service: established, 330(t), 331; estimates on soil erosion, 322n; relation to Soil Conservation and Domestic Allotment Act activities, 331–33; activities and expenditures of, 334–41; land-purchase program, 339–40; land holdings of, 351; conservation method, 327, 374–76, 377, 463; costs of program, *1932–1953,* 336(t), 475, 556–57(t); *see also* Agricultural Conservation Program Service; Soil Erosion Service

Soil-conserving crops, 252–53, 327–28, 332, 341

Soil-conserving payments, *see* Conservation payments

Soil-depleting crops: definition, 252–53, 571; payments for shifting to soil-conserving crops, 327–28, 332; costs of stabilization programs for, *1932–1953,* 564–65(t); *see also* Conservation payments

Soil Erosion Service, 184n, 330, 385n, 463

Soup: exports by Commodity Credit Corporation, *1941–1952,* 304(t); costs of stabilization programs for, *1932–1953,* 566–67(t)

South: changes in agricultural economy of, 226

Southern Commercial Congress, 126

Soybeans: use of orders for marketing, 247; designated as Steagall commodity, 262n; subsidies for production of, World War II, 299; price-support pro-

visions in Agricultural Act of 1948, 264; disposal of surplus stocks by Foreign Operations Administration, 315; price base for, 539; costs of stabilization programs for, *1932–1953,* 566–67(t)

Specialty crops: Agricultural Adjustment Administration program for, 244

Spinach: costs of stabilization programs for, *1932–1953,* 566–67(t)

Squash: costs of stabilization programs for, *1932–1953,* 566–67(t)

Stability in agriculture: as goal in farm policy, 488

Stabilization Act (1942), 261–62, 396

Stabilization corporations: under Federal Farm Board, 91, 93–101, 224, 382; compared with Commodity Credit Corporation, 258, 381, 385, 388, 392, 407, 411, 415, 514; ever-normal granary idea implicit, 419; costs of, *1932–1953,* 561(t), 563(t), 565(t), 567(t), 569(t); *see also* Federal Farm Board; Cotton; Wheat

Stabilization Extension Act (1944), 262n, 299

Stabilization of prices and farm income: prices and wages, World War II, 295–98, 301; cost of programs for, *1932–1953,* 473, 474(t), 477, 556–57(t), 560–70(t), *1953,* 479(t)

Standard Containers Act, 88

State rural rehabilitation corporations, 184, 195–96, 200

Steagall Amendment (1941): provisions, 261–63, 396–97; provision for "comparable prices" for designated nonbasic commodities, 539; defense of, 449

Steagall commodities: list, 262n; high support levels provided, *1941* ff., 414; potatoes added, 316; difficulties with potatoes, 406; supports modified in Agricultural Act of 1948, 264, 265, 267; *see also* Butter; Cheese; Milk; Potatoes; Wool, *etc.*

Stewart, Andrew: comment by, 504n

Stock market collapse of 1929: effects of, 48–49

Storage: investment in crops, *1940, 1953,* 45–46; facilities provided by Commodity Credit Corporation, 402–03; of wheat, 496–98; cost of, per day, 515; problem of, 491, 530

Submarginal lands program: origins of, 175, 184n; land utilization projects on, 176, 182, 369; lands turned over to Forest Service, 334, 339; handled by Resettlement Administration, 185, 188; as administered by Soil Conser-